# HYPERSONIC
# FLOW THEORY

### WALLACE D. HAYES

*Princeton University and Space Technology Laboratories*

### RONALD F. PROBSTEIN

*Brown University and Avco Research Laboratory*

1959

ACADEMIC PRESS · NEW YORK and LONDON

EDITING SUPPORTED BY THE BUREAU OF ORDNANCE,
U. S. NAVY, UNDER CONTRACT NORD 7386.

To Professor Theodore von Kármán,

for the essential and leading part he has played in the development of the aeronautical sciences and for his catalytic role in nurturing international cooperation in aeronautics, the authors affectionately dedicate this volume.

# PREFACE

Hypersonic flow theory is a branch of the science of fluid mechanics which is in active development at present. In this book we have endeavored to present the fundamentals of this subject as we understand them, together with a reasonably comprehensive report on the state of knowledge at this time. We feel that a book such as this one is needed now, even though numerous refinements and extensions of the theory will certainly be made later. In concentrating on the fundamental concepts of hypersonic flow, however, we hope to have produced a text which will be lasting as well as timely. The book is directed to students and research workers in the field of modern gasdynamics, and to hypersonic aerodynamicists. It should also be of interest to scientists and engineers desiring some insight into this relatively new field.

The scope of the book is indicated by the title. We have not included specific material on such aerodynamic subjects as the dynamics of hypersonic flight or hypersonic wing theory. Some of the material included is directly pertinent to these subjects, of course. We have not included any magnetohydrodynamic theory or any developments involving treatment of the Boltzmann equation. And we have generally taken the point of view of classical fluid mechanics and have not delved deeply in the field of high temperature gasdynamics.

This book serves as a vehicle for original work of the authors, otherwise unpublished. Most of this original work was done in the course of the preparation of the book to fill obvious gaps in the outlined subject matter. Some, of course, was done because specific questions suggested by our treatment of the subject invited further development.

In planning this book we set ourselves a number of guiding principles: The stress at all times is placed on the basic theory and on the related fundamental concepts. We have generally avoided empirical approaches and semi-empirical theories. Empirical results are mentioned only where they are so much in vogue as to demand attention or where they may contribute in some way to an understanding of hypersonic flow phenomena. Thus we present without apology theories which are correct but which cannot be applied accurately to hypersonic flows encountered in practice, provided they furnish fundamental concepts and lead to basic understanding. And theories which are incorrect or not rational we have ignored regardless of the excellence of their agreement with experiment. Experimental results have been included only for comparison with theoretical results, and not for their own interest. We feel that empirical approaches are certainly of value to the engineer, but would detract seriously from a book on theory.

We consider the material in this book to be essential to a hypersonic aerodynamicist. But we must emphasize that this book is not a handbook in any sense, and that we have made no attempt to present design information. The point here is that the understanding which comes from an appreciation of the theory is the soundest basis for engineering ability.

We hope the book will be useful as a text in graduate courses, in courses designed to introduce the student not only to hypersonic flow theory but also to modern approaches in theoretical aerodynamics in general. A course in gasdynamics or compressible fluid theory should be a prerequisite. Material from the book has been used in graduate classes of the authors.

Although the book is formally self-contained, the reader will find a background in the theory of compressible fluid flow most helpful. As to mathematical level, no effort to impose any artificial limit in this level was made. The requisite mathematical background is about what is needed for most compressible flow theory—primarily a knowledge of partial differential equations and vector analysis. The last three sections of Chapter III involve the concepts of dyadics or tensors. The reader will find an ability to appreciate approximations and their limitations most helpful.

Only directly cited references have been listed here. Although the list of references is thus governed by the plan of the book and is not intended as a general bibliography on hypersonic flow, it forms a reasonably comprehensive bibliography on hypersonic flow theory. An attempt has been made to include references for all results reported here except those which appear here for the first time.

We have endeavored to keep the notation as uniform as practicable throughout the text, while at the same time reasonably consistent with accepted usage. The principal symbols used have been listed in a symbol index, with which is included a brief discussion of our notation.

The first draft of Chapters I through V was prepared by the senior author, and that of Chapters VI through X by the second author. The original work presented here is generally to be attributed according to this divison. However, all parts of the text have been carefully gone over by both authors, and many changes from the first draft have been made. Thus the book is really to be considered of joint authorship, without divided responsibility.

The book started as a projected 80-page contribution to *Advances in Applied Mechanics* undertaken by the senior author at the suggestion of Professor Theodore von Kármán. The second author joined the effort, and the concept of the contribution simply grew out of that of a short review paper into that of a reasonably comprehensive text. We are most grateful to the editors of *Advances in Applied Mechanics* for their release of our commitment for the review article and their encouragement of our expanding the work into a text. The writing of the book was mostly completed in 1957. Some of our original results have been duplicated independently by others, and these works have been cited herein.

This book is dedicated to Professor von Kármán, who was responsible for its inception. Both authors are pleased to acknowledge a personal debt to him, the senior author directly and the second author through Professor Lester Lees. Our debt is more than a personal one, however, and includes a more basic one. Our work rests heavily on the present state of development of the aeronautical sciences in many lands. Without the influence on these sciences of Professor von Kármán and his numerous able students of various generations our book could not have been written.

We hope we have caught in proof most of the miscellaneous inevitable errors which appear in the preparation of a technical book. We shall be grateful to readers who wish to inform us of errata or to comment on the content.

WALLACE D. HAYES

RONALD F. PROBSTEIN

*February*, 1959

# ACKNOWLEDGMENTS

More than a formal acknowledgment is due to the Space Technology Laboratories and to the Avco Research Laboratory. The Space Technology Laboratories furnished the senior author much support during the early part of the preparation of this book, and a number of the original results in the book are based on work done for them. The Avco Research Laboratory has furnished the second author continuing support, and has given invaluable aid to the project in many ways. Without the sympathetic backing of these two organizations this book would not have been completed in its present form. We also wish to thank Arthur R. Kantrowitz and his colleagues at the Avco Research Laboratory for the stimulation of numerous discussions and of their own research. They had intended earlier to write a book on high temperature gasdynamics, and there was a certain amount of joint planning with the purpose of making the two books complementary. Unfortunately, the plans for their book have now been shelved.

We have been indirectly but strongly supported in this work by Air Force contracts, at Princeton University through the Office of Scientific Research and at Brown University through the Aeronautical Research Laboratory of the Wright Air Development Center. A particular debt is due to Roscoe H. Mills, Chief of the Fluid Dynamics Research Branch of the Aeronautical Research Laboratory, for his farsighted and vigorous support of research in American universities in the field of hypersonic flow. Many of the results reported in this book are derived from research done under the sponsorship of this Branch.

We are grateful to S. M. Bogdonoff and other members of his Gas Dynamics Laboratory for valuable discussions and for technical assistance. For their help with details of theoretical treatments we should like to thank George D. Waldman, Nelson H. Kemp, William B. Bush, and D. Roger Willis. We gratefully acknowledge Sir Geoffrey Taylor's valuable comments on an early draft of Section 3.1; on the basis of his comments we modified our point of view on Newton's work. We should also like to thank Lester Lees, C. C. Lin, B. T. Chu, Nicholas Rott, R. E. Meyer, James A. Fay, and S. A. Schaaf for their comments on early drafts of various chapters of the book.

For his skillful and patient handling of the preparation of the figures we express our grateful appreciation to C. S. Leonard, Jr. For the typing of the manuscript and the competent handling of secretarial details we are indebted to Mrs. Meredith Knowlton and Mrs. Brenda R. Faulkner. We thank F. N.

Frenkiel, the series editor, for valuable counsel and assistance with certain details.

Photographs for the book were furnished us by the (former) National Advisory Committee for Aeronautics and by the Gas Dynamics Laboratory of Princeton University. We are indebted to O. M. Belotserkovskii of the Academy of Sciences of the U.S.S.R. for graphical results.

Finally, we sincerely thank our publishers for their cooperative attitude in our joint endeavor and the printers for the high quality of their work.

*February*, 1959                                W. D. H.        R. F. P.

# CONTENTS

# HYPERSONIC
# FLOW THEORY

# CHAPTER I

# GENERAL CONSIDERATIONS

## 1. Introductory remarks

Within recent years the development of aircraft and guided missiles has brought a number of new aerodynamic problems into prominence. Most of these problems arise because of extremely high flight velocities, and are characteristically different in some way from the problems which arise in supersonic flight. The term "hypersonic" is used to distinguish flow fields, phenomena, and problems appearing at flight speeds far greater than the speed of sound from their counterparts appearing at flight speeds which are at most moderately supersonic. The appearance of new characteristic features in hypersonic flow fields justifies the use of a new term different from the well established term "supersonic".

These new characteristically hypersonic features may be roughly divided into those of a hydrodynamic nature which arise because the flight Mach number is large, and those of a physical or chemical nature which arise because the energy of the flow is large. If the gas involved is rarefied, so that the mean free path is not negligibly small compared with an appropriate characteristic macroscopic scale of the flow field, the same division applies to a certain extent if we include kinetic theory with hydrodynamics. Rarefied gas flows are encountered in flight at extreme altitudes.

The new features of a hydrodynamic nature are mostly of a kind allowing us to make certain simplifying assumptions in developing theories for hypersonic flow. However, certain important features which appear introduce additional complications over those met with in gasdynamics at more moderate speeds. In hypersonic flow the technique of linearization of the flow equations and the use of the mean-surface approximation for boundary conditions have a vanishing range of applicability. We find also that the entropy gradients produced by curved shock waves make the classical isentropic irrotational approach inapplicable. In many cases the boundary layer creates an important disturbance in the external inviscid flow field, and boundary layer interaction phenomena can be important in hypersonic flow. Generally, it is these hydrodynamic features of hypersonic flow which form the subject matter of the present book.

The new features of a physical or chemical nature appearing in hypersonic flows are mostly connected with the high temperatures generally associated

1

with the extremely strong shock waves present in such flows. At high temperatures in air or in other gases of interest vibrational degrees of freedom in the gas molecules may become excited, the molecules may dissociate into atoms, the molecules or free atoms may ionize, and molecular or ionic species unimportant at lower temperatures may be formed. In any of these processes there may be important time delays, so that relaxation phenomena may appear. At sufficiently high temperatures the gas may radiate, giving a method for the transfer of energy which is negligible at lower temperatures. With the presence of different molecular or ionic species in large gradients of concentration, temperature, and pressure, the processes of diffusion become important. Finally, there are phenomena connected with the interaction of gas particles (or dust particles) with solid surfaces; here appear, for example, the accommodation coefficients of rarefied gas theory, catalytic recombination of dissociated atoms on the surface, and ionization of the surface material. These features of hypersonic flow belong to the field of high temperature gasdynamics, and, generally, are not treated in this book from a physical point of view. The authors expect that other monographs or books covering the subject matter of high temperature gasdynamics will appear in the not-too-distant future.

We must recognize, of course, that there is interplay between the hydrodynamics and the physics of hypersonic flow, that each affects the other. However, the influence of the physical phenomena on the flow is usually a local one, so that the principal features of the inviscid flow field may be obtained without a knowledge of the physical phenomena. This fact lends justification to our treatment of hypersonic flow from a hydrodynamic point of view. However, we must keep in mind that physical phenomena may not only strongly influence local details of hypersonic flow fields, but in extreme cases might control the nature of the entire flow. On the other hand, a knowledge of the hydrodynamic flow field is necessary for any estimation of physical effects. For the most part, though, only a rather rough picture of the flow field is needed, so that a treatment of high temperature gasdynamics independent of hypersonic flow theory is also justifiable.

In the present book we shall be concerned with the problem of determining the details of the flow field about a body placed in a high velocity gas stream. This gas stream is taken to be uniform with respect to all its basic properties, i.e., chemical composition, thermodynamic state, and velocity components. Insofar as possible, we shall treat the gas as a general fluid, and consider the perfect gas of constant ratio of specific heats as a special case. The Mach number of the free stream $M_\infty$ is the ratio of the velocity of the free stream to the velocity of sound there, and is a basic parameter of the problem. In order that a flow may be termed hypersonic it is necessary that this parameter be large.

We naturally ask the question as to how large the free stream Mach number must be before we have a hypersonic flow. No direct answer may be given, as it depends upon the shape of the body, the particular gas involved, and upon the part of the flow field being considered. Some of the characteristic features of hypersonic flow appear on the forward parts of blunt bodies with $M_\infty$ as low as three. Some features of hypersonic flow which some investigators consider essential do not appear unless $M_\infty$ is about ten or larger. In short, we must recognize a certain arbitrariness in the term hypersonic which can be resolved only by reference to the particular flow and characteristic feature of immediate concern. The applicability of any part of hypersonic flow theory depends on the validity of the particular assumptions needed. Whether or not a flow is to be called hypersonic in the sense of a specific part of the theory must be assessed on the basis of this required validity.

## 2. General features of hypersonic flow fields

We shall begin our study of hypersonic flow theory by examining qualitatively the flow fields as they appear in observed hypersonic flows. Here we must make a distinction between the flow around a blunt body and that around a slender body (see Figs. 1–1 and 1–2). At the same time we must recognize that there exist bodies of intermediate shapes and that a slender body may be somewhat blunted at its nose. In all cases we observe that there is a strong fore-and-aft asymmetry in the flow pattern, and that the flow field is always completely undisturbed upstream of the body to within a very short distance of the nose of the body. The front of the body is enveloped by a shock wave, which extends downstream in the shape of a slightly flared skirt. The flow in front of this shock is undisturbed and the flow field of interest lies entirely behind the shock. Of principal interest to us is the flow field between the shock and the body. Here we notice that the inclination of surfaces in the flow field to the oncoming stream is very significant. The enveloping shock lies very close to body surfaces which have a sufficiently large positive inclination to the free stream direction. The region between the body and the shock here is termed the shock layer. No shock lies near body surfaces which have an appreciable negative inclination. The pressures on such surfaces are much less than those found in the thin shock layers, although usually greater than the pressure in the free stream. Far aft the shock wave becomes weak, and a wake is observed directly downstream of the body. The skirt-shaped relatively weak shock far downstream is termed the shock tail.

Within the shock layer the temperature and pressure are very much greater than in the free stream, with no limit on the ratios of these quantities across the shock. On the other hand, although the density is appreciably greater than in the free stream, the density ratio across the shock is limited to finite values. If the temperature of the body is of the order of the temperature of the free stream, a large heat transfer takes place from the gas to the body. In this case the boundary layer may have densities higher than those found in the inviscid part of the shock layer. In general, the temperature of the body is an essential parameter in the determination of real-fluid effects, and even becomes an essential parameter for determining the forces exerted on the body if the gas is at low density, e.g. in a free molecule flow.

The shock waves enveloping the body are curved, and we observe large lateral entropy gradients in the flow. In accordance with the Crocco vorticity law, this flow is also highly rotational. The wake which extends behind the body is only partly attributable to viscous effects, and with no viscosity or heat conduction we should still observe an extensive wake behind the body as a result of the large entropy increase in the fluid which has passed near the body. Within the relatively wide entropy wake is observed the narrower viscous wake, often turbulent, and characterized by a decrease in total enthalpy if the body is cold.

As the shock grows weak in the shock tail far behind the body, the shock inclination approaches the free stream Mach angle $\sin^{-1}$ $(1/M_\infty)$. In hypersonic flow this angle is very small. The entropy wake, or region of entropy increase, is formed behind the part of the shock wave which is relatively strong. This entropy wake has a lateral dimension which may be quite large but is limited.

Figure 1–1 gives a picture of a hypersonic flow on a blunt body, a right circular cylinder with its flat face traveling forward. Figure 1–1(a) is a free flight shadowgraph in air at a Mach number of 3. The dished appearance of the front face, the apparent thickness of the shock wave, and the bulged-out appearance of the sides are due to optical distortion. At a larger value of the Mach number the shock shape in front of the body would be but little altered, but the shock skirt and the other shock waves would have smaller inclination angles and would lie closer to the axis. This photograph was chosen because of the excellent picture it gives of the expansion about the rear corner of the body, the dead-water region behind the body, and the development of the highly turbulent wake. These features, of course, are all found in supersonic flows. The shock wave emanating from the side of the body probably results from recompression following overexpansion of the flow around the front corner of the body. The third shock is the rear shock from the recompression accompanying the necking-down of the dead-water region to form the wake. Figure 1–1(b) is a sketch showing qualitatively the characteristic features of this flow. Characteristic of all blunt-body flows is the subsonic region and the stagnation point behind the strong

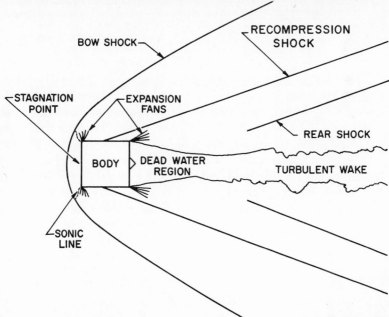

FIG. 1–1. Circular cylinder with flat face forward in air at $M_\infty = 3$. (a) Free flight shadowgraph (Ames Aeronautical Laboratory, courtesy National Advisory Committee for Aeronautics). (b) Sketch of flow field.

shock at the foremost point on the body. The flow in the shock layer on the front of this body is highly rotational and nonuniform.

Figure 1–2 gives a picture of a hypersonic flow on a slender pointed body with a base flare. This is a free flight shadowgraph (with countercurrent air flow) at a Mach number of 9.6, Reynolds number of 10 million, and a free stream temperature of 290°R. The reader will observe the small inclinations of the shock waves, the boundary layer on the body, and the relatively weak rear shock. The body is at a slight angle of attack, with a resulting weak lateral asymmetry of the flow field. Laminar separation of the boundary

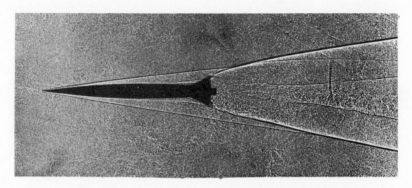

Fig. 1–2. Free flight shadowgraph in Free-Flight Wind Tunnel of a slender flared body in air at $M_\infty = 9.6$. (Ames Aeronautical Laboratory, courtesy of National Advisory Committee for Aeronautics).

layer occurs on the upper side, and a shock wave starts at the separation point and intersects the flare. Transition occurs in the separated boundary layer on the lower side. Characteristic of hypersonic slender-body flows is the fact that the velocity in the disturbed region is changed but very little from the velocity of the free stream, even though the other flow properties such as pressure, density, and speed of sound may be changed markedly. As long as the body is slender the speed of sound within the disturbed region remains low enough so that the entire flow field remains hypersonic. The concept of a shock layer may still be applied over the forward part of the body, but the concept is less appropriate for flows about slender bodies than for flows about blunt bodies. The shock waves observed with a slender body are much weaker than those with a blunt body, so that the entropy wake is less pronounced.

We must look a little more critically at conditions near the nose of a slender body in hypersonic flow. The remarks just made are based upon an idealized sharp tip on which a shock wave of small inclination may lie. In constructional practice it is next to impossible to provide a tip which is sharp enough to represent this idealization. In addition, the local heating in the vicinity of a very sharp tip may be so great that the sharp tip will rapidly melt away. Thus we must recognize the fact that slender bodies are really slightly blunted. At the tip of such a slender body a local blunt body hypersonic flow is observed, with the attendant local strong shock wave and large entropy increase. The entropy wake from this local flow pattern lies in a layer next to the body which is generally initially thicker than the viscous boundary layer. Viscous effects play little or no part in determining the initial structure of this entropy layer, but the entropy layer has an important effect on the development of the viscous boundary layer and vice versa. In fact, if the blunting of the slender body is slight it is generally difficult to identify distinct entropy and viscous boundary layers. If the blunting of the slender body is appreciable, the recognizable entropy wake is generally too extensive to be identifiable as an entropy layer.

Figure 1–3 is an interferogram of the flow over a flat plate at zero incidence at a Mach number of 12.7 in helium. The bluntness is a flat face normal to the flow direction of width 0.00093 inches, and the Reynolds number based on this width and free stream conditions ($Re_{t_\infty}$) is 808. The length of the plate shown in the photograph (about 35 fringes) is about 2 inches. The flow field below the plate is three-dimensional and should be disregarded. The shock wave above the plate is clearly visible, as is a layer of reduced density next to the plate. The decreased density in this layer is to a large extent attributable to the entropy jump across the strong shock very near the nose. However, it appears difficult to recognize a distinct viscous boundary layer within this layer of reduced density, and it is likely that viscosity plays a part in creating the identifiable outer boundary to this layer. Although the concept of a definable narrow entropy boundary layer may not be a usable one, the recognition of the highly nonuniform entropy field behind a blunt nose is essential.

At sufficiently high free stream Mach numbers the value of the Mach number $M_\infty$ is not a particularly important factor in determining the general shape of the shock wave near the body. The separation of the shock wave from the body depends primarily upon the density of the gas between them, which in turn depends upon the ratio of the density in the free stream to that just behind the shock. If this density ratio $\epsilon$ is small the shock lies close to the body; if it is not small the shock is farther from the body. Although this ratio is a variable dependent upon the inclination angle of the shock, it is useful to use it conceptually as a basic parameter. The density ratio across a shock will be treated in Section 1.4.

In these remarks we have not distinguished between, say, bodies of revolution and two-dimensional bodies. Important differences between bodies of these two types do exist, but appear primarily in fine details of hypersonic flow patterns and in the quantitative results. These differences will be pointed out in the text where they appear in the development. An understanding of these differences is not essential for an appreciation of the qualitative features of hypersonic flow fields.

Fig. 1–3. Wind tunnel interferogram of a slightly blunted flat plate in helium at $M_\infty = 12.7$ and $Re_{t_\infty} = 808$. (Courtesy Gas Dynamics Laboratory, Princeton University).

## 3. Assumptions underlying hypersonic flow theory

In various parts of this book we shall make a number of assumptions which will be familiar to the reader with a general background in fluid mechanics. In the earlier chapters we shall be developing inviscid hypersonic flow theory, with the basic assumption that all real-fluid effects such as viscosity may be neglected. This is the familiar assumption of all ideal-fluid theory. Later we shall investigate viscous boundary layers in hypersonic flow, with the basic boundary layer assumptions as well as the assumption that the molecular mean free path of the gas in the boundary layer is small compared with the boundary layer thickness. After a general consideration of low-density effects, we shall present the basic theory of hypersonic free molecule flow, with the basic assumption that the molecular mean free path in the free stream is large compared with an appropriate dimension of the body.

The assumptions mentioned above are mostly quite standard, and not particularly characteristic of hypersonic flow theory. The reader as yet wholly unacquainted with hypersonic flow will encounter certain other assumptions here which are characteristically hypersonic. Some of these appear in the treatment of the interaction of shock waves and boundary layers, and will be discussed there. Some of these underlie the inviscid theory, and deserve our attention at this point.

We shall pick out four basic assumptions which appear in inviscid hypersonic flow theory. Only one or two of these are needed for any particular development, and our main purpose in assembling and discussing them here together is to obtain a comprehensive picture of the assumptions used in inviscid hypersonic flow theory and their relation to each other. An assumption of the type being considered is always of the form that a particular quantity or parameter is small compared with one (or large compared with one). A particular theory based upon such an assumption is generally valid in an asymptotic sense as the chosen parameter is made to approach zero (or infinity) by a limiting process. Since products and ratios of parameters are themselves parameters the assumptions may appear in varying strength: for example, if a quantity $\epsilon^{1/2}$ is small, the quantity $\epsilon$ must be "very small"; or if $\sin \theta_b$ is small and $M_\infty \sin \theta_b$ is large, $M_\infty$ must be "very large". In addition to the four hypersonic assumptions, the assumption needed for linearized supersonic or hypersonic flow is included for the sake of completeness.

The inviscid hypersonic assumptions are:

| | | |
|---|---|---|
| A. | $M_\infty \gg 1$ | "Basic hypersonic" |
| B. | $\sin \theta_b \ll 1$ | "Slender body" |
| C. | $M_\infty \sin \theta_b \gg 1$ | "Strong shock" |
| D. | $\epsilon \ll 1$ | "Small density ratio" |
| E. | $M_\infty \sin \theta_b \ll 1$ | "Linearization" |

Here $\theta_b$ is an appropriate maximum value of the inclination angle of the body or of a streamline with respect to the free stream direction. The limiting statement corresponding to an assumption may be designated by the letter followed by -lim, and a strong form of an assumption by the letter followed by -strong. Thus, for example, we designate the limiting process $M_\infty \to \infty$ by A-lim and the assumption $\epsilon^{1/2} \ll 1$ by D-strong. Note that assumption A involves only conditions in the free stream flow and that assumption B involves only the shape of the body. Assumptions C and E are mixed in nature, while assumption D primarily concerns the properties of the gas behind the shock.

By the definition of hypersonic flow, assumption A is required for all hypersonic flow theories. Briefly, the physical significance of this assumption is that the internal thermodynamic energy in the material in the free stream is small compared with the kinetic energy of this stream. Assumption A ensures that the Mach angle in the free stream is small. The physical significance of the other assumptions will appear naturally in the sections concerning the quantities involved in the assumptions (in particular $\epsilon$ in Section 1.4) or concerning the theories dependent upon the assumptions.

The concept which we shall term the Mach number independence principle (Section 1.6) depends on assumption C. Here we must notice that assumption C may not be applied to the entire shock tail if $M_\infty$ is finite. In the vicinity of the shock tail the local flow inclination angle must be used in place of $\theta_b$ and this angle decreases toward zero as the shock grows weaker downstream. If we wish to apply the Mach number independence principle over the entire field we must use assumption A-lim.

The classical hypersonic similitude of Tsien and Hayes and the associated small-disturbance theory of Van Dyke require assumption B. The similar solutions of the small-disturbance theory require in addition assumption C and the assumption of a perfect gas of constant ratio of specific heats. The combination of assumptions B and C implies and requires assumption A-strong. Small-disturbance theory forms the subject of Chapter II.

Newtonian flow theory and various theories for thin shock layers related to Newtonian theory, treated in Chapters III to V, depend upon assumption D. The requirements for Newtonian theory are particularly stringent, as it is assumption D-strong which is needed in this case and there are restrictions on the body shape in order that the shock shape may be assumed known.

The application of supersonic linearized flow theory to hypersonic flow requires assumption E, which with A implies and requires assumption B-strong. This theory is not characteristic of hypersonic flow and, since assumption B-strong cannot be considered realistic, is not significant. Nonlinearity is an essential feature of hypersonic flow, and we shall not consider the linear theory further.

A word about the nature of the basic hypersonic limiting process A-lim is in order. The free stream Mach number is the ratio between the free stream velocity and the free stream sound speed. In the limiting process A-lim in which $M_\infty$ approaches infinity we may consider as one possibility that the free stream velocity approaches infinity and that the free stream thermodynamic state remains fixed. However, such a process does not make physical sense, as then the energy of the gas and the temperatures in the shock layer increase without limit, and no true limiting state occurs. In the limiting process A-lim we may also consider that the free stream sound velocity is made to approach zero, while the free stream velocity and density are kept constant. Thus we consider the absolute temperature, pressure, and sound speed of the oncoming gas to approach zero. In such a limiting process a proper limiting state does appear. For a perfect gas with constant ratio of specific heats this distinction is unimportant, but for actual gases at elevated temperatures the distinction is usually an essential one.

## 4. The normal shock wave

Shock waves are an essential feature of any hypersonic flow, and we shall begin our analytical treatment of hypersonic flow with a study of them. The normal shock is treated first.

The subscripts $\infty$ and $s$ will refer to conditions upstream and downstream, respectively, of the normal shock. The normal shock is governed by three basic conservation equations, corresponding to the three physical principles of conservation of mass, of momentum, and of energy. These equations are

$$(1.4.1a) \qquad\qquad \rho_\infty v_\infty = \rho_s v_s \qquad = m,$$

$$(1.4.1b) \qquad\qquad p_\infty + \rho_\infty v_\infty^2 = p_s + \rho_s v_s^2 = P,$$

$$(1.4.1c) \qquad\qquad h_\infty + \tfrac{1}{2}v_\infty^2 \ = h_s + \tfrac{1}{2}v_s^2 \ = H_n,$$

where $m$, $P$, and $H_n$ are constant. The quantity $h$ is the specific enthalpy, defined with respect to the specific internal energy $e$ by the relation

$$(1.4.2) \qquad\qquad h = e + p/\rho,$$

and $v$ is the flow velocity, directed normal to the shock. Both $e$ and $h$ are so defined as to be zero at zero absolute temperature. The quantity $H$ is the total enthalpy, and the subscript $n$ refers to the fact that the shock is considered normal. We shall generally know beforehand the properties of the gas in front of the shock, and shall want to know them behind. For this we must have an equation of state for the material behind the shock in order to relate $p_s$, $\rho_s$, and $h_s$. In this book, the term "equation of state" is used in a sense encompassing all the usual thermodynamic variables, and not in the limited sense specifying pressure as a function of volume and temperature. The equation of state required may be of the form

$$(1.4.3) \qquad\qquad h = h(S, p),$$

where $S$ is the specific entropy; $T$ and $\rho$ are immediately obtainable from

(1.4.3) by differentiation, according to the well known thermodynamic formulas

$$(1.4.4) \qquad T = \left(\frac{\partial h}{\partial S}\right)_p ; \qquad \frac{1}{\rho} = \left(\frac{\partial h}{\partial p}\right)_S .$$

We should note that we are here assuming the existence of such an equation of state. This assumption is not always a valid one, and fails in particular if the gas is far from thermal equilibrium (but not frozen—see below).

A number of additional relations may be obtained from (1.4.1). Some of these are

$$(1.4.5a) \qquad v_\infty \pm v_s = m(1/\rho_\infty \pm 1/\rho_s) = v_\infty(1 \pm \epsilon),$$

$$(1.4.5b) \qquad p_s - p_\infty = m(v_\infty - v_s) = \rho_\infty v_\infty^2(1 - \epsilon),$$

$$(1.4.5c) \qquad h_s - h_\infty = \tfrac{1}{2}v_\infty^2(1 - \epsilon^2),$$

$$(1.4.5d) \qquad \frac{p_s - p_\infty}{1/\rho_\infty - 1/\rho_s} = m^2.$$

Here $\epsilon$ is the density ratio across the shock, defined by

$$(1.4.6) \qquad \epsilon = \frac{\rho_\infty}{\rho_s} .$$

We may eliminate $v_\infty^2$ between (1.4.5b) and (1.4.5c) to obtain the Hugoniot relation

$$(1.4.7) \qquad h_s - h_\infty = \frac{p_s - p_\infty}{2\rho_\infty}(1 + \epsilon) = \tfrac{1}{2}(p_s - p_\infty)(1/\rho_\infty + 1/\rho_s).$$

The importance of the Hugoniot relation lies in the fact that in it the velocities and the conservation constants of (1.4.1) have been eliminated. It provides a relation connecting the thermodynamic state quantities on the two sides of the shock. With the aid of the equation of state we may use the Hugoniot relation to plot a curve of the possible states of the gas behind the shock corresponding to a given state in front of the shock. In order to determine which of these states is actually obtained, some additional determining quantity or boundary condition must be given. For example, a specification of $v_\infty$, of $v_\infty - v_s$, or of $p_s$ will determine the shock. A more detailed investigation of the Hugoniot relation with sufficient conditions for uniqueness of a shock under various determining conditions may be found, for example, in Hayes [7, Arts. 1 and 2].

We now rewrite the Hugoniot relation in a form which expresses the density ratio $\epsilon$ explicitly

$$(1.4.8) \qquad \epsilon = \frac{p_s/\rho_s}{(h_s + e_s) - (h_\infty + e_\infty) + p_\infty/\rho_s} .$$

We now consider the basic hypersonic limiting process (A-lim), in which the temperature and pressure before the shock approach zero and $M_\infty$ approaches infinity. The terms $h_\infty + e_\infty$ and $p_\infty$ in (1.4.8) are dropped, and we obtain

$$(1.4.9) \qquad \epsilon_{\text{lim}} = \frac{p_s/\rho_s}{h_s + e_s}.$$

From this we see that the density ratio in the limiting case of a very strong shock depends only upon the thermodynamic state of the gas behind the shock, and that this limiting density ratio is finite.

In hypersonic flow theory we shall be interested primarily in a general fluid and shall consider the case of a perfect gas as a special case. The ratio of specific heats $c_p/c_v$, an important parameter for a perfect gas, is of essentially no significance in the gasdynamics of a general fluid such as a dissociating gas. Accordingly, we shall refer to the ratio of specific heats only with respect to a perfect gas, and shall not give this ratio a symbol per se. Instead, we shall use the symbol $\gamma$ to refer to other dimensionless parameters which necessarily coincide with the ratio of specific heats only if the gas is perfect and this ratio is constant. Of these parameters the most important probably is the "isentropic exponent" or "effective ratio of specific heats" $\gamma_e$ defined as $\rho a^2/p$, where $a$ is the speed of sound defined below. Except for flows such as those in shock tunnels or with particular fluids, the fluid in the free stream may be considered perfect, and we shall refer to $\gamma_e$ in the free stream simply as $\gamma$.

In order to obtain an expression for $\epsilon$ in terms of the Mach number of the oncoming flow we introduce the notation for quantities before the shock

$$(1.4.10a) \qquad M_n = \frac{v_\infty}{a_\infty},$$

$$(1.4.10b) \qquad \gamma = \frac{\rho_\infty a_\infty^2}{p_\infty},$$

$$(1.4.10c) \qquad \epsilon_\infty = \frac{p_\infty/\rho_\infty}{h_\infty + e_\infty}.$$

The quantity $a$ is the isentropic velocity of sound in the fluid medium, defined by the relation

$$(1.4.11) \qquad a^2 = \left(\frac{\partial p}{\partial \rho}\right)_S.$$

This quantity is necessarily identified with the actual speed of sound waves only for waves of sufficiently low frequency that real-fluid effects play no role. The quantity $M_n$ is the Mach number of the oncoming flow normal to the shock, equal to $M_\infty$ for a normal shock. In considering oblique shocks we shall define $M_n$ as the normal component of the free stream Mach number $M_\infty$, and thus make a distinction between the two quantities.

We now express the pressure ratio across the shock with the aid of (1.4.5b)

(1.4.12)
$$\frac{p_s}{p_\infty} = 1 + \gamma M_n^2(1 - \epsilon).$$

If we treat $\epsilon_{\text{lim}}$ as defined in (1.4.9) as a constant and combine (1.4.12) with (1.4.8) we obtain a quadratic equation for $\epsilon$. The solution of this may be expressed

(1.4.13)
$$\epsilon = \tfrac{1}{2}(1 + \epsilon_{\text{lim}})(1 + \gamma^{-1}M_n^{-2})$$
$$-\tfrac{1}{2}\sqrt{[(1 - \epsilon_{\text{lim}}) - (1 + \epsilon_{\text{lim}})\gamma^{-1}M_n^{-2}]^2 + 4(1 - \epsilon_{\text{lim}}\epsilon_\infty^{-1})\gamma^{-1}M_n^{-2}}.$$

The positive sign on the radical in (1.4.13) corresponds to the trivial solution $\epsilon = 1$. For $M_n$ large (1.4.13) may be expanded as

(1.4.14)
$$\epsilon = \epsilon_{\text{lim}}\left[1 + \frac{\epsilon_\infty^{-1} - \epsilon_{\text{lim}}}{1 - \epsilon_{\text{lim}}}\gamma^{-1}M_n^{-2}\right] + O(M_n^{-4}),$$

or with $|1 - \epsilon_{\text{lim}}\epsilon_\infty^{-1}|$ small, as

(1.4.15)
$$\epsilon = \epsilon_{\text{lim}} + (1 + \epsilon_{\text{lim}})\gamma^{-1}M_n^{-2} - \frac{(1 - \epsilon_{\text{lim}}\epsilon_\infty^{-1})\gamma^{-1}M_n^{-2}}{(1 - \epsilon_{\text{lim}}) - (1 + \epsilon_{\text{lim}})\gamma^{-1}M_n^{-2}}$$
$$+ (1 - \epsilon_{\text{lim}}\epsilon_\infty^{-1})^2 O(M_n^{-4}).$$

If the relation

(1.4.16)
$$\epsilon_\infty = \epsilon_{\text{lim}}$$

holds, as is the case with a perfect gas of constant ratio of specific heats, we obtain simply

(1.4.17)
$$\epsilon = \epsilon_{\text{lim}} + (1 + \epsilon_{\text{lim}})\gamma^{-1}M_n^{-2}.$$

It is not necessary for the fluid to be a perfect gas for (1.4.16) to hold, but the relation should probably be considered accidental otherwise. However, it is possible to change $\epsilon_\infty$ by redefining $e$ and $h$ so that they have a value different from zero at absolute zero temperature. Hence it is possible to satisfy (1.4.16) for one particular shock, but it is not generally possible to satisfy this relation for all shocks with a given $\rho_\infty$ and $p_\infty$.

In the special case of a perfect gas with constant ratio of specific heats this ratio equals $\gamma$, and also $\epsilon_\infty = \epsilon_{\text{lim}}$. The limiting density ratio is

(1.4.18)
$$\epsilon_{\text{lim}} = \frac{\gamma - 1}{\gamma + 1},$$

and (1.4.17) becomes

(1.4.19)
$$\epsilon = \frac{\gamma - 1}{\gamma + 1}\left(1 + \frac{2}{\gamma - 1}M_n^{-2}\right).$$

The purpose of the foregoing calculations for the density ratio is to provide a basis for estimating the value of this quantity and for acquiring an understanding of its variations. We note first the consequences of different ways of changing $M_n$, corresponding to the different ways of applying the basic hypersonic limiting process $M_\infty \to \infty$ (A-lim) discussed in the previous section. If $M_n$ is changed or made to approach infinity in such a way that the state properties behind the shock are unchanged, $\epsilon_{\lim}$ is unchanged, and (1.4.13) to (1.4.15) above give explicit statements as to the effects of $M_n$ on $\epsilon$. If $M_n$ is changed in such a way that $\rho_\infty$ and $v_\infty$ are unchanged, $\epsilon_{\lim}$ changes but slightly; for large $M_n$ the quantity $\epsilon_{\lim}$ is constant within a relative error of $O(M_n^{-2})$, and (1.4.14) is of the correct form for an appropriate description of the effects of $M_n$. However, in this case the coefficient of $M_n^{-2}$ in an expansion in powers of $M_n^{-2}$ is different from that given in (1.4.14). But if the thermodynamic state in front of the shock is fixed, and $M_n$ is changed by changing $v_\infty$, the value of $\epsilon_{\lim}$ may vary considerably; these equations for $\epsilon$ then give no explicit information on the variation of $\epsilon$ with $M_n$, except for the special case of a perfect gas. Unfortunately, the variations in $M_n$ with the angle of an oblique shock in a given flow are of the latter type.

We next ask how close $\epsilon$ is to $\epsilon_{\lim}$ if $M_n$ is large. Equation (1.4.14) tells us that the relative error in using $\epsilon_{\lim}$ for $\epsilon$ is of the order of $\epsilon_\infty^{-1} M_n^{-2}$. This means that in an analysis in which $\epsilon_{\lim}$ is used for $\epsilon$ it is necessary not only that $M_n^2$ be large but that $\epsilon_\infty M_n^2$ be large. The quantity $\epsilon_\infty M_n^2$ or its equivalent appears in certain hypersonic analyses as a basic parameter.

What values can $\epsilon_{\lim}$ have in actual gases? As long as the gas behind the shock is a perfect gas and is physically equivalent to the gas in front, (1.4.18) applies. In this case $\epsilon_{\lim}^{-4}$ is equal to the number of classical degrees of freedom excited, plus one. All monatomic gases have $\epsilon_{\lim} = \frac{1}{4}$, and diatomic gases at moderate temperatures have $\epsilon_{\lim} = \frac{1}{6}$. At higher temperatures in polyatomic gases, vibrational degrees of freedom become excited, and $\epsilon_{\lim}$ drops moderately.

A striking decrease in $\epsilon_{\lim}$ occurs only if some physical mechanism appears which causes a large contribution to $h_s + e_s$ without a corresponding contribution to $p_s/\rho_s$. A mechanism which absorbs energy from the dynamic degrees of freedom of the gas is generally of this type; here the practically important examples are dissociation and ionization. The energy of dissociation appears as a potential energy contribution to $h + e$, which does not contribute to the temperature or to $p/\rho$. With dissociation the number of molecules (and the gas constant) in a diatomic gas doubles, and this results in an increase in $p/\rho$. However, the effect of the large energy of dissociation far exceeds the effect of the increase in the number of molecules in practical cases. In air at elevated temperatures $\epsilon_{\lim}$ may drop to a value of the order of 0.07 or less because of the effect of dissociation (see, for example, Feldman

[1] or Moeckel [2]). The effect of ionization is similar to that of dissociation. If there is a significant time delay in the transfer of energy to or from a vibrational degree of freedom or to or from energy of dissociation, relaxation phenomena appear. If the gas is at a sufficiently high temperature, it may transfer a significant quantity of energy away from the region of the shock by radiation. Either with relaxation or with radiation we may consider three different possibilities: First, all but a negligible portion of the energy transfer may be accomplished within a thin layer which may be considered as the shock wave itself. In this case only the structure of the shock is affected, except that if there is radiation present the energy lost must be accounted for by a corresponding decrease in the total enthalpy $H_n$, i.e. by a correction of the energy conservation equation (1.4.1c). Second, there may be only a negligible portion of the energy transferred within a clearly identifiable thickness of the shock wave. In this case the preceding analysis holds again, provided that the equation of state used takes into account the fact that any degree of freedom involved in the relaxation is unexcited. The process of relaxation or radiation must then be taken into account in the flow field behind the shock. Third, the situation may be intermediate between the first two, and a significant portion of the energy transfer may occur both within the thickness of the shock and behind the shock. In this case it is difficult to define a thickness for the shock wave and the problem of determining the flow field becomes fundamentally more difficult.

If a relaxation process takes place in the gas but with a characteristic delay time which is sufficiently short (as in the first possibility mentioned above), the departure at any instant of the state of the gas in the flow field from a thermodynamic equilibrium state will be small. In this case we may ignore the relaxation phenomenon and use the "equilibrium" equation of state for the gas. If the characteristic time of the relaxation is sufficiently large, the energy transferred to or from the vibrational degree of freedom or to or from dissociation may be negligible not only within the thickness of the shock (as in the second possibility mentioned above) but within the entire flow field of interest. In this case the gas is said to be in frozen equilibrium, and there exists a "frozen" equation of state which we may use to calculate the flow field of interest. In inviscid flow theory a single equation of state is assumed to hold for the fluid, but it is immaterial whether this equation of state is based on thermodynamic equilibrium or is a frozen equation of state (see Section 7.1). In the intermediate case for which appreciable relaxation transfers of energy occur within the flow field of interest behind the shock, inviscid theory does not apply, and additional flow equations are needed. The dynamics of such a relaxing fluid lie outside the scope of the present book.

Although frozen equilibrium fits the requirements of inviscid flow theory we shall generally treat the fluid as though it were in thermodynamic equilibrium. The fluid which is of most practical interest to us is air, and Figs. 1–4 present plots of the thermodynamic properties of argon-free air in thermodynamic equilibrium, obtained from Feldman [1] (See also Korobkin and Hastings [1] and Hansen [2]). Each of these three figures is in the form of a Mollier diagram, with specific enthalpy and entropy as the ordinate and

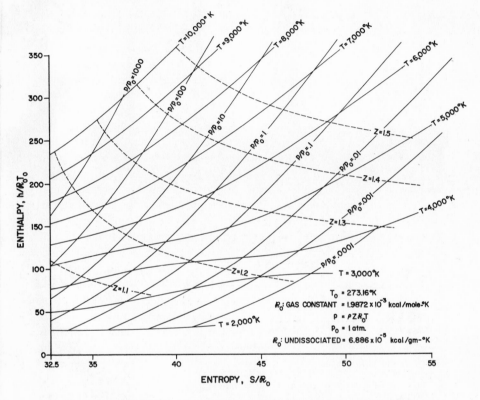

Fig. 1–4a. Mollier diagram for argon-free air. Pressure, temperature, and compressibility factor (Feldman [1]).

abscissa, respectively. Curves of constant pressure, temperature, and the compressibility factor defined in (7.1.34) appear on Fig. 1–4a, and curves of constant density and speed of sound on Fig. 1–4b. On Fig. 1–4c are plotted curves of constant altitude and velocity in front of a normal shock for which the stagnation thermodynamic state behind the shock corresponds to the enthalpy and entropy given.

One way of obtaining conditions behind a shock with the aid of such a set of diagrams or an equivalent set of tables is with a successive approximation procedure. Let us assume that the quantities $v_\infty$, $p_\infty$, $h_\infty$, and $\rho_\infty$ are known. An initial guess of $\epsilon$ is made, with which values for $p_s$ and $h_s$ are obtained from (1.4.5b, c). The corresponding value of $\rho_s$ is taken from the plot of thermodynamic properties or interpolated from the equivalent set of tables. An improved value of $\epsilon$ is then obtained from (1.4.6) and the process is repeated. It may be shown that this procedure is convergent. For air, charts for $\epsilon$ and

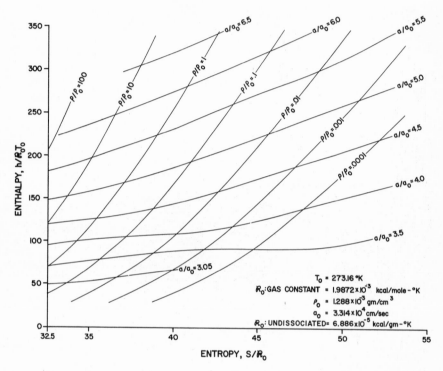

Fig. 1–4b. Mollier diagram for argon-free air. Density and speed of sound (Feldman [1]).

other thermodynamic properties behind normal and oblique shocks are available for various flight speeds and altitudes (see, for example, Feldman [1] and Moeckel [2]).

We turn finally to a discussion of the dimensionless parameters for which the symbol $\gamma$ is used and which coincide with the ratio of specific heats for a perfect gas when this ratio is constant. We shall define three of these, $\gamma_\epsilon$, $\gamma_e$, and $\gamma_*$. The first of these is defined as the ratio of enthalpy to internal energy,

$$(1.4.20) \qquad\qquad \gamma_\epsilon = \frac{h}{e}.$$

We may note that $\epsilon_{\lim}$ from (1.4.9) may be expressed

$$(1.4.21) \qquad \epsilon_{\lim} = \frac{\gamma_\epsilon - 1}{\gamma_\epsilon + 1},$$

where $\gamma_\epsilon$ is taken immediately behind the shock. The quantity $\epsilon_\infty$ of (1.4.10c) satisfies the same relation, with $\gamma_\epsilon$ taken in front of the shock. The connection between (1.4.21) and (1.4.18) is evident. The quantity $\gamma_\epsilon$ is changed if $e$ and $h$ are redefined so that they have a value different from zero at absolute zero temperature.

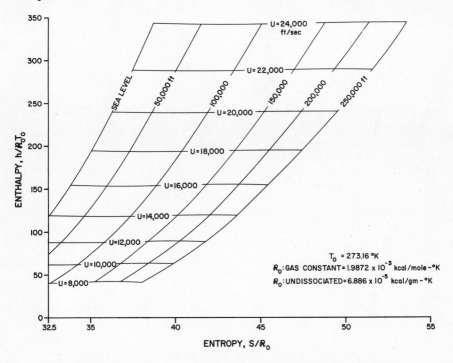

FIG. 1–4c. Mollier diagram for argon-free air. Altitude and velocity in front of a normal shock for given thermodynamic stagnation conditions behind the shock (courtesy Avco Research Laboratory).

The second of these quantities, $\gamma_e$, is called the isentropic exponent or effective ratio of specific heats and is defined (see, for example, Moeckel [2] and Hansen [2])

$$(1.4.22) \qquad \gamma_e = \frac{\rho a^2}{p} = \left(\frac{\partial \ln p}{\partial \ln \rho}\right)_S = \left(\frac{\partial h}{\partial e}\right)_S.$$

We may relate $\gamma_e$ and $\gamma_\epsilon$ by the relation

$$(1.4.23) \qquad \gamma_e = \gamma_\epsilon + \frac{1}{\gamma_\epsilon - 1}\left(\frac{\partial \gamma_\epsilon}{\partial \ln \rho}\right)_S,$$

and it is clear that if $\gamma_\epsilon$ is constant along an isentrope, then $\gamma_e = \gamma_\epsilon$. The quantity $\gamma_e$ is important in that it relates the speed of sound to the pressure and density. For a perfect gas $\gamma_e$ equals the ratio of specific heats even if this ratio is not constant but is a function of temperature.

The third of these quantities, $\gamma_*$, is defined

$$(1.4.24) \qquad \gamma_* = \frac{1}{a^2}\left(\frac{\partial \rho a^2}{\partial \rho}\right)_S = \frac{1}{\rho a^2}\left(\frac{\partial^2 p}{\partial (\ln \rho)^2}\right)_S = \left(\frac{\partial \rho a^2}{\partial p}\right)_S.$$

The relation between $\gamma_*$ and $\gamma_e$ may be written

$$(1.4.25) \qquad \gamma_* = \gamma_e + \frac{1}{\gamma_e}\left(\frac{\partial \gamma_e}{\partial \ln \rho}\right)_S = \gamma_e + \left(\frac{\partial \gamma_e}{\partial \ln p}\right)_S$$

$$= \gamma_e + \frac{p}{\rho}\left(\frac{\partial \gamma_e}{\partial h}\right)_S,$$

and it is clear that if $\gamma_e$ is constant along an isentrope, then $\gamma_* = \gamma_e$. The quantity $\gamma_*$ is important in any isentropic process in which the change in speed of sound is important. Let us define the parameter $\Gamma$

$$(1.4.26) \qquad \Gamma = \tfrac{1}{2}(\gamma_* + 1) = \frac{1}{a}\left(\frac{\partial \rho a}{\partial \rho}\right)_S.$$

The parameter $\Gamma$ has the following properties for a general fluid:

1. The parameter $\Gamma$ must be greater than zero to ensure proper behavior of shock waves and other gasdynamic discontinuities such as detonations and deflagrations (see Hayes [7]). If this condition were not met various anomalous results would ensue, as for example the existence of expansion or rarefaction shocks.
2. The parameter $\Gamma$ is the correct replacement for the quantity $\tfrac{1}{2}(\gamma + 1)$ which appears in first-order viscous or inviscid wave theory (see Hayes [2; 7, Art. 5]).
3. The parameter $\Gamma$ is the correct replacement for the quantity $\tfrac{1}{2}(\gamma + 1)$ in the classical theory of transonic similitude and in all second-order subsonic and supersonic theories.
4. The quantity $\gamma_*$ equal to $2\Gamma - 1$ is a correct replacement for $\gamma$ in the combination $(\gamma - 1)/(\gamma + 1)$ appearing in the theory of Prandtl-Meyer flow. This theory is fundamental to the method of characteristics and is presented in Section 7.1.

The quantities $\gamma_e$ and $\gamma_*$ are both defined with respect to an isentropic process. A specification of these related quantities would characterize the behavior of a material with respect to isentropic changes. Knowing either $\gamma_e$ or $\gamma_*$ gives us no information with regard to the effects of changes in the entropy of the material.

## 5. Oblique and curved shocks

Over almost all of its extent, the enveloping shock on a body in hypersonic flow is oblique and curved. We shall extend our results on the normal shock to include the effects of obliquity, and shall examine briefly some of the effects of shock curvature.

Looking first at the case of the oblique shock pictured in Fig. 1–5, we imagine an observer who travels along the shock with a velocity equal to

$$(1.5.1) \qquad u_\infty = u_s = U \cos \sigma,$$

where $U$ is the free stream velocity and $\sigma$ is the inclination angle of the shock with respect to the free stream direction. With respect to such an observer the shock wave appears to be a normal one with an upstream velocity and Mach number equal to

$$(1.5.2a) \qquad v_\infty = \epsilon^{-1} v_s = U \sin \sigma,$$

$$(1.5.2b) \qquad M_n = U \sin \sigma / a_\infty = M_\infty \sin \sigma.$$

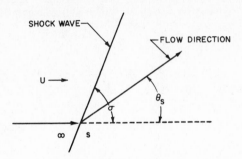

FIG. 1–5. Oblique shock.

The total enthalpy $H_n$ with respect to this observer is not the same as the total enthalpy $H$ of the free stream, but is related to it by

$$(1.5.3) \qquad H - H_n = \tfrac{1}{2} u_\infty^2 = \tfrac{1}{2} U^2 \cos^2 \sigma.$$

The thermodynamic properties of the gas on either side of the shock are the same for the moving observer as for a fixed observer. What is most important here is the basic idea that any oblique shock may be considered in terms of a normal one.

We may now calculate the angle between the shock and the flow direction behind the shock. The result is immediate

$$(1.5.4) \qquad \tan (\sigma - \theta_s) = v_s / u_s = \epsilon \tan \sigma,$$

where $\theta_s$ is the angle of deflection of streamlines passing through the shock.

We may note that if $\epsilon$ is small and the shock is not nearly normal, the streamlines behind the shock must lie close to it. If we differentiate (1.5.4) we obtain

$$(1.5.5) \quad (1 + \epsilon^2 \tan^2 \sigma)\frac{d\theta_s}{d\sigma} = (1 - \epsilon)(1 - \epsilon \tan^2 \sigma) - \tan \sigma \frac{d\epsilon}{d\sigma}.$$

With $\sigma$ equal to the Mach angle in the free stream, $\epsilon = 1$, $\theta_s = 0$, and $d\epsilon/d\sigma < 0$, so that $d\theta_s/d\sigma > 0$. For a normal shock with $\sigma = \frac{1}{2}\pi$, $\theta_s = 0$, and $d\theta_s/d\sigma = -\epsilon^{-1}(1 - \epsilon) < 0$. It is clear that the quantity $d\theta_s/d\sigma$ is zero for at least one intermediate value of $\sigma$, given by $\tan \sigma = \epsilon^{-1/2}$ if $\epsilon$ is constant. In general there is only one such angle, and this point on the curve of possible shock solutions is termed the detachment point. The flow deflection angle $\theta_s$ takes its maximum value at the detachment point. Shocks are termed weak or strong according to whether $\sigma$ is less than or greater than the value of $\sigma$ at detachment. However, except when we are considering this type of division, we shall be using the word "strong" to refer to a shock for which $M_n$ is large and $\epsilon$ close to $\epsilon_{\lim}$.

The sonic point refers to a shock for which the velocity behind the shock is sonic, with the condition

$$(1.5.6) \qquad\qquad u_s^2 + v_s^2 = a_s^2.$$

In general there is only one such point, and shocks are divided by this point into those termed supersonic and those termed subsonic, according to whether the velocity behind the shock is supersonic or subsonic. Normally the detachment point is subsonic and the sonic point is weak; this is the case in a perfect gas. However, Hayes in unpublished work has shown that an anomalous case is possible, with the detachment point supersonic and the sonic point strong. Such a case may only exist at high free stream Mach numbers. We shall implicitly assume that only the normal case occurs.

With the basic hypersonic limiting process $M_\infty \to \infty$ (A-lim) the sonic and detachment points generally remain distinct. In the special case of a perfect gas with constant ratio of specific heats these two points coalesce in the limit as $M_\infty$ becomes very large.

In considering curved shock waves we note first that the entropy of the gas just behind the shock is a function of the shock inclination angle. The mass flow $m$ across the shock is given by

$$(1.5.7) \qquad\qquad m = \rho_\infty v_\infty = \rho_\infty U \sin \sigma.$$

If now (1.4.5d), (1.4.7), and (1.5.7) are differentiated with respect to the shock angle, and combined with the differential state equation

$$(1.5.8) \qquad\qquad dh = T\, dS + \frac{1}{\rho}\, dp,$$

we arrive at a differential relation connecting the shock angle and the entropy behind the shock $S_s$

$$(1.5.9) \qquad T_s \frac{dS_s}{d\sigma} = U^2 \sin \sigma \cos \sigma \, (1 - \epsilon)^2.$$

We shall consider here only the relatively simple case of a curved shock in two-dimensional flow, and shall be interested primarily in the vorticity. To consider a more general type of curved shock would only lead us into more complicated mathematics and would not give a more useful result for the vorticity. A left-handed cartesian coordinate system is set up as shown in Fig. 1–6 with origin at the point of interest on the shock. The entropy

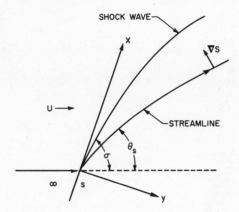

FIG. 1–6. Coordinate system (left-handed) for a curved shock.

behind the shock is constant along a streamline, and $|\nabla S|$ is used to designate the magnitude of the entropy gradient aligned as indicated in Fig. 1–6. Crocco's vorticity law as applied to a steady isocompositional two-dimensional isoenergetic (constant total enthalpy) flow states simply that the product of the vorticity and the speed is equal to $T$ times the magnitude of the entropy gradient. If we now calculate the magnitude of the entropy gradient in terms of the derivative of entropy immediately behind the shock and express the vorticity law with correct sign we obtain

$$(1.5.10) \qquad T_s |\nabla S_s| = \frac{T_s \, dS_s/dx}{\sin (\sigma - \theta_s)} = - \frac{U \cos \sigma}{\cos (\sigma - \theta_s)} \, \zeta_s,$$

where $\zeta$ is the vorticity defined here as

$$(1.5.11) \qquad \zeta = \frac{\partial u}{\partial y} - \frac{\partial v}{\partial x}$$

in the left-handed coordinate system of Fig. 1–6. Combining (1.5.10) with (1.5.4) and (1.5.9) gives us

$$(1.5.12) \qquad \zeta_s = -U\epsilon^{-1}(1-\epsilon)^2 \cos \sigma \frac{d\sigma}{dx}.$$

The term $d\sigma/dx$ is simply the curvature of the shock, and (1.5.12) gives a direct relation between shock curvature and vorticity behind the shock.

The relation (1.5.12) was first found by Truesdell [1], and has been later rediscovered by others who were unaware of Truesdell's work. Lighthill [3, pp. 14 and 15] found an extension of the result to a general curved shock, obtaining the vorticity immediately behind the shock in terms of the principal curvatures of the shock surface. Hayes [6] obtained a generalized result with a purely dynamic derivation in which the constancy of total enthalpy and Crocco's vorticity law are not used. The derivation of (1.5.12) utilizing Crocco's law has been followed above in order to emphasize the connection between entropy gradient and vorticity.

The vorticity produced by a curved shock is clearly strongly dependent upon $\epsilon$, and becomes very large as $\epsilon$ becomes small for a given shock inclination and curvature. However, behind a point on a shock for which the shock is normal, $\cos \sigma = 0$, and the vorticity is zero. Relation (1.5.12) may be readily shown to be valid in axisymmetric flow as well as in two-dimensional flow. If $\zeta_s$ is taken to be the component of vorticity perpendicular to both the streamline immediately behind the shock and the free stream direction, (1.5.12) is valid in general.

## 6. Mach number independence principle

The definition of hypersonic flow used by Oswatitsch [1; 2] involved the concept of the basic hypersonic limiting process $M_\infty \to \infty$ (A-lim). On the basis of his analysis of the flow of a perfect gas, he concluded that in the limit of very large values of $M_\infty$, the flow pattern and pressure coefficients on a body were independent of the value of $M_\infty$. The same result had been found by Sir Isaac Newton (see Section 3.1), for his model of a rarefied gas. We shall restate this important idea in a way which does not depend upon the gas being a perfect one.

The word similitude usually is used to refer to an equivalence between two physical problems which are different from each other in some fundamental way. Oswatitsch stated his result as a similitude. An inviscid perfect gas with constant ratio of specific heats is a self-similar fluid which for any flow field permits the general Mach number similitude obtained from dimensional analysis. The general similitude expressed by Oswatitsch utilizes this property of a perfect gas. When the result is properly restated for a general ideal (inviscid) fluid, it really states that in the limit $M_\infty \to \infty$ two flows with different values of $M_\infty$ are fundamentally identical, i.e., are not different from each other in any fundamental way. Although the result expressed for a general fluid may certainly be termed a similitude, it is preferable to consider it as an "independence principle". Such an independence principle is thus a special type of a similitude which is stronger than a general similitude.

In order that the flow field may be independent of the free stream Mach number $M_\infty$ it is necessary that at any point on the shock the density ratio $\epsilon$ be independent of $M_\infty$. From (1.4.14) it may be seen that $M_\infty$ must be sufficiently high that $M_n^{-2}$ or $(M_\infty \sin \sigma)^{-2}$ will be small compared with $\epsilon_\infty$ and that $\epsilon$ may be replaced by $\epsilon_{\mathrm{lim}}$. In order that $\epsilon_{\mathrm{lim}}$ be independent of $M_\infty$ as $M_\infty$ approaches infinity it is necessary that $\rho_\infty$ and $U$ be fixed in the basic hypersonic limiting process (A-lim) and that $a_\infty$ approach zero. These considerations have already been briefly discussed in Section 1.4. The requirement that $(M_\infty \sin \sigma)^{-2}$ be small is equivalent to our strong shock assumption (assumption C), which is thus a basic assumption for the independence principle. If the quantity $\epsilon_\infty$ is itself small, we need a stronger form of the assumption (C-strong).

With the condition that $M_\infty$ is sufficiently large that the strong shock approximation is valid, we may state the Mach number independence principle: The flow around a body and behind the bow shock depends only upon the density $\rho_\infty$ and the uniform velocity $U$ of the given gas in the free stream, and is independent of the free stream pressure $p_\infty$, enthalpy $h_\infty$, temperature $T_\infty$, and speed of sound $a_\infty$. A physical interpretation of the independence principle is that in a flow with $\rho_\infty$ and $U$ fixed the entire flow field becomes frozen as $a_\infty$ is reduced to extremely small values, and a proper limiting flow field is approached.

The justification of this principle comes readily out of the results of the previous two sections. The flow of interest about the body is separated from the free stream by a shock wave which is everywhere strong and for which $\epsilon$ may be taken to be $\epsilon_{\mathrm{lim}}$. The pressure, enthalpy, and other quantities immediately behind the shock are dependent only upon $\rho_\infty$, $U$, and $\sigma$, and may be considered independent of $p_\infty$ and $h_\infty$. Conditions immediately behind the shock may be considered to serve as boundary conditions for the flow field. Thus, a flow solution obtained for one sufficiently large value of $M_\infty$ will serve for another large value of $M_\infty$ if $\rho_\infty$ and $U$ are the same. With the assumption of uniqueness of the flow solution the independence principle follows immediately.

Since the flows behind the shock at two appropriate values of $M_\infty$ are essentially identical under our conditions, it is clear that the independence principle applies also to real-fluid effects such as those due to viscosity, and to the physical gasdynamics effects mentioned in the first section. The only possible exception to this is the structure of the shock wave itself. However, the mean molecular collision time in the gas in the free stream is much greater than the transit time of the gas through the shock wave, and the vector velocity of individual molecules differs but negligibly from the free stream velocity. We may conclude that the independence principle applies also to the structure of the shock wave.

The Mach number independence principle as we have stated it thus holds for boundary layers in hypersonic flows provided that the exterior inviscid flow follows the independence principle. Where the Mach number is sufficiently large, as for what we shall term (in Chapter IX) the strong interaction region, the independence principle holds even though the inviscid flow field is completely determined by the boundary layer. The independence principle does not hold on a flat plate for what we shall term weak interactions. The independence principle does hold for rarefied gas flows and free molecule flows with $M_\infty \sin \theta_b$ large.

Mathematically phrased, the Mach number independence principle states that if $\rho_\infty$ and $U$ are fixed, the solution within a fixed finite domain approaches a limiting solution uniformly in the limit $M_\infty \to \infty$.

As we have already remarked, as long as $M_\infty$ is finite, there is some point on the tail of the shock for which assumption C fails, and the independence cannot apply to the entire flow field including the shock tail. However, the body and the subsonic part of its wake are within the zone of action of only a relatively limited portion of the shock, and the flow on the body cannot be affected by the solution for the shock tail. Thus the failure of the independence principle on the shock tail is of no significance for the flow near the body.

## 7. Real-fluid effects

The flow of any fluid is influenced by a number of effects which are usually termed "real-fluid" effects, and which are neglected in ideal-fluid theory. These effects have their roots in the behavior of individual molecules, and the parameters that are important are the mean free path of kinetic theory and the mean free time between one collision and the next for a given molecule. A basic distinction must be made among the cases for which the mean free path of the gas is small, is of the same order of magnitude, or is large compared with an appropriate characteristic macroscopic scale of the flow field. In some cases it may be more convenient to make the corresponding distinction with respect to the mean collision time. In any case the temperature of the body is a fundamentally important parameter for the determination of real-fluid effects.

If the mean free path and the mean collision time are sufficiently small and the velocity and temperature gradients moderate we may consider the gas as a continuum in quasi-equilibrium for which the equilibrium equation of state may be used. In this case we shall refer to the real-fluid effects as "viscous" effects. Included among viscous effects besides viscosity are heat conduction, relaxation, the various types of diffusion, and irreversible chemical reaction. All of these viscous effects are dissipative in that they cause an increase in world entropy, and are subject to the laws of the relatively new science called Irreversible Thermodynamics. We shall be concerned with these viscous effects in hypersonic flow in Chapters VIII and IX.

At the other extreme, if the mean free path and the mean collision time are sufficiently large, we may completely neglect collisions between molecules for the purpose of determining effects on the body. In this case we have "free molecule flow", for which we need the laws of interaction of the gas molecules with the body. These laws are most simply, although empirically, expressed through the accommodation coefficients mentioned earlier. In Chapter X we shall present the basic theory of free molecule flow.

The intermediate or transition regime, for which the mean free path and mean collision time are of the same order of magnitude as an appropriate macroscopic scale and time, is called the rarefied gas flow regime or the superaerodynamic regime. If the mean free path in the fluid near the body is small but not quite negligibly so the phenomenon of slip flow may occur. The phenomenon of slip flow may not be too important in practical hypersonic flows on blunt bodies (see Section 10.1). If the mean free path is large but not quite large enough to ensure free molecule flow we may have to consider first-order collisions. The intermediate or transition regime and its importance are discussed in Section 10.1. The domain of rarefied gas flow includes many important unsolved problems for the theoretician. Analysis here must use the full formulation of the kinetic theory and requires nontrivial solutions to the Boltzmann equation. An example of an important unsolved problem of this type is the determination of the structure of a strong shock wave. About all that is clearly known about this problem is that the thickness of the shock is of the order of a few mean free paths in the gas behind the shock. A continuum approach for the problem of obtaining useful approximate solutions for certain rarefied gas flows is described in Section 10.2.

We shall now look at the relative orders of magnitude of the thicknesses of the various layers appearing in a viscous flow. The order of magnitude of the speed of sound behind the shock is given by

$$(1.7.1) \qquad\qquad a_s \sim \epsilon^{1/2} U \sin \sigma,$$

and the order of magnitude of the mean free path by

$$(1.7.2) \qquad\qquad \lambda_s \sim \frac{v_s}{a_s} = \frac{\mu_s}{\rho_s a_s},$$

where $\nu$ and $\mu$ are the kinematic and dynamic coefficients of viscosity, respectively. We use the symbol $\sim$ here to mean "of the same order of magnitude as". This mean free path measures the shock wave thickness if the shock is moderately strong. We neglect for the present the important difference between $\nu$ behind the shock and in the boundary layer and the difference between a cold and a hot body; this difference will be considered further in Chapters IX and X. With this rough approximation we may express the boundary layer thickness by

$$(1.7.3a) \qquad\qquad \delta^2 \sim \frac{\nu c}{U}$$

for a slender body, where $c$ is a chord length, and by

$$(1.7.3b) \qquad\qquad \delta^2 \sim \frac{\nu R_s}{\epsilon^{1/2} U}$$

for the nose of a blunt body, where $R_s$ is the radius of curvature of the shock. In these equations we are anticipating results to be obtained later. The shock layer thicknesses may also be expressed

$$(1.7.4a) \qquad\qquad \Delta \sim \epsilon c \sin \sigma$$

for the slender body (with a strong shock), and

$$(1.7.4b) \qquad\qquad \Delta \sim \epsilon R_s$$

for the blunt body. Combining these order-of-magnitude results gives us

$$(1.7.5a) \qquad\qquad \lambda_s \Delta \sim \epsilon^{1/2} \delta^2$$

for the slender body, and

$$(1.7.5b) \qquad\qquad \lambda_s \Delta \sim \epsilon \delta^2$$

for the blunt body.

With either a blunt body or a slender body we may conclude that if $\delta$ is small compared with $\Delta$ then $\lambda_s$ will be yet smaller compared with $\delta$, especially if $\epsilon$ is small. Thus, as long as we can distinguish a boundary layer as a narrow region distinct from the shock layer, we can consider the shock wave as infinitesimally thin. Also, we may then be assured of being in the usual continuum viscous regime. These questions are discussed later in Chapters IX and X.

For the most part, boundary layer theory in hypersonic flow is no different from boundary layer theory at lower speeds. On blunt bodies in particular, local flow velocities are subsonic or moderately supersonic over much of the region of interest. Boundary layers may be laminar or turbulent, and problems of transition on blunt bodies should be about the same as for supersonic flows, provided we have temperature distributions in the supersonic flow which are similar to those encountered in hypersonic flows. Apart from a characteristically hypersonic type of similar solution, the differences noted in hypersonic boundary layers in general are more of degree than of kind. The effects of temperature differences are more notable in hypersonic flows simply because temperature differences in hypersonic flows are generally larger. The importance of high temperatures in causing deviations from the perfect gas law and in making diffusion effects significant justifies our considering these effects as characteristically hypersonic. Boundary layer interactions are more prominent, because boundary layer thicknesses can easily be large enough in hypersonic flows to make the interaction problem particularly important.

We can roughly divide the interactions of viscous boundary layers with shock waves into two types, into "boundary layer induced" interactions and "shock induced" interactions. In the former category we include those cases in which the displacement thickness distribution of the boundary layer controls the strength of the shock from the front edge of the boundary layer. In the latter category we include those cases in which the boundary layer is already established upstream of the interaction and the interacting shock would have existed with no boundary layer at all. We shall not treat shock induced interactions in this book. Although this distinction is not an absolute one, it is a useful one, as the analytic approaches to the two types of interaction are quite different.

# CHAPTER II

# SMALL-DISTURBANCE THEORY

## 1. Introduction and basic equations

The variety of hypersonic flow theory appropriate for slender bodies is termed the small-disturbance theory. Here the word small has been used because the velocity perturbations are small compared with the free stream velocity and the pressures are small compared with the free stream dynamic pressure. However, the velocity perturbations are not small compared with the free stream sound velocity, and the pressure perturbations are not small compared with the free stream static pressure. Hence the disturbances are not at all small in the sense usually associated with linearized theory, and the small-disturbance theory is an essentially nonlinear one.

The small-disturbance theory is inherently connected with classical hypersonic similitude; the similitude may be considered as a direct result of the theory, or the basic equations of the theory appear as a consequence of applying the similitude concept. The idea of hypersonic similitude is due to Tsien [1], who investigated the two-dimensional and axisymmetric irrotational equations of motion. By showing equivalence of a steady hypersonic flow on a slender body with an unsteady flow in one fewer space dimensions, Hayes [1] pointed out that the similitude should apply to three-dimensional slender bodies in rotational flow. Subsequently other investigators, including Hamaker, Neice, and Wong [1], Goldsworthy [1], Oswatitsch [1; 2], Ehret, Rossow, and Stevens [1], and Rossow [1], have looked into various aspects of hypersonic similitude.

The establishment of hypersonic similitude, however, does not provide hypersonic flow solutions. The appropriate equations of motion must be written down and solutions obtained. Although some solutions were obtained previously by Goldsworthy [1] and Linnell [1] for particular cases, the first comprehensive study made outside of Russia was that of Van Dyke [2]. The Russian work is discussed at the end of this section. Van Dyke also coined the term "small-disturbance theory". We shall here follow a development which is similar to his, but with two important differences. We shall use a development which is suitable for a general inviscid fluid instead of only for a perfect gas, and which is suitable for treating unsteady flows. We shall also be following more closely the original equivalence idea of Hayes [1].

A parameter $\tau$ is introduced, whose purpose will be to serve as a measure of the maximum inclination angle of Mach waves in the flow field. In order to be able to define it in terms of known quantities, we shall require in the steady flow case that it be of the order of the maximum body inclination angle. Thus we define it as the thickness ratio or as the angle of attack of the body, whichever is larger. In unsteady flow we should use a maximum value of the lateral velocity of the surface divided by the free stream velocity if that quantity is of larger order than the thickness ratio. Thus $\tau$ is always defined in terms of the maximum inclination of individual particle paths near the body. If $M_\infty \tau$ is of the order of one or larger, the quantity $\tau$ as defined will serve as a measure of the maximum inclination angle of the Mach waves. If $M_\infty \tau$ is small, corresponding to linearized or almost linearized flow, we must replace $\tau$ by $M_\infty^{-1}$ where it is used as a measure of relative orders of magnitudes of various quantities. We shall assume in general that $M_\infty \tau$ is not small, and consider separately the modifications of the theory necessary when $M_\infty \tau$ is small. The slender-body assumption $\sin \theta_b \ll 1$ (B) which underlies the small-disturbance theory is equivalent to the requirement that $\tau$ is small. Although we shall be treating primarily the steady case, we shall keep the formulas in a form appropriate for discussing the unsteady case.

We assume that at the shock the inclination of individual particle paths is also of the order of magnitude $\tau$. Considering the steady case, and assuming that the shock is not a nearly normal one, we may conclude from (1.5.4) or may cite the result (4.1.10) obtained later that

$$(2.1.1) \qquad \tan \sigma = \frac{\tan \theta_s}{1 - \epsilon} + O\left(\frac{\epsilon \tan^3 \theta_s}{(1 - \epsilon)^3}\right).$$

Since $\tan \theta_s$ is of the order of magnitude $\tau$ so also is $\tan \sigma$ presuming only that $1 - \epsilon$ is not small.

With the shock inclination angle small, with $\tan \sigma$ of the order of $\tau$, we conclude not only that the lateral velocity components behind the shock are of order $U\tau$, but that the axial perturbation velocity component is of order $\tau$ times this, or of order $U\tau^2$. This suggests the transformation

$$(2.1.2) \qquad q_x = \tau q_x',$$

through which a reduced axial perturbation velocity component is introduced which is of the same order of magnitude as the lateral velocity. The subscript on the velocity component $q$ indicates its direction, and $x$ is the axial cartesian coordinate.

With the rough result of (1.7.1) we note that the Mach angle behind the shock is of the order of magnitude $\epsilon^{1/2}\tau$, and that the flow there is still hypersonic. Since $\epsilon^{1/2}$ is less than one, the inclination of the characteristics (in steady flow) is of the order of magnitude $\tau$. This suggests the transformation

$$(2.1.3) \qquad\qquad x = \tau^{-1}x',$$

through which reduced derivatives of various quantities in the axial direction are of the same order of magnitude as lateral derivatives.

With the transformations (2.1.2) and (2.1.3) we are ready to write down the equations of motion for the flow. We shall use vector notation, with the understanding that the vectors are two-dimensional, defined with respect to the $(y, z)$ space of the lateral coordinates. In accordance with the equivalence concept, the equations are expressed with respect to an observer who is fixed with respect to the fluid in the undisturbed free stream. In the coordinate system of such an observer, the axial velocity which appears is the perturbation, and the free stream velocity $U$ appears only in the formulation of boundary conditions.

The equations of continuity, momentum, and entropy are now expressed for the flow field:

$$(2.1.4a) \qquad \frac{\partial \rho}{\partial t} + \nabla \cdot (\rho \mathbf{q}) = -\tau^2 \frac{\partial \rho q_x'}{\partial x'},$$

$$(2.1.4b) \qquad \frac{\partial \mathbf{q}}{\partial t} + \mathbf{q} \cdot \nabla \mathbf{q} + \frac{1}{\rho} \nabla p = -\tau^2 q_x' \frac{\partial \mathbf{q}}{\partial x'},$$

$$(2.1.4c) \qquad \frac{\partial q_x'}{\partial t} + \mathbf{q} \cdot \nabla q_x' + \frac{\partial p}{\rho \partial x'} = -\tau^2 q_x' \frac{\partial q_x'}{\partial x'},$$

$$(2.1.4d) \qquad \frac{\partial S}{\partial t} + \mathbf{q} \cdot \nabla S = -\tau^2 q_x' \frac{\partial S}{\partial x'}.$$

The entropy equation here replaces the more usual energy equation. We are assuming the flow to be inviscid, and the entropy equation is more convenient for our purposes.

The boundary conditions at infinity are simply that the velocity is everywhere zero, and that the thermodynamic state of the fluid is uniform and is given. Thus $\rho_\infty$, $p_\infty$, $h_\infty$, and $a_\infty$ are known. The location of the surface of the body is expressed by an equation of the form

$$(2.1.5) \qquad\qquad f(x', y, z, t) = 0.$$

The boundary condition to be satisfied on the body is

$$(2.1.6) \qquad \frac{\partial f}{\partial t} + \mathbf{q} \cdot \nabla f = -\tau^2 q_x' \frac{\partial f}{\partial x'}.$$

In linearized and transonic small-disturbance theories a useful and permissible procedure is to satisfy this boundary condition on a suitable cylindrical mean surface instead of on the body itself. In hypersonic flow this procedure is never permissible because of the large gradients of the flow variables normal to the surface, and the boundary condition (2.1.6) must be satisfied on the boundary surface proper. The original paper of Tsien [1] was in error on this small but essential point.

The shape of the shock wave is given by an equation similar to (2.1.5), by

$$(2.1.7) \qquad g(x', y, z, t, \tau) = 0.$$

The conditions to be satisfied on the shock are all expressed in terms of the change in various quantities across the shock. Brackets are introduced here to mean the difference between the quantity inside the brackets after the shock and the same quantity before the shock. Thus, for example, the pressure jump is expressed

$$(2.1.8) \qquad [p] = p_s - p_\infty.$$

With this notation we may express the three conditions of (1.4.1) in the form

$$(2.1.9a) \qquad \left[ \rho \left( \frac{\partial g}{\partial t} + \mathbf{q} \cdot \nabla g \right) \right] = -\tau^2 \left[ \rho q_x' \frac{\partial g}{\partial x'} \right],$$

$$(2.1.9b) \qquad \left[ \rho \left( \frac{\partial g}{\partial t} + \mathbf{q} \cdot \nabla g \right)^2 + (\nabla g)^2 p \right]$$
$$= -\tau^2 \left[ 2\rho \left( \frac{\partial g}{\partial t} + \mathbf{q} \cdot \nabla g \right) q_x' \frac{\partial g}{\partial x'} + \left( \frac{\partial g}{\partial x'} \right)^2 p \right] + O(\tau^4),$$

$$(2.1.9c) \qquad \left[ \frac{1}{2} \left( \frac{\partial g}{\partial t} + \mathbf{q} \cdot \nabla g \right)^2 + (\nabla g)^2 h \right]$$
$$= -\tau^2 \left[ \left( \frac{\partial g}{\partial t} + \mathbf{q} \cdot \nabla g \right) q_x' \frac{\partial g}{\partial x'} + \left( \frac{\partial g}{\partial x'} \right)^2 h \right] + O(\tau^4).$$

In addition we have a condition corresponding to the two components of momentum not included in (2.1.9b), that the direction of the velocity jump is normal to the shock wave

$$(2.1.10a) \qquad [\mathbf{q}] = A \nabla g,$$

$$(2.1.10b) \qquad [q_x'] = A \frac{\partial g}{\partial x'}.$$

In (2.1.10) the quantity $A$ is a scalar proportionality factor, a function of position on the shock surface. Since $A$ is initially undetermined, the two-dimensional vector equation (2.1.10a) expresses a single condition. With the values of $A$ specified by (2.1.10a), equation (2.1.10b) expresses another single condition.

With $\tau$ sufficiently small we may neglect terms of order $\tau^2$ in (2.1.4) to (2.1.9), so that the right-hand sides of all these equations may be taken to be zero. We are here making the slender-body assumption (B). Omitting (2.1.4c), equations (2.1.4) to (2.1.10a) are the correct equations governing two-dimensional unsteady flow, with the variable $x'$ appearing only as a parameter. These equations give an analytic formulation of the principle that a three-dimensional hypersonic slender-body flow is equivalent to a two-dimensional unsteady flow. Once a solution to the two-dimensional unsteady problem has been obtained, (2.1.4c) and (2.1.10b) may be solved to obtain $q_x'$. The equations (2.1.4) to (2.1.10) with terms of order $\tau^2$ dropped are referred to as the small-disturbance equations.

An observation of Van Dyke [2] on the order of error is of interest and is quoted here: "The error in the various first-order small-disturbance theories decreases progressively from $O(\tau^{2/3})$ in transonic flow to $O(\tau)$ in linearized supersonic flow to $O(\tau^2)$ in hypersonic flow. Therefore, under the plausible assumption (confirmed by later examples) that these mathematical order estimates give a reasonable indication of the actual physical magnitude of error, the practical need for a second-order solution is seen to be greatest for transonic flow and least at hypersonic speeds."

We turn now briefly to the case of linearized or almost linearized flow, with $M_\infty \tau$ small compared with one. The same analysis we have made above could then be made with $M_\infty^{-1}$ in place of $\tau$, with the same arguments that $q_x'$ is of the same order of magnitude as the other unreduced velocity components and that derivatives with respect to $x'$ are of the same order of magnitude as derivatives with respect to the other unreduced coordinates. The terms to be dropped in order to obtain the small-disturbance equations would then be of order $M_\infty^{-2}$. It is not necessary to change our analysis above, however, if we simply recognize that the right-hand terms bearing the factor $\tau^2$ are really of order $M_\infty^{-2}$, and that, for example, $q_x'$ as defined by (2.1.2) is really of order $(M_\infty \tau)^{-1}$ times the other unreduced velocity components. Thus we are able to include the case of small $M_\infty \tau$ in our original analysis. But it is clear that we must assume not only that $\tau^2$ is small but that $M_\infty^{-2}$ is small, and that the basic hypersonic assumption (A) is needed for the small-disturbance theory in addition to the slender-body assumption (B).

The concept of the equivalence of a three-dimensional physical problem to a two-dimensional unsteady problem with a parameter or a two-dimensional or axisymmetric physical problem to a one-dimensional unsteady problem with a parameter has been very fruitful. This is because this concept has permitted immediate adaptation of certain known unsteady gasdynamic solutions to hypersonic problems and because it has provided a reduction of one in the number of essential independent variables in many unsteady problems. In addition, it gives an immediate physical conceptual picture of the meaning of hypersonic similitude. We shall refer to this concept as the equivalence principle. This principle states, in essence, that the flow as viewed in any transverse plane is independent of the flow in any other transverse plane. In the two-dimensional physical case we may liken the flow in a given transverse plane to the flow in a cylinder driven by a piston.

In case the basic flow field is a steady one the dependence upon $x'$ and $t$ is always a dependence upon the single variable $x' + U\tau t$. We have then, for example, that

$$(2.1.11) \qquad \frac{\partial f}{\partial t} = U\tau \frac{\partial f}{\partial x'}$$

and the basic equations may readily be changed to the steady-state form for an observer moving with the body. If the time-varying point of view is kept, the quantity $-(U\tau)^{-1}x'$ is a phase parameter indicating the delay or advance in time of the motion at the particular value of $x'$ as compared with that at $x' = 0$. In this case $x'$ is not a basic independent parameter, and the solutions with different values of $x'$ are identical except for a shift in the time scale equal to the phase parameter as defined above. On the other hand, in the unsteady case $x'$ is a basic independent parameter, and a different two-dimensional unsteady problem must be solved for each value of $x'$.

In the treatment above the quantity $\tau$ is considered as a constant which is small. To establish a similitude or to set up an expansion scheme to improve the small-disturbance solution we must consider $\tau$ as a parameter and the functional behavior with respect to $\tau$ of the various quantities occurring must be investigated. With the body shape given we may consider the function $f$ of (2.1.5) independent of $\tau$, but the shock shape function $g$ of (2.1.7) and the other variables of the problem are not. A direct procedure is to expand all quantities involved in power series in $\tau^2$. Equations (2.1.4) to (2.1.10) yield successive sets of equations independent of $\tau$ by the process of equating like powers of $\tau^2$. Perhaps it may also be desirable or necessary to deform the lateral coordinates according to the well-known P-L-L (Poincaré-Lighthill-Lin; see Lin [1]) method in order to obtain uniform convergence, with relations such as

$$(2.1.12a) \qquad y = \eta + \tau^2 y_1(\eta,\zeta) + \ldots$$

$$(2.1.12b) \qquad z = \zeta + \tau^2 z_1(\eta,\zeta) + \ldots .$$

Higher approximations based on the small-disturbance theory present an as-yet largely unexplored field.

The well known slender-body theory of subsonic, transonic, and supersonic flow (for bodies which have small aspect ratio as well as small thickness ratio) appears at first glance to be very similar to the hypersonic small-disturbance theory. In the slender-body theory the flow pattern is considered to be two-dimensional, with the axial variable acting as a parameter. This similarity is illusory, and there are significant differences between the two theories. Besides the requirement of small angles of incidence there are other very restrictive requirements for the validity of the slender-body theory, not only that the aspect ratio be small but also that the incidence angle vary smoothly along the body. The two-dimensionality of the slender-body theory is only a local property which holds sufficiently near the body, and does not exist over the entire flow field. And the pressure on the body is determined by the theory with an arbitrary additive function of the axial variable; this function can only be determined with the aid of the full three-dimensional equations, imposing conditions relatively far from the body. Thus the slender-body theory, useful in its place, lacks by far the generality of the hypersonic small-disturbance theory.

In Russia, some developments of the small-disturbance theory were made at an early date. Following the concept of the equivalence principle stated by Hayes [1], Bam-Zelikovich, Bunimovich, and Mikhailova [1] developed an appropriate theory and gave a more complete proof of the equivalence principle. Apparently completely independently, Il'yushin [1] developed the theory, and proved the equivalence principle.

Il'yushin's term for the equivalence principle is the "law of plane sections". He presents a careful order-of-magnitude analysis not unlike that given above, but restricted to a perfect gas. The unification of linearized theory with that for which $M_\infty \tau$ is not small is accomplished by using $\tau + M_\infty^{-1}$ in place of $\tau$ as a measure of wave inclination, in his analogues of our (2.1.2) and (2.1.3). Il'yushin considers a large number of examples analytically, including the case of a cone at zero incidence for which the exact solution of Taylor and Maccoll [1] was available but apparently not known to him. He also obtains the law of hypersonic similitude, referred to by him as the "method of affine models". In a footnote to his paper, which was published in 1956, he states that the paper was issued in a limited printing in 1948 and that it is reprinted without change. It is clear that this large delay in publication must have resulted from secrecy restrictions. Il'yushin gives no reference to any other work in gasdynamics, not even to the contemporary work of Bam-Zelikovich, Bunimovich, and Mikhailova of which he must have been aware.

The paper of Bam-Zelikovich, Bunimovich, and Mikhailova [1], although apparently not subject to any secrecy restrictions within Russia, has been unavailable to the authors. Our conclusions regarding their work are based primarily upon references to it in the literature.

## 2. Hypersonic similitude

Before we express the classical hypersonic similitude, let us look briefly at the concept of similitude itself. A similitude or similarity rule expresses an equivalence between two physical situations between which there is some intrinsic dissimilarity and which are thus not identical in all essential respects. The description of a physical situation may be expressed in functional form, with some quantity of physical interest expressed as a function of all the parameters (and functions) which determine the physical situation. The result which a similitude accomplishes is a reduction in the number of independent parameters on which the function depends. In general, a regrouping of the parameters in the original functional formulation is necessary in accomplishing this reduction.

The classical dimensional similitude afforded by dimensional analysis fits into this general definition, with the necessary regrouping of parameters yielding new dimensionless parameters according to the Pi theorem. It must be emphasized that we do not generally have full dimensional similitude in fluid mechanics. Dimensional similarity between two different fluid flows depends either upon certain self-similar properties of the fluid or upon a particular correspondence between the equations of state of two different fluids. This correspondence must be regarded as accidental unless the two fluids are themselves self-similar, or unless the equations of state are otherwise idealized, as with the ideal dissociating gas of Lighthill [3, §2.4] or with a van der Waal's gas. The self-similar fluid of most practical importance is the perfect gas of constant ratio of specific heats $\gamma$, and two perfect gas flows with the same value of $\gamma$ can be dimensionally similar. However, our policy in this treatment is to consider such a perfect gas as a special case.

The only general similitude for a general inviscid fluid is the geometric one between flows of the same fluid which is afforded by the scale transformation, in which the basic distance coordinates and the time coordinates are all changed by the same constant factor. The similitude states that, with a given inviscid flow, there can exist a similar one with a different scale but with the same values of the velocity and the thermodynamic state variables of the fluid at corresponding points. The functional dependence of any of these quantities may be expressed in a form independent of the absolute scale. The existence of steady conical flows depends upon the scale transformation, and thus such flows can exist in a general inviscid fluid. This scale similitude is taken for granted in all the inviscid flow theory treated here. Thus, for example, the lateral coordinates $y$ and $z$ will be kept in an unreduced form in this section, with no loss of generality.

The establishment of a similitude must be based upon an analysis of the physical situation in which certain simplifying assumptions have been made. These assumptions which have been used in the analysis become the fundamental assumptions underlying the resulting similitude. In general, the greater are the number of assumptions made, the smaller are the number of independent parameters remaining in the functional formulation and the more powerful is the similitude in relating equivalent systems. Conversely, the fewer are the demands made of the number of different systems which must be related as equivalent, the fewer are the assumptions which need to be made and the more general is the similitude in the classes of systems to which it may be applied.

In inviscid fluid theory the assumption is made that the viscosity is so small it may be neglected. The generalized Prandtl-Glauert similitude of supersonic flow theory assumes that the equations of motion may be linearized and permits a functional specification of the results in which there is no dependence upon the Mach number per se. The more usual Prandtl-Glauert similitude requires also the mean-surface approximation and permits results expressed as independent of the parameter $\sqrt{M_\infty^2 - 1}\, \tau$ per se, where $\tau$ is the thickness ratio or angle of attack.

Hypersonic similitude is the similitude which arises from the small-disturbance analysis of the previous section. Thus the assumptions underlying hypersonic similitude are the same as those made for the small-disturbance theory, and the characteristic one of these is the slender-body assumption (B) that $\tau$ is small. With the geometric similitude given by the scale transformation not considered, hypersonic similitude considers two flows as equivalent if both flows are given by the same solutions of the small-disturbance equations. With a general fluid the fluid must be the same for both flows. We shall consider primarily the case of steady flow, but shall discuss the unsteady case briefly in Section 2.7.

For classical hypersonic similitude we consider a family of bodies with related shapes, given by

$$(2.2.1) \qquad\qquad f(\tau x, y, z) = 0$$

in a system of coordinates fixed with respect to the body. The quantity $\tau$ remains defined as the thickness ratio (or angle of attack). Besides the angle of attack, various other geometric parameters must vary in proportion to $\tau$, such as aspect ratio and gap ratio. The body is placed in a uniform steady hypersonic flow with $U$, $\rho_\infty$, and $p_\infty$ given in the free stream. Taking the pressure as typical of the dependent variables, we may express the functional dependence of $p$, in general, as

$$(2.2.2) \qquad\qquad p = p(x, y, z;\ \tau, U, \rho_\infty, p_\infty).$$

Equation (2.2.2) is written for a particular fluid under consideration, and the functional dependence of $p$ upon the equation of state is understood. If $\tau$ is small, so that the small-disturbance theory is applicable, this functional dependence may be re-expressed as

$$(2.2.3) \qquad\qquad p = p(\tau x, y, z;\ U\tau, \rho_\infty, p_\infty).$$

The primary feature of hypersonic similitude is the reduction by one of the number of quantities upon which $p$ depends, from (2.2.2) to (2.2.3). Thus, in (2.2.3), there is no dependence of $p$ upon the parameter $\tau$ per se. Equation (2.2.3) may be reexpressed in terms of the pressure coefficient

$$(2.2.4) \qquad C_p = \tau^2 \Pi(\tau x, y, z; \ U\tau, \rho_\infty, p_\infty).$$

Similar expressions may be obtained for the other variables of the flow, with the lateral velocities proportional to $U\tau$ and the axial perturbation velocity to $U\tau^2$. The applicability of the concept of hypersonic similitude to a general fluid has been exploited independently by H. K. Cheng [1].

For an example we shall consider a simple Prandtl-Meyer flow under hypersonic conditions, and shall use the result (7.1.15) of Chapter VII for the turning angle. We replace the term representing $\sqrt{M^2 - 1}$ by $M$, and replace $H - h$ except in the differential by $\frac{1}{2}U^2$. The result is a simplified form of (7.1.15) appropriate for hypersonic flow

$$(2.2.5) \qquad \nu = -\frac{1}{U}\int \frac{dh}{a} = -\frac{1}{U}\int \frac{dp}{\rho a},$$

in which the integral is taken along an isentropic path and the turning angle $\nu$ is defined to be zero in the free stream. Note that the integral is one taken only with respect to thermodynamic variables. With $\rho_\infty$ and $p_\infty$ fixed both the initial point and the path of the integral are determined, and the value of $p$ will be given by the value of the integral. Thus we have

$$(2.2.6) \qquad p = p(U\nu, \rho_\infty, p_\infty).$$

The ray angle is simply the Mach angle less the turning angle in a Prandtl-Meyer flow, or

$$(2.2.7) \qquad \frac{y}{x} = \frac{a}{U} - \nu$$

in our hypersonic flow. The quantity $a$ has a functional dependence of the same form as does $p$ in (2.2.6). Hence we may write

$$(2.2.8) \qquad \frac{Uy}{x} = a - U\nu = Y(U\nu, \rho_\infty, p_\infty).$$

Assuming the functional relation in (2.2.8) may be reversed, we may express $U\nu$ in (2.2.8) in terms of $Uy/x$ and substitute in (2.2.6). The result is a new functional expression for $p$,

$$(2.2.9) \qquad p = p\left(\frac{Uy}{x}, \rho_\infty, p_\infty\right),$$

which is a relatively very simple special case of (2.2.3). It may be readily shown that the quantities $q_y$ and $U\tau q_x'$ have the same functional dependence as does $p$. Note that these results are for a general fluid.

If the fluid is a perfect gas with a constant ratio of specific heats $\gamma$, the single parameter $\gamma$ characterizes the complete equation of state. The addition of $\gamma$ as an independent parameter in (2.1.2) to (2.2.4) takes care of the functional dependence upon the equation of state. In addition, because of the self-similar properties of such a gas, we may drop the variables $\rho_\infty$ and $p_\infty$ provided that $U\tau$ is reduced to dimensionless form. To do this we need any quantity dependent upon the free stream state which has the dimensions of velocity. It is convenient to choose the free stream speed of sound for this purpose, already expressed for a general fluid (1.4.10b) by

$$(2.2.10) \qquad a_\infty^2 = \frac{\gamma p_\infty}{\rho_\infty}.$$

The quantity $U\tau$ is divided by $a_\infty$ and thus reduced to $M_\infty \tau$. This quantity $M_\infty \tau$ is the basic similarity parameter $K$ of classical hypersonic similitude

$$(2.2.11) \qquad K = M_\infty \tau.$$

Since $a_\infty$ is a function of $\rho_\infty$ and $p_\infty$, $K$ may be substituted for $U\tau$ in (2.2.3) or (2.2.4) if desired.

For a perfect gas, then, (2.2.4) may be reexpressed in the form

$$(2.2.12) \qquad C_p = \tau^2 \Pi(\tau x, y, z; \ K, \gamma).$$

The pressure coefficient of (2.2.4) or (2.2.12) may be expressed either relative to zero pressure or, more conventionally, relative to the free stream pressure. The free stream pressure coefficient relative to zero pressure must be of the form indicated by (2.2.12) but independent of the space coordinates, and is

$$(2.2.13) \qquad \frac{p_\infty}{\frac{1}{2}\rho_\infty U^2} = \frac{2\tau^2}{\gamma K^2}$$

for any fluid. A lift coefficient based upon a lateral projected area has the same dependence as does $C_p$, except that the coordinate variables do not appear. The same is true for a drag coefficient which is based on a projected frontal area. Using a lateral projected area as reference for both coefficients, we have

$$(2.2.14a) \qquad C_L = \tau^2 \Lambda(K, \gamma),$$

$$(2.2.14b) \qquad C_D \doteq \tau^3 \Delta(K, \gamma).$$

The complete similarity of shape imposed by (2.1.5) requires that the angle of attack $\alpha$ and the aspect ratio $\mathcal{R}$ of the body vary proportionally with $\tau$, and (2.2.14a) is usually expressed with $\alpha^2$ in place of $\tau^2$. The similitude gives no information on a hypersonic flow in which $\alpha$ and $\tau$ are varied independently.

We now turn to the Mach number independence principle or similitude of Oswatitsch discussed earlier, and ask what is the result of combining the two concepts. To use the independence principle, we must consider a limiting process in which $p_\infty$ approaches zero with the other parameters of the problem held fixed. The combined result, expressed for the pressure, is

$$(2.2.15) \qquad p = p(\tau x, y, z; \ U\tau, \rho_\infty)$$

to replace (2.2.3), or

$$(2.2.16) \qquad C_p = \tau^2 \Pi(\tau x, y, z; \ U\tau, \rho_\infty)$$

to replace (2.2.4). The functional dependence upon the equation of state is again understood.

For the perfect gas of constant ratio of specific heats, $a_\infty$ goes to zero in the limiting process, and the basic similitude parameter $K$ goes to infinity. By the independence principle we may neglect dependence upon $K$, and obtain

$$(2.2.17) \qquad C_p = \tau^2 \Pi(\tau x, y, z; \ \gamma)$$

in place of (2.2.12). The free stream pressure of (2.2.13) is zero in this limit. Oswatitsch [1, §5] has given suitable equations of motion for such a combined theory in two-dimensional and axisymmetric flow. We must note the severe limitations on such a combined theory. For its application not only must $\tau$ be small but $K$ must be very large. In terms of our earlier discussion on assumptions, A-strong or A-lim is required.

Comparisons of exact theoretical results and experimental results with the predictions of hypersonic similitude indicate a wide range of validity for the similitude. An experimental check of the similitude for yawed cones is shown in Fig. 2–1, taken from Hamaker, Neice, and Wong [1]. Some comparisons of exact theoretical results with results of the small-disturbance theory appear in Figs. 2–2 to 2–9 which accompany Sections 2.3 and 2.5; others appear in the references cited at the beginning of Section 2.1. This general agreement lends weight to the equivalence principle upon which hypersonic similitude is based. However, at moderately low Reynolds numbers on slender bodies the effects of the displacement thickness of the boundary layer (see Chapter IX) may be large enough to invalidate the similitude. If the Reynolds numbers on similar bodies are controlled so that the displacement thickness varies in direct proportion to the body thickness, hypersonic similitude should still hold (see Section 9.3). But in applying the small-disturbance theory with the displacement thickness taken into account, this displacement thickness may not be known a priori because of interactions of the type discussed in Chapter IX. In comparing experimental results with the results of the small-disturbance theory, a correction for the boundary layer thickness may be advisable. Such corrections were made, for example, by Kubota [1].

A full development of a viscous hypersonic similitude has not as yet been made, and we shall not attempt such a development here. We may note that

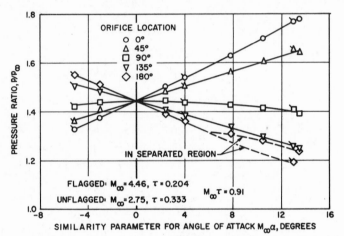

FIG. 2–1. Experimental check of hypersonic similitude for the pressure on yawed cones (Hamaker, Neice, and Wong [1]).

in such a similitude the quantity $\bar{\chi}$ or $M_\infty \, d\delta^*/dx$ of Chapter IX must be the same at corresponding points on two similar bodies. The drag coefficient with viscous effects included is proportional to $\tau^3$ as in (2.2.14b), as is the skin friction coefficient. An additional condition is needed to ensure that the quantity $g_b$ of Chapter VIII is fixed in the similitude. A development of viscous hypersonic similitude will appear in Hayes and Probstein [1].

### 3. Unified supersonic-hypersonic similitude

The Prandtl-Glauert similitude for general bodies in linearized steady supersonic flow has the quantity $\beta\tau$ as a basic similitude parameter, where

$$(2.3.1) \qquad \beta = \sqrt{M_\infty^2 - 1}.$$

In hypersonic flow $\beta$ is very close to $M_\infty$, and the similitude parameters merge. At moderate values of the Mach number the flow may be considered linearized if $\tau$ is small, and the classical hypersonic similitude as just presented is clearly incorrect. It has long been clear that the two similitudes for the two steady flow regimes may be joined by the simple process of replacing $M_\infty$ by

$\beta$ in hypersonic similitude. An examination of the derivation of the small-disturbance theory shows that the error incurred in this replacement is of no greater order than that of the errors inherent in the original theory.

This idea was explored and justified heuristically by Van Dyke [1; 2] for the case of a perfect gas of constant ratio of specific heats. The correct form of the unified similitude is obtained by replacing the parameter $K = M_\infty \tau$ by a "unified" hypersonic similarity parameter

$$(2.3.2) \qquad\qquad K' = \beta \tau$$

in the equations of functional dependence such as (2.2.12). In place of (2.2.13) we have

$$(2.3.3) \qquad\qquad \frac{p_\infty}{\frac{1}{2}\rho_\infty U^2} = \frac{2\tau^2}{\gamma K'^2} - \frac{2}{\gamma\beta^2 M_\infty^2} \,.$$

It is convenient to define a density coefficient to measure the difference between the density in the flow field and in the free stream,

$$(2.3.4) \qquad\qquad C_\rho = \frac{\rho - \rho_\infty}{\frac{1}{2}\rho_\infty U^2} \cdot \frac{p_\infty}{\rho_\infty} \,.$$

It may be noticed that the free stream density contribution to this density coefficient is the same as the free stream pressure contribution to the pressure coefficient and is given simply by the negative of (2.3.3).

We summarize here the unified similitude as given by Van Dyke for a perfect gas: The pressure coefficient relative to free stream pressure is given by (2.2.13) with $K$ replaced by $K'$, or by

$$(2.3.5) \qquad\qquad C_p = \tau^2 \Pi(\tau x, y, z; \ K', \gamma).$$

The density coefficient $C_\rho$ defined in (2.3.4) is given by an expression of exactly the same form. The velocity components $q_y, q_z$, and $q'_x = \tau^{-1}q_x$ are given by functional expressions of the form

$$(2.3.6) \qquad\qquad q_y = U\tau Q(\tau x, y, z; \ K', \gamma).$$

Note that the free stream pressure coefficient and the free stream density coefficient do not fit (2.3.5) because of the term $-2/\gamma\beta^2 M_\infty^2$ in (2.3.3), and hence that the absolute pressure and density do not follow the unified similitude.

In case the fluid is a general one and not a perfect gas the unification replaces (2.2.4) by

$$(2.3.7) \qquad\qquad C_p = \tau^2 \Pi(\tau x, y, z; \ K', \rho_\infty, p_\infty),$$

in which the understood hypersonic dependence on the particular equation of state is indicated by the presence of $\rho_\infty$ and $p_\infty$. If $K'$ is small enough so that only second-order effects need to be taken into account, we may replace (2.3.7) by

(2.3.8) $$C_p = \tau^2 \Pi(\tau x, y, z; \ K', \gamma_*),$$

where $\gamma_*$ is given by

(2.3.9) $$\gamma_* = \frac{1}{a^2}\left(\frac{\partial \rho a^2}{\partial \rho}\right)_s.$$

The quantity $\gamma_*$ was defined previously in (1.4.24), and a discussion of its relation to second-order supersonic theory is included at the end of Section 1.4.

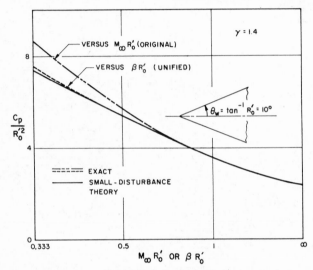

FIG. 2–2. Comparison of original and unified supersonic-hypersonic similarity law for a wedge of 10° half-angle (Van Dyke [2]).

Finally, if $K'$ is small enough so that only linear effects need be taken into account, the dependence on $\gamma_*$ may be dropped from (2.3.8). The resultant relation is the one given by the general Prandtl-Glauert similitude.

This unified form of hypersonic similitude is much superior in practice to the original form, permitting the results of experiment to be correlated well over a much wider range of Mach numbers than if $K = M_\infty \tau$ is taken as the similitude parameter. A comparison of the two forms of hypersonic similitude is given for the case of the flow on a wedge in Fig. 2–2. Henceforth we shall consider hypersonic similitude in steady flow to have this unified form.

### 4. Strip theory

There is another similitude which exists in hypersonic flow theory, for slender bodies which are flat. This similitude is known in linearized theory under the name of "strip theory". Strip theory has the essential features of a similitude, although this fact has not been generally recognized.

In order to demonstrate this similitude we may start with the small-disturbance equations and follow a process of reduction similar to that used for the classical hypersonic similitude. The body is assumed to be a "flat" one, with a characteristic lateral scale determined by an aspect ratio $Æ$. The meaning of flat will be that the body shape is close to a mean cylindrical surface, here considered to be the $(x, z)$ plane. For this strip theory the restrictions on the shape of the body are very similar to those of the mean-surface or quasi-cylinder assumptions of linearized theory, though these assumptions remain invalid in hypersonic flow. The coordinate $z$ is the lateral coordinate along the body, and $y$ is the coordinate normal to the mean surface. The body shape is expressed by a relation of the form

$$(2.4.1) \qquad f(\tau x, y, \tau Æ^{-1}z, t) = 0$$

instead of by (2.1.5), and the aspect ratio $Æ$ is considered as a parameter of the problem. We shall be interested in the case for which $\tau Æ^{-1}$ is small. By using the scale transformation discussed at the beginning of Section 2.2 we may put (2.4.1) into the more recognizable form

$$(2.4.2) \qquad f\left(\frac{x}{c}, \frac{y}{\tau c}, \frac{z}{Æc}, \frac{t}{\tau c}\right) = 0,$$

where $c$ is a reference axial dimension of the body.

The shape of the shock wave is assumed to be given by a relation of the same form as that for the body, and it is assumed that the shock forms a "flat" surface in the same sense as does the body. The value of $q_z$ behind the shock is then of order $\tau^2 Æ^{-1}U$ instead of $\tau U$ as in the general case. This suggests the transformation analogous to (2.1.2) by letting

$$(2.4.3) \qquad q_z = \tau Æ^{-1}q_z'.$$

with $q_z'$ of the same order of magnitude as $q_y$. We complete the analogy with the transformation corresponding to (2.1.3) by letting

$$(2.4.4) \qquad z = \tau^{-1}Æz'.$$

We may now complete the analysis and obtain equations analogous to (2.1.4) through (2.1.10). The terms on the right-hand side are now of order $\tau^2 Æ^{-2}$ instead of $\tau^2$.

The transformation (2.4.4) is clearly appropriate to produce derivatives with respect to $z'$ which are of the same order of magnitude as derivatives with respect to $y$ or $x'$. But we should justify that $q_z'$, which is of order $U\tau$

behind the shock, will remain of that order throughout. We pick out the appropriate small-disturbance momentum equation

$$(2.4.5) \qquad \frac{\partial q'_z}{\partial t} + q_y \frac{\partial q'_z}{\partial y} + \frac{\partial p}{\rho \partial z'} = -\tau^2 \cancel{R}^{-2} q'_z \frac{\partial q'_z}{\partial z'}.$$

and note that it is the pressure gradient term which controls changes in $q'_z$. That $q'_z$ remains of order $U\tau$ is then justified by the fact that $\partial p / \partial z'$ must be of the same order of magnitude as $\partial p / \partial x'$ or $\partial p / \partial y$.

Finally, we must justify the assumption made that the shock shape is flat if the body is flat. The thickness of the shock layer and body together is of the order $\tau c$ or $M_\infty^{-1} c$, whichever is greater, while the lateral dimensions of the shock are the same as those of the body, or $\cancel{R}c$. For the shock shape to be flat both $\tau\cancel{R}^{-1}$ and $M_\infty^{-1}\cancel{R}^{-1}$ must be small. The quantity $\tau\cancel{R}^{-1}$ must be small anyway, and the requirement that $M_\infty\cancel{R}$ be large follows unless the similitude parameter $K = M_\infty\tau$ is small. As in the development of the small-disturbance theory, we should replace $\tau$ in our order-of-magnitude analysis by the Mach angle $M_\infty^{-1}$ if $K$ is small, i.e. if we are near the linearized flow case.

For steady flow it is convenient to replace $M_\infty$ by $\beta$, whereby the quantity $M_\infty\cancel{R}$ becomes the reduced aspect ratio $\beta\cancel{R}$ of linearized supersonic theory. We note, incidentally, that the requirement for the applicability of strip theory in linearized supersonic flow is simply that $\beta\cancel{R}$ be large.

If $\tau^2\cancel{R}^{-2}$ (and also $M_\infty^{-2}\cancel{R}^{-2}$) is sufficiently small we may drop the right-hand sides in the reduced equations of which only (2.4.5) is given here. The resultant equations are the one-dimensional unsteady flow equations in $y$, with both $x'$ and $z'$ as parameters. To express the similitude we must first recognize that with $\cancel{R}$ variable, the quantity $\tau\cancel{R}^{-1}$ must appear in equations of the form (2.2.4). Thus to take the aspect ratio into account we should have expressed the functional dependence of the pressure coefficient in the form

$$(2.4.6) \qquad C_p = \tau^2 \Pi(\tau x, y, z;\ U\tau, \tau\cancel{R}^{-1}, \rho_\infty, p_\infty)$$

for the general case of slender-body flow instead of in the form of (2.2.4). With the similitude afforded by strip theory, with $\tau\cancel{R}^{-1}$ small, we may replace (2.4.6) by

$$(2.4.7) \qquad C_p = \tau^2 \Pi(\tau x, y, \tau\cancel{R}^{-1}z;\ U\tau, \rho_\infty, p_\infty).$$

The strip theory similitude amounts to this elimination of dependence upon $\tau\cancel{R}^{-1}$. Further reduction for the case of a perfect gas or the development of a unified form to fit the supersonic case may be carried out exactly as was done above for classical hypersonic similitude. With strip theory valid, the analogy of a two-dimensional physical flow to flow in a cylinder driven by a piston applies also to three-dimensional flows.

Strip theory is applicable to more general shapes, with the requirement that the body surface approximate a smooth reference cylinder or mean surface. The coordinate system must be constructed suitably, with one lateral coordinate normal to the mean surface and the other tangential to it. The reference lateral scale cannot be greater than a characteristic lateral dimension of the mean surface, such as the radius of an annular wing.

## 5. Examples of small-disturbance solutions

In order to illustrate the small-disturbance theory we shall present the results of the application of the theory to a few simple problems. The cases we shall consider are those of the wedge, the plane ogive, the cone, and the ogive of revolution. Our results are all taken from the basic report of Van Dyke [2] (see also Van Dyke [3]), to which the reader is referred for details of the calculations. In accordance with our statement made at the end of Section 2.3 we have followed Van Dyke in using the unified form of the hypersonic similitude parameter in expressing the results. The assumption of a perfect gas of constant ratio of specific heats is made throughout, and the diatomic value of $\gamma$ equal to 1.4 or 1.405 was used in computing the curves.

In either the two-dimensional case or the axisymmetric case the body shape is given by a function $R(x)$ in Van Dyke's notation, equal to $y$ or $r$. The slope of the body at the nose is given by

$$(2.5.1) \qquad R_0' = R'(0) = (\tan \theta_b)_0$$

with the prime denoting differentiation. The quantity $R_0'$ is the quantity $\tau$ of our presentation of the small-disturbance theory, and the basic similitude parameter is thus $\beta R_0'$. In Figs. 2–3 through 2–9 taken from Van Dyke [2] are plotted various quantities against $\beta R_0'$. For convenience in including the limit $\beta R_0' = \infty$ the abscissas of these plots have been made linear in $(\beta R_0')^{-1}$.

For the wedge the small-disturbance result was found by Linnell [1] (see also Ivey and Cline [1]) and is

$$(2.5.2) \qquad \frac{C_p}{R_0'^2} = \frac{2\tan\sigma_0}{R_0'} = \frac{\gamma+1}{2} + \sqrt{\left(\frac{\gamma+1}{2}\right)^2 + \frac{4}{\beta^2 R_0'^2}}$$

with the unified parameter substituted for $M_\infty R_0'$. This result may be obtained from the results of Sections 1.4 and 1.5, and it may be noted that within the accuracy of the small-disturbance theory the quantity $\frac{1}{2}(\gamma+1)$ expressed in (2.5.2) is simply $2/(1 - \epsilon_{\lim})$. Note also that (2.5.2) expresses a result both for pressure and for shock position. This result with $\gamma = 1.4$ is plotted on Fig. 2–3, together with pressure curves for thick wedges for comparison. Also for comparison is the same curve for $\gamma = 1$; the ordinate of this curve at $\beta R_0' = \infty$ gives the Newtonian value, from the so-called Newtonian theory to be discussed later.

The body shape for the plane ogive is expressed in the form

$$(2.5.3) \qquad y = R_0'x + \tfrac{1}{2}R_0''x^2 + O(x^3),$$

and $R_0''$ is the curvature of the body evaluated at the nose. The curvature of the shock $d \tan \sigma/dx$ evaluated at the nose divided by the body curvature

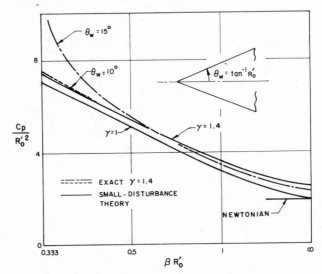

FIG. 2–3. Pressure coefficient on a wedge in small-disturbance theory
(Van Dyke [2]).

$R_0''$ is denoted by $l$ and is plotted for $\gamma = 1.4$ in Fig. 2–4. The pressure gradient along the body evaluated at the nose is given in Fig. 2–5. For comparison, some exact results of Kraus [1] for thick ogives have been shown, and also the values given by the Newtonian theory. It may be noted that for the "uncorrected Newtonian" pressure without the necessary centrifugal correction of Busemann (see Section 3.1), the ordinate in Fig. 2–5 would be 4.

For the cone and ogive of revolution the calculations were made for $\gamma = 1.405$ in order to permit a direct comparison with the solutions tabulated by Kopal [1]. For the cone, the ratio of cone angle to shock angle $R_0'/\tan \sigma_0$ is plotted in Fig. 2–6, and the pressure coefficient is plotted in Fig. 2–7. Also plotted in Fig. 2–7 are the corresponding linearized, second-order, and Newtonian results, and some exact results for thick cones taken from Kopal [1].

For the ogive of revolution, the ratio $l$ of the shock curvature to body curvature at the nose is given in Fig. 2–8. Also presented here are some exact results of Shen and Lin [1] for thick ogives. The pressure gradient

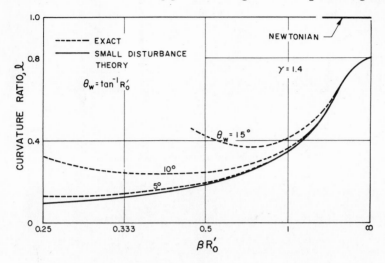

FIG. 2–4. Initial ratio of shock to body curvature for a plane ogive (Van Dyke [2]).

along the body evaluated at the nose is given in Fig. 2–9, with Newtonian, tangent-cone, and cone-expansion results also given for comparison. The tangent-cone approximation is discussed in Section 7.3. The cone-expansion

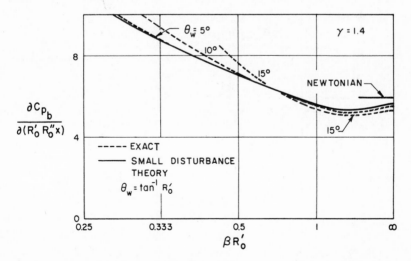

FIG. 2–5. Initial pressure gradient on a plane ogive (Van Dyke [2]).

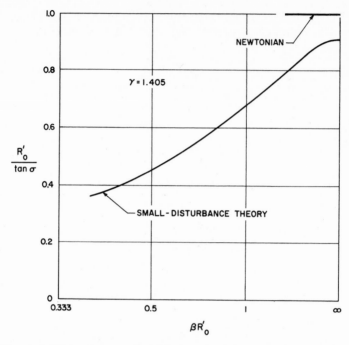

FIG. 2–6. Ratio of cone angle to shock angle (called $\delta/\tau$ in Van Dyke [2]).

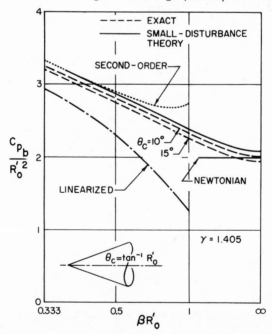

FIG. 2–7. Pressure coefficient on a cone (Van Dyke [2]).

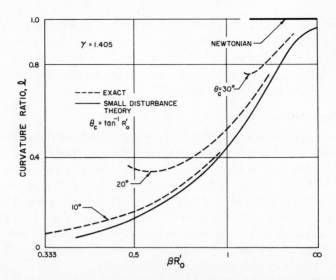

FIG. 2–8. Initial ratio of shock to body curvature for an ogive of revolution (Van Dyke [2]).

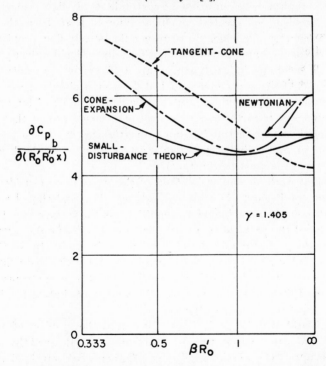

FIG. 2–9. Initial pressure gradient on an ogive of revolution (Van Dyke [2]).

method is the same as the shock-expansion method, applied to the three-dimensional flow field immediately behind the locally conical shock at the nose. The shock-expansion approximation is discussed in Section 7.2. As with the plane ogive, the ordinate in Fig. 2–9 for the incorrect "uncorrected Newtonian" pressure would be 4.

## 6. Similar solutions

We shall examine next a particular group of solutions to the small-disturbance equations, comprising those solutions for two-dimensional and axisymmetric steady flow which are self-similar. Such solutions are termed similar solutions, and have the property that the solution in the lateral variable $y$ or $r$ at one value of $t$ (or of $x$ for the corresponding hypersonic steady flow) is similar to the solution at any other value of $t$. This self-similar property permits a decrease in the number of essential independent variables from two to one, and yields a treatment using ordinary differential equations instead of partial differential equations.

Most of the investigations of similar solutions have been carried out with unsteady problems with suitable symmetry in mind, although many of them are directly applicable to our related hypersonic steady flow problems. The unsteady problems of greatest practical interest have been those with spherical symmetry, for which no corresponding steady flow problems exist (barring, of course, hypersonic flows in a four-dimensional universe). Many well known solutions in gasdynamics are self-similar; examples include Prandtl-Meyer flows, supersonic attached flows on a circular cone, and the flows in idealized shock tubes. But the similar solutions of interest to us here are different from the more classical ones mentioned in that the gas must have self-similar thermodynamic properties (i.e. must be a perfect gas of constant $\gamma$), and a similar behavior must be required of shock waves of varying strength ($\epsilon$ must be constant).

The earliest work on similar solutions of the type we are considering was carried out by Bechert [1] and by Guderley [1]. Guderley derived the appropriate equations and boundary conditions for the problems we shall treat below, reduced the problem to a single first-order differential equation, and applied his theory to the problem of implosions. In his treatment Guderley gives a detailed study of the various singular points of the basic differential equation. Bechert's earlier work was mostly limited to a polytropic gas and is therefore of little practical interest. His main contribution lies in introducing the concept of such solutions.

During World War II, G. I. Taylor [1] solved the problem of a violent spherical explosion; publication of his results was delayed by security restrictions until 1950. Following Taylor's approach Sakurai [1; 2], S. C. Lin [1], Latter [1], Lees and Kubota [1], and Kubota [1] treated a number of related problems.  Lin also noted that the result he had obtained for a violent cylindrical explosion would apply to an axisymmetric hypersonic steady flow.  Cheng and Pallone [1] and Lees and Kubota developed the analogy further and presented comparisons of the theory with experiment. All these authors were apparently unaware of the extensive early work of various Russian authors.

In Russia the term used for these solutions is "automodel", etymologically equivalent to "self-similar".  Two authors are predominant in the Russian development of similar solutions, Sedov and Stanyukovich.  Sedov obtained the equations of Guderley in somewhat more general form [1], and obtained an analytic solution for the problem of a violent spherical explosion [2], the same problem for which Taylor obtained a numerical solution.  Presentations of his theory appear in editions of his book on similitude [3], beginning with the second edition.  Following Sedov's approach, Krasheninnikova [1] and Chernyi [2; 3] treated a number of related problems.  The analogy with steady hypersonic flows following the equivalence principle was developed by Grodzovskii [1] and Chernyi [4; 5; 6].  Stanyukovich, e.g. in [1], has also investigated several types of similar solutions;  a part of his recent book [2] is devoted to such solutions.

The approach we shall use is that of Sedov, with part of his notation unchanged and part altered to fit the remainder of this volume.  The gas is assumed to be a perfect gas with constant ratio of specific heats $\gamma$, and the flow is assumed to have planar, cylindrical, or spherical symmetry.  Uniformly in this book we shall use the integer $j$ to denote one less than the number of lateral space dimensions involved.  Thus $j$ takes the value 0 in the planar case, the value 1 in the cylindrical case, and the value 2 in the spherical case. In the standard Russian notation the symbol $\nu$ is used for $1 + j$.

Sedov's parameters $\nu$, $\delta$ (4th Edition) or $q$ (3rd Edition), $k$, $s$, and $m$ used in Sedov [3] are replaced in our development by

(2.6.1a) $$\nu = 1 + j,$$

(2.6.1b) $$\delta \text{ or } q = k,$$

(2.6.1c) $$k = \omega - 3,$$

(2.6.1d) $$s = 0,$$

(2.6.1e) $$m = -1.$$

The parameters $s$ and $m$ are set equal to 0 and $-1$, respectively, with no loss of generality in the problems we are considering.  The change from Sedov's $k$ to $\omega$ is motivated by the fact that we shall be most interested in the case for which $\omega = 0$.

The basic problem posed is one in one space dimension and time, for which the three equations of motion may be written

$$(2.6.2a) \qquad v_t + vv_r + \rho^{-1}p_r = 0,$$

$$(2.6.2b) \qquad \rho_t + (\rho v)_r + jr^{-1}\rho v = 0,$$

$$(2.6.2c) \qquad (p\rho^{-\gamma})_t + v(p\rho^{-\gamma})_r = 0,$$

with subscripts denoting partial differentiation, with $r$ used to denote the one spatial coordinate, and with $v$ the velocity in the $r$ direction. If $j = 0$, $r$ is simply $y$. Dimensionless variables $V$, $R$, and $P$ replacing the dependent variables above are defined

$$(2.6.3a) \qquad v = rt^{-1}V,$$

$$(2.6.3b) \qquad \rho = Ar^{-\omega}R,$$

$$(2.6.3c) \qquad p = Ar^{2-\omega}t^{-2}P,$$

where $A$ is a constant with suitable dimensions, and $\omega$ is a dimensionless parameter; $\omega$ will equal 0 for the solutions of most practical interest. These new variables are required to be functions only of a single dimensionless independent variable $\lambda$, which is defined by the relation

$$(2.6.4) \qquad \lambda = Brt^{-k},$$

where $B$ is a constant with suitable dimensions and $k$ is a dimensionless exponent. The variable $\lambda$ is constant on a path for which $r$ is proportional to $t^k$, or to $x^k$ in an equivalent steady hypersonic flow. Substituting (2.6.3) and (2.6.4) into (2.6.2) we obtain the set of ordinary differential equations

$$(2.6.5a) \qquad \lambda\left[(V - k)V' + \frac{P'}{R}\right] = -V(V - 1) - (2 - \omega)\frac{P}{R},$$

$$(2.6.5b) \qquad \lambda\left[V' + (V - k)\frac{R'}{R}\right] = -(1 + j - \omega)V,$$

$$(2.6.5c) \qquad \lambda(V - k)\left[\frac{P'}{P} - \gamma\frac{R'}{R}\right] = -2(V - 1) - \omega(\gamma - 1)V,$$

in which the primes indicate differentiation with respect to $\lambda$.

In order to reduce the set of differential equations (2.6.5) to a single one, the new dependent variable $z$ is introduced to replace the variable $P$,

$$(2.6.6) \qquad z = \frac{\gamma P}{R}.$$

This variable is also dimensionless, and is equal to $t^2/r^2$ (or $x^2/U^2r^2$ for the equivalent steady problem) times the square of the speed of sound. From (2.6.5) may be obtained the single differential equation

$$(2.6.7) \quad \frac{dz}{dV} = \frac{z\begin{Bmatrix}[2(V-1)+j(\gamma-1)V](V-k)^2 \\ +(\gamma-1)(1-k)V(V-k)-[2(V-1)+\kappa(\gamma-1)]z\end{Bmatrix}}{(V-k)\{V(V-1)(V-k)-[(1+j)V-\kappa]z\}},$$

in which $P$, $R$, and $\lambda$ do not appear. The solution of this equation under appropriate boundary conditions is the essential step in the problem. The parameter $\kappa$ appearing in (2.6.7) is defined by

$$(2.6.8) \quad \kappa = \frac{2(1-k)+k\omega}{\gamma}.$$

Once a solution for $z(V)$ is obtained from (2.6.7), $\lambda$ and $R$ may be obtained by quadratures over $V$. The relations to be used are also obtainable from (2.6.5), and are

$$(2.6.9a) \quad \frac{d\ln\lambda}{dV} = \frac{z-(V-k)^2}{V(V-1)(V-k)-[(1+j)V-\kappa]z},$$

$$(2.6.9b) \quad \frac{d\ln(V-k)R}{d\ln\lambda} = -\frac{(1+j-\omega)V}{(V-k)}.$$

Let us now briefly examine the equations obtained. We shall call a line in the $(r, t)$ space for which $\lambda$ is constant, for which $r$ is proportional to $t^k$, a "similarity line". And we shall term a straight line through the origin in this space a "radial line". These two families of lines do not coincide unless $k = 1$. At a point for which $V = k$ the similarity line corresponds to a streamline; thus $V = k$ is the boundary condition on a flow boundary whose trajectory is a similarity line. At a point for which $z = (V - k)^2$ the similarity line is one of the two characteristics in the flow field. Except in certain singular cases the variable $\lambda$ has an extremum at such a point, which therefore is a type of branch point. The similarity line in this case is a limiting line of the flow field, an envelope of the characteristics. In general, $z$ must be greater than $(V - k)^2$ for flows of physical interest. The sign of $z - (V - k)^2$ changes across a shock wave which lies on a similarity line. For further details the reader is referred to Sedov [3].

In order to obtain a similar solution we must provide boundary conditions with suitable similar properties. In this respect the shock conditions are most critical, and unless $k = 1$ we must assume that the pressure in front of the shock is small enough that we may take the $\epsilon_{\text{lim}}$ given by (1.4.18) in place of $\epsilon$. In addition, the density in front of the shock must be proportional to a power $-\omega$ of the distance variable $r$. In the problems of interest to us the density in front of the shock will be constant, and we shall set $\omega = 0$ later. The shock trajectory must be a similarity line in order for the entire solution to be similar. With the gas in front of the shock at rest and the density there given by

$$(2.6.10) \qquad\qquad \rho_\infty = Ar^{-\omega}$$

the independent variables take on the values

$$(2.6.11a) \qquad\qquad V_\infty = 0,$$
$$(2.6.11b) \qquad\qquad R_\infty = 1,$$
$$(2.6.11c) \qquad\qquad P_\infty = 0,$$
$$(2.6.11d) \qquad\qquad z_\infty = 0,$$

in front of the shock. The shock conditions, with $\epsilon$ given by (1.4.18), give us the boundary values for the variables immediately behind the shock

$$(2.6.12a) \qquad\qquad V_s = \frac{2k}{\gamma + 1},$$

$$(2.6.12b) \qquad\qquad R_s = \frac{\gamma + 1}{\gamma - 1},$$

$$(2.6.12c) \qquad\qquad P_s = \frac{2k^2}{\gamma + 1},$$

$$(2.6.12d) \qquad\qquad z_s = \frac{2\gamma(\gamma - 1)k^2}{(\gamma + 1)^2}.$$

The subscripts $\infty$ and $s$ here are equivalent to Sedov's 1 and 2.

If the other boundary condition is on a flow boundary whose trajectory is a similarity line, the boundary condition on $V$ is simply

$$(2.6.13) \qquad\qquad V_b = k.$$

A detailed examination of the basic differential equation (2.6.7) shows that the corresponding value of $z_b$ is infinite, finite, or zero as the exponent $k$ is less than, equal to, or greater than one. The pressure and the quantity $P_b$ remain finite, while the density and $R_b$ must be zero, finite, or infinite, respectively, for these three cases. Also, the exponent $k$ must be greater than a minimum value in order that $\lambda_b$ be positive (body thickness positive). This value of $k$ corresponds to a particular solution characterized by constant total energy. We shall not go into all the detailed considerations on which these conclusions are based; the reader may consult Sedov's book [3] or the article of Lees and Kubota [1]. We must investigate the solution of constant total energy in order to determine the critical minimum value of the exponent

$k$. This particular solution is of considerable interest in its own right. It can represent the solution on the after part of a blunted slender body in steady hypersonic flow.

The constant-energy solution is the same as that mentioned above for a violent explosion, obtained numerically by Taylor and analytically by Sedov. This solution is often referred to as the "blast wave" solution. A total energy integral is defined by

$$(2.6.14) \qquad E(t) = \int \left( \frac{p}{\gamma - 1} + \frac{\rho v^2}{2} \right) r^j \, dr,$$

with the integral taken over the entire flow field; for a similar solution this lies between two fixed values of $\lambda$, corresponding to the shock and to the body or analogous boundary. The quantity $E$ is the energy per unit area on one side of the plane $r = 0$ in the planar case, the energy per unit depth per radian in the cylindrical case, and the energy per unit solid angle in the spherical case. Using (2.6.3) and (2.6.4) we may re-express the energy integral

$$(2.6.15) \qquad E = A B^{-(3+j-\omega)} t^{(3+j-\omega)k-2} \int_{\lambda_b}^{\lambda_s} \left( \frac{P}{\gamma - 1} + \frac{R V^2}{2} \right) \lambda^{2+j-\omega} \, d\lambda.$$

A constant-energy solution is one for which this energy is constant, or for which

$$(2.6.16) \qquad k = \frac{2}{3 + j - \omega}.$$

In general, there may be no moving flow boundary in the flow corresponding to a constant-energy solution, as with finite pressure the boundary would perform work on the system. The boundary condition which replaces (2.6.13) is that the solution extend to $\lambda = 0$. The variable $z$ must be infinite there, and examination of (2.6.7) and (2.6.9a) shows that $(1 + j)V - \kappa$ must vanish. We first note that with (2.6.16), the expression for $\kappa$ (2.6.8) may be restated

$$(2.6.17) \qquad \kappa = \frac{(1 + j)k}{\gamma}$$

for constant-energy solutions. The boundary condition which replaces (2.6.13) is thus

$$(2.6.18) \qquad V_b = \frac{k}{\gamma}; \quad \lambda_b = 0.$$

As before, the density and $R_b$ are zero and the pressure is finite. But because of the form of (2.6.3c) the quantity $P_b$ is infinite. We have implicitly assumed that $2 - \omega > 0$ and $k < 1$ above.

Sedov's analytic solution to the constant-energy problem is

$$(2.6.19) \qquad z = \frac{(\gamma - 1)V^2(k - V)}{2(V - k/\gamma)} \, ,$$

which satisfies the boundary conditions given above. That (2.6.19) is a solution to the basic equation (2.6.7) is not evident at a glance but may be readily checked. Sedov found the solution by using energy considerations. In the solution of interest here the energy is constant not only for the entire flow field but also between any two similarity lines. Thus there may be no energy transfer across a similarity line. Noting that the velocity of a similarity line is $krt^{-1}$, we may set the energy transfer per unit area across such a line equal to zero,

$$(2.6.20) \qquad \left(\frac{p}{\gamma - 1} + \frac{\rho v^2}{2}\right)\left(v - \frac{kr}{t}\right) + pv = 0.$$

The first term above represents transport of internal and kinetic energy, and the second term represents work done. The solution (2.6.19) of Sedov is directly obtainable from (2.6.20).

The total energy integral may be expressed in the form

$$(2.6.21) \qquad E = AB^{-2/k}e(\gamma, j, \omega)$$

for the constant-energy case, where $e$ represents the integral appearing in (2.6.15). In order to correlate the total energy in a flow or explosion of this type with the initial density distribution and the kinematics of the shock wave, it is necessary to calculate the quantity $e$. And of course it is necessary to multiply $E$ by an appropriate depth or angle factor, for example by the total solid angle $4\pi$ with a spherical explosion.

In expressing the complete constant-energy solution it is convenient to introduce two parameters $\varphi$ and $\Phi$ which serve to give us expressions of simpler form. We repeat (2.6.16) and write

$$(2.6.22a) \qquad k = \frac{2}{3 + j - \omega} \, ,$$

$$(2.6.22b) \qquad \varphi = k[\gamma + 1 + j(\gamma - 1)],$$

$$(2.6.22c) \qquad \Phi = k\left(\frac{\gamma + 1 - \varphi}{\varphi} + \frac{\gamma - 1}{2\gamma - \varphi}\right) ;$$

the quantity $\Phi$ is Sedov's $\alpha_1$.

We now define the following functions of $V$, each of which may be shown from (2.6.12a) to take the value 1 immediately behind the shock:

$$(2.6.23a) \qquad F_1(V) = \frac{\gamma + 1}{2k}\, V,$$

$$(2.6.23b) \qquad F_2(V) = \frac{\gamma + 1}{\gamma - 1}\left(1 - \frac{1}{k}\, V\right),$$

$$(2.6.23c) \qquad F_3(V) = \frac{\gamma + 1}{\gamma - 1}\left(\frac{\gamma}{k}\, V - 1\right),$$

$$(2.6.23d) \qquad F_4(V) = \frac{\gamma + 1}{\gamma + 1 - \varphi}\left(1 - \frac{\varphi}{2k}\, V\right).$$

The function $F_3$ takes the value zero on the axis, as we may note from (2.6.18). We now define the constant $B$ of (2.6.4) so that $\lambda_s = 1$. The quadratures of (2.6.9) together with the basic solution (2.6.19) then yield the results for a given value of the time

$$(2.6.24a) \qquad \frac{r}{r_s} = \lambda = F_1^{-k}\, F_3^{\frac{k(\gamma-1)}{2\gamma - \varphi}}\, F_4^{-\Phi},$$

$$(2.6.24b) \qquad \frac{v}{v_s} = \frac{\gamma + 1}{2k}\, \lambda V = F_1^{1-k}\, F_3^{\frac{k(\gamma-1)}{2\gamma - \varphi}}\, F_4^{-\Phi},$$

$$(2.6.24c) \qquad \frac{\rho}{\rho_s} = \frac{\gamma - 1}{\gamma + 1}\, \lambda^{-\omega}\, R = F_1^{k\omega}\, F_2^{-\frac{k(2+2j-\gamma\omega-\omega)}{2-\varphi}}\, F_3^{\frac{k(1+j-\gamma\omega)}{2\gamma - \varphi}}\, F_4^{\frac{2(1+j)-\omega\varphi}{2-\varphi}\Phi},$$

$$(2.6.24d) \qquad \frac{T}{T_s} = \frac{(\gamma + 1)^2}{2\gamma(\gamma - 1)k^2}\, \lambda^2 z = F_1^{2(1-k)}\, F_2\, F_3^{-\frac{k(1+j-\gamma\omega)}{2\gamma - \varphi}}\, F_4^{-2\Phi},$$

$$(2.6.24e) \qquad \frac{p}{p_s} = \frac{T}{T_s}\frac{\rho}{\rho_s} = F_1^{2(1-k)+k\omega}\, F_2^{-1-\frac{k(\gamma-1)(2+2j-\omega)}{2-\varphi}}\, F_4^{\frac{2(\varphi-1+j)-\omega\varphi}{2-\varphi}\Phi},$$

$$(2.6.24f) \qquad \frac{r_0}{r_s} = \left(\frac{F_1}{F_2}\right)^{-k}\left(\frac{F_3}{F_2}\right)^{\frac{k\gamma}{2\gamma - \varphi}}\left(\frac{F_4}{F_2}\right)^{\frac{\varphi}{2-\varphi}\Phi}.$$

These results were obtained by combining results taken from Sedov's book [3], Chapter IV of the fourth edition, §§11 and 14. The quantity $T$ is the absolute temperature. The quantity $r_0$ is the Lagrangian coordinate of a particle, equal to its original radius before the shock wave reached it. For further details, graphs, and tables the reader is referred to Sedov's book. Equations (2.6.24) are given in Sedov [3] only for the case with $\omega = 0$ and $j$ general and for the case with $j = 2$ and $\omega$ general. Equations (2.6.24) have been written in a form with $j$ and $\omega$ general, based on Sedov's more specific results and on his general equations.

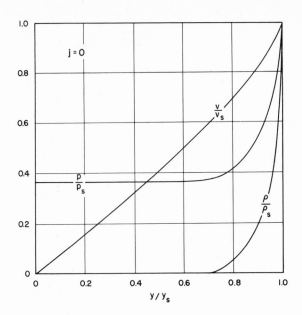

FIG. 2–10. Constant-energy similar solution, two-dimensional case;
$\gamma = 1.4$ (Sedov [3]).

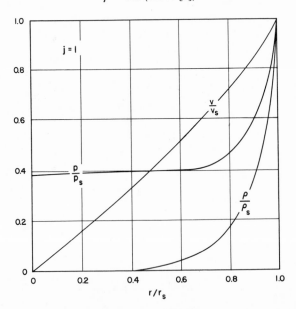

FIG. 2–11. Constant-energy similar solution, axisymmetric case;
$\gamma = 1.4$ (Sedov [3]).

We have kept $\omega$ arbitrary above solely in order to preserve the generality of Sedov's constant-energy solution. We are actually interested only in the case for which $\rho_\infty$ is constant, i.e. for which $\omega = 0$ and for which $k = 2/(3 + j)$ for the constant-energy solution.

And since we are concerned here with hypersonic small-disturbance theory rather than with explosion theory we shall confine our interest in the numerical solutions to the planar and cylindrical cases ($j = 0, 1$), corresponding to two-dimensional and axisymmetric steady flows. In Fig. 2–10 the functions $v/v_s$, $\rho/\rho_s$, and $p/p_s$ are plotted versus $y/y_s$ for the planar case with $\gamma = 1.4$. We have here replaced the symbol $r$ by the more appropriate symbol $y$. In Fig. 2–11 the same functions are plotted versus $r/r_s$ for the cylindrical case, also with $\gamma = 1.4$. Tables for these functions may be found in Sedov's book [3].

The unsteady similar solutions we have been studying correspond to solutions in steady hypersonic flow only with the application of the equivalence principle, with the identification of the similar solutions as approximate solutions according to the small-disturbance theory. In the cases for which $k$ is greater than the value (2.6.16) corresponding to the constant-energy solution, the corresponding body has a thickness distribution which is zero at the nose and increases monotonically in the axial direction. If $k$ is less than one the body is somewhat blunted at the nose and the equivalence principle fails locally there. If $k$ is greater than one the body shape is cusped and the equivalence principle fails at some sufficiently large downstream station. If $k$ is one the body is a wedge or a cone and the validity of the equivalence principle depends only on the value of the constant angle of the body. The bodies of more practical interest have $k$ less than one, and we expect that the local failure of the equivalence principle near the nose should not affect the applicability of the similar solutions at sufficient distances downstream. Numerical results for the axisymmetric case are available in Kubota [1] and Grodzovskii [1]. Figures 2–12 giving $r_b/r_s$ and the pressure coefficient in terms of $k$ for various values of $\gamma$ are taken from Kubota [1]. He also presents experimental results for similar bodies of revolution with $k = 3/4$ and $k = 2/3$, and obtains acceptable agreement with the theory within the limitations imposed by viscous effects and the relatively low value of $M_\infty = 7.7$ available for his tests. His symbol for our $k$ is $m$.

The application of the constant-energy solution to hypersonic flow is a more difficult matter than for solutions of larger $k$. As $k$ approaches the value given for $\omega = 0$ by (2.6.16), equal to $\frac{2}{3}$ for two-dimensional bodies and to $\frac{1}{2}$ for bodies of revolution, the ratio of shock layer thickness to body thickness for the similar solutions approaches infinity. With $k$ equal to the constant-energy value the body thickness must be zero with a finite shock layer thickness. However, a body which is truly of zero thickness creates no

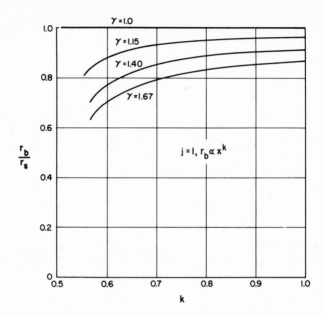

FIG. 2–12a. Ratio of body radius to shock radius in axisymmetric similar solution (Kubota [1]).

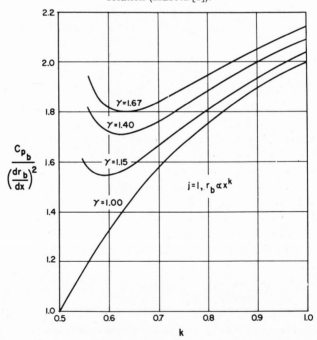

FIG. 2–12b. Pressure coefficient on body in axisymmetric similar solution (Kubota [1]).

disturbance in an inviscid flow, and some mechanism is necessary to simulate the violent explosion of the equivalent unsteady similar solution. This mechanism is the creation of a local strong disturbance by a blunt nose on a body which, after the nose, has effectively constant thickness. The prediction of the similar constant-energy solution applies then to the asymptotic behavior of the flow, and not to the local solution near the blunt nose.

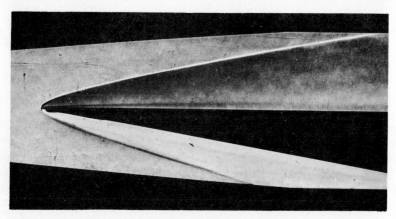

Fig. 2–13. Schlieren photograph of a blunted flat plate in helium at $M_\infty = 11.6$ and $\mathrm{Re}_{t_\infty} = 16,500$ (courtesy Gas Dynamics Laboratory, Princeton University).

Fig. 2–13 is a Schlieren photograph of a flow over a blunted flat plate in a uniform flow of helium at $M_\infty = 11.6$. The leading edge has a flat face with a thickness of 0.017 inches, and the height of the part of the wind tunnel which is shown at the right of the photograph is $1\frac{1}{2}$ inches. As with Fig. 1–3, the flow on the bottom surface should be disregarded. The Reynolds number based on leading edge thickness $\mathrm{Re}_{t_\infty}$ is about 16,500, and the effect of the boundary layer is negligible. The shock shape is close to a power-law shape, with a measured value of $k$ from three tests of $0.66 \pm 0.01$. This may be compared with the theoretical value of 0.667. Although this agreement with the theory may be considered excellent for the shock shape, agreement for the pressure distribution on the plate is unsatisfactory.

An imposing set of assumptions underlie the applications of similar solutions to steady hypersonic flows, and some of these assumptions must be examined in more detail. Besides the assumption that the gas is a perfect one, the density ratio must be constant, and we must make the strong shock assumption (C) for this. Thus we have the same assumptions as are necessary to combine the Mach number independence principle with hypersonic similitude, and must make the requirement (A-strong) that $M_\infty$ be extremely large. And, as long as $M_\infty$ is finite and there is some nonzero counterpressure in the undisturbed gas the strong shock assumption must fail at some point on the shock tail. Thus with finite counterpressure the similar solution cannot be truly asymptotic, as it will not approximate the true solution at arbitrarily large distances downstream. This limitation is more severe for a gas with $\gamma$ small, since with such a gas the requirement that $\epsilon \approx \epsilon_{lim}$ is more severe. Methods for modifying similar solutions to take finite counterpressure approximately into account have been given by Sakurai [1; 2], Sedov [3], and Kubota [1]. In his comparisons between theory and experiment, Kubota has used a second approximation which takes the effect of finite counterpressure into account.

Another assumption concerns the initiation of the solution. The gas at the center of the similar constant-energy solution for a violent explosion has infinite entropy, as does also the gas nearest the flow boundary in the other solutions with $k$ less than one. This gas cannot "cool down" by expansion, and maintains infinite temperature and finite pressure. In all these solutions (with $k < 1$), and particularly with the constant-energy solution, there is a "hot core" of gas which continues to exert a significant pressure. This effect may be readily noticed in the pressure curves of Figs. 2–10 and 2–11. If the explosion is not quite "violent" in the sense of the constant-energy solution but is initiated by finite forces over a finite time interval the resulting explosion should have a relatively "cool core" during the earlier history of the phenomenon. Here again, this effect is more significant for a gas with $\gamma$ small, in which we should expect relatively small variations in temperature. In the limit as $\gamma$ approaches one streamlines become similarity lines, all the material traversed by the shock remains within a very thin layer near the shock, and the hot core consists entirely of material which was at or very near the origin at the time of initiation. The pressure ratio near the origin $p_b/p_s$ in the constant-energy solution approaches $1/2$ as $\gamma$ approaches one. In a hypersonic steady flow we should expect a cool core and lower pressures near the axis, because the initiation of the solution cannot be "violent" and the entropy of the gas has a definite upper limit determined by the entropy jump across a normal shock. The existence of a cool core in flows with $\gamma$ close to one is important in assessing whether the Newtonian free layers treated in Section 3.3 are realistic. The core in a hypersonic flow contains the entropy layer discussed in Section 1.2. If the Reynolds number based on nose dimension is small the boundary layer is an important part of the core. The comments we have made in Section 2.2 on the effects of viscous boundary layers on hypersonic similitude apply equally here. Guiraud [2] has considered this cold-core effect in a study of the blunt-nosed flat plate.

As we have indicated, then, we can expect the constant-energy solution to be much more realistic for hypersonic flows in a gas with $\gamma$ large than in a gas with $\gamma$ small. Thus, an acceptable correlation should be expected to be obtainable at high $M_\infty$ with a monatomic gas such as helium, and this expectation is borne out for the shock shape in Fig. 2–13. But the constant-energy solution should become meaningless with regard to applicability to hypersonic steady flows as $\gamma$ approaches one, and cannot predict pressure on the axis accurately even with $\gamma = 5/3$.

If the quantity $k$ is considered as a variable which characterizes the actual shock shape, for example if we define $k$ by

$$(2.6.25a) \qquad k(t) = t \frac{d^2 r_s}{dt^2} \frac{dt}{dr_s} + 1,$$

or by

$$(2.6.25b) \qquad k(t) = \left[ 1 + r_s \frac{d^2 r_s}{dt^2} \left( \frac{dt}{dr_s} \right)^2 \right]^{-1},$$

we may inquire qualitatively into how $k$ should be affected by the phenomena we have discussed. A finite counterpressure in the undisturbed gas is associated with a finite sound velocity; this results in an increased shock velocity, particularly when the shock is weak. The effect of counterpressure is thus to increase $k$ over that for the similar solution. And, of course, $k$ eventually approaches one in the shock tail. A cool core decreases the core pressure and increases the pressure gradients through the relatively high-density region near the shock; accordingly, the deceleration of the shock is increased, and the local value of $k$ is decreased below that for the similar solution. This effect is less important in the later history of a solution, while the effect of finite counterpressure grows more important. The two effects may effectively balance each other over an appreciable part of an actual solution, and we must guard against interpreting such a fortuitous check of the shock shape in an experiment with that predicted by a constant-energy solution as an unqualified confirmation of the applicability of the solution. In general, we expect the quantity $k$ to be monotonic increasing.

Finally, a word about implosion solutions. In the analysis above we have considered only explosion solutions, with the time $t$ going from $0$ to $\infty$; implosion solutions are solutions for which the time goes from $-\infty$ to $0$. The planar implosion case $j = 0$ is trivial, and corresponds to the intersection of two equal uniform shocks. But the cylindrical case $j = 1$ is of interest to us, and corresponds to a focusing axisymmetric shock. Such a shock may be produced in a duct of circular cross section, for example; however, very near the convergence point of the implosion solution the equivalence principle must fail, and a lambda shock must appear in the steady hypersonic flow.

For similar implosion solutions we need to substitute $-t$ for $t$ in the defining relations of this section. But if we also change the sign of $v$, so that a positive $V$ corresponds to negative $v$, the entire analysis given above is unchanged, including the establishment of boundary conditions for flow boundaries and for shock waves with the gas in front undisturbed. The solution of Guderley [1] represents the asymptotic behavior of quite arbitrary implosions, and is particularly interesting. The solution is required to satisfy the boundary conditions

(2.6.26a) $$\lambda_b = \infty,$$

(2.6.26b) $$z_b = 0,$$

(2.6.26c) $$V_b = 0.$$

Since the boundary point given above and the shock boundary point of (2.6.12) lie on different sides of the curve $z = (V - k)^2$ in the $(z, V)$ space, the integral curve must pass through a singular point in traversing this line. This singular point is a saddle point in this space, and corresponds to the numerators and denominators of (2.6.7) and (2.6.9a) vanishing simultaneously. An integral curve which possesses this property and which satisfies the boundary conditions may be found only with a particular value of $k$ which depends upon the constant parameters of the problem.

With constant density in the undisturbed flow, i.e. with $\omega = 0$, Chisnell [1] and Culler and Fried [1] have obtained by independent and completely dissimilar analyses the same approximate formula

$$(2.6.27) \qquad k = \frac{1}{1 + \dfrac{j\alpha_0}{(\alpha_0 + 1)(\alpha_0 + 2/\gamma)}} = \frac{1}{1 + \dfrac{j}{1 + 2/\gamma + \gamma\alpha_0}},$$

where $\alpha_0$ is the symbol used by Culler and Fried for

$$(2.6.28) \qquad \alpha_0 = \sqrt{\frac{2}{\gamma(\gamma - 1)}}.$$

Chisnell notes that $\alpha_0$ is the Mach number of the flow following a moving strong shock. This approximation is remarkably accurate. With $j = 1$, it gives a value of $k$ which is too low by about $0.3\%$ at $\gamma = 1.1$, and which is in error by not more than about $0.05\%$ for $\gamma$ between 1.4 and 2.0.

Actually, the boundary condition (2.6.26) is not essential, and the essential boundary condition is that the integral curve pass through the saddle point. The solution for the inner regions with $\lambda$ smaller than at the saddle point is completely independent of the physical solution for the outer region with $\lambda$ larger than this critical value. The solution in the outside region need not be a similar one at all at finite values of $-t$, and the solution has an asymptotic validity for small values of $-t$ with quite general implosions with suitable symmetry. The reason for this independence is that no characteristic from the outer region can penetrate into the inner region. Guderley's solution continues for $t > 0$ with a solution of the explosion type, with different shock conditions but with the same boundary conditions at $\lambda = 0$ as with the constant-energy solution.

## 7. Unsteady flow theory

The question of the appropriate similitude for unsteady hypersonic flow was first examined by Lin, Reissner, and Tsien [1] in a paper which treated unsteady flow at all flight speeds. As with the earlier paper of Tsien [1] the investigation is limited to irrotational motions, and the error of Tsien of using the mean-surface approximation in the boundary conditions is repeated. The simplification obtainable by taking the point of view of an observer fixed in the undisturbed fluid was not pointed out by the authors, but is evident in their hypersonic equations. This paper does establish that Hayes' equivalence principle is applicable to unsteady flows, within the limitations inherent in the paper, although the authors did not specifically mention this fact.

The fact that the equivalence principle holds in unsteady flows was first noted by Hamaker and Wong [1], who demonstrated the equivalence analytically for potential flow and concluded that it should hold in general. Hamaker and Wong were primarily interested in the connection between unsteady hypersonic similitude and the dynamic similitude of bodies in free flight. They showed that complete dynamic similarity (with aerodynamic forces) can be obtained provided the body has certain symmetry and is not rolling.

The unsteady application of the equivalence principle was further exploited by Lighthill [2]. He likened the problem to that of the gas flow in a tube driven by a piston, and suggested the use of three terms in the isentropic expression for the pressure on a piston as a power series in its velocity. Within the accuracy of the first two terms in such a series we may neglect changes in the entropy, and Lighthill points out that the maximum error in the third term is small enough that this term is worth retaining for engineering purposes. Lighthill obtains analytic expressions for aerodynamic coefficients for a pitching symmetrical airfoil, with the assumption of a perfect gas. The accuracy of Lighthill's approximation in any particular case may be tested roughly by examining the magnitude of the next term in the series.

The relation which Lighthill used may be expressed

$$(2.7.1) \qquad \frac{p}{p_\infty} = 1 + \gamma \frac{v}{a_\infty} + \frac{\gamma(\gamma+1)}{4}\left(\frac{v}{a_\infty}\right)^2 + \frac{\gamma(\gamma+1)}{12}\left(\frac{v}{a_\infty}\right)^3$$

in our notation. This relation comes from the isentropic form of the Busemann expansion; compare (7.3.2) which includes the effect of a shock. Since $v$ is of the order of $U\tau$, it is necessary that $M_\infty\tau$ be small for the application of Lighthill's formula. However, since the error is in the fourth term, acceptable accuracy may be obtainable with $M_\infty\tau$ of the order of about 1/3. Lighthill shows that his results are consistent with those of other investigators. Subsequently, Ashley and Zartarian [1] extended Lighthill's calculations and introduced the term "piston theory". This term is now generally applied to this branch of unsteady flow theory.

Recently Landahl [1] has developed a theory for unsteady flow which takes into account the terms of order $M_\infty^{-2}$ which are neglected in piston theory. His theory is restricted to small values of $M_\infty\tau$, but its validity extends to smaller values of $M_\infty$ than that of piston theory. Landahl's theory serves in particular to estimate the accuracy of piston theory when this is applied at moderate values of the Mach number. Good agreement is obtained with the results of Van Dyke [4] which include second-order effects.

In this book we are primarily interested in steady hypersonic flows, and here we shall only present heuristic arguments to delimit the validity of the small-disturbance theory in unsteady flow. In steady flow a parameter $\tau$ was defined, equal to the thickness ratio or the angle of attack of the body, whichever is greater. In unsteady flow $\tau$ must also be no less than the ratio of the maximum lateral velocity of any part of the body to the free stream velocity.

Provided the functional dependence of the body shape upon the distance and time is smooth and provided a suitably defined axial scale characterizing the time variations is of the order of the chord of the body or larger, the analysis we have given earlier or the somewhat more limited analysis of Lin, Reissner, and Tsien [1] is applicable, and the small-disturbance theory is correct to within an error of order $\tau^2$. If the variations with time are slow, such as with a slowly accelerating body or with oscillating flow at low frequency, quasi-stationary theory applies and the equivalence principle remains valid, regardless of the distribution of the disturbances in the axial variable.

If the changes in body shape are not smooth in time and distance, failure of the equivalence principle may occur. To see this, let us imagine that at a point on the wing a local, violent disturbance to the flow occurs. According to the small-disturbance theory this disturbance should propagate normal to the body only, along a line fixed in the undisturbed fluid. But of course the disturbance propagates in all directions, and this diffraction effect is felt within a space of dimension of the order of $\tau c$, where $c$ is the chord. For such an isolated disturbance the failure of the equivalence principle is felt only locally.

In general the unsteady flows of interest are not characterized by isolated violent disturbances; the flow patterns from smoother disturbances are themselves smoother, and clear-cut diffraction patterns do not appear. In order to see how failure of the equivalence principle may occur let us imagine that the unsteady disturbance may be broken up into superposable parts, each of which is sinusoidal both in time with frequency $f$ and in distance along the body with wavelength $\lambda$. For a given combination of $f$ and $\lambda$ the disturbance may be divided into one representing a traveling wave going upstream with velocity $f\lambda$ and a wave going downstream with the same velocity. The latter appears to an observer moving downstream with velocity $f\lambda$ as a steady flow of velocity $|U - f\lambda|$. In order for the equivalence principle to apply it is necessary that the local Mach number corresponding to this velocity be high, or that

$$(2.7.2) \qquad\qquad |U - f\lambda| \gg a.$$

Since $a$ is of order $U\tau$ we may reexpress this condition

$$(2.7.3) \qquad\qquad \left|1 - \frac{f\lambda}{U}\right| \gg \tau.$$

Assuming we are considering only finite bodies the flow is primarily a transient one for the first wavelength or so, and this transient flow follows the equivalence principle. This transient flow will predominate over the entire body if the wavelength is large compared with the size of a diffraction pattern, or if

$$(2.7.4) \qquad\qquad \frac{\lambda}{c} \gg \tau.$$

This condition is satisfied automatically if $\lambda$ is of the same order as $c$.

In effect, then, the equivalence principle may be considered valid and the small-disturbance theory applicable for oscillatory unsteady flows provided either condition (2.7.3) or (2.7.4) holds, where $\lambda$ is a suitably chosen axial scale of the disturbance and $f$ is the frequency. Implicit in the investigations cited earlier is the assumption that the axial scale of the disturbance is of the same order of magnitude as the chord, hence that (2.7.4) is satisfied automatically.

With regard to the unsteady application of strip theory it is first necessary that the condition for strip theory in steady flow be satisfied, that $\tau \mathcal{R}^{-1}$ be small. Then a condition equivalent to (2.7.4) must be satisfied, where $\lambda$ is now a suitably chosen lateral scale for the unsteady motion. If the aspect ratio $\mathcal{R}$ is defined with respect to this lateral scale, the two conditions may be seen to be identical.

CHAPTER III

# NEWTONIAN THEORY

## 1. The gasdynamics of Sir Isaac Newton

The name of Sir Isaac Newton has been given to one branch of hypersonic flow theory, the branch based upon the zero density ratio assumption (D-lim), with the shock layer infinitesimally thin. Before we enter into an exposition of this theory let us inquire briefly as to what Newton's accomplishments in gasdynamics were, and as to why his name is attached to this body of modern hypersonic flow theory.

The investigations of Newton which are of interest to us were made in the last part of the seventeenth century, long before the concepts of thermodynamics, kinetic theory, viscous stresses, etc. were developed. Hence it is not surprising that some of Newton's analyses and results may appear to be in error in the light of today's knowledge. He had to invent a model for molecular interaction to serve in place of our present kinetic theory models, he made no distinction between the isentropic process in a sound wave and the isothermal process of a leisurely laboratory experiment, and his analysis of resistance in an incompressible fluid was based on an unrealistic model. In the present context, he did not have the notion of the shock wave or of the shock layer, and he apparently did not realize the magnitude of the flow velocities necessary for compressibility to play the dominating role in a fluid flow about a body. Newton's general approach was deductive, starting from a set of basic laws and a hypothetical model of a physical problem, leading to the logical solution of the problem based on the model. The results permitted some evaluation of the consistency of the model used, but not necessarily of its physical correctness.

A criticism of Newton's scientific results based upon our superior knowledge of two and a half centuries later is hardly of interest to us here. What is of interest is an appreciation for Newton's picture of the mechanics of matter, to serve as a framework in which to discuss his remarkable deductive accomplishments. The reference we shall use in our examination is Cajori's edition of the translation of the third edition of Newton's *Principia Mathematica* by Andrew Motte, Newton [1]. The portions of most direct interest are in Book II, Section VII, Propositions 32 through 35 (Theorems 27 and 28, Problem 7), and Note 35 in Cajori's appendix. According to Cajori, Proposition 34 of the second and third editions was Proposition 35 of the first edition.

70

Newton knew that gases such as air and steam are elastic, and that the relation between the density and the pressure ("compression") is what is now known as Boyle's law. He knew that liquids such as water and quicksilver are practically inelastic and have much higher densities than do gases. And he knew that water and steam were the same substance. He thus considered fluids to be either elastic, with variable density, or nonelastic ("compressed"), with the density an intrinsic property of the medium. In the absence of kinetic theory, Newton postulated repulsive ("centrifugal") forces between neighboring particles of an elastic fluid as a possible mechanism which would explain its elasticity. With this model the pressure of the elastic fluid arises primarily from these repellent forces. He finds that consistency with Boyle's law (the perfect gas law) is obtained with the assumption that the repellent force between two neighboring particles is inversely proportional to the distance between them (see Book II, Proposition 23). Newton also introduces the concept of a rare medium which consists of small particles with large distances between them, evidently with the additional assumption that the repellent forces between the particles may be neglected.

We shall examine Newton's conclusions on the basis of the model he postulated for a perfect gas, with an attempt to interpret his findings into present day terminology objectively. Thus we shall consistently interpret the interparticle forces inversely proportional to distance in terms of the pressure of a perfect gas. In assessing his results we should keep in mind that they depend deductively on a hypothetical model consistent with a realistic gas law, even though the details of the model would not be considered realistic today. We shall find that he clearly foreshadowed the concepts of Mach number similarity and of the Mach number independence principle, and that he obtained comprehensive and instructive results for hypersonic free molecule flows under hypothetical surface conditions.

In Proposition 32 Newton establishes the complete similarity of the motions of two similar systems of particles, provided, with the interpretation above, that the pressures are proportional to density times the squares of the velocities involved. His way of saying this is that the particles act on each other only "with accelerative forces that are inversely as the diameters of the correspondent particles, and directly as the squares of the velocities." The reader may note that acceleration times distance has the same dimensions as pressure divided by density. In Proposition 33 Newton extends this similarity to the resistance of a body in such a medium. His similarity condition may be re-expressed, that the velocity of the body must be proportional to the velocity of sound, with his definition of the velocity of sound. Thus his result may be expressed, that the drag coefficient of bodies of a given shape in similar elastic fluids is a function only of the Mach number. Newton did not specifically relate his similarity condition to the velocity of sound. We may note that Cranz [2, p. 45] derived Mach similarity from Newtonian similarity.

In Corollary II of Proposition 33 Newton first notes that "in a medium, whose parts when at a distance do not act with any force on one another, the resistance is as the square of the velocity, accurately." This case corresponds to our limiting case of infinite Mach number with the medium at absolute zero temperature. By the use of a similarity argument he then demonstrates that at very large velocity the repulsive forces (or pressure) may be neglected. He restates his conclusion in Corollary III: "Hence the resistance of a body moving very swiftly in an elastic fluid is almost the same as if the parts of the fluid were destitute of their centrifugal forces, and did not fly from each other; provided only that the elasticity of the fluid arise from the centrifugal forces of the particles, and the velocity be so great as not to allow the particles time enough to act." In these two corollaries Newton has demonstrated an equivalent of the Mach number independence principle or similitude of Oswatitsch for the perfect gas he is considering.

In Propositions 34 and 35 Newton considers a rare medium, in which it is evident he postulates no interaction between individual particles and considers only the force of impact between a body and the particles lying in the space swept out by the body. In Proposition 34 he assumes, but not explicitly, that the impact law for the transfer of normal momentum is independent of the angle of incidence of the body surface, and that there is no transfer of tangential momentum. He concludes, thus, that the impulse or the force of impact of a particle on the body is proportional to the sine of the angle of incidence and is directed normal to the body. The component of this impulse from a single particle contributing to the resistance is proportional to the square of the sine of the angle of incidence. In the Scholium to this proposition, Newton gives the result for the shape of the body of given length and base diameter which has minimum resistance according to his model. His calculation leading to the result has been found in his correspondence, and, according to Cajori, represents the earliest solution of a problem in the calculus of variations. A modern derivation of Newton's solution may be found in Eggers, Resnikoff, and Dennis [1], together with test results on such bodies.

In Proposition 35 Newton calculates the resistance of a sphere according to different impact laws. In his Case 1 he considers the impact to be completely elastic, while in Case 2 he considers the impact to be completely inelastic (for the normal component of momentum). The resistance for Case 1 is simply twice that for Case 2. In a free molecule flow, Newton's case 1 corresponds to specular reflection, with all accommodation coefficients zero. Case 2 corresponds to an accommodation coefficient of zero for the tangential momentum or shear, and an accommodation coefficient of one for normal momentum or pressure if the body is very cold; if the body is not cold this normal accommodation coefficient must be greater than one. Except for normal momentum or pressure in Case 2, none of Newton's cases may be considered at all realistic for actual rarefied gas flows no matter what the body temperature is. The unrealistic model of specular reflection is sometimes treated as an interesting special case in modern theoretical investigations.

But for flows at high Mach number with a high density, essentially inviscid shock layer, Newton's analysis may be realistic. At very high Mach number the medium is essentially a rarefied one in front of the shock, and becomes a continuum only within the shock layer. With a very thin shock layer the shock has approximately the same angle of inclination as the body, and the normal momentum of an impinging molecule is lost inelastically and is transmitted to the body through the shock layer. With the shock layer inviscid the tangential component of the momentum of an impinging molecule is conserved. In order for the shock layer to be sufficiently thin, the strong form of the small density ratio assumption $\epsilon^{1/2} \ll 1$ (D-strong) discussed earlier is needed. This practical case corresponds to Newton's Case 2.

Epstein [1] was the first to obtain by a gasdynamic analysis the pressure result corresponding to Newton's Case 2

$$(3.1.1) \qquad\qquad p_s - p_\infty = \rho_\infty U^2 \sin^2 \theta_b.$$

He obtained this result for the case of a two dimensional wedge at velocities such that radiation energy losses would provide an infinitesimal density ratio across the shock. Epstein did not relate his result to the results of Newton. The connection between the shock wave result (3.1.1) and the analysis of Newton was noted independently by Busemann [1, pp. 276–277] and by Sänger [1, pp. 120–121] (the latter with an erroneous factor of $\frac{1}{2}$).

While the authors cited above were the first to obtain the sine-squared pressure law on the basis of the modern theory of oblique shocks, the sine-squared pressure law had been known previously for many years by ballisticians (cf. Cranz [1, § 12]). These earlier ballisticians used the law empirically, with an unknown multiplicative constant, and only considered the Newtonian law as one of several possible empirical laws. Newton was himself undoubtedly the most fundamental contributor to the science of ballistics, and it is probable that ballisticians have been well acquainted with Newton's results ever since the publication of the *Principia*. In any case the association of Newton's name with the sine-squared pressure law has existed for at least thirty years, and probably much longer.

The pressure result (3.1.1) as expressed is correct in the limiting case of zero density ratio provided the shock and body shapes may be assumed to be the same. Note that (3.1.1) has been given for the pressure immediately behind the shock. This pressure is equal to the pressure on the body only in case each particle follows an unaccelerated or essentially free path after impact with the shock layer, corresponding to the model for Newton's Case 2. This is the case for the flow on a wedge or on a cone at zero incidence. On a curved body, a particle is constrained within the continuum flow in the shock layer to follow a curved path, and the forces required to curve the particle paths must be taken into account. The result is a pressure difference across the shock layer equal to the momentum flow in the layer times the curvature of the layer. The necessity for this centrifugal (in present-day sense, not in Newton's) force correction to obtain the pressure on the body was discovered by Busemann [1, pp. 276–277], who gave formulas for the correction. With a convex body the pressure on the body is less than that given by (3.1.1), and may drop to zero for a point on the body for which the surface still has positive incidence to the free stream.

In hypersonic flow theory, the inclusion of the centrifugal correction of Busemann is essential to a logical theory which is correct in a limiting sense. The use of a "modified Newtonian" sine-squared pressure formula without the centrifugal correction was proposed by Lees [3, Section (4)] on an empirical basis, and is common now for purposes of comparison with experiment. The modification of (3.1.1) consists of a multiplicative factor which makes the formula give the correct stagnation pressure, and the pressure is interpreted as the pressure on the body. This formula is valuable because it is easy to compute and gives a simple basis of comparison. It is not based on any rational theory, however, and its empirical basis should be kept in mind.

With the recognition that the centrifugal correction to the pressure on the body must be included in a rational theory of hypersonic flow, we may turn our attention briefly to the question of terminology. The usual terms used are "Newtonian plus centrifugal" or "corrected Newtonian". A logical and appropriate possibility would be "Newton-Busemann". For simplicity we shall in this book use simply "Newtonian" to refer to the rational theory with the Busemann correction and the term "Newton-Busemann" for the correct pressure law. Since we are here primarily concerned with hypersonic flow *theory*, we must look on the uncorrected Newtonian pressure law applied to pressure on the body as being in error.

## 2. Two-dimensional and axisymmetric bodies

The basic assumption which underlies the Newtonian theory is the strong form of the small density ratio assumption, D-lim or D-strong in our terminology. Real gases, even those in which dissociation plays an essential role, are characterized by values of $\epsilon_{lim}$ whose square roots cannot be considered small, and Newtonian theory provides at best an extremely rough picture of actual hypersonic flows; it is extremely unlikely that many of the results we shall obtain in this chapter may be applied directly. The results of the succeeding four chapters will give us some understanding of the meaning of Newtonian theory in its relation to hypersonic flows. Before we get into our detailed analysis of Newtonian flow theory, it is appropriate to inquire as to whether this theory is of any more than academic interest in a study of hypersonic flow. There are two principal reasons for our studying New-tonian flow. The first is that one promising line of attack upon general blunt-body flows uses an expansion procedure in the density ratio $\epsilon$, and the approximation of zeroth order in such an approach is a Newtonian one. We must, of course, understand thoroughly the zeroth approximation in order to exploit any expansion procedure. The second reason is that a pursuit of the Newtonian theory to its logical conclusions can shed light on phenomena in real gas flows. Many of the logical conclusions of Newtonian theory are anomalous, and involve infinite mass, zero pressure, concentration of force, and multiple condensation of the material. The presence of such anomalies, of course, depends on the limiting process $\epsilon \to 0$ (D-lim). These apparently completely unrealistic anomalous phenomena may have signifi-cant vestigial counterparts in hypersonic gas flows. An appreciation of the former is necessary for an understanding of the latter. Hence the anomalies of Newtonian theory are not to be avoided but rather to be sought out, in order to discover phenomena which may be important in hypersonic flow but which have no counterparts in flows at moderate speeds. In addition, the methods developed in Newtonian theory suggest analogous methods in more realistic theories. An example of this is the constant-density solution with cross flow given in Section 4.5, in which the method is suggested directly by the method of Section 3.6.

Newtonian flow theory is based upon the concept of an infinitesimally thin shock layer which coincides with the surface of the body, with the assumption that there is no friction between the layer and the body surface. On the basis of these assumptions and with no further specification as to the structure of the shock layer, we can obtain formulas for the steady-state pressures and forces on two-dimensional and axisymmetric bodies with suitable restrictions on the shape.

In general, however, some knowledge of the structure of the thin shock layer is desired or needed. For this purpose we need to specify in more detail the nature of the shock layer. We may in principle set up a number of models for the shock layer, or postulated rules of structure and behavior, all of which are consistent with the basic hypothesis that there is no friction between the layer and the body surface. We shall find it convenient here to consider the three distinct conceptual models for the shock layer structure, of which the first two are essentially identical. In our treatment of the shock layer structure we shall use the first model almost exclusively. The models considered are:

A. *The laminar layer model.* In this model, which is the one we shall consider as standard for Newtonian flow, the shock layer is considered to be composed of an infinite number of independent laminae. Each lamina is infinitesimally thin, and carries in it fluid which has entered the shock layer at some other point. This fluid has travelled between the point of entry and the point at which the shock layer is being examined along a path of zero lateral curvature on the body or shock layer surface. Such a path is known as a geodesic. With this model, the succession of laminae from the body side of the shock layer to the shock side furnishes us with a scale on which we must be able to identify the fluid with respect to its point of entry. In other words, we must be able to set up a one-to-one correspondence between the individual laminae within the layer and the points of entry into the shock layer of the corresponding streamlines. A given lamina can contain only material from one source. For any given point at which the shock layer structure is being investigated there will be a locus of the corresponding points of entry, called the "locus of entering streamlines". The one-to-one correspondence is a mapping of this locus onto the scale of laminae.

The above description of the model is for the steady flow case. In the unsteady case the additional time coordinate must be taken into account, and the specification of the analogue to the locus of entering streamlines is more involved. This case is treated in Section 3.7.

B. *The limiting perfect gas model.* According to this model we consider that the material is a perfect gas under the limiting processes $\gamma \to 1$ and $M_\infty \to \infty$, with zero viscosity. Such a model ought to be more realistic than other Newtonian models, as it does correspond to a gas flow and the only artificiality appears in the restrictions needed to make $\epsilon$ zero. On the whole this model will behave identically with the standard laminar layer model. The main purpose of considering such a model is to obtain suggestions as to whether the standard model should be modified when applied to unusual problems, and to obtain an idea as to when, if ever, the standard model necessarily diverges in behavior from the gas model.

The equivalence of this model with the laminar layer model may be obtained from the momentum equation, which states that the acceleration of a particle is minus the pressure gradient divided by the density. With the density approaching infinity in the limiting process considered, the particle acceleration approaches zero if the pressure gradient remains finite. In the direction normal to the shock surface the pressure gradient may approach infinity as the shock layer becomes infinitesimally thin, and the component of particle acceleration in this direction is not generally zero but is controlled by the geometry of the shock layer. In the directions parallel to the shock surface the pressure gradient is controlled by the shock pressure jump and must remain finite. Accordingly, the particle acceleration components tangential to the shock surface approach zero in the limiting process, and the particle path in the shock layer approaches a geodesic on the shock surface.

An assumed gas other than a perfect gas may equally be used in this conceptual limiting process as long as $\epsilon$ approaches zero and $\epsilon$ divided by the speed of sound in the shock layer also approaches zero. Such a gas would furnish us another model, also equivalent to the laminar layer model.

C. *The homogeneous layer model.* In this model the shock layer at a point has a characteristic velocity, and all the material in the layer moves at that velocity. A parcel of fluid entering the shock layer suddenly takes on the velocity of the layer, and at the same time makes a contribution to the momentum of the layer tangential to the body. This increment of momentum affects the velocity of the layer, and this velocity is determined by momentum balance considerations. Such a model is not realistic, as it requires the material in the shock layer to be infinitely viscous but with zero friction at the wall. In a limiting case of a gas at very low Reynolds number in the shock layer this model would require zero accommodation coefficient for tangential momentum for collisions of molecules with the body surface. However, the homogeneous layer model is extremely simple and often can give us easily obtainable results which may be compared with the less unrealistic results of the other Newtonian models. Most of the anomalies which appear with the standard laminar layer model are absent with the homogeneous layer model.

We now turn to the application to two-dimensional and axisymmetric bodies and introduce a stream function $\psi$ which represents mass flow per unit depth for two-dimensional flows, and mass flow per unit azimuthal angle (in radians) for axisymmetric flows. In the undisturbed free stream this function is simply

$$(3.2.1a) \qquad\qquad \psi = \rho_\infty U y$$

for two-dimensional flow, and

$$(3.2.1b) \qquad\qquad \psi = \tfrac{1}{2}\rho_\infty U r^2$$

for axisymmetric flow. It is convenient to combine these formulas, replacing $r$ by $y$ and introducing the integral parameter $j$, into the single formula

$$(3.2.2) \qquad\qquad \psi = \frac{\rho_\infty U}{1 + j} y^{1+j}.$$

Note that $\psi$ is essentially frontal area times $\rho_\infty U$. The integer $j$ is the integer of (2.6.1), with $j = 0$ for two-dimensional flow and $j = 1$ in axisymmetric flow. With $j = 1$ the coordinate $y$ is to be read as $r$, the radial cylindrical coordinate.

We introduce also the quantity $P$ which, times $U$, is the momentum in the shock layer per unit depth for two-dimensional flows, and per radian of azimuthal angle for axisymmetric flows. The change in the shock layer momentum between two points is simply the impinging mass flow times the tangential component of the free stream velocity, written as

$$(3.2.3) \qquad\qquad dP = \cos \sigma \, d\psi.$$

In this equation $\sigma$ is the shock inclination angle and a factor $U$ has been cancelled. In integrated form this expression is

$$(3.2.4) \qquad\qquad P = \int_0^c \cos \sigma \, d\psi,$$

here expressed as an indefinite integral evaluated as zero at the point 0 at which the shock layer begins.

The pressure increase divided by $\rho_\infty U^2$ is one half the pressure coefficient $C_p$, defined by

$$(3.2.5) \qquad\qquad \tfrac{1}{2}C_p = \frac{p - p_\infty}{\rho_\infty U^2}.$$

Immediately behind the shock momentum considerations give us the formula

$$(3.2.6) \qquad\qquad \tfrac{1}{2}C_{p_s} = \sin^2 \sigma$$

(this result is not applicable to the homogeneous layer model without a careful specification of its meaning for this model). On a convex body this is decreased by the Busemann centrifugal pressure correction equal to the momentum per unit depth $Uy^{-j}P$ times the curvature of the body $-\sin \sigma \, d\sigma/dy$ (see Fig. 3–1). The pressure on the body may thus be expressed

$$(3.2.7) \qquad\qquad \tfrac{1}{2}C_{p_b} = \sin^2 \sigma - \frac{d\cos\sigma}{d\psi} P_1,$$

where the subscript 1 on $P$ indicates that the integral (3.2.4) has been taken to the outer edge of the shock layer. The result (3.2.7) is termed the "Newton-Busemann" pressure law and is identical with the one originally given by Busemann [1] for the two-dimensional case.

The drag of the body divided by $U$ will be denoted $\tfrac{1}{2}\psi_1 C_D$, and is expressed

$$(3.2.8) \qquad\qquad \tfrac{1}{2}\psi_1 C_D = \psi_1 - \cos \sigma_1 P_1,$$

where the subscript 1 here denotes the outer edge of the body and $\psi$ is defined to be zero where the shock layer begins. The drag coefficient here is based on frontal area. With a two-dimensional body the drag for the two sides should be calculated separately, and with an annular body of revolution the drag for the inner and outer portions should be calculated separately. We may obtain (3.2.8) either directly from momentum considerations or from integration of (3.2.7) over $\psi$.

With two-dimensional bodies we may calculate the contribution to the

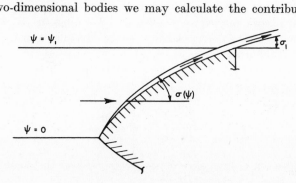

FIG. 3–1. Newtonian shock layer.

lift of the flow on one side of the body. This is given, per unit depth of the body, by

$$(3.2.9) \qquad \tfrac{1}{2}\psi_1 C_L = \pm\sin\sigma_1 P_1,$$

and may also be obtained directly from momentum considerations or from appropriate integration of (3.2.7). This lift coefficient is also based on frontal area. A body of revolution (or a symmetric two-dimensional body) at zero incidence has zero lift, and (3.2.9) has no meaning applied to axisymmetric flow. We may note, though, that the axisymmetric theory can apply to a meridional section of a body of revolution. In this case a suitable integral will give a formula similar to (3.2.9) for a net lift on the body.

The formulas given above permit us to obtain by quadratures the pressures and forces on two-dimensional and axisymmetric shapes. Some examples of these calculations will be given later, and many may be found in the literature. See for example Ivey, Klunker, and Bowen [1] and Ivey and Morrissette [1], who developed the theory proposed by Busemann [1].

We shall now obtain a few results for the structure of the shock layer, with the laminar layer model. The mass per unit area in the shock layer is denoted by $\rho_\infty m$, and is given by

$$(3.2.10) \qquad m = \frac{y^{-j}}{\rho_\infty U}\int_0^{\psi}\frac{d\psi}{\cos\sigma}.$$

The quantity $m$ has the dimensions of distance. With the homogeneous layer model, the velocity of the layer is simply $UP/\psi$. The mass per unit area is simply the mass flow per unit depth $y^{-j}\psi$ divided by this velocity, or

$$(3.2.11) \qquad\qquad m_{\text{hom}} = \frac{y^{-j}\psi_1^2}{\rho_\infty UP_1}.$$

Returning to the standard laminar layer model, the velocity of the flow in the layer is simply $U \cos \sigma$, where $\sigma$ is the angle of the body where the streamline of interest entered the shock layer. The quantity $\cos \sigma$ considered as a function of $\psi$ thus describes the velocity distribution in the layer. If $m$ in (3.2.10) is defined in terms of an integral over part of the layer, we may consider $\cos \sigma$ as a function of $m$. Distance along the layer is given by the integral of $dx/\cos \sigma$ or $dy/\sin \sigma$. The time that a particle has spent in the layer is thus given by

$$(3.2.12) \qquad\qquad t = \frac{1}{U \cos \sigma_0} \int_0^\cdot \frac{dx}{\cos \sigma},$$

where the subscript 0 on $\sigma_0$ here denotes conditions at the point of entry of the particle under consideration.

The Newtonian flow results for two-dimensional and axisymmetric shapes may be applied to bodies of considerably greater generality. Let us consider a body which is composed of a number of surfaces fitted together along sharp intersection lines or corners. Let us require that each individual surface be a piece of a two-dimensional surface (of a general cylinder with generatrix perpendicular to the flow direction) or a piece of a body of revolution whose axis is parallel to the flow direction. We require that all the corners of intersection be convex, and that each of these corners acts as a leading edge for both of its two defining surfaces. Then, on each surface we may set up strips (or meridional sections for pieces from bodies of revolution) which are of infinitesimal width. Within the assumptions of Newtonian flow theory the flow on each of these strips is independent from that on its neighbor, and the pressures and shock layer structure may be calculated for the strip on the basis of the two-dimensional or axisymmetric theory given in this section. It is possible to construct a more general convex body as a limiting case of such a composite surface, to which our simple Newtonian theory could be applied. Because of the strong restriction that none of the corners may be a trailing edge for a surface, we are limited in this concept to very special bodies. As a class, these bodies may be termed "Newtonian bodies without cross flow".

A further generalization is made possible by introducing the classical concept of cylindrical flow, with pieces from general cylinders whose generatrices are not perpendicular to the flow direction permitted in the composite body surface. With such surfaces the calculation of pressures and structure becomes more complicated and the restrictions on orientation of the corners become more involved. We shall investigate these cylindrical flows in Section 3.6, but shall not go into their application in composite bodies.

### 3. Simple shapes and free layers

We now continue our treatment of two-dimensional and axisymmetric flows, considering the impulse $P_1$ as the basic dependent variable, but with the subscript 1 dropped. We first consider $P$ to be a function of $\sigma$, with $\psi(\sigma)$ given by

$$(3.3.1) \qquad \psi = \int \frac{dP}{d\sigma} \frac{d\sigma}{\cos \sigma}.$$

The pressure may be expressed

$$(3.3.2) \qquad \tfrac{1}{2}C_{p_b} = \sin^2 \sigma + \sin \sigma \cos \sigma \, P \, \frac{d\sigma}{dP},$$

and the drag as before in (3.2.8). With this formulation we shall now define two families of shapes which we term "simple"; the simplicity of these bodies lies in their pressure expressions rather than in their geometries.

A "simple cosine shape" is defined by the relation

$$(3.3.3) \qquad P(\sigma) = \rho_\infty U A (\cos \sigma)^n,$$

where $A$ and $n$ are constants. The pressure coefficient for this shape is

$$(3.3.4) \qquad \tfrac{1}{2}C_{p_b} = 1 - \left(1 + \frac{1}{n}\right) \cos^2 \sigma.$$

The integral (3.3.1) may be evaluated explicitly to give

$$(3.3.5) \qquad \psi = \frac{nP}{(n-1)\cos \sigma} = \frac{n\rho_\infty U A}{n-1}(\cos \sigma)^{n-1}.$$

The shape with $\psi$ chosen to be zero at $y = 0$ is determined by relation (3.2.2) between $\psi$ and $y$, and by the integral for $x$

$$(3.3.6) \qquad x = \int \cot \sigma \, dy = -\frac{n-1}{1+j}\left[\frac{(1+j)nA}{n-1}\right]^{\frac{1}{1+j}} \int (\cos \sigma)^{\frac{n-1}{1+j}} \, d\sigma.$$

For a general exponent this integral may be expressed in terms of an incomplete Beta function. Note that we may express

$$(3.3.7a) \qquad -\int_{\pi/2} (\cos \sigma)^m \, d\sigma = \tfrac{1}{2}B\left(\frac{m+1}{2}, \tfrac{1}{2}; \cos^2 \sigma\right),$$

$$(3.3.7b) \qquad \int_0 (\sin \sigma)^m \, d\sigma = \tfrac{1}{2}B\left(\frac{m+1}{2}, \tfrac{1}{2}; \sin^2 \sigma\right),$$

where

$$(3.3.8) \qquad B(\alpha, \beta; t) = \int_0^t t^{\alpha-1}(1-t)^{\beta-1}\,dt$$

is the incomplete Beta function. This function may itself be expressed as a hypergeometric function. The integrals in (3.3.7) and (3.3.8) are indefinite integrals which are specified to be zero at the lower limit indicated. A special case of interest is that for which

$$(3.3.9) \qquad n = 2 + j,$$

which gives

$$(3.3.10a) \qquad x = [(2+j)A]^{\frac{1}{1+j}}(1-\sin\sigma),$$

$$(3.3.10b) \qquad y = [(2+j)A]^{\frac{1}{1+j}}\cos\sigma.$$

This shape is a circle, corresponding to a circular cylinder in the two-dimensional case and to a sphere in the axisymmetric case. Note that the pressure difference from stagnation is 3/2 times the uncorrected Newtonian value (the correct value immediately behind the shock) for the cylinder, and 4/3 times for the sphere.

With $n > 1$ all these simple cosine shapes are finite and convex. At a point on the body the pressure is zero, and if the solution were continued the pressure would become negative. What must happen is that the shock layer must separate at this point and fly free. Such "free layers" are discussed below. Near the nose of one of these bodies the shape has the form

$$(3.3.11) \qquad y \propto x^k,$$

where

$$(3.3.12) \qquad k = \frac{n-1}{n+j}.$$

If $n$ is negative we obtain bodies which are infinite in extent and concave. A body of this type cannot start with $P = 0$, and some sort of forebody is needed on which an initial impulse in the shock layer of the correct magnitude is developed. Equations (3.3.11) and (3.3.12) still apply, but describe the asymptotic shape of the body at large distances. We must have $n < -j$ for these shapes.

The other family of simple shapes, denoted "simple sine shapes", is defined by the relation

$$(3.3.13) \qquad P = \rho_\infty UA(\sin\sigma)^n,$$

where $A$ and $n$ are again constants. For these shapes the pressure is given by

$$(3.3.14) \qquad \tfrac{1}{2}C_{p_b} = \left(1 + \frac{1}{n}\right)\sin^2\sigma.$$

and the stream function by

$$(3.3.15) \qquad \psi = n\rho_\infty U A \int_0^{} (\sin \sigma)^{n-1}\, d\sigma,$$

in terms of another integral reducible to an incomplete Beta function. Only in the two-dimensional case is the quadrature for $x$ explicitly obtainable. We obtain with $j = 0$

$$(3.3.16) \qquad x = \frac{nA}{n-1}\,(\sin \sigma)^{n-1}.$$

For $n = 2$ the two-dimensional body is again a circular cylinder, but in this case the concave side of a quadrant of a circle faces the stream.

With $n > 1 + j$ the simple sine shapes are all finite and concave. The local behavior near the nose again follows (3.3.11), but in this case the exponent $k$ is given by

$$(3.3.17) \qquad k = \frac{n}{n-1-j}.$$

With $n$ negative we obtain bodies which are infinite and convex and, if the pressure is to remain nonnegative, we must have $n \leq -1$. As with the simple cosine shapes of negative $n$, the body cannot start with $P = 0$, and again we must have a forebody to furnish an initial impulse in the shock layer of correct magnitude. The case $n = -1$ corresponds to a free layer with $k = 1/(2 + j)$ describing the asymptotic shape at large distances, and with the pressure behind the layer equal to zero. The case $n = -2$ gives a pressure on the body half that immediately behind the shock, with $k = 2/(3 + j)$ for the asymptotic shape. This case corresponds to the constant-energy similar solution of the small-disturbance theory in the limit $\gamma \to 1$. It should be noted that this value of $k$ is the same as that given by (2.6.16) or (2.6.22a) with $\omega$ there equal to zero.

For slender bodies derived from simple sine shapes we may calculate the drag coefficient in terms of the thickness ratio and the parameter $n$ or $k$. An approximate integral for $x$, valid at small distances with $n$ positive, and valid only at large distances with $n$ negative, is

$$(3.3.18) \qquad x = \frac{ky}{\sin \sigma},$$

where $k$ is to be taken from (3.3.17). We define the thickness ratio $\tau$ as the ratio of $y$ to $x$ at the base of the body, and obtain

$$(3.3.19) \qquad \tau = \frac{y_1}{x_1} = \frac{\sin \sigma_1}{k}.$$

The drag coefficient based on frontal area may be expressed

$$(3.3.20) \qquad \tfrac{1}{2}C_D = \frac{1}{\psi_1} \int_0^{\psi_1} (\tfrac{1}{2}C_{p_b})\, d\psi$$

$$= \frac{n+1}{n+2} \sin^2 \sigma_1.$$

This result may also be obtained from (3.2.8) by an appropriate approximate analysis. Expressing $n$ in terms of $k$ from (3.3.17), the drag coefficient takes the form

$$(3.3.21) \qquad \tfrac{1}{2}C_D = \frac{(2+j)k - 1}{(3+j)k - 2}\, k^2\tau^2.$$

This result was obtained by Cole [1]. He notes that for the two-dimensional case $C_D/2\tau^2$ takes on the minimum value of 0.918 at $k = 0.864$, and that for the axisymmetric case it takes on the minimum value of 2/3 at $k = 2/3$. He notes also the condition for finite drag that $k$ must be greater than $2/(3+j)$, equivalent to the condition $n < -2$.

We now turn to a different formulation of the problem with $\psi$ considered as the independent variable. With primes used to denote differentiation with respect to $\psi$, the relation determining $\sigma$ is

$$(3.3.22) \qquad \cos \sigma = P'.$$

The pressure is expressed

$$(3.3.23) \qquad \tfrac{1}{2}C_{p_b} = 1 - P'^2 - PP'',$$

and the drag

$$(3.3.24) \qquad \tfrac{1}{2}\psi C_D = \psi - PP',$$

with the subscript 1 dropped. For determining the body shape with this formulation we note first that

$$(3.3.25) \qquad dx = \cot \sigma\, dy = \frac{P'\, dy}{\sqrt{1 - P'^2}}.$$

Differentiation of (3.2.2) gives

$$(3.3.26) \qquad dy = (\rho_\infty U)^{\frac{-1}{1+j}}[(1+j)\psi]^{\frac{-j}{1+j}}\, d\psi,$$

whence we obtain

$$(3.3.27) \qquad dx = (\rho_\infty U)^{\frac{-1}{1+j}}[(1+j)\psi]^{\frac{-j}{1+j}} \frac{P'\, d\psi}{\sqrt{1 - P'^2}}.$$

With $P(\psi)$ given the quadrature of (3.3.27) gives us the shape. We may recognize the simple cosine shapes in this formulation as being those for which

$$(3.3.28) \qquad P = C\psi^{\frac{n}{n-1}},$$

with $C$ a constant, and the simple sine shape with $n = 2$ as one for which

$$(3.3.29) \qquad P = \psi\left(1 - \frac{\psi}{4\rho_\infty UA}\right).$$

A Newtonian free layer is a Newtonian shock layer whose position is determined not by the geometry of a body but by the condition that the pressure behind it is zero. The general shape of a free layer in two-dimensional or axisymmetric flow may be obtained following various approaches. Probably the most direct is the one using $\psi$ as an independent variable, and we shall follow this approach. The pressure coefficient in (3.3.23) must be set equal to zero. This is equivalent to setting the drag in (3.3.24) equal to a constant, or

$$(3.3.30) \qquad PP' = \psi - \psi_0,$$

with $\psi_0$ a constant. The integral of (3.3.30) gives

$$(3.3.31) \qquad P = \sqrt{(\psi - \psi_0)^2 + P_0^2}$$

where $P_0$ is another constant, and shows that $P$ takes the minimum value $P_0$ at $\psi = \psi_0$. We evaluate also the quantity

$$(3.3.32) \qquad \frac{P'}{\sqrt{1 - P'^2}} = \frac{\psi - \psi_0}{P_0}.$$

We may now evaluate $x$ from (3.3.27), keeping in mind the relation (3.2.2) between $\psi$ and $y$, as

$$(3.3.33) \qquad x = \frac{\rho_\infty U}{(1+j)P_0}\left[\frac{y^{2+j}}{2+j} - y_0^{1+j}y\right] + x_0.$$

Here $y_0$ is the value of $y$ at $\psi = \psi_0$ and may be imaginary in the axisymmetric case $j = 1$, and $x_0$ is an arbitrary constant. In two-dimensional flow the curve is a parabola, in axisymmetric flow a cubic curve. In any case the asymptotic shape is of the form (3.3.11) with a value of $k$ equal to $1/(2+j)$, consistent with the simple sine shape with $n = -1$. The Newtonian free layer is depicted in Fig. 3–2a.

We must now inquire as to whether this free layer may be considered in any way realistic for actual gas flows. An obvious step is to compare the asymptotic shock shape of a free layer with the asymptotic similar shapes in gas flows considered in Section 2.6. The limiting case of these similar solutions gives us the shape associated with a constant-energy similar flow, for which the parameter $k$ is distinctly greater than that for a free layer. Other similar gas flows with finite bodies have still larger values of $k$. From this inconsistency we might cursorily conclude that the free layer is unrealistic; we have noted in Section 2.6, however, that the constant-energy similar solution is itself unrealistic for steady hypersonic flows with $\gamma$ close to 1. And it is only for a gas with $\gamma$ very close to 1 that any Newtonian flow

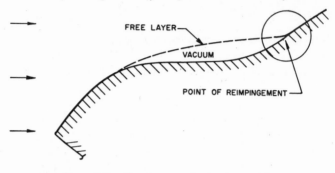

FREE LAYER

VACUUM

POINT OF REIMPINGEMENT

FIG. 3–2a. Free layer and reimpingement.

can be expected to be realistic. We may expect that the effect of a "cool core" would be to give a lower effective value of $k$. Thus we should not conclude that the free layer is unrealistic on the basis of a comparison with the constant-energy similar flow.

The correctness of the concept of a Newtonian free layer depends on the maintenance of the integrity of the layer, without appreciable thickening of the layer or loss of material to the vacuum region behind. We outline here the justification of the fact that the layer remains intact in a limiting sense, following the limiting perfect gas model for Newtonian flow. We consider that the body shape is given, that $M_\infty = \infty$ in the flow, and that the gas is a perfect one with $\gamma$ very close to 1. And we consider first that the body is a pointed one, so that the velocity in each lamina is of the order of $U$. Using conservation of total enthalpy, the velocity of sound is of the order $(\gamma - 1)^{1/2} U$. With finite pressure through the layer, its thickness is roughly proportional to $\gamma - 1$. We imagine that the layer shoots over a sharp edge and suddenly becomes free. A sound signal is propagated through the layer in a time proportional to the thickness divided by the sound speed; this time is proportional to $(\gamma - 1)^{1/2}$ with varying $\gamma$. In the limit as $\gamma \to 1$ this time approaches zero, and in the limit the entire shock layer is affected immediately by the fact that the layer has become free.

The material on the back side of the shock layer immediately begins to expand into the space between the shock layer and the body behind the corner. The Mach number within the layer is of the order $(\gamma - 1)^{-1/2}$, and we may apply the equivalence principle locally to the shock layer itself.

Thus we may liken this expansion to a sudden one-dimensional expansion following a piston which is being withdrawn. If $\gamma - 1$ is very small this unsteady flow is one at constant velocity of sound, and the pressure on the piston is expressible in terms of the initial pressure $p_b$ by

$$(3.3.34) \qquad\qquad p = p_b \exp{(-M)},$$

where $M$ is the velocity of the piston divided by the constant velocity of sound. This Mach number is of the order of the Mach number of the primary flow in the layer times the angle of divergence, and if this angle is finite, $M$ is of order $(\gamma - 1)^{-1/2}$. From (3.3.34) we see that the pressure on the body in the space approaches zero as $\gamma \to 1$. Even though the rarefaction wave sent from the corner to the shock reflects as a pressure wave (see Table 7–1), it may be shown that this reflected wave does not affect our limiting result. If the slope of the body is continuous at the Newtonian separation point, i.e. if there is no corner, the process described is delayed so that the pressure drop does not take place suddenly. However, this delay is of the order $(\gamma - 1)^{1/2}$ in time or distance, and an effective separation point defined by a chosen low body pressure will approach the Newtonian separation point in the limit $\gamma \to 1$.

The considerations above are for a pointed body, for which the shock layer may be considered itself hypersonic. With a blunt body the fluid nearest the body is at a relatively low velocity, at zero velocity at the body within the Newtonian approximation. With $\gamma$ very close to one, we can express the Mach number $M_b$ of the flow nearest the wall by a direct application of Bernoulli's law as

$$(3.3.35) \qquad\qquad M_b^2 = 2 \ln{(p_0/p_b)},$$

where $p_0$ is the stagnation pressure. If the Newtonian separation point occurs in a region of continuous body slope or at a corner with $p_b/p_0$ appreciably less than $\exp{(-\frac{1}{2})}$, then $M_b^2$ is appreciably greater than one although still of order one. The equivalence principle does not hold for the expansion, and the pressure on the body immediately downstream of the corner or Newtonian separation point is not vanishingly small. However, the rarefaction wave sent from the back of the layer toward the shock is rapidly reflected as a rarefaction almost fully from the strong vorticity in the lower part of the shock layer. This conclusion is based on (7.2.19) and the discussion following it. The end effect of these reflections is to make the presence of the low velocity flow near the wall unimportant, and to cause the pressure to be determined primarily by the high velocity flow. The case of Newtonian separation at a corner which is far enough forward on a blunt body so that $p_b/p_0$ is greater than $\exp{(-\frac{1}{2})}$ ($M_b^2 < 1$) is considerably more complicated. In any case, we may expect the pressure behind the corner to be primarily determined by the high velocity flow. Thus we may expect the pressure behind the Newtonian separation point to approach zero as $\gamma \to 1$ for a blunt body as well as for a pointed body, although this approach may be slower than with a pointed body.

Although the foregoing arguments justify that the free layer may be considered to be realistic, they also indicate the limitations inherent in the concept. We first note that the quantity $\gamma - 1$ we have been considering is essentially the same as $2\epsilon$. The requirement that the layer remain thin is then that $\epsilon^{1/2}$ be small. This requires the strong form of the small density

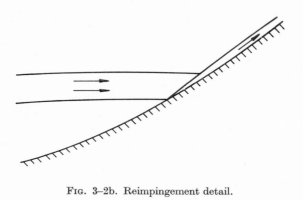

Fig. 3–2b. Reimpingement detail.

ratio assumption (D-strong); however, as we shall see later in Chapter IV, this assumption is required for the validity of most results in Newtonian flow. We have also assumed that Newtonian separation occurs at a corner or at least with the body curvature initially appreciably larger than the free layer curvature, so that there is an appreciable space between the free layer and the body. Even with $\epsilon^{1/2}$ small, this space should be amply large for the free layer to be realistic. If $\epsilon^{1/2}$ is finite and the space behind the free layer is constrained, we should expect an important effect of finite back pressure in this space. This effect would involve a thickening of the layer, and would be more pronounced with a blunt body. Freeman [1], in investigating flows on blunt bodies with $\epsilon$ small, has noted a singular behavior of his theory near the Newtonian separation point. This behavior is undoubtedly connected with the limitations on the concept of Newtonian separation, and undoubtedly also indicates a nonanalytic dependence upon $\epsilon$ of the solution in the separation region.

The shape of the Newtonian free layer after it leaves the body is independent of the shape of the body downstream of the separation point, provided that a space is left between them. If the body shape is such that it intersects the course of the free layer, the layer will reimpinge on the body (see Figs. 3–2). The free layer is itself hypersonic, and we should not expect phenomena in any way similar to those observed when a free jet of incompressible fluid strikes a wall. Instead, we should expect that the Newtonian impact process be essentially repeated, and that the free layer lose its momentum component normal to the wall and preserve the component tangential to the wall. This transfer of momentum results in a concentration of forces along the line of impingement and a further condensation of the material. This force distribution is a force per unit distance and not a pressure; a similar force would be exerted by an attached Newtonian layer at a concave corner of the body. In the idealization of Newtonian flow such singular or anomalous force distributions are not uncommon. Although they may appear unreasonable they are logical consequences of the Newtonian assumptions and models. If such singular behavior appears in a Newtonian flow we can expect some corresponding local behavior in a real-gas flow with $\epsilon$ small. In the case of the phenomenon of impingement, however, the shock layer in a real gas may be closer to one of the constant-pressure type discussed next.

The Newtonian free layer is a special case of a more general family of layers characterized by constant pressure on the body side of the layer. Except for the free layer (zero pressure case), such constant-pressure layers may be either convex or concave. A constant-pressure shape is asymptotic to a straight line of slope $\tan \sigma$ equal to $\sqrt{\frac{1}{2}C_p/(1 - \frac{1}{2}C_p)}$, and may be obtained with the methods used for investigating the free layer. A constant-pressure layer may reimpinge on a body just as may a free layer. The space between a constant-pressure layer and the body must be filled with "dead" fluid at the specified pressure, at a high density which in the Newtonian limit approaches infinity. Since this space normally would have finite volume, we have the anomalous result that an infinite mass of fluid is stored therein.

With constant-pressure layers permitted the Newtonian flow on a general body becomes nonunique, as the possible constant-pressure layers on a given two-dimensional or axisymmetric body form a two-parameter family. For this very general family we permit the possibility that the pressure jumps discontinuously behind the layer at a separation point. If the flow separates at a corner, or if we require the pressure on the body to be continuous where the flow separates at a point which is not a corner, there is a reduction in the freedom of choice of solution and we are left with a one-parameter family. With the slope of the body continuous and its curvature finite, a constant-pressure layer may only separate under a pressure which is greater than that which would occur without separation. If the body curvature is continuous and the pressure is required to be continuous, a constant-pressure layer can separate only in a region of decreasing pressure or at a leading edge.

A constant-pressure layer other than a free layer which extends to infinity in the free stream must be rejected because of unacceptable downstream boundary conditions. If now we also reject solutions in which the layer reimpinges on the body the possible solutions form a zero-parameter family. In this case the solution is not necessarily unique, but we would have at most a finite number of solutions to choose from. In real gas flows the thin but finite viscous boundary layer does provide a mechanism for upstream influence in the shock layer, and a separation point far upstream from a pressure-increasing obstacle is quite generally observed in experiments. Hence we suggest here that a configuration with a Newtonian constant-pressure layer without discontinuities in the pressure (except at a corner) and

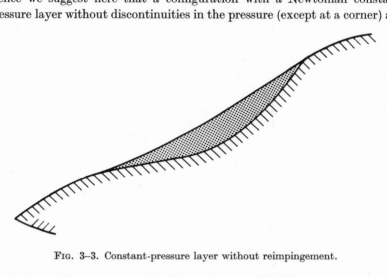

FIG. 3–3. Constant-pressure layer without reimpingement.

without reimpingement of the layer may be an appropriate limiting configuration to represent real gas flows, in case the attached solution reaches zero pressure and the solution with a free layer involves reimpingement. The condition of contact with the body without reimpingement is somewhat analogous to the well known Kutta condition of airfoil theory, in that it is an ideal-fluid condition with an origin in real-fluid effects, and which provides uniqueness within inviscid theory. The constant-pressure layer without reimpingement is depicted in Fig. 3–3.

Another interesting generalization of the Newtonian free layer appears when the Newtonian theory is applied to the problem of a two-dimensional hypersonic sail. We define a "Newtonian sail" as a membrane which is a surface in a Newtonian flow. A membrane has the property that it may support no bending loads but will, in general, experience a two-dimensional stress in its surface. On the reverse side of the sail we specify a constant pressure. We shall restrict ourselves to a generalization of the free layer and not consider the analogous generalization of the constant-pressure layer. Accordingly, we specify this constant back pressure to be zero. And finally, we require that the pressure on the front of the sail be nonnegative. Each differential element of the sail must be in equilibrium under the forces exerted on it.

The stress in the membrane is a symmetric two-dimensional tensor, whose principal axes will be aligned with the natural coordinate system for either a two-dimensional or an axisymmetric sail. For a two-dimensional sail the principal stress component in the direction of the cylindrical axis of the sail exerts no forces on any element of the sail and may be completely disregarded. From the requirement of equilibrium in the tangential direction we may conclude that the other principal stress component is constant. We denote this stress by $UT$ and may derive an expression for the pressure on the back of the sail which is the same as (3.3.23) but with $P$ replaced by $P - T$. Setting this back pressure equal to zero we obtain

$$(3.3.36) \qquad 0 = 1 - P'^2 - P''(P - T).$$

This relation we may integrate immediately to obtain an equation analogous to (3.3.30),

$$(3.3.37) \qquad (P - T)P' = \psi - \psi_0.$$

When we integrate this expression with the requirement of nonnegative pressure on the front of the sail we obtain in place of (3.3.31)

$$(3.3.38) \qquad T - P = \sqrt{(\psi - \psi_0)^2 + P_0^2}.$$

The succeeding development proceeds exactly as for the free layer, but with a change in sign in (3.3.32) and (3.3.33). The resulting shape $(j = 0)$ is again a parabolic cylinder, but with the vertex of the parabola pointed downstream instead of upstream. Which shape of the family of possible shapes the sail assumes may be determined by the ratio of the length of the sail to its chord, by the tension in the sail, or by an elastic relation between the length and the tension.

An analysis of a two-dimensional hypersonic sail using the uncorrected Newtonian pressure law instead of the Newton-Busemann pressure law has been made by Daskin and Feldman [1]. With the uncorrected pressure law the shape of a two-dimensional sail is a catenary with its vertex pointed downstream. Daskin and Feldman did not note that the shape they obtained is a catenary, and did not attempt the solution for a sail with the complete pressure law.

Another two-dimensional sail configuration is possible, involving the constant-pressure layer discussed above. The shock layer is a constant-pressure layer which just grazes the rear of the sail; with no forebody this shape is simply the straight line chord from the leading edge of the sail to the rear edge. Behind the dead-water region the sail takes a circular arc shape. Which of the family of possible circular arc shapes the sail assumes is again determined by the ratio of length to chord, by the tension, or by an elastic relation between length and tension.

For an axisymmetric sail we must consider the azimuthal or meridional principal stress component in the membrane. We let $UT$ be the longitudinal force per unit radian in the membrane; if the azimuthal stress component is nonzero, $T$ is not a constant but a function $T(\psi)$. When we include the effect of the azimuthal stress in the condition for equilibrium of an element of the sail, we again arrive at (3.3.36) but with an additional term $P'T'$ on the right-hand side. We conclude that the first integral (3.3.37) is valid also for an axisymmetric sail, whether $T$ is constant or not.

For an axisymmetric sail with zero azimuthal stress and constant $T$, the analysis above may be followed again and yields (3.3.33) with $j = 1$ and with reversed sign. Again the sail shape is the mirror image in a transverse plane of a free layer shape. For a sail with nonzero azimuthal stress we must inquire as to how the stress components and sail shape are specified or related. If the sail shape itself is specified, i.e. if the unstressed membrane shape is given and the membrane is inextensible, the sail behaves as though it were rigid and we may solve the problem completely with the methods of Section 3.2.

The problem of an elastic axisymmetric sail is nontrivial in the sense of this section, however. We assume that the unstressed shape of the sail is known, and that its complete elastic behavior under an arbitrary axisymmetric stress system is specified. A Lagrangian coordinate identifying position on the unstressed sail is defined and is used as the independent variable. Two elastic stress relations and (3.3.37) yield three ordinary differential equations for the three unknown dependent variables $\psi$, $P$, and $T$. With three boundary conditions from the conditions of the mounting of the sail we may obtain the complete solution. We shall not investigate the elastic sail further.

Finally, we introduce the concept of an "isotropic sail". An isotropic sail is a Newtonian sail for which the stress tensor in the membrane is isotropic, or for which the membrane has zero rigidity in shear. The condition of tangential equilibrium of a sail element requires that the stress, which now may be considered a scalar, be a constant over the entire sail. Thus we could refer jocularly to such an isotropic sail as a "Newtonian soap bubble". In the axisymmetric case $T$ is $r/U$ times this constant stress, and we may rewrite (3.3.37) as

$$(3.3.39) \qquad (P - A\psi^{1/2})P' = \psi - \psi_0,$$

where $A$ is a constant. This differential equation may be solved numerically and the profile shape obtained from (3.2.1b) and (3.3.27).

## 4. Optimum shapes

The problem of determining the shape of a body so that its drag is a minimum is an old problem, one which occupied Newton in the seventeenth century. Newton's results and those of Eggers, Resnikoff, and Dennis [1] are based on analyses which omit the centrifugal correction to the pressure on the body. We set as our present task the determination of optimum minimum-drag shapes using the complete pressure relation (3.2.7). We have available an explicit formula for the drag (3.2.8), but note that this formula is somewhat different in form from that obtained using the uncorrected pressure expression. We shall find it convenient to distinguish between two different types of optimum shapes which we shall develop, designated by the terms "absolute optimum" and "proper optimum".

We shall concern ourselves primarily with the classical problem in which the quantities specified are the length and thickness of the body. The approach used here will be directly applicable or adaptable to problems with different isoperimetric conditions. In considering bodies of revolution we shall not include annular bodies; if desired, such bodies may be treated by the same methods. We shall work within the formulation of the problem in which $y(x)$ is the basic function treated. The formulations using the function $x(y)$ or the function $P(x)$ could also have been used, but the use of $y(x)$ appears direct and the most conventional.

Equation (3.2.8) for the drag is fundamental to any optimization considerations and is repeated here,

$$(3.4.1) \qquad\qquad \tfrac{1}{2}\psi_1 C_D = \psi_1 - \cos \sigma_1 P_1.$$

The subscript 1 refers to conditions at the rear of the body. With the thickness of the body given the quantity $\psi_1$ is fixed, and a minimum to the drag is obtained by requiring the product $\cos \sigma_1 P_1$ to be a maximum. The two factors in this product are of different types, as $\cos \sigma_1$ depends only upon the shape of the body at its base, while $P_1$ is an integral taken over the entire body. We now make the apparently naive assumption that the two factors are independent and that we may maximize the product by maximizing the factors separately. The maximum of $\cos \sigma_1$ is simply 1, and is obtained by setting $\sigma_1 = 0$. The maximum of $P_1$ will be obtained by using the calculus of variations. With $\cos \sigma_1 = 1$ the requirement that the thickness of the body be given is inessential, and our analytical treatment may be directly applied to problems in which the body thickness is not specified. However, then variations in the quantity $\psi_1$ appearing on the right side of (3.4.1) must be taken into account.

The step of setting $\cos \sigma_1 = 1$ is a critical one, which will have to be examined carefully later. With $\cos \sigma_1 = 1$ we may express the drag with the aid of (3.2.4) as

$$(3.4.2) \qquad \tfrac{1}{2}\psi_1 C_{D_{\sigma_1 = 0}} = \int_0^{\psi_1} (1 - \cos \sigma)\, d\psi = 2 \int_0^{\psi_1} \sin^2 \frac{\sigma}{2}\, d\psi.$$

For comparison, the corresponding expression for the drag using the uncorrected expression for the pressure is

$$(3.4.3) \qquad \tfrac{1}{2}\psi_1 C_{D_{\text{uncorr}}} = \int_0^{\psi_1} \sin^2 \sigma\, d\psi.$$

For a slender body the approximate result is immediate,

$$(3.4.4) \qquad C_{D_{\sigma_1 = 0}} = \tfrac{1}{2} C_{D_{\text{uncorr}}}$$

This result was obtained by von Kármán [1], who did not, however, discuss the limitations involved.

We now express $P_1$ in terms of the function $y(x)$ with $\cos \sigma = 1/\sqrt{1 + y'^2}$ as

$$(3.4.5) \qquad P_1 = \rho_\infty U \int_0^{x_1} \frac{y' y^j\, dx}{\sqrt{1 + y'^2}},$$

where $x_1$ is the length of the body. Two auxiliary integrals of interest in various isoperimetric conditions are the integral for the volume per unit depth or radian

$$(3.4.6) \qquad (1 + j)V = \int_0^{x_1} y^{1+j}\, dx,$$

and the corresponding integral for the surface area

$$(3.4.7) \qquad S = \int_0^{x_1} \sqrt{1 + y'^2}\, y^j\, dx.$$

With the Lagrangian multipliers $\lambda_V$ and $\lambda_S$ the problem posed for the calculus of variations (compare Eggers, Resnikoff, and Dennis [1]) is the maximization of the integral of $F$ over $x$, where

$$(3.4.8) \qquad F = \left[ \frac{y'}{\sqrt{1 + y'^2}} + \lambda_V y + \lambda_S \sqrt{1 + y'^2} \right] y^j.$$

Since $F$ is a function of $y$ and $y'$ alone and does not depend explicitly upon

$x$, we may apply immediately the first integral of the Euler equation of the calculus of variations. This first integral is

$$(3.4.9) \qquad F - y' \frac{\partial F}{\partial y'} = A,$$

where $A$ is a constant. With the $F$ in (3.4.8) this takes the form

$$(3.4.10) \qquad \frac{y'^3}{(1 + y'^2)^{3/2}} + \lambda_V y + \frac{\lambda_S}{\sqrt{1 + y'^2}} = Ay^{-j}.$$

Equation (3.4.10) is a first-order differential equation in $x$ and $y$ whose solution gives us the desired shapes. Note that three undetermined constants appear in (3.4.10) and that a fourth must appear in the general solution of the differential equation. This freedom is necessary to satisfy the various boundary and isoperimetric conditions. Of course, in special cases (3.4.10) is simplified: If there is no specification on the volume, $\lambda_V$ is zero; if there is no specification on the surface area, $\lambda_S$ is zero; if there is no specification on the length of the body $A$ is zero (compare Eggers, Resnikoff, and Dennis [1]). If there is no specification on the thickness of the body, the boundary condition $y'_1 = 0$ must be satisfied at the base of the body, except with $\lambda_S > 0$. Exceptions to normal behavior and other difficulties will appear in the most general case, and a complete study will require use of the parts of the theory of the calculus of variations dealing with wall conditions, discontinuities in slope, and second variations. See, for example, Courant and Hilbert [1].

The simpler solutions of (3.4.10) are given in Table 3–1. Note that with $A = 0$ and the body length unspecified the solutions are the same for two-dimensional as for axisymmetric flow. With $\lambda_V$ and $\lambda_S$ both zero in axisymmetric flow, the solution may be expressed parametrically as

$$(3.4.11a) \qquad x = \tfrac{3}{4}y_0[\xi(\xi^2 - \tfrac{1}{2})\sqrt{\xi^2 - 1} - \tfrac{1}{2}\cosh^{-1}\xi],$$

$$(3.4.11b) \qquad y = y_0\xi^3,$$

where the parameter $\xi$ goes from 1 to $\infty$. In axisymmetric flow with body length specified the body generally has a flat portion on the nose, as do the corresponding solutions of Newton and of Eggers, Resnikoff, and Dennis. The radius of this flat portion in solution (3.4.11) is $y_0$. For $\xi$ large (3.4.11) approaches the form

$$(3.4.12) \qquad y = y_0\left(\frac{4x}{3y_0}\right)^{3/4}.$$

Eggers, Resnikoff, and Dennis obtain a solution analogous to (3.4.11) with an asymptotic solution of a form similar to (3.4.12). They note that their asymptotic solution is a very accurate approximation to their complete solution in the case of reasonably slender bodies. It can be shown that this is even more true with our solution (3.4.11).

The solutions we have obtained correspond to optimum bodies only if we may set $\cos \sigma_1 = 1$. In general, however, the shapes obtained have finite

TABLE 3–1

*Solutions to the variational equation*

| $A$ | $j$ | $\lambda_V$ | $\lambda_g$ | Solution |
|---|---|---|---|---|
| $0$ | $0$ or $1$ | $\dfrac{1}{y_m}$ | $0$ | $x = y_m - (y_m^{2/3} - y^{2/3})^{3/2}$ |
| $0$ | $0$ or $1$ | $0$ | $-\dfrac{a^3}{1 + a^2}$ | $y = ax$ |
| $\dfrac{b}{\sqrt{1 + a^2}}$ | $0$ | $0$ | $b - \dfrac{a^3}{1 + a^2}$ | $y = ax$ |
| $y_0$ | $1$ | $0$ | $0$ | Equations (3.4.11) |

slope at the base, and the question naturally arises as to whether our solutions have meaning. Mathematically, there is no objection to a discontinuity in slope, and we may require that the slope be zero at the base proper although the slope remains finite to within an infinitesimal distance of the base. Physically, such a solution requires that the direction of the shock layer be changed quite suddenly, and this would require a negatively infinite pressure acting over an infinitesimal part of the body at the base. Of course, we must reject such a mechanism as being unrealistic even by the rather liberal standards of Newtonian flow theory.

Another solution is available, however, and consists of a mechanism by which the direction of the shock layer is changed by means of a positively infinite pressure acting over an infinitesimal part of the outside of the layer at the base. This leads to the concept of a "thrust cowl" which will turn the flow in the shock layer smoothly into the proper direction. In order that this be done without significant losses, it is necessary that the chord of the cowl be large compared with the thickness of the Newtonian layer. But since this thickness is infinitesimal, the chord of the thrust cowl is itself infinitesimal in the Newtonian limit. This Newtonian thrust cowl is depicted in Fig. 3–4.

If the body in question has positive pressure everywhere the one thrust cowl at the base is sufficient. If the body has a region of negative pressure we must replace the body with a number of positive-pressure segments separated by corners fitted with thrust cowls. If in the Newtonian limit the number of these segments and cowls is increased without limit the body may be made to approach equivalence to a body with negative pressure. The realism of this picture is admittedly more dubious than that of a body

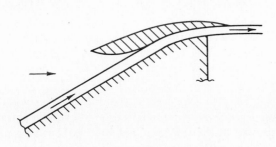

FIG. 3–4. Newtonian thrust cowl.

with a single thrust cowl, but the picture is useful in permitting us to complete conceptually the class of bodies without detachment of the layer and with the condition $\sigma_1 = 0$ satisfied.

With the condition $\sigma_1 = 0$ satisfied and with thrust cowls provided as needed, then, we can find optimum shapes under a variety of isoperimetric conditions. We shall refer to these shapes as being "absolute optimum" shapes. In a real gas flow with a thin shock layer a thrust cowl may be used to decrease the net drag of a body. The advantage of such a cowl will be greater the thinner is the shock layer, and the closer we are to being able to utilize the Newtonian absolute optimum shapes.

We now turn to a different kind of optimum shape for minimum drag, for which we shall use the expression "proper optimum". For a proper optimum shape we set up different rules from those applicable to absolute optimum shapes. In particular, the possibility of using a thrust cowl is ruled out, and the possibility of having a discontinuity in the slope of the body is eliminated by the requirement that the pressure on the body be everywhere positive or zero. The pressure is itself expressed as an indefinite integral of the shape and, to the writers' knowledge, the classical calculus of variations does not provide a method for this type of isoperimetric condition. We shall use an attack based upon intuition, with the help of general results from the calculus of variations. We shall concentrate on the simplest problem, that of a two-dimensional body with given chord length and thickness; we suggest as an interesting problem the extension of the method given here to other isoperimetric conditions and to general axisymmetric shapes. We shall, however, include the axisymmetric case for a slender body of given chord and thickness.

We first note that our nonnegative pressure condition is violated for the absolute optimum shape only by the negatively infinite pressure at the base. Personifying the optimum body shape, we note that it is doing its best to have very low pressure far aft. Within the rules of the proper optimum, the best that the optimum shape can do in this regard is to have zero pressure over a finite section adjoining the base of the body. This suggests that a proper optimum body should consist of a forebody bearing positive pressures and an afterbody which is quite arbitrary (see, for example, Fig. 3–6). The afterbody lies within a free layer which separates from the forebody and which returns to the body at the base. The free layer must pass by the base unobstructed into the region behind the body.

If the shape of the free layer were predetermined we could draw its trace on a plot of tan $\sigma$ versus $x$. Minimum drag would still be obtained by maximizing $P$ at the end of the forebody and we should solve a problem in the calculus of variations with the end point not fixed but required to lie on this trace. A basic result of the theory of the calculus of variations is that such a boundary condition does not affect the basic differential equations obtained; in our case the same Euler equations and solutions would therefore apply for the forebody as the equations and solutions appropriate to the absolute optimum problem. The shape of the free layer is not predeterminable, but we guess that the forebody should have an absolute optimum shape anyway. We shall not attempt a complete proof that this guess is justified but shall outline a partial proof for the two-dimensional body of given chord and thickness. This is the simplest problem, as the absolute optimum shape is simply a straight line in this case. After presenting this justification we shall present examples.

Our method will consist of assuming the contrary and showing that a contradiction results. Our comparison shapes will, however, be limited to those consisting of a forebody followed by a free layer; hence our proof is only a partial one. We need certain properties of the free layer solution. The derivation of these properties is straightforward and will not be given here. We are interested in the change in the lateral coordinate $y$ of a two-dimensional free layer in traversing a given distance in the axial direction. The properties we shall need are that the change in the lateral coordinate varies monotonically with the initial impulse with given initial angle, and that if the rear part of the forebody is shortened so that the free layer starts earlier, the value of $y$ at the base must decrease monotonically with the amount of the body cut off.

We now suppose that the proper optimum shape has a forebody which is not the absolute optimum shape (a straight line in this case). The free layer shape is continued upstream from the separation point, and a straight line is drawn from the vertex tangent to the free layer (see Fig. 3–5). A shape

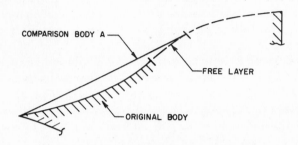

FIG. 3–5a. Proper optimization—first case.

for which this point of tangency lies aft of the base clearly has greater drag than does a simple wedge and is not considered. Also, it may be shown that the vertex must lie on the convex or upstream side of the free layer and that the point of tangency must exist. Two cases now exist, that for which the point of tangency lies in the part of the free stream layer downstream of the

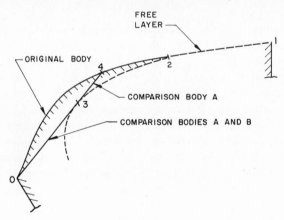

FIG. 3–5b. Proper optimization—second case.

separation point (Fig. 3–5a), and that for which the point of tangency lies on the extension of the free layer upstream of the separation point (Fig. 3–5b). We consider the two cases separately.

In the first case we consider comparison body $A$ to consist of the straight line to the point of tangency (Fig. 3–5a). Since this body has maximum impulse between the vertex and the tangency point and the initial angles are the same, the free layer from $A$ will overshoot the base. Now we consider the body to be shortened to give comparison body $B$, with the property that the free layer just reaches the base. The drag of the original body is clearly greater than that of body $A$, and the drag of body $A$ is greater than that of body $B$. Since body $B$ satisfies the conditions required of a proper optimum body, the original body could not have been the proper optimum body as was assumed.

In the second case we consider comparison body $A$ to consist of the straight line extended beyond the tangency point 3 to its intersection with original body 4, followed by a thrust cowl at this intersection point to direct the layer along the original body, followed by the remaining part of the original body to the separation point 2. The numbers here refer to points labelled on Fig. 3–5b. Comparison body $B$ consists simply of the straight line to the point of tangency, while $B'$ is the same plus the free layer section between the point of tangency 3 and the separation point 2. The impulse at the intersection point 4 for body $A$ is greater than that for the original body, because between the vertex and point 4 body $A$ has an absolute optimum shape. The contribution of the segment 4–2 to the impulse is the same for both bodies, and the impulse at point 2 is greater for body $A$. We may write this result as

$$(3.4.13) \qquad\qquad P_{A2} > P_{02}.$$

We must now compare the increments in impulse developed along the extended free layer segment 3–2 and the corresponding part of body $A$, 3–4–2. We first must note that minus the Euler differential expression is the kernel of the first variation integral in the theory of the calculus of variations (see Courant and Hilbert [1]), equal to $3y'y''/(1 + y'^2)^{5/2}$ in this case. This kernel has the same sign as does the curvature $y''/(1 + y'^2)^{3/2}$ because $y'$ is positive, and is negative for a concave shape (corresponding to a convex body) such as that for a free layer. An infinitesimal increase of $y$ over a concave section of a shape decreases the impulse $P$ developed over that section. It is possible to construct a sequence of nested shapes each of which is concave where it does not coincide with the segment 3–4–2, and which provides a continuous transition between the free layer segment 3–2 and the segment 3–4–2. The impulse decreases monotonically on this sequence of shapes, and we may conclude that the impulse at point 2 on body $B'$ is greater than for body $A$, or

$$(3.4.14) \qquad\qquad P_{B3} + P_{3-2} > P_{A2}.$$

From (3.4.13) and (3.4.14) we obtain immediately

$$(3.4.15) \qquad\qquad P_{B3} > P_{02} - P_{3-2}.$$

But the quantity $P_{02} - P_{3-2}$ is the impulse which the original free layer extended upstream would have at point 3, and the drag of the original body may be calculated from (3.4.1) at point 3, using this impulse. Hence the drag of body $B$ is less than that of the original body. Also, from (3.4.15), the free layer which will come from body $B$ separating at point 3 will over-shoot the base. We consider body $B$ shortened to give comparison body $C$ with the property that the free layer from $C$ just reaches the base. Since body C has less drag than does body $B$ and satisfies the conditions required of a proper optimum body, our assumption that the original body was the proper optimum body must have been false.

Recognizing that our proof is a partial one and that a neater proof of the result (3.4.14) would be desirable, let us accept the result that the forebody must have an absolute optimum shape. We are left with a one-parameter family of shapes satisfying the specifications and need only to minimize the drag with respect to the parameter. Let $a$ be the slope of the forebody and $sc$ its chord, where $c$ is the chord of the entire body. Let $\tau$ be the thickness ratio of the entire half-body on one side of the vertex (see Fig. 3–6).

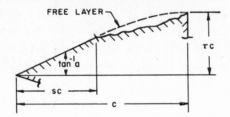

FIG. 3–6. Two-dimensional proper optimum shape.

The change in $y$ in the free layer is thus $(\tau - as)c$, and the change in $x$ is $(1 - s)c$. Putting in the condition which comes from a determination of the initial impulse in the free layer, we may write the condition that the free layer just reach the base in the two-dimensional case as

$$(3.4.16) \qquad \tfrac{1}{2}(\tau - as)^2 + \frac{as(\tau - as)}{1 + a^2} = \frac{a^2s(1 - s)}{1 + a^2}.$$

This equation can be obtained from (3.3.33), with $j = 0$ and with a factor $c^2$ divided out.

The drag of the body equals the drag of the forebody, and is

$$(3.4.17) \qquad \tfrac{1}{2}\tau C_D = as\left(1 - \frac{1}{1 + a^2}\right) = \frac{a^3s}{1 + a^2}.$$

The quantity $s$ may be eliminated from (3.4.16) by using (3.4.17), and we obtain

$$(3.4.18) \qquad \tau^2 \left[ 1 - C_D + \frac{(1 + a^2)^2}{4a^4} C_D^2 \right] - \frac{\tau C_D}{a} = 0.$$

The quantity $\tau$ is kept constant, and an extremum of the drag is obtained by setting the derivative of (3.4.18) with respect to $a$ equal to zero. This procedure yields

$$(3.4.19) \qquad \frac{\tau C_D}{a^2} \left[ 1 - \frac{1 + a^2}{a^3} \tau C_D \right] = 0.$$

That a minimum to the drag is obtained by setting the bracket in (3.4.19) equal to zero is readily verified, and a comparison with (3.4.17) tells us that

$$(3.4.20) \qquad s = \tfrac{1}{2}$$

for minimum drag. A peculiar simplicity of this result lies in the fact that it is independent of thickness ratio, and no simple reason for this is apparent to the authors.

Results for the drag in terms of thickness ratio are best expressed parametrically, for example, in terms of $a$ using (3.4.17) and (3.4.18). We may avoid the solution of a quadratic in a parametric representation by introducing a new parameter $\kappa$, which varies from $\tfrac{1}{2}$ for very thick bodies to $\tfrac{1}{2}\sqrt{3}$ for very thin bodies. In terms of $\kappa$ the results may be expressed

$$(3.4.21a) \qquad \tau = a\kappa,$$

$$(3.4.21b) \qquad a = \frac{\sqrt{3 - 4\kappa^2}}{2\kappa - 1},$$

$$(3.4.21c) \qquad \tfrac{1}{2}C_D = \frac{3 - 4\kappa^2}{8\kappa(1 - \kappa)},$$

$$(3.4.21d) \qquad \frac{1}{2\tau^2} C_D = \frac{(2\kappa - 1)^2}{8\kappa^3(1 - \kappa)}.$$

For slender bodies the results are simpler. Besides the basic result of (3.4.20) we have, setting $\kappa = \tfrac{1}{2}\sqrt{3}$ in (3.4.21a and d),

$$(3.4.22a) \qquad a = \frac{2}{\sqrt{3}} \tau = 1.155\tau,$$

$$(3.4.22b) \qquad \frac{1}{2\tau^2} C_D = \frac{4\sqrt{3}}{9} = 0.770.$$

We shall compare this drag result with others after looking at the axisymmetric case.

The methods and basic approach presented are clearly applicable to two-dimensional problems with different isoperimetric conditions and to corresponding axisymmetric problems. It is clear, however, that both the justification arguments and the algebra of computing the optima will be even more involved and detailed. Moreover, we would have to go into such questions as whether the free layer surface area should be included in an isoperimetric condition on surface area. We shall limit ourselves here with the introduction of the concept of the proper optimum, and with the relatively simple illustrative examples presented.

However, we shall give the axisymmetric solution corresponding to the two-dimensional one above, but only for the slender body case. The quantity $s$ is defined as before, and $a$ is defined by the equation giving the shape of the forebody

$$(3.4.23) \qquad y = \tfrac{4}{3}asc\left(\frac{x}{sc}\right)^{3/4},$$

which is equivalent to (3.4.12). The values of $y$ and $y'$ at the separation point 2 with $x = sc$ are given by

$$(3.4.24) \qquad y_2 = \tfrac{4}{3}asc,$$

$$(3.4.25) \qquad y_2' = a.$$

A new parameter $\beta$ is introduced as the ratio between the thickness at the base and $y_2$, or

$$(3.4.26) \qquad \tau c = \beta y_2,$$

from which we obtain

$$(3.4.27) \qquad \tau = \tfrac{4}{3}a\beta s.$$

The drag of the forebody is given by the approximate expression

$$(3.4.28) \qquad \tfrac{1}{2}(\tfrac{1}{2}\tau^2 c^2)C_D = \int_0^{y_2} (1 - \cos \sigma)y \, dy + \tfrac{1}{2}(1 - \cos \sigma_2)y_2^2,$$

from which we may calculate

$$(3.4.29) \qquad \tfrac{1}{2}\tau^2 C_D = \tfrac{20}{9}a^4 s^2.$$

Within the body of approximations which we are using, the term in $y_0$ in (3.3.33) does not appear, and the free layer shape may be expressed as

$$(3.4.30) \qquad \tfrac{1}{3}y^3 = \tfrac{16}{9}a^3 s^2 c^2(x - x_0),$$

where $x_0$ is a constant. The coefficient on the right hand side has been evaluated by matching the impulse from the forebody with the impulse in the free layer. The condition that the free layer just reach the base is thus

$$(3.4.31) \qquad \tfrac{1}{3}(\tfrac{4}{3})^3 a^3 s^3 c^3 (\beta^3 - 1) = \tfrac{16}{9} a^3 s^2 (1 - s) c^3.$$

We then solve (3.4.31) for $s$ and obtain

$$(3.4.32) \qquad s = \frac{9}{4\beta^3 + .5}.$$

Next we divide (3.4.29) by $\tau^4$ from (3.4.27), eliminate $s$ using (3.4.32), and obtain another expression for the drag

$$(3.4.33) \qquad \frac{1}{2\tau^2} C_D = \frac{5}{4^4 3^2} \left( \frac{4\beta^3 + 5}{\beta^2} \right).$$

The drag expressed in (3.4.33) has a minimum at

$$(3.4.34) \qquad \beta = (\tfrac{5}{2})^{1/3} = 1.3572,$$

with a minimum value of

$$(3.4.35) \qquad \frac{1}{2\tau^2} C_D = \tfrac{5}{16}\beta^2 = 0.5756.$$

The value of $s$ at this minimum is

$$(3.4.36) \qquad s = \tfrac{3}{5}.$$

The numerical results for two-dimensional and axisymmetric bodies are presented in Table 3–2. The values of the absolute optimum drag which are used as reference in the last column of Table 3–2 are

$$(3.4.37a) \qquad \frac{1}{2\tau^2} C_{D_{\text{abs. opt.}}} = \tfrac{1}{2}$$

in the two-dimensional case, and

$$(3.4.37b) \qquad \frac{1}{2\tau^2} C_{D_{\text{abs. opt.}}} = \tfrac{27}{64}$$

in the axisymmetric case. These values are readily obtained from (3.4.2) or (3.4.5) with (3.4.1).

An attempt to determine optimum shapes in the axisymmetric case under the same conditions we have set was made by Gonor and Chernyi [1]. They started with an equation equivalent to (3.4.1), but they disregarded variations in $\sigma_1$ and merely accepted the value of $\sigma_1$ forthcoming from their analysis. They maximized the quantity $P_1$, and were accordingly led to essentially the same problem in the calculus of variations which we have considered. The slender body shape they arrived at was therefore the $\tfrac{3}{4}$ power shape, for which they correctly noted a 30% reduction in drag below that for the cone. As is evident from our treatment and from Table 3–2, their shapes are not optimum shapes.

For the slender body case, an alternate approach is available, which we shall briefly outline without considering isoperimetric conditions. For slender bodies the basic Newton-Busemann pressure law (3.2.7) may be rewritten (cf. Cole [1])

$$(3.4.38) \qquad \tfrac{1}{2} C_{p_b} = y'^2 + \frac{1}{1+j} \, y y''.$$

TABLE 3–2

*Comparative drags of optimum slender bodies*

| Shape | $\dfrac{1}{2\tau^2} C_D$ | $\dfrac{C_D}{C_{D_{\text{abs,opt.}}}}$ |
|---|---|---|
| *Two-dimensional:* | | |
| Wedge | 1.000 | 2.000 |
| 0.864 Power (Cole [1]) | 0.918 | 1.836 |
| Proper Optimum | 0.770 | 1.540 |
| Absolute Optimum (wedge) | 0.500 | 1.000 |
| *Axisymmetric:* | | |
| Cone | 1.000 | 2.370 |
| 3/4 Power, uncorrected | 0.844 | 2.000 |
| 3/4 Power | 0.703 | 1.667 |
| 2/3 Power (Cole [1]) | 0.667 | 1.580 |
| Proper Optimum | 0.576 | 1.364 |
| Absolute Optimum (3/4 power) | 0.422 | 1.000 |

The drag may be represented by the integral

$$(3.4.39) \qquad \tfrac{1}{2} \psi_1 C_D = \int_0^1 F(y, y', y'') \, dx,$$

where

$$(3.4.40) \qquad F = y^j y'^3 + \frac{1}{1+j} \, y^{1+j} y' y''.$$

We may minimize (3.4.39) using the usual technique, with the fact that the first integral to the Euler equation for (3.4.39) is

$$(3.4.41) \qquad y'' F_{y''} + y' F_{y'} - F - y' \frac{d}{dx} (F_{y''}) = A,$$

where $A$ is a constant. Putting $F$ from (3.4.40) into (3.4.41) we obtain

(3.4.42)                                $y'^3 = Ay^{-j},$

which we recognize as equivalent to (3.4.10) with the Lagrange multipliers zero. But while discontinuities in slope were permitted in our absolute optimum analysis, they are not permitted here, as the pressure given by (3.4.38) must remain finite. The concept of the proper optimum with the use of the free layer must somehow come out of the isoperimetric condition that $F$ be everywhere nonnegative. This approach promises us nothing beyond what we have already obtained, and we shall not pursue it further. But it can undoubtedly give us for the slender body case an alternate justification of our proper optimum shapes.

We now ask what these results can teach us as to what optimum bodies should be like in real gas flows. The process of optimization is one by which momentum losses are minimized. These losses are of two kinds, the loss in momentum of the flow in entering the shock layer, and the loss in the axial component of the momentum from inclination of the momentum leaving the body. The thrust cowl of an absolute optimum body has as its aim the elimination of the second loss.

In a real gas flow with a shock layer of finite thickness a penalty in pressure and frictional drag must be paid for a thrust cowl. In addition, there will be practical difficulties in structural support and aerodynamic heating which may eliminate the thrust cowl for the designer. The practical realization of a design based upon the proper optimum concept, however, appears feasible especially when we realize that frictional resistance should be very low on the after section of the body corresponding to the free layer section.

We first note that our absolute optimum shape which appears on the proper optimum forebody (without isoperimetric conditions) is essentially identical to the shape which appears as optimum in the theory of linearized supersonic flow (for the axisymmetric case, see von Kármán [1]). We may guess, then, that an uncowled optimum shape should have a forebody with our absolute optimum shape, a wedge in the two-dimensional case and a $\frac{3}{4}$ power shape body in the axisymmetric case. This forebody should be followed by an afterbody designed to have low pressures on it. The chord ratio $s$ should be intermediate between our Newtonian value ($\frac{1}{2}$ or $\frac{3}{5}$) and one, and should be closer to the former if the shock layer is thin and closer to the latter if the shock layer is very thick or if the body is to perform best at moderate supersonic speeds. In any case, with the shock layer thin, the optimum shape will surely not be realized with a simple power law shape.

We have concerned ourselves so far in this section exclusively with the problem of minimizing the drag of bodies for which no specification is made as to lift; the axisymmetric bodies are at zero incidence and provide no lift anyway. Let us now look at a simple optimization problem involving lift in two-dimensional Newtonian flow. The problem of maximizing only the ratio of lift to drag is not a properly posed problem in inviscid flow, as this ratio is simply the inverse of the angle of attack for a flat plate and may be made as large as we please. We shall consider a body of given chord $c$ with the lift specified but with no other isoperimetric conditions, and shall minimize the drag. Following our absolute optimum concept we shall not require that the shock angle $\sigma$ be continuous at the trailing edge.

We use (3.2.8) or (3.4.1) for the drag and (3.2.9) for the lift, and first consider that the shock angle at the trailing edge $\sigma_1$ and the quantity $\psi_1$ be fixed. We note that an increase in $P_1$ would increase the lift and decrease the drag. An accompanying decrease in $\sigma_1$ to return the lift to its pre-specified value would further decrease the drag. Hence any optimum shape must be one for which $P_1$ is maximum, or one of the absolute optimum shapes we have considered. In the absence of other isoperimetric conditions this shape is a straight line, and we conclude that our body must be a flat plate with an angle of attack which we denote $\alpha$. Of course, the quantity $\alpha$ is not necessarily the same as $\sigma_1$.

Defining $c$ as the actual width of the flat plate we have

$$(3.4.43) \qquad \psi_1 = \rho_\infty U c \sin \alpha$$

and

$$(3.4.44) \qquad P_1 = \psi_1 \cos \alpha = \tfrac{1}{2} \rho_\infty U c \sin 2\alpha.$$

The lift and drag coefficients for the body based on $c$ are simply $\sin \alpha$ times the corresponding coefficients based on frontal area. The lift coefficient based on $c$ is thus

$$(3.4.45) \qquad C_L = \sin 2\alpha \sin \sigma_1,$$

while the corresponding drag coefficient is

$$(3.4.46) \qquad C_D = 2 \sin \alpha - \sin 2\alpha \cos \sigma_1.$$

We next require that both $C_L$ and $C_D$ be stationary under a variation in $\alpha$ and $\sigma_1$, or that the Jacobian determinant vanish:

$$(3.4.47) \qquad \begin{vmatrix} 2 \cos 2\alpha \sin \sigma_1 & \sin 2\alpha \cos \sigma_1 \\ 2 \cos \alpha - 2 \cos 2\alpha \cos \sigma_1 & \sin 2\alpha \sin \sigma_1 \end{vmatrix} = 0.$$

We obtain immediately the condition

$$(3.4.48) \qquad \cos \sigma_1 = \frac{\cos 2\alpha}{\cos \alpha}.$$

Putting condition (3.4.48) back into (3.4.45) and (3.4.46) yields for our optimum conditions

$$(3.4.49) \qquad C_L = 2 \sin^2 \alpha \sqrt{3 - 4 \sin^2 \alpha}$$

and

$$(3.4.50) \qquad C_D = 4 \sin^3 \alpha.$$

Combining (3.4.49) and (3.4.50) gives the ratio of lift to drag

$$(3.4.51) \qquad \frac{C_L}{C_D} = \frac{\sqrt{3 - 4 \sin^2 \alpha}}{2 \sin \alpha}.$$

These results may also be obtained by eliminating $\sigma_1$ between (3.4.45) and (3.4.46) and minimizing $C_D$ with $C_L$ fixed.

The analysis above is only valid for $\alpha$ between 0 and $\pi/4$. Within this range $\sigma_1$ from (3.4.48) is always greater than $\alpha$. Since the Newtonian shock

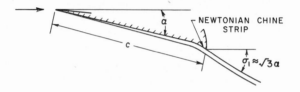

FIG. 3–7. Optimum wing with given lift.

layer must be deflected from its inclination angle $\alpha$ on the flat plate to the inclination angle $\sigma_1$, the flat plate must be fitted with a narrow strip which we term a "Newtonian chine strip". Such a strip is analogous to a Newtonian thrust cowl. The chine strip has a chord of larger order of magnitude than the thickness of the shock layer but which is still infinitesimal in the Newtonian limit (see Fig. 3–7). No analogue to the concept of the proper optimum appears in this case. If the angle of attack $\alpha$ is small, we may replace (3.4.48) by the approximate expression

$$(3.4.52) \qquad \sin \sigma_1 = \sqrt{3} \sin \alpha.$$

The corresponding relation between $C_D$ and $C_L$ is

$$(3.4.53) \qquad C_D = \sqrt{2}(3)^{-3/4} C_L^{3/2} = 0.620 C_L^{3/2}.$$

The coefficient in this expression was minimized in our optimum procedure; for a flat plate the coefficient has the value $\frac{1}{2}\sqrt{2}$ or 0.707. We may note, incidentally, that a wing with this geometry flying in trim (i.e. with balanced moments) under these optimum loading conditions would be statically unstable.

The Newtonian chine strip appears in another problem, that of a Newtonian body of maximum drag. For a body of maximum drag $P$ must again be a maximum, and the chine strip must turn the shock layer so that it shoots almost directly forward, with $\cos \sigma_1$ in (3.4.1) equal to minus one. The effect is similar to that which is the basis for the Pelton wheel. For a slender body the maximum drag is given approximately by

$$(3.4.54) \qquad\qquad \tfrac{1}{2}C_{D_{max}} = 2,$$

with the drag coefficient based on frontal area.

The process discussed in Section 3.3 in which a constant-pressure layer is formed which just grazes the rear edge of the body would destroy the results we have obtained requiring Newtonian chine strips. It appears plausible, though, that with $\epsilon$ low enough and the Reynolds number large enough it might be possible to obtain a practical realization of the deflection process envisioned in the concept of the Newtonian chine strip.

In looking back over the results of this section, we should note particularly that they all depend upon the maximization of the impulse in the shock layer. In fact we can look on this maximization of the impulse as a central optimization principle. The primary aerodynamic forces, lift and drag, are expressed directly in terms of the impulse in the shock layer and its direction as the layer leaves the body. Accepting the principle that we have full control over this direction, we have the greatest control over lift and drag if the impulse is at a maximum.

The problem of determining optimum body shapes is an extremely important one in practical aerodynamics. It is appropriate, then, to comment on the applicability of the results and methods of this section to practical hypersonic aerodynamics in a fluid in which we may expect reasonably thin shock layers. We may expect that hypersonic flows as met with in actual flight will occur primarily at extremely high altitudes and at low densities, and that we shall always be faced with strong viscous effects. This means that the frictional drag must be taken into account in the optimization procedure, and should have an importance roughly equal to that of the inviscid hypersonic drag. Thus the detailed results of this section are probably not applicable. However, much of the philosophy of this section and the methods developed should be applicable. And with certain simple assumptions as to the dependence of the frictional drag on the parameters of the problem, certain parts of our results should be applicable. In particular, this should be the case if the frictional drag is a function only of those quantities which are held fixed in an optimization.

## 5. Shock layer structure and cross flow phenomena

In the analysis we have made of Newtonian flow on two-dimensional and axisymmetric bodies we have not had to concern ourselves with the structure of the shock layer. However, in analyzing Newtonian flow on general bodies in which the flow in the shock layer is not unidirectional we must analyze this structure. Before turning to the general problem let us first look briefly at the shock layer structure for certain two-dimensional and axisymmetric problems. The basic formula (3.2.10) needed has already been given.

In our investigation of shock layer structure we shall consistently use a notational convention to distinguish between the point at which a particle entered the shock layer and the point at which it is being observed. The subscript 1 will appear on quantities to designate their value at the point at which the structure is being investigated. Also, we shall use the subscript 1 to refer to a quantity at the top of the shock layer. These two usages are consistent because it is for a particle at the top of the shock layer that the point of entry and the point of investigation coincide. The lack of subscript 1 will generally refer to a particle within the shock layer and will generally designate the value of a quantity at the point of entry of that particle.

We look first at the case of the sphere for which the solution is given by (3.3.10). Letting $R_s$ be the radius of the sphere, we express first the relation between $\psi$ and $\sigma$

$$(3.5.1) \qquad\qquad \psi = \tfrac{1}{2} \rho_\infty U R_s^2 \cos^2 \sigma.$$

The quantity $m$ of (3.2.10) may be calculated as an indefinite integral for a point designated by the subscript 1

$$(3.5.2) \qquad\qquad m = \frac{1}{\rho_\infty U y_1} \int_0^\cdot \frac{d\psi}{\cos \sigma} = R_s \frac{\cos \sigma}{\cos \sigma_1}.$$

The quantity $m$ at $\psi = \psi_1$ is given for this case,

$$(3.5.3) \qquad\qquad m_1 = R_s$$

to be independent of position. The quantity $m_1$, which always has the dimensions of distance, equals the mass per unit area in the shock layer divided by the free stream density $\rho_\infty$. The variable $m$ is analogous to the Howarth-Dorodnitsyn variable $\int_0 \rho \, dy$ which is used in boundary layer theory, and will be used in the remainder of this chapter as a basic independent variable.

Our reasons for using $m$ as a basic variable are simple. We need a clearly defined scale normal to the shock layer with which to identify individual laminae of our laminar layer model. The intuitive distance scale is unavailable because the Newtonian shock layer is infinitesimally thin. But the variable $m$ is clearly defined within the laminar layer model and is available to serve as the desired scale. If the Howarth-Dorodnitsyn variable is used as a scale in a non-Newtonian hypersonic flow, it will approach $\rho_\infty m$ in the Newtonian limit. The quantity $m$ is the only variable which is suitable in the general Newtonian problem with cross flow present.

We denote the velocity in the shock layer by $Uq$; the quantity $q$ is thus a dimensionless velocity. We may express the distribution of $q$ in the layer for the case of the sphere either in terms of $\psi$ or of $m$ as

$$(3.5.4) \qquad q = \cos\sigma = \frac{\sqrt{2\psi/\rho_\infty U}}{R_s} = \frac{m\cos\sigma_1}{R_s},$$

or

$$(3.5.5) \qquad \frac{q}{q_s} = \frac{\cos\sigma}{\cos\sigma_1} = \sqrt{\frac{\psi}{\psi_1}} = \frac{m}{m_1}.$$

We notice that the distribution of $q$ in terms of $m$ is triangular. The velocity at the bottom of the layer, with $m = 0$ there, is zero for this case according to Newtonian theory.

We turn now to the case of the circular cylinder, with

$$(3.5.6) \qquad \psi = \rho_\infty U R_s \cos\sigma,$$

and

$$(3.5.7) \qquad q = \frac{\psi}{\rho_\infty U R_s}.$$

In this case the integral (3.2.10) for $m$ does not converge and we cannot express $q$ in terms of $m$. The mass per unit area is infinite everywhere on the body in this case. This anomaly will be resolved later when we obtain improved solutions for blunt two-dimensional bodies. We shall use $m$ as the basic independent variable despite the anomaly which appears in this case; no solution exists for the structure of the Newtonian shock layer on a blunt two-dimensional body.

We shall look at one other simple shape, the two-dimensional concave quadrant of a circle, corresponding to (3.3.16) with $n = 2$. The quantity $m$ is given by

$$(3.5.8) \qquad m = -R_s \ln\cos\sigma,$$

and the velocity profile may be expressed

$$(3.5.9) \qquad q = 1 - \frac{\psi}{\rho_\infty U R_s} = \exp\left(-\frac{m}{R_s}\right).$$

In this case the velocity is greatest at the bottom of the layer.

The homogeneous layer model we shall not consider in detail. Here we simply record the quantity $m_{\text{hom}}$ (corresponding to $m_1$) calculated from (3.2.11) for the sphere and circular cylinder. For the sphere this is

$$(3.5.10) \qquad\qquad m_{\text{hom}} = \tfrac{3}{4} R_s,$$

which may be compared with (3.5.3). For the circular cylinder it is

$$(3.5.11) \qquad\qquad m_{\text{hom}} = 2 R_s,$$

which is to be compared with an infinite value of $m_1$. In both cases the value with the homogeneous layer model is less than with our standard laminar layer model. This is explained by the fact that in the homogeneous layer model no part of the velocity profile is at a very low value. As we have mentioned, we shall not consider this model realistic.

As we have indicated, the variable $m$ serves as a scale which may be used to identify the laminae which make up the shock layer. The one-to-one correspondence which we shall require of this layer is between points on

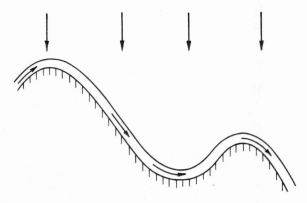

Fig. 3–8a. Roller coaster problem—homogeneous layer model.

this scale of $m$ and points on the "locus of entering streamlines" (see Section 3.2). We shall require that this mapping be continuous along any connected linear segment of the locus of entering streamlines. We also require that this mapping be continuous under a continuous change in the point at which the structure is being investigated. This requirement is illustrated in two examples given below. The uppermost value of $m$ must correspond to the streamline which enters the layer at the point investigated. If these requirements are not met we must either abandon the laminar layer model or must accept new and usually anomalous phenomena in the flow field. The latter choice appears physically more sound.

To begin our discussion of these concepts we shall consider a two-dimensional problem, termed the "roller coaster problem" (see Fig. 3–8). In this problem a developed Newtonian shock layer lies on a body for which the angle $\theta_b$ increases to a value greater than $\pi/2$ and then decreases. The value of $\cos \theta_b$ thus decreases and becomes negative, then becomes positive again. With the homogeneous layer model there is no difficulty with this problem, provided only that the impulse $P$ does not become negative in the "uphill"

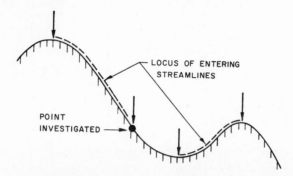

FIG. 3–8b. Roller coaster problem—locus of entering streamlines.

stretch before getting over the hump. And if $P$ does become negative the problem may be resolved with the homogeneous layer model by having the shock layer flow the other way.

With the laminar layer model, on the other hand, a basic difficulty appears. Considering the shock layer structure at a point at the bottom of the trough for which $\cos \theta_b = 0$, the locus of entering streamlines extends from the point in both directions. A continuous one-to-one correspondence between points in the layer and entering streamlines is impossible at this point as well as for other points (see Fig. 3–8b). Here in a simple example, then we have a failure of the laminar layer model and may expect to find a new phenomenon which we must accept in order to resolve the problem. This phenomenon is a "pool" of infinitely high-density fluid at zero velocity and at the pressure $\rho_\infty U^2$. The resolution of the problem with the laminar layer model is shown in Fig. 3–8c. Newtonian anomalies in this solution are an infinite mass of fluid in the pool and zero velocity of the flow coming out of the pool.

Referring to Fig. 3–8b, we note that a general point has a locus of entering streamlines which has two branches, one connected to the point being investigated and the other disjoined from it. The point at the bottom of the trough is a singular point, for which the two branches of the locus of entering streamlines are connected, with the point itself the branch point. The configuration or topology of the two branches is different for a point on one side of the singular point from that for a point on the other side. And in the final solution with the pool, a point on the body above the pool is "shielded" by the pool from its second branch of entering streamlines on the other side of the trough. This shielding process permits us to keep the laminar layer model for points above the pool. These features all have their analogues in more general flows.

On a general body in steady flow we can draw lines for which the axial coordinate is constant. With the flow axis aligned vertically these lines are

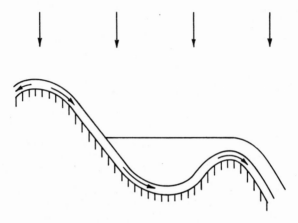

FIG. 3–8c. Roller coaster problem—laminar layer model.

contour lines. The orthogonal trajectories of these contour lines on the body surface are the paths of steepest descent, and we shall refer to the direction of such a path at any point as the "fall line" direction. This fall line direction is determined at any point by the intersection of the body with a plane

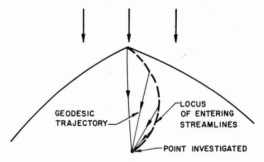

FIG. 3–9. Locus of entering streamlines.

through the external streamline going into the point and the normal to the body surface at the point.

A particle striking a surface which loses all normal component of its momentum without change in the tangential components assumes the fall line direction. Within our laminar layer model this is what happens to a particle in Newtonian flow. The particle subsequently experiences no forces except for those forces normal to the surface required to make the particle follow the surface. Under these conditions the particle follows a path on the surface which has zero lateral curvature. Such a path is termed a geodesic, and the reader should consult a text on differential geometry if he wishes a detailed treatment of geodesics and their properties. Here we only note, for example, that a geodesic on a sphere is a great circle, and that a geodesic on a developable surface such as a general cone is a straight line on the developed surface.

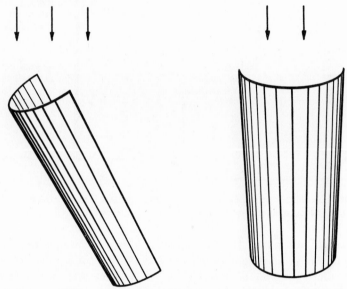

FIG. 3–10a. Drain trough problem—sketch.

The entering streamlines form a two-parameter family, as do the subsequent geodesic trajectories on the surface. The trajectories which pass over a given point on the surface form a one-parameter family, and the locus of points at which the trajectories start is our locus of entering streamlines (see Fig. 3–9). The locus begins at a stagnation point or at a leading point or edge of the body and ends at the point in question.

We now turn to another problem in which the assumption of a continuous one-to-one correspondence is violated, which we term the "drain trough problem". The problem considered is that of a surface which is inclined to the free stream and whose principal characteristic is that it is laterally concave (see Fig. 3–10). At a sufficient distance from the leading edge there will be singular points whose loci of entering streamlines are branched, such as point A in Fig. 3–10b. These singular points themselves form a locus on the body. The locus of entering streamlines for a neighboring point, such as point B in Fig. 3–10b, consists of two distinct branches. A one-to-one correspondence established between $m$ and entering streamlines for an ordinary point cannot be continuous as the point is made to cross the locus of singular points, and our basic requirement is violated.

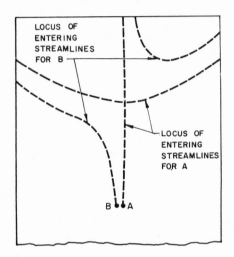

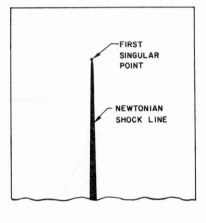

FIG. 3–10b. Drain trough problem—loci of entering streamlines.

FIG. 3–10c. Drain trough problem—Newtonian shock line.

Physically, we can say that the difficulty arises because material arrives at a point from various points on the surface in such a way that a continuous solution would be possible only if two streams were allowed to occupy the same space, only if a lamina is allowed to contain material from two sources. The alternative is that a collision or shock process ensues. Within the limiting perfect gas model the flow in the shock layer is still hypersonic and at infinite Mach number, and with a second shock the Newtonian process is repeated and a second condensation takes place. The original Newtonian process reduced a spatial distribution of mass, mass flow, and momentum to a surface distribution. The second Newtonian process we are here concerned with reduces a surface distribution of these quantities to a linear distribution. The resultant flow is termed a "Newtonian shock line", and is illustrated in Fig. 3–10c. The Newtonian shock line begins at the first singular point on the body and follows a path on the body for which the lateral curvature of the path times the momentum flow in the shock line is balanced by lateral momentum fed into the line from the sides. In general, this path is not the locus of singular points. This shock line is the new and anomalous phenomenon which we must accept in order to resolve the problem.

If the path of the shock line along the body is concave with respect to the body, a force per unit distance is exerted on the body by the shock line. This force is simply equal to the momentum flow in the shock line times the component of the curvature of the shock line normal to the surface. If the path were convex with respect to the body a negative force per unit distance would be required. This possibility must be rejected and the shock line must fly free, in a manner analogous to that of a free layer. But in the case of a free shock line, the free stream cannot exert the singular forces needed to make the shock line curved, and its path is a straight line. If at the first singular point the surface is convex in the direction a shock line would otherwise take, a shock line is not formed. Instead, a Newtonian free layer is formed which erupts into the free stream. And if immediately after a shock line separates and becomes free the conditions on the surface are such that a regular Newtonian layer still cannot exist, a free shock layer is formed which erupts from the body and is connected to the free shock line like a web.

In either the solution with a Newtonian shock line or that with an erupting shock layer a point on the surface on one side of the line or layer is shielded by it from certain parts or branches of its locus of entering stream-lines. The structure of the shock layer at this point is determined by the flow entering at those parts of the locus which are not shielded, which correspond to entering particles which actually reach the point in question. Thus the original difficulty of multiple correspondence between the structure of the layer and the locus of entering streamlines is removed through this shielding effect, and we are permitted to keep the laminar layer model.

Other even more anomalous behavior may be deduced for body shapes related to that for our drain trough problem. For example, we may imagine a body with a geometry such that a free shock line will reimpinge on the body. Assuming a Newtonian process in this reimpingement, there will result an isolated force on the body at the reimpingement point. Such an isolated force represents a two-fold condensation with respect to the force distribution represented by conventional aerodynamic pressure.

We return now to our study of the regular Newtonian layer, assuming that singular behavior of the type just discussed does not appear. In our development, we shall always express pressures in terms of the dimensionless pressure coefficient. In defining this coefficient we have reduced the pressure using the known quantities $\rho_\infty$ and $U$ describing the free stream. With respect to the new dynamic quantities we shall introduce, we shall use $\rho_\infty$ and $U$ in their definitions in order to eliminate the dimensions of mass and of time. We wish to make no specification as to body dimensions, and accordingly do not choose to complete the reduction to dimensionless form by using a reference length in our definitions. Thus our basic variables will all have dimensions involving length. The reader will recognize that we have already carried out this plan in the definition of $m$, as given in (3.2.10), or of $q$, as defined earlier in this section. We have used dynamic forms for $\psi$ and $P$ in the first four sections of Chapter III primarily in order to have a consistent definition of $\psi$ throughout the book.

All our results will be invariant with respect to the scale transformation discussed in the third paragraph of Section 2.2, and this property will be evidenced by dimensional consistency of the results. Reduction of our quantities to dimensionless form by use of a specified reference distance dimension would be a trivial process.

At each point in a regular Newtonian layer a scale in terms of $m$ exists which we may use in describing the structure of the shock layer. The structure of the shock layer is described in terms of the velocity $U\mathbf{q}$ of the material in the layer, expressed functionally

$$(3.5.12) \qquad\qquad \mathbf{q} = \mathbf{q}(m).$$

This vector is a two-dimensional vector in the curved two-dimensional space of the surface of the shock layer or body, and is dimensionless. The total mass per unit area is represented by the quantity

$$(3.5.13) \qquad\qquad m_1 = \int_0^{m_1} dm,$$

which is a scalar in this two-dimensional space with the dimensions of length. We define the total mass flow vector

$$(3.5.14) \qquad\qquad \mathbf{M}_1 = \int_0^{m_1} \mathbf{q}\, dm;$$

this vector has two components. And we define the total momentum

$$(3.5.15) \qquad\qquad \boldsymbol{\mathfrak{P}}_1 = \int_0^{m_1} \mathbf{q}\mathbf{q}\, dm;$$

this quantity is a symmetric dyadic or tensor in this space, and has three independent components. Both $\mathbf{M}_1$ and $\boldsymbol{\mathfrak{P}}_1$ have the dimensions of length. The subscript 1 indicates that the integral of (3.5.14) or (3.5.15) is taken through the entire layer. We shall use the same quantities without the subscript to indicate the corresponding indefinite integrals evaluated as zero at $m = 0$, representing quantities that are functions of $m$. Thus, for example, we have $\mathbf{M}_1 = \mathbf{M}(m_1)$. In two-dimensional or axisymmetric flow $\mathbf{M}$ and $\mathfrak{P}$ each have only one nonzero component. The nonzero components of $\mathbf{M}$ and $\mathfrak{P}$ are related to the $\psi$ and $P$ we have used in the first four sections by the relations

(3.5.16)
$$|\mathbf{M}| = \frac{\psi}{\rho_\infty U y^j},$$

and

(3.5.17)
$$|\mathfrak{P}| = \frac{P}{\rho_\infty U y^j}.$$

The curvature of the surface is also a symmetric dyadic or tensor in the two-dimensional space of the shock layer, and has three independent components. We denote this quantity as $\mathfrak{K}$. As with any symmetric dyadic or tensor there exist principal axes with respect to which the cross component vanishes. The inverses of the two principal components of the curvature tensor are termed the principal radii of curvature. We define $\mathfrak{K}$ to have positive components for a convex body; with this definition the customary convention for curvature requires us to define the unit vector normal to the body $\mathbf{n}$ as directed into the body.

The inclination of the shock layer surface $\sigma$ is the angle of the surface with the free stream direction, measured in the plane defined by the free stream direction and the normal to the surface. The quantity $\sin \sigma$ is the direction cosine between the surface normal and the free stream direction. The pressure immediately behind the shock is given as before by (3.2.6). The centrifugal correction needed to obtain the pressure on the body is obtained by taking the double dot product of the dyadics $\mathfrak{P}_1$ and $\mathfrak{K}$, giving

(3.5.18)
$$\tfrac{1}{2} C_{p_b} = \sin^2 \sigma - \mathfrak{K} : \mathfrak{P}_1.$$

This double dot product of the two dyadics is the same as the corresponding double contracted product of the two tensors, and is a scalar. For the pressure at an intermediate value of $m$ in the layer we must use a momentum integral similar to (3.5.15) but not taken over the entire layer. We obtain for the pressure at an intermediate point

(3.5.19)
$$\tfrac{1}{2} C_p = \sin^2 \sigma - \mathfrak{K} : (\mathfrak{P}_1 - \mathfrak{P}).$$

In a three-dimensional Newtonian sail, the stress is a general two-dimensional symmetric tensor in the surface of the sail. We denote this stress tensor or dyadic by $U\mathfrak{T}$. The condition of equilibrium of an infinitesimal element of the sail may be given

(3.5.20)
$$\nabla \cdot \mathfrak{T} = 0.$$

This is a vector equation, and expresses two conditions on the quantity $\mathfrak{T}$.

With zero pressure on the back side of the sail, the equation analogous to (3.3.36) for equilibrium of an element in the normal direction is

$$(3.5.21) \qquad 0 = \sin^2 \sigma - \mathfrak{K} : (\mathfrak{P}_1 - \mathfrak{T}).$$

If the sail is isotropic the stress dyadic may be expressed

$$(3.5.22) \qquad \mathfrak{T} = \mathfrak{T}\mathfrak{J},$$

where $\mathfrak{J}$ is the idemfactor. Condition (3.5.20) requires that $\nabla \mathfrak{T}$ is zero, and hence that $\mathfrak{T}$ is constant.

It is clear that in a general problem with cross flow any of the various phenomena discussed for two-dimensional and axisymmetric bodies may arise, including free layers, constant-pressure layers, and reimpingement. Many new phenomena must exist in a general flow, however, besides those connected with the Newtonian shock line which we have already discussed. For example, we can make a free shock layer reimpinge on a surface on which there is already a regular shock layer; we can make two free layers collide and coalesce in midstream; or we can control the pressure behind a constant-pressure layer by ventilation from the sides. An extended deductive exploration of such anomalous phenomena appears of dubious value at the present time, and we shall turn to other problems. We shall next investigate how the structure of a regular layer with cross flow is to be obtained.

## 6. Shock layer structure with cross flow

If for a given point we know the locus of entering streamlines and the topology of its mapping onto the sequence of laminae, we can quite directly determine the sequence of values for the dimensionless velocity $\mathbf{q}$ in the shock layer there. In addition to this sequence we need the quantitative scale $m$ for it in order to have a suitable description of the structure of the shock layer. As for the simpler two-dimensional and axisymmetric flows, a method based on the principle of the conservation of mass is used to calculate the quantity $m$.

Referring to Fig. 3–11, it is necessary to have the locus of entering streamlines not only for the point of interest, here labelled 1, but for a neighboring point an infinitesimal distance away, here labelled 1'. The two-dimensional vector $\boldsymbol{\delta}_1$ is the infinitesimal distance vector from point 1 to point 1'. A linear scale must be set up on the locus of entering streamlines for point 1, and an expression for the area of a differential parallelogram lying between the two loci must be obtained. In Fig. 3–11 this element of area is $\delta \, dl$. We now equate the mass flow entering this differential area element with that passing between the two points and between $m$ and $m + dm$ on our desired scale. We obtain

$$(3.6.1) \qquad \rho_\infty U \sin \sigma \, \delta dl = \rho_\infty U \boldsymbol{\delta}_1 \times \mathbf{q} \cdot \mathbf{n}_1 \, dm,$$

where $\sigma$ is the surface inclination at the point of entry of the streamline in question, and $U\mathbf{q}$ is the corresponding vector velocity at point 1. In obtaining (3.6.1) we have used the fact that a vector cross product in a two-dimensional space is really a scalar; however, in order to conform to

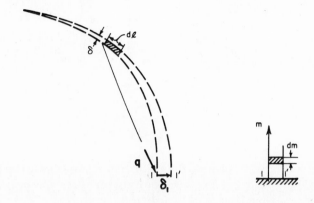

FIG. 3–11. Calculation of $m$ with cross flow.

conventional notation, we have indicated the cross product dotted with the unit normal vector $\mathbf{n}$ to the surface. The magnitude of $\mathbf{q}$ is, of course, simply $\cos \sigma$. Solving (3.6.1) for $dm$, we obtain

$$(3.6.2) \qquad dm = \frac{\sin \sigma \; \delta dl}{\boldsymbol{\delta}_1 \times \mathbf{q} \cdot \mathbf{n}_1}.$$

The quadrature of (3.6.2) gives us the desired relation between $m$ and points on the locus of entering streamlines.

There is a certain arbitrariness in this procedure in that we may choose any orientation for $\boldsymbol{\delta}_1$ that we please, and our final result must be independent of this choice. We may take advantage of this freedom in order to choose an orientation which will make the calculation simpler. As another possibility, we may check our calculation by repeating it with a different orientation for the two points.

Our first example is that of cylindrical flow, which consists of a constant velocity in the direction of the axis of a general cylinder superposed on a two-dimensional flow about the cylinder. Cylindrical flows are generally obtained by placing a cylinder in a uniform flow at an angle of yaw or sweepback, and we shall take this point of view. The coordinate $x$ is taken along the surface normal to the generatrix of the cylinder, and $y$ is taken along the axis, with $\mathbf{j}$ a unit vector in the $y$ direction. The two-dimensional solution for the unyawed cylinder is presumed known, and the two-dimensional quantities $m_1$, $\psi_1/\rho_\infty U$, and $P_1/\rho_\infty U$ are denoted in vector form as

$m_{2-d}$, $\mathbf{M}_{2-d}$, and $\mathfrak{P}_{2-d}$. In this notation we recognize that the latter two quantities are a two-dimensional vector and tensor, respectively, each with only one nonzero component.

In the yawed flow the velocity $U$ normal to the cylinder is reduced by the factor $\cos \Omega$, where $\Omega$ is the angle of yaw, and the constant superposed axial velocity is $U \sin \Omega$. However, in our analysis we shall use the complement of $\Omega$, termed $\sigma_0$; in the case of a blunt body $\sigma_0$ is the inclination angle of the surface at the two-dimensional stagnation point. Thus we shall have

(3.6.3a) $$\sigma_0 = \tfrac{1}{2}\pi - \Omega,$$

(3.6.3b) $$\sin \sigma_0 = \cos \Omega,$$

(3.6.3c) $$\cos \sigma_0 = \sin \Omega.$$

Our reason for using $\sigma_0$ in place of $\Omega$ is to permit a more direct comparison of the example of cylindrical flow with the example of the flow near an axis of symmetry considered later.

We may now directly calculate the quantities $m_1$, $\mathbf{M}_1$, and $\mathfrak{P}_1$ for the yawed body. The results are

(3.6.4a) $$m_1 = m_{2-d},$$

(3.6.4b) $$\mathbf{M}_1 = \mathbf{M}_{2-d} \sin \sigma_0 + \mathbf{j} m_{2-d} \cos \sigma_0,$$

(3.6.4c) $$\mathfrak{P}_1 = \mathfrak{P}_{2-d} \sin^2 \sigma_0 + (\mathbf{M}_{2-d}\mathbf{j} + \mathbf{j}\mathbf{M}_{2-d}) \sin \sigma_0 \cos \sigma_0 + \mathbf{j}\mathbf{j} m_{2-d} \cos^2 \sigma_0.$$

Since the curvature tensor has but one nonzero component, only the $\mathfrak{P}_{2-d}$ component of (3.6.4c) comes into the expression for the pressure. The inclination of the body is governed by the relation

(3.6.5) $$\sin \sigma = \sin \sigma_0 \sin \sigma_{2-d}$$

obtainable from the law of cosines of spherical trigonometry, and the pressure on the body by the relation

(3.6.6) $$\tfrac{1}{2}C_{p_b} = \sin^2 \sigma_0 (\sin^2 \sigma_{2-d} - \mathfrak{R} : \mathfrak{P}_{2-d}).$$

Thus the pressure coefficient is simply that for the two-dimensional flow times $\cos^2 \Omega$. It is evident that this principal result for the flow on a yawed infinite cylindrical body could have been readily obtained without the use of our cross flow theory.

We now look at the locus of entering streamlines, shown in the plane of the developed cylinder in Fig. 3–12. The geometry of this locus is determined by the condition

$$(3.6.7) \qquad \frac{y_1 - y}{\cos \sigma_0} = \frac{x_1 - x}{\sin \sigma_0 \cos \sigma_{2-d}},$$

where $\cos \sigma_{2-d}$ is a function of $x$. Note that the quantity expressed in (3.6.7) is essentially the time the particle has spent in the layer before reaching point 1. With allowance for the change in the definition of $x$ and of $\sigma_0$, this

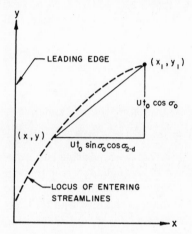

FIG. 3–12. Developed cylinder with cylindrical flow.

expression is in agreement with (3.2.12). If the neighboring point 1′ is chosen to have the same value of $x$ as does point 1, the area element between the two loci of entering streamlines is simply $\delta_1 \, dx$ and the cylindrical structure of the shock layer is easily obtained by our general method.

So far, our cylindrical analysis has given us very little new. A new aspect appears when we permit the cylindrical body to be finite rather than infinite, with part of the leading edge a curve in the $(x, y)$ plane different from the $x = constant$ curve representing the leading edge or stagnation line of the basic cylinder. If the locus of entering streamlines for a point starts at this leading edge rather than at the leading edge of the cylinder, the shock layer structure for the point will lack part of the complete cylindrical solution. This part is on the bottom of the layer and corresponds to the part of the locus of entering streamlines cut off by the leading edge. Such a solution is not cylindrical in the proper sense, but is easily obtainable from the two-dimensional results and equation (3.6.7) for the locus of entering streamlines.

If the two-dimensional body is sharp-nosed, with $\cos \sigma_{2-d}$ nonzero at the leading edge, the loci of entering streamlines are finite in length and the trajectory from a point on the leading edge has a nonzero angle on the $(x, y)$ plane. If the body is sufficiently long, then, a portion of the body will have a shock layer with the complete cylindrical structure. If the two-dimensional body is blunt, on the other hand, the fact that the body is finite is felt over the entire body. With the body blunt, and $\cos \sigma_{2-d} = 0$ at the leading edge, each locus of entering streamlines is infinite in extent and must be cut off by the leading edge if the body is finite. One result of this effect is that on a blunt two-dimensional body such as the circular cylinder the anomaly of infinite $m_1$ disappears if the body is finite and is yawed. The structure on a finite blunt cylindrical leading edge will be investigated as a special case of our next problem.

We consider now the problem of the flow near a straight axis of symmetry. A surface is considered which has the equation

$$(3.6.8) \qquad z(x, y) = \tfrac{1}{2}K(y)x^2 + O(x^4),$$

and for which the curvature tensor is approximately

$$(3.6.9) \qquad \mathfrak{K} = \mathbf{ii}K + (\mathbf{ij} + \mathbf{ji})K'x + \tfrac{1}{2}\mathbf{jj}K''x^2.$$

This surface is inverted so that with positive curvature the shape is convex, and the surface is inclined at an angle $\sigma_0$ to the free stream so that a streamline striking the body at $x = 0$ has the line $x = 0$ as its subsequent trajectory. The body is assumed to have a definite leading edge at $y = 0$. If $K$ is a constant the body is a section of a yawed blunt cylindrical body. If $K$ is inversely proportional to $y$ the body represents the neighborhood of a symmetry axis on a yawed cone. Our investigation will be a purely local one, with terms of higher order in $x$ neglected, and with geodesics approximated by straight lines on an $(x, y)$ plot.

The locus of entering streamlines is given by an equation similar to (3.6.7), with $Kx$ in place of $\cos \sigma_{2-d}$. The equation for the locus is

$$(3.6.10) \qquad x = \frac{x_1}{1 + K(y)(y_1 - y) \tan \sigma_0}.$$

The neighboring point to point 1 is placed at the same value of $y$, and the component of $\mathbf{q}$ normal to $\boldsymbol{\delta}_1$ is simply $\cos \sigma_0$. The ratio $\delta/\delta_1$ is equal to $x/x_1$, and the area element is $\delta \, dy$. From (3.6.2) we obtain

$$(3.6.11) \qquad dm = \frac{\tan \sigma_0 \, dy}{1 + K(y)(y_1 - y) \tan \sigma_0},$$

and the quadrature of this equation gives us $m_1$ on the body, which is locally independent of $x$.

The slope of the body may be shown to be given by

$$(3.6.12) \qquad \sin \sigma = \sin \sigma_0(1 - \tfrac{1}{2}K^2x^2) - \cos \sigma_0(\tfrac{1}{2}K'x^2),$$

and this quantity in (3.2.6) gives the pressure immediately behind the shock. The quantities $\mathbf{M}_1$ and $\mathfrak{P}_1$ may be expressed

(3.6.13a)     $\mathbf{M}_1 = \mathbf{i}M_1 x_1 \sin \sigma_0 + \mathbf{j}m_1 \cos \sigma_0,$

(3.6.13b)     $\mathfrak{P}_1 = \mathbf{ii}\mathfrak{P}_1 x_1^2 \sin^2 \sigma_0 + (\mathbf{ij} + \mathbf{ji})M_1 x_1 \sin \sigma_0 \cos \sigma_0 + \mathbf{jj}m_1 \cos^2 \sigma_0,$

where

(3.6.14a)     $M_1 = \dfrac{1}{x_1} \displaystyle\int_0^{m_1} Kx \, dm = \tan \sigma_0 \int_0^{y_1} \dfrac{K \, dy}{[1 + K(y_1 - y)\tan \sigma_0]^2},$

(3.6.14b)     $\mathfrak{P}_1 = \dfrac{1}{x_1^2} \displaystyle\int_0^{m_1} K^2 x^2 \, dm = \tan \sigma_0 \int_0^{y_1} \dfrac{K^2 \, dy}{[1 + K(y_1 - y)\tan \sigma_0]^3}.$

The relation between (3.6.13) and (3.6.4) is evident. The pressure on the body is given by (3.5.18), using (3.6.12) and the relation

(3.6.15)     $\mathfrak{K} : \mathfrak{P}_1 = x_1^2[K\mathfrak{P}_1 \sin^2 \sigma_0 + 2K'M_1 \sin \sigma_0 \cos \sigma_0 + \tfrac{1}{2}K''m_1 \cos^2 \sigma_0],$

in which $K$ and its derivatives are evaluated at $y = y_1$. The bracket in (3.6.15) is a function of $y_1$ alone.

For a simple example we consider the finite yawed cylindrical body mentioned earlier. The quantity $K$ is a constant, equal to $R_s^{-1}$. Quadrature of (3.6.11) gives

(3.6.16)     $m_1 = R_s \ln \left(1 + \dfrac{y_1 \tan \sigma_0}{R_s}\right),$

and of (3.6.14b) gives

(3.6.17)     $\mathfrak{P}_1 = \dfrac{1}{2R_s} \left[1 - \left(\dfrac{R_s}{R_s + y_1 \tan \sigma_0}\right)^2\right].$

The pressure on the body, expressed as a function of $x_1$ and $y_1$, is

(3.6.18)     $\tfrac{1}{2}C_{p_b} = \sin^2 \sigma_0 \left[1 - \dfrac{3x_1^2}{2R_s^2} + \dfrac{x_1^2}{2(R_s + y_1 \tan \sigma_0)^2}\right].$

As $y_1$ increases without limit, the third term in the bracket of (3.6.18) goes to zero. The remaining part of (3.6.18) is equivalent to (3.3.4) with $n = 2$, with account taken of the difference in geometry.

We turn next to the problem of a conical body. As we have defined it, a conical body will have a symmetry axis along a ray where the body is tangent to a right circular cone with axis in the free stream direction. The semiangle of this right circular cone is $\sigma_0$. Along the symmetry axis the conical body will osculate a different right circular cone of semiangle $\beta$. The basic dimensionless parameter of the problem, denoted $\kappa$, is the ratio of the tangents of these two semiangles. In this case we express the quantity $K$ of (3.6.8) as

$$(3.6.19) \qquad K(y) = \frac{1}{y \tan \beta} = \frac{\kappa}{y \tan \sigma_0}$$

in an equation which also defines $\kappa$. We have, therefore,

$$(3.6.20) \qquad K' = \frac{-\kappa}{y^2 \tan \sigma_0},$$

and

$$(3.6.21) \qquad \tfrac{1}{2} K'' = \frac{\kappa}{y^3 \tan \sigma_0}.$$

The pressure immediately behind the shock, calculated with the help of (3.6.12), is

$$(3.6.22) \qquad \tfrac{1}{2} C_{p_s} = \sin^2 \sigma_0 - \frac{x_1^2 \cos^2 \sigma_0}{y_1^2} \kappa(\kappa - 1).$$

The quantity $x_1/y_1$ in (3.6.22) is simply the angle from the symmetry axis measured on the cone surface.

With $K$ given from (3.6.19) we may calculate $m_1$, $M_1$, and $\mathfrak{P}_1$ from (3.6.11) and (3.6.14). The results of these quadratures are

$$(3.6.23\text{a}) \qquad m_1 = \frac{y_1 \tan \sigma_0}{(\kappa - 1)^2} [\kappa \ln \kappa - (\kappa - 1)],$$

$$(3.6.23\text{b}) \qquad M_1 = \frac{\kappa}{(\kappa - 1)^2} [(\kappa - 1) - \ln \kappa],$$

$$(3.6.23\text{c}) \qquad \mathfrak{P}_1 = \frac{\kappa}{2y_1 \tan \sigma_0}.$$

Applying these quantities to (3.6.15), we may obtain the pressure on the body

$$(3.6.24) \quad \tfrac{1}{2} C_{p_b} = \sin^2 \sigma_0 - \frac{3x_1^2 \cos^2 \sigma_0}{2y_1^2} \frac{\kappa^2}{(\kappa - 1)^2} [(\kappa - 1)(\kappa - 3) + 2 \ln \kappa].$$

In the limit of $\kappa$ very large (3.6.24) approaches the same form that (3.6.18) does with $y_1$ very large, with allowance for the different functions $K(y)$ in the two cases.

The problem of Newtonian flow on a general cone may be attacked by an analysis on the developed surface. General analytical results in closed form are available only in certain special cases, such as the axis of symmetry case or the case of a very slender cone, and a nontrivial problem would require numerical or graphical computations. The conical approach to the conical symmetry axis problem takes advantage of the fact that one of the principal curvatures is zero, but in general the analysis is about at the same level of complexity as that for the symmetry axis approach we have used here. The results of the two analyses for the cone agree; in fact, the result (3.6.24) was first obtained following the conical approach. The approach we have chosen illustrates the centrifugal pressure correction in its general form.

Our final example is that of a general stagnation point, intermediate between the two-dimensional stagnation point on a body such as a circular cylinder and the axisymmetric stagnation point on a body such as a sphere. Again, we shall seek only a local solution, within a region small enough that from a front view a geodesic appears as a straight line. No solution for an entire body without two-dimensional or axial symmetry has been found which has the simplicity found for the circular cylinder and sphere. The system of coordinates is one in a projection of the surface in a plane normal to the flow direction, with the origin at the stagnation point. The axes are aligned in the directions of principal curvature. The basic parameter in this problem, again denoted $\kappa$, is the ratio of principal curvatures

$$(3.6.25) \qquad \kappa = \frac{K_1}{K_2} = \frac{R_2}{R_1},$$

where $K_1$ is the curvature in the $x$ direction and $K_2$ the curvature in the $y$ direction. There is a possibility of confusion here with respect to our use of the subscript 1. We use the subscripts 1 and 2 to indicate the $x$ and $y$ directions only upon the quantities $K$, $R = K^{-1}$, and a dimensionless pressure correction term $\pi$ to be defined later. On all other quantities the subscript 1 will indicate, as before, the point under investigation or the top of the shock layer. Our results will all have to remain unchanged if we interchange $x$ and $y$, $\kappa$ and $\kappa^{-1}$, and the subscripts 1 and 2 on $K$, $R$, and $\pi$. This invariance gives us a ready method of checking our results. No solution is obtainable with $\kappa$ negative, and we consider only positive values of $\kappa$.

The velocity of a particle in the shock layer is given by

$$(3.6.26) \qquad \mathbf{q} = \mathbf{i} K_1 x + \mathbf{j} K_2 y$$

in terms of the coordinates of the point of entry. The equation for the trajectory of the particle is

$$(3.6.27) \qquad \frac{x_1 - x}{K_1 x} = \frac{y_1 - y}{K_2 y},$$

where $x_1$ and $y_1$ are the coordinates of a point on the trajectory. With $x_1$ and $y_1$ fixed and with $x$ and $y$ variable, (3.6.27) is the equation for the locus of entering streamlines. We rewrite (3.6.27)

$$(3.6.28) \qquad \left(x + \frac{x_1}{\kappa - 1}\right)\left(y - \frac{\kappa y_1}{\kappa - 1}\right) + \frac{\kappa x_1 y_1}{(\kappa - 1)^2} = 0,$$

in which form the locus may be recognized as an equilateral hyperbola (see Fig. 3–13). The paths of steepest descent here are of the form $x = Ay^\kappa$.

We now choose the neighboring point $1'$ to have the same value of $x_1$ as does point 1. The area element between the two loci is $\delta\,dx$ with $\delta$ their

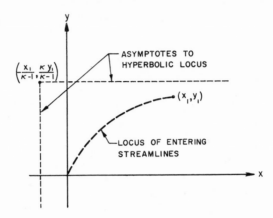

Fig. 3–13. General stagnation point.

separation in the $y$ direction. The two loci are related through an affine transformation, and the ratio $\delta/\delta_1$ is equal to $y/y_1$. Applying (3.6.2) we obtain

$$(3.6.29) \qquad dm = \frac{y\,dx}{K_1 y_1 x} = \frac{\kappa R_1\,dx}{(\kappa - 1)x + x_1}\,,$$

for which the integral giving the correspondence between $m$ and the coordinates of the point of entry is

$$(3.6.30) \qquad m = \frac{\kappa R_1}{\kappa - 1}\ln\left[1 + \frac{(\kappa - 1)x}{x_1}\right] = -\frac{R_2}{\kappa - 1}\ln\left[1 - \frac{(\kappa - 1)y}{\kappa y_1}\right].$$

The total quantity $m_1$ is simply

$$(3.6.31) \qquad m_1 = \frac{\kappa R_1}{\kappa - 1}\ln\kappa = \frac{R_1 R_2}{R_2 - R_1}\ln\frac{R_2}{R_1}\,,$$

and it may readily be verified that this reduces to (3.5.3) for $\kappa = 1$ and that $m_1$ approaches infinity as $\kappa$ is made indefinitely large.

The velocity profile in the shock layer may be described in terms of the velocity components

$$(3.6.32a) \qquad q_x = \frac{K_1 x_1}{\kappa - 1}\left[\exp\left(\frac{(\kappa - 1)m}{\kappa R_1}\right) - 1\right],$$

$$(3.6.32b) \qquad q_y = \frac{\kappa K_2 y_1}{\kappa - 1}\left[1 - \exp\left(-\frac{(\kappa - 1)m}{\kappa R_1}\right)\right].$$

The velocity profile for one component is concave and for the other is convex, except for $\kappa = 1$. With $\kappa = 1$, both components of the velocity profile become triangular, in agreement with (3.5.4).

The impulse tensor may be expressed in the form

$$(3.6.33) \qquad \mathfrak{P}_1 = \mathbf{ii}K_1x_1^2\pi_1 + \mathbf{jj}K_2y_1^2\pi_2 + (\mathbf{ij} + \mathbf{ji})\mathfrak{P}_{xy},$$

in terms of which the pressure on the body is expressed

$$(3.6.34) \qquad \tfrac{1}{2}C_{p_b} = 1 - (1 + \pi_1)K_1^2x_1^2 - (1 + \pi_2)K_2^2y_1^2,$$

with $\pi_1$ and $\pi_2$ constants to be determined, and $\mathfrak{P}_{xy}$ a cross component of $\mathfrak{P}_1$ which does not influence the pressure. Using (3.5.15) and the relations given for this problem, we may calculate the coefficients appearing in (3.6.34). The results are

$$(3.6.35a) \quad 1 + \pi_1 = (\kappa - 1)^{-3}[(\kappa - 1)(3\kappa - 1)(\tfrac{1}{2}\kappa - 1) + \kappa \ln \kappa],$$

$$(3.6.35b) \quad 1 + \pi_2 = (\kappa - 1)^{-3}[(\kappa - 1)(\kappa - 3)(\kappa - \tfrac{1}{2}) + \kappa^2 \ln \kappa].$$

It may be verified that $1 + \pi_1$ approaches $3/2$ as $\kappa$ approaches infinity, and approaches the value $4/3$ for $\kappa = 1$, in agreement with our two-dimensional and axisymmetric results.

We close our discussion of cross flow by recording the results obtained for the general stagnation point with the homogeneous layer model. The value of $m_{\text{hom}}$ is

$$(3.6.36) \qquad m_{\text{hom}} = \frac{6R_1R_2}{2(R_1 + R_2) + \sqrt{R_1^2 + 14R_1R_2 + R_2^2}},$$

which is to be compared with (3.6.31). The pressure on the body may be expressed in the form (3.6.34), with

$$(3.6.37a) \qquad 1 + \pi_{1_{\text{hom}}} = \frac{1}{12\kappa}(19\kappa + 1 - \sqrt{\kappa^2 + 14\kappa + 1}),$$

$$(3.6.37b) \qquad 1 + \pi'_{2_{\text{hom}}} = \frac{1}{12}(19 + \kappa - \sqrt{\kappa^2 + 14\kappa + 1}).$$

The lack of importance of these results justifies our not allotting them much space here, and we leave their derivation as an exercise for the reader with curiosity. Equation (3.6.36) reduces to (3.5.10) in the axisymmetric case and to (3.5.11) in the two-dimensional case, and $1 + \pi_{1_{\text{hom}}}$ reduces to $4/3$ and $3/2$, respectively, in these cases. Although $\kappa$ can be negative with the homogeneous layer model, it cannot lie between the values $-7 \pm 4\sqrt{3}$, or between $-0.0718$ and its reciprocal.

## 7.  Unsteady flow

Our previous analysis of Newtonian flow has been entirely limited to steady flow, and we have made full use of the simplifications which result from this limitation.  We next turn to the problem of developing a basic theory for unsteady Newtonian flow.  The introduction of the time as a basic independent variable produces about the same additional complication as does an additional space variable;  in other words, we may expect two-dimensional unsteady flow to be about as difficult from a conceptual and calculational point of view as is three-dimensional steady flow.  And just as we found anomalies of various kinds in three-dimensional flows we may expect to find them in a thorough study of unsteady flow, undoubtedly in greater variety.  Here we shall not make any particular attempt to look for anomalous behavior, but shall content ourselves with a general development in which suitably proper behavior of the solution is implicitly assumed.

Our use of vector analysis will necessarily be somewhat involved.  In our analysis of three-dimensional steady flow we dealt mostly with two-dimensional vectors (and dyadics or tensors) in the curved two-dimensional space of the shock surface.  Since in unsteady flow the shock surface is a moving one we must now deal with velocity vectors and other vectors which are three-dimensional.  Part of our problem will be to resolve these vectors into normal and tangential components with respect to the shock surface, of which the tangential components will be two-dimensional vectors in the surface analogous to those of the last two sections.  And we shall have to adequately specify the motion of the shock surface itself.  The method of treatment is similar to that used by Hayes [6] for a different problem.  In unsteady flow the particle trajectories lie in a three-dimensional curved space consisting of the shock surface with the addition of the coordinate time, and our concept of the locus of entering streamlines will have to be modified accordingly.

We assume that the body has a surface whose motion is known, and that the shock layer follows the body surface without separation.  As a first step, we consider the motion of a single particle which is constrained to move on the surface but on which the only force exerted is directed normal to the surface.  All velocities are reduced in our notation by being divided by a constant reference velocity $U$;  this velocity, which cannot be defined unambiguously in all cases of unsteady flow, is the one which appears in the definition of the pressure coefficient $C_p$.  In most cases $U$ is to be identified as the average flight speed of a body.  The dimensionless velocity of the particle is $\mathbf{q}$, and that of a point on the body $\mathbf{q}_b$.  Note that this is a body velocity and not the velocity of a fluid particle at the body boundary.  The unit vector normal to the surface directed into the body is denoted $\mathbf{n}$; this convention is consistent with our definition of the curvature as positive on a convex body. The velocity vector $\mathbf{q}$ is decomposed into a normal vector and a tangential vector,

(3.7.1) $$\mathbf{q} = \mathbf{n}q_n + \mathbf{q}_t,$$

with

(3.7.2) $$q_n = \mathbf{q} \cdot \mathbf{n},$$

and

(3.7.3) $$\mathbf{q}_t = \mathbf{n} \times (\mathbf{q} \times \mathbf{n}).$$

A tangential vector, one which is normal to $\mathbf{n}$, is a two-dimensional vector in the surface of the type we have considered earlier. A normal vector, one which is parallel to $\mathbf{n}$, may be considered as a scalar with respect to the two-dimensional space of the shock surface.

The relative velocity $\mathbf{q}_r$ is defined as

(3.7.4) $$\mathbf{q}_r = \mathbf{q} - \mathbf{q}_b,$$

with $\mathbf{q}_b$ here the body velocity at the point where the particle is. The condition that the particle be constrained to lie always on the body surface is simply that $\mathbf{q}_r$ be a tangential vector, or that

(3.7.5) $$\mathbf{q}_r \cdot \mathbf{n} = 0.$$

The angular velocity of the body surface as measured by an observer moving with the velocity $\mathbf{q}_b$ may be defined as a tangential vector $U\boldsymbol{\omega}_b$ with the properties

(3.7.6) $$\mathbf{n} \times \boldsymbol{\omega}_b = -U^{-1}\frac{d\mathbf{n}}{dt} = (\nabla\mathbf{q}_b) \cdot \mathbf{n} = \nabla(\mathbf{q}_b \cdot \mathbf{n}) + \mathbf{q}_b \cdot \boldsymbol{\Re},$$

with $\nabla$ the two-dimensional Nabla operator in the surface. In defining $\boldsymbol{\omega}_b$ we have again eliminated the dimension time by division by $U$. Any normal component of $\boldsymbol{\omega}_b$ has no effect on our analysis. In (3.7.6) we have used the fact that the curvature tensor or dyadic may be expressed

(3.7.7) $$\boldsymbol{\Re} = -\nabla\mathbf{n},$$

and have used the symbol $d/dt$ to denote the time derivative with respect to an observer moving with the body velocity $\mathbf{q}_b$. The fact that $\boldsymbol{\Re}$ is symmetric may be readily shown, e.g. by noting that $\mathbf{n}$ is the gradient of a scalar. The angular velocity of the surface as measured by an observer moving with the particle is

(3.7.8) $$\boldsymbol{\omega} = \boldsymbol{\omega}_b + \mathbf{q}_r \cdot \boldsymbol{\Re} \times \mathbf{n},$$

also defined as a tangential vector. This angular velocity appears in the expression for the time derivative of $\mathbf{n}$ with respect to an observer moving with the particle,

(3.7.9) $$\frac{D\mathbf{n}}{Dt} = U\boldsymbol{\omega} \times \mathbf{n}.$$

We have here used capital $D$ in the derivative to indicate a material derivative. The normal component of the acceleration of a point on the body is denoted

$$(3.7.10) \qquad a_b = U^{-1} \frac{d\mathbf{q}_b}{dt} \cdot \mathbf{n}$$

with the dimension time eliminated, and we shall treat it as a scalar. The tangential component of this body acceleration will not enter into our analysis.

The reader may have noticed that the description of the motion of the body surface is arbitrary to some extent. An alternate equally valid description of the surface motion may be obtained by adding an arbitrary tangential vector $\delta\mathbf{q}_b$ to the body velocity $\mathbf{q}_b$. While we could make the description unique by requiring $\mathbf{q}_b$ to be a normal vector, such a procedure would greatly complicate most calculations; for example, the curvature at a body point on a rigid body would become a function of time. It is definitely preferable for us to retain this arbitrariness and to make sure our results are independent of the choice of the description of the body motion. This independence is checked by checking the invariance of our basic equations under the transformation

$$(3.7.11a) \qquad \mathbf{q}_b = \mathbf{q}'_b + \delta\mathbf{q}_b ; \qquad \delta\mathbf{q}_b \cdot \mathbf{n} = 0,$$

$$(3.7.11b) \qquad \boldsymbol{\omega}_b = \boldsymbol{\omega}'_b + \delta\mathbf{q}_b \cdot \mathfrak{K} \times \mathbf{n},$$

$$(3.7.11c) \qquad a_b = a'_b + 2\boldsymbol{\omega}'_b \times \delta\mathbf{q}_b \cdot \mathbf{n} + \delta\mathbf{q}_b \cdot \mathfrak{K} \cdot \delta\mathbf{q}_b.$$

The relative velocity $\mathbf{q}_r$ from (3.7.4) is changed in this transformation.

Using (3.7.9) we next carry out the time derivative of $\mathbf{q}_t$ defined in (3.7.3) and obtain

$$(3.7.12) \qquad U^{-1} \frac{D\mathbf{q}_t}{Dt} = \mathbf{n}(\boldsymbol{\omega} \times \mathbf{q} \cdot \mathbf{n}) + U^{-1}\mathbf{n} \times \left(\frac{D\mathbf{q}}{Dt} \times \mathbf{n}\right) + \mathbf{n} \times \boldsymbol{\omega}(\mathbf{q} \cdot \mathbf{n}).$$

The first term on the right hand side is the contribution of the change in direction of $\mathbf{q}_t$ normal to the surface, and this term is not of particular interest to us. The second term is the component of the particle acceleration tangential to the surface. The third term represents an interaction between angular velocity and normal velocity component.

Our analysis thus far has been purely kinematic, and it is at this point that we turn to dynamical considerations. We take our frame of reference to be unaccelerated, so that the acceleration of a particle is proportional to the force on it. We assume that the motion of the particle on the surface is frictionless, so that the force exerted by the surface on the particle is in the direction normal to the surface. With these assumptions the tangential component of the particle acceleration, i.e. the second term of (3.7.12), is identically zero. From (3.7.12) we obtain

$$(3.7.13) \qquad \left(\frac{D\mathbf{q}_t}{Dt}\right)_t = U\mathbf{n} \times \boldsymbol{\omega}(\mathbf{q} \cdot \mathbf{n}).$$

The force on the particle divided by its mass is equal to its acceleration, and may be calculated with respect to an observer who moves with a body point, with the velocity $\mathbf{q}_b$. The result is

$$(3.7.14) \qquad \frac{D\mathbf{q}}{Dt} = U\mathbf{n}(a_b + 2\boldsymbol{\omega}_b \times \mathbf{q}_r \cdot \mathbf{n} + \mathbf{q}_r \cdot \mathfrak{K} \cdot \mathbf{q}_r),$$

in which the second term will be recognized as a Coriolis term. The similarity between the right hand side of (3.7.14) and of (3.7.11c) may be noted. This equation, together with the definition (3.7.4) for $\mathbf{q}_r$, will serve as the basis for our calculation of the centrifugal pressure correction in unsteady Newtonian flow, while (3.7.13) is needed for the calculation of the shock layer structure. Note that if $\mathbf{q}_r$ had any normal component it would be annihilated in (3.7.14). Hence we may substitute $\mathbf{q}_t - \mathbf{q}_b$ in place of $\mathbf{q}_r$ in (3.7.14) with no other change, and this we shall do.

We now consider the Newtonian impact process in the unsteady case. The particle before impact has the velocity $U\mathbf{U}$, with $\mathbf{U}$ defined as dimensionless consistent with our definition of other velocities. If the atmosphere in which the body is moving is motionless, we define $U$ as the velocity of our frame of reference, and $\mathbf{U}$ is simply a constant unit vector. The normal component of momentum relative to the body is proportional to $(\mathbf{U} - \mathbf{q}_b) \cdot \mathbf{n}$, and this quantity is transferred in Newtonian impact to the body. The tangential momentum relative to the body is conserved, and we have

$$(3.7.15) \qquad \mathbf{n} \times [(\mathbf{U} - \mathbf{q}_b) \times \mathbf{n}] = \mathbf{n} \times (\mathbf{q}_r \times \mathbf{n}) = \mathbf{q}_r.$$

From (3.7.15) and (3.7.4) an expression for the initial value of $\mathbf{q}_t$ immediately after impact is obtained,

$$(3.7.16) \qquad \mathbf{q}_{t_1} = \mathbf{n} \times (\mathbf{U} \times \mathbf{n}).$$

Here we have used the subscript 1 as before to denote conditions immediately after impact, at the top of the shock layer.

We are now ready to write down the equations for the pressure at a point on a body in unsteady Newtonian flow. The external flow is assumed to be a uniform one of constant density $\rho_\infty$ and velocity $U$, with the vector $\mathbf{U}$ a constant unit vector. The mass per unit time per unit area impinging on the body is $\rho_\infty U$ times $(\mathbf{U} - \mathbf{q}_b) \cdot \mathbf{n}$. The pressure immediately behind the shock is then given by the relation

$$(3.7.17) \qquad \begin{aligned} \tfrac{1}{2}C_{p_s} &= [(\mathbf{U} - \mathbf{q}_b) \cdot \mathbf{n}]^2 \\ &= (\mathbf{U} \cdot \mathbf{n})^2 - 2(\mathbf{U} \cdot \mathbf{n})(\mathbf{q}_b \cdot \mathbf{n}) + (\mathbf{q}_b \cdot \mathbf{n})^2. \end{aligned}$$

The quantity $(\mathbf{U} \cdot \mathbf{n})$ is the $\sin \sigma$ of our steady flow analysis, and (3.7.17) appears as a generalization of (3.2.6).

Assuming that the shock layer structure is known in terms of $\mathbf{q}_t$ as a function of $m$, we form the quantities

$$(3.7.18a) \qquad\qquad m_1 = \int_0^{m_1} dm,$$

$$(3.7.18b) \qquad\qquad \mathbf{M}_1 = \int_0^{m_1} \mathbf{q}_t \, dm,$$

$$(3.7.18c) \qquad\qquad \mathfrak{P}_1 = \int_0^{m_1} \mathbf{q}_t \mathbf{q}_t \, dm,$$

which are equivalent to those defined in (3.5.13) to (3.5.15). If the integrals in (3.7.18) are indefinite ones defined to be zero at the bottom of the layer, we would omit the subscripts 1 and could use the unsubscripted quantities to express the pressure in the layer in an equation analogous to (3.5.19). Here we only obtain the centrifugal pressure correction on the body, using Newton's third law and (3.7.14). This pressure correction is

$$(3.7.19) \quad \tfrac{1}{2}C_{p_s} - \tfrac{1}{2}C_{p_b} = \mathfrak{R} : \mathfrak{P}_1 - 2\mathbf{q}_b \cdot \mathfrak{R} \cdot \mathbf{M}_1 + \mathbf{q}_b \cdot \mathfrak{R} \cdot \mathbf{q}_b m_1$$
$$+ 2\boldsymbol{\omega}_b \times \mathbf{M}_1 \cdot \mathbf{n} - 2\boldsymbol{\omega}_b \times \mathbf{q}_b \cdot \mathbf{n} m_1 + a_b m_1,$$

and includes a number of terms besides the one giving the generalized Busemann centrifugal correction.

To calculate the velocities in the unsteady shock layer of a general body we must obtain an analogue to the locus of entering streamlines. To do this we must consider the three-dimensional space consisting of the body surface with time as an additional coordinate. A particle which enters the shock layer at a given point and at a given instant follows a trajectory in this three-dimensional space which is to be calculated with the help of (3.7.13) and (3.7.16). These trajectories form a three-parameter family. The trajectories which pass through a given point at a given instant form a one-parameter family, and the locus in the three-dimensional space of the entering points of the trajectories of this family is our unsteady form of the locus of entering streamlines. From such a calculation we would obtain the sequence of velocities $\mathbf{q}_t$ in the shock layer at a given point at a given instant.

To complete the picture of the shock layer by obtaining the scale variable $m$ we again need an analysis based on continuity. We choose two neighboring points to the point investigated and form a parallelogram with a known differential area on the body at the instant investigated. The locus of the loci of entering streamlines through points on the periphery of the differential area is a tube in the three-dimensional space. The quantity $U(\mathbf{U} - \mathbf{q}_b) \cdot \mathbf{n}$ is proportional to the entering mass flow per unit area. A differential element of volume in the tube times this quantity is equal to the differential area element on the surface times $dm$. We may thus obtain a relation similar to (3.6.2) which connects $m$ with the locus of entering streamlines. The arbitrariness which we had in the choice of neighboring point in the steady case appears in the unsteady case in a different form. An alternate procedure to that given above may be used, in which one of the neighboring points is chosen at the same instant and the other at a different instant but on the normal through the point investigated. This

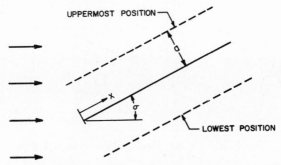

Fig. 3–14a. Oscillating flat plate—sketch.

procedure yields an expression for one of the components of $d\mathbf{M}$ rather than for $dm$, and the two procedures must be consistent. Again, we may choose the procedure which appears simplest, and we may use the arbitrariness to furnish us with a method of checking our results.

The method outlined above for the general case is not one which is at all easy to apply analytically. The principal difficulty is that the three-dimensional space involved is generally curved and incapable of being represented metrically (as opposed to topologically) in a three-dimensional cartesian space. We would be forced in most cases to a cinematographic or stroboscopic representation, with a sequence of instantaneous pictures of the two-dimensional surface at small time intervals. In such a representation, a locus of entering streamlines would consist of a point on each picture. In the two-dimensional unsteady case we can represent the two-dimensional time-distance space as a surface in a three-dimensional cartesian space.

We present here only one very simple example of the calculation of the structure of an unsteady Newtonian shock layer. The problem is that of a flat plate at constant angle of attack $\sigma$ which oscillates sinusoidally in a direction normal to its surface with angular frequency $Uk$ and half-amplitude $a$ (see Fig. 3–14a). The quantity $k$ here is a wave number and has the dimensions of inverse distance. We take distance along the plate from the leading edge as $x$ and consider the trajectories on a plot of $x$ versus $t$. From (3.7.13) and (3.7.16) all particles have the same constant value of $q_t$, equal to $\cos \sigma$. On the $(x, t)$ plot the trajectories are all straight lines of slope $U \cos \sigma$ (see Fig. 3–14b). Accordingly, the locus of entering streamlines for a point is a straight line of the same slope through the point, and is given by

$$(3.7.20) \qquad\qquad x_1 - x = U(t_1 - t) \cos \sigma.$$

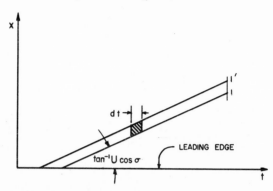

FIG. 3–14b. Oscillating flat plate—calculation of $m$.

With $x = x_0 = 0$ at the leading edge, the corresponding value of $t$ at the leading edge is

$$(3.7.21) \qquad\qquad t_0 = t_1 - \frac{x_1}{U \cos \sigma}.$$

The distance of the flat plate from its central position is $a \sin Ukt$, its normal velocity is

$$(3.7.22) \qquad\qquad \mathbf{q}_b \cdot \mathbf{n} = -ak \cos Ukt,$$

and its acceleration is

$$(3.7.23) \qquad\qquad a_b = ak^2 \sin Ukt.$$

The entering mass flow per unit area is given by

$$(3.7.24) \qquad\qquad (\mathbf{U} - \mathbf{q}_b) \cdot \mathbf{n} = \sin \sigma + ak \cos Ukt.$$

We may now calculate $m_1$ (see Fig. 3–14b), and obtain

$$(3.7.25) \qquad m_1 = \int_{t_0}^{t_1} (\sin \sigma + ak \cos Ukt)U \, dt$$

$$= x_1 \tan \sigma + a \sin Ukt_1 - a \sin (Ukt_1 - kx_1 \sec \sigma).$$

The problem chosen is one in which neither curvature nor Coriolis terms appear, and the pressure on the body may be calculated directly from (3.7.17) and (3.7.19),

(3.7.26)   $\frac{1}{2}C_{p_b} = \sin^2 \sigma + 2ak \sin \sigma \cos Ukt_1 - ak^2x_1 \tan \sigma \sin Ukt_1$
$$+ a^2k^2 \cos 2Ukt_1 + \frac{1}{2}a^2k^2(1 - \cos 2Ukt_1) \cos (kx_1 \sec \sigma)$$
$$- \frac{1}{2}a^2k^2 \sin 2Ukt_1 \sin (kx_1 \sec \sigma).$$

Of the terms appearing in this expression, the first is present in steady flow, the second is a damping term, and the third is an effective-mass term. The remainder of the terms are quadratic in $ak$, and are small if $ak$ is small.

Certain assumptions are implicit in the foregoing analysis. A principal one is that the mass flow of (3.7.24) is never negative, and that $ak < \sin \sigma$. If the mass flow is negative, incidentally, an intermittent shock layer forms on the reverse side of the plate. A more stringent assumption is that the pressure on the body is never negative. If the pressure as given by the analysis becomes negative, a free layer must form with zero pressure behind it; the appropriate solution with the free layer will be much more complicated than the one given and will involve a reattachment process and perhaps a reimpingement of a more violent nature. A simple necessary condition for the pressure on the body to be never negative in our solution (3.7.26) is that $ak^2c < \sin \sigma \cos \sigma$, where $c$ is the chord of the plate. The condition for nonnegative mass flow is also a necessary condition for nonnegative pressure.

We turn now to the problem of a body for which the deviations from steady flow are small and for which a linearized perturbation theory is adequate. We consider that the quantities $\mathbf{q}_b$, $\boldsymbol{\omega}_b$, and $a_b$ are of the first order of smallness, and express the increment in the pressure from (3.7.17) and (3.7.19). We define an angle change $\delta\boldsymbol{\theta}_b$ for the body such that

(3.7.27)                     $\delta\mathbf{n} = \delta\boldsymbol{\theta}_b \times \mathbf{n}$,

and

(3.7.28)                     $\dfrac{d\boldsymbol{\theta}_b}{dt} = \boldsymbol{\omega}_b$.

In terms of $\delta\boldsymbol{\theta}_b$ the linearized increment in pressure on the body is given by

(3.7.29)       $\frac{1}{2}\delta C_{p_b} = 2(\mathbf{U} \cdot \mathbf{n})(\mathbf{U} \times \delta\boldsymbol{\theta}_b - \mathbf{q}_b) \cdot \mathbf{n} + 2\mathbf{q}_b \cdot \mathfrak{R} \cdot \mathbf{M}_1$
$$- 2\boldsymbol{\omega}_b \times \mathbf{M}_1 \cdot \mathbf{n} - a_b m_1 - \delta\mathfrak{R} : \mathfrak{P}_1 - \mathfrak{R} : \delta\mathfrak{P}_1.$$

The quantities $m_1$, $\mathbf{M}_1$, and $\mathfrak{P}_1$ in this equation are defined with respect to the reference steady flow. The effect of the unsteady flow on the structure of the shock layer does appear in this linearized pressure expression, although only in the last term involving $\delta\mathfrak{P}_1$. Hence, an analysis of unsteady shock layer structure is needed even for the linearized problem, but the additional analysis over that already necessary for the steady flow problem is appreciably simpler than that for the general case. We shall not go into the details of such an incremental analysis here.

If the body is a rigid body we may define the body variables in terms of their values at a given point in the body which is chosen as origin of our coordinate system. We express the linearized relations

(3.7.30a) $$\delta\boldsymbol{\theta}_b = \boldsymbol{\theta}_c$$

(3.7.30b) $$\boldsymbol{\omega}_b = \boldsymbol{\omega}_c = \frac{d\boldsymbol{\theta}_c}{dt},$$

(3.7.30c) $$\mathbf{q}_b = \mathbf{q}_c + \boldsymbol{\omega}_c \times \mathbf{r}_b,$$

(3.7.30d) $$a_b = (\mathbf{a}_c + \boldsymbol{\alpha}_c \times \mathbf{r}_b) \cdot \mathbf{n},$$

in which the quadratic terms have been dropped, and quantities with subscript $c$ are for the chosen center of the body. The quantity $\boldsymbol{\alpha}_c$ is the angular acceleration of the body, and $\mathbf{r}_b$ is the distance vector from the center. Combining (3.7.29) with (3.7.30), with $\delta\mathfrak{R} = 0$, there results

(3.7.31) $$\tfrac{1}{2}\delta C_{p_b} = 2\boldsymbol{\theta}_c \cdot [(\mathbf{U} \cdot \mathbf{n})\mathbf{n} \times \mathbf{U}]$$
$$+ 2\mathbf{q}_c \cdot [\mathfrak{R} \cdot \mathbf{M}_1 - \mathbf{n}(\mathbf{U} \cdot \mathbf{n})]$$
$$+ 2\boldsymbol{\omega}_c \cdot [(\mathbf{n}\mathbf{U} \cdot \mathbf{n} - \mathfrak{R} \cdot \mathbf{M}_1) \times \mathbf{r}_b + \mathbf{n} \times \mathbf{M}_1]$$
$$- \mathbf{a}_c \cdot \mathbf{n}m_1 + \boldsymbol{\alpha}_c \cdot \mathbf{n} \times \mathbf{r}_b m_1 - \delta\mathfrak{P}_1 : \mathfrak{R}.$$

This pressure times $\mathbf{n}\, dS_b$ is integrated to obtain the total force on the body, where $dS_b$ is the differential element of area of the body surface.

Let us close our treatment of unsteady Newtonian flow with a listing of some of the subjects which we have not investigated. The question of anomalies has been mentioned. It should be possible to obtain a three-fold condensation in unsteady Newtonian flow, i.e. a "Newtonian shock point". The reimpingement of a free layer presents new aspects, as for example local pressures which instantaneously correspond to an infinite force on the body; such a phenomenon may be termed a "slap". The linearized calculation of $\delta\mathfrak{P}_1$ in (3.7.29) has not been developed; the calculation of complete force coefficients for quasisteady and oscillatory motions needs such a development. The pseudosteady problem of a body flying at constant velocity on a curved path or with a constant rate of roll has not been investigated. Unsteady Newtonian free layers and sails have not been considered. It is clear that there is ample room for exploration in this subject and that, following the philosophy we have expressed earlier, such exploration should help us develop insight into general unsteady hypersonic flows.

# CHAPTER IV

# CONSTANT-DENSITY SOLUTIONS

## 1. The wedge

A fairly common misconception held by students of fluid mechanics is that "incompressible" and "constant density" are synonymous. Any aerodynamicist knows that, while low speed air flows are essentially at constant density, air is a highly compressible fluid. Any oceanographer knows that, while sea water is essentially incompressible, it is far from being a constant-density fluid. The essential point here is that the density in a compressible fluid can be essentially constant if the changes in pressure experienced by the fluid in the flow are small. We shall consider constant-density hypersonic flows, though we should never consider the fluid in a hypersonic flow as incompressible.

In hypersonic flow the approximation that the flow is at a constant density is a useful one in certain cases, and is exact in the case of steady flow on a wedge. The approximation is limited to those cases in which the pressure changes in the flow field are small. Except for the case of a wedge, this limitation usually implies the restriction that the shock layer be thin, and this limitation in turn implies a relationship with Newtonian theory. The applicable cases are in two categories, those for which the shock inclination angle $\sigma$ is essentially constant, and those for which the region of interest is near a stagnation point.

There are two principal reasons for our studying constant-density solutions. The first is that we obtain from them new valid information beyond that available from Newtonian theory and with an analysis of minimum complexity. And we obtain thereby some insight into how Newtonian theory should be applied to practical flows. The second reason is that the constant-density solutions are needed as first approximations to more general solutions based upon the assumption that the shock layer is moderately thin.

Our first step in investigating these constant-density solutions will be to obtain as general a solution as is feasible, without regard to applicability. We then consider the case in which the shock layer is thin, and compare these results with those available from Newtonian theory. Finally, we shall discuss the limitations on the validity of our results, and shall estimate the effects of variations in the density.

The basic equation needed for the wedge has already been obtained (1.5.4), and is repeated here for convenience

(4.1.1) $$\tan (\sigma - \theta_s) = \epsilon \tan \sigma$$

(see Fig. 4–1). Variants of this equation which are useful are

(4.1.2) $$\frac{\epsilon}{1 - \epsilon} = \frac{\cos^2 \sigma(\tan \sigma - \tan \theta_s)}{\tan \theta_s} = \frac{\cos \sigma \sin (\sigma - \theta_s)}{\sin \theta_s},$$

(4.1.3) $$\sin \theta_s = (1 - \epsilon) \sin \sigma \cos (\sigma - \theta_s).$$

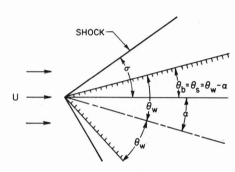

FIG. 4–1. Flow on a wedge.

From (4.1.1) we may also obtain the equation

(4.1.4) $$\tan \theta_s \tan^2 (\sigma - \theta_s) - (1 - \epsilon) \tan (\sigma - \theta_s) + \epsilon \tan \theta_s = 0,$$

which we may solve for $\tan (\sigma - \theta_s)$. The result is

(4.1.5a) $$\tan (\sigma - \theta_s) = \epsilon^{1/2} f(\eta_w)$$

with

(4.1.5b) $$\eta_w = \epsilon^{1/2}(1 - \epsilon)^{-1} \tan \theta_s,$$

where

(4.1.6) $$f(\eta) = \frac{1}{2\eta} \mp \sqrt{\frac{1}{4\eta^2} - 1} = \frac{2\eta}{1 \pm \sqrt{1 - 4\eta^2}}.$$

The function $f(\eta)$ is termed the "detachment function", and is plotted in Fig. 4–2. Combining (4.1.1) and (4.1.5) gives us also

(4.1.7) $$\tan \sigma = \epsilon^{-1/2} f(\eta_w).$$

This detachment function is basic for the solution on a wedge, and appears again in the solution for the cone. The detachment function does not give us an immediate solution if $\theta_s$ is given, as then $\epsilon$ is an unknown. It does, however, give us the solution if $\sigma$ is known, provided we have determined $\epsilon$ as a function of $\sigma$. With given free stream conditions, $\epsilon$ is a function of $\sigma$ alone.

The relations just given are in terms of the flow inclination angle $\theta_s$ immediately behind the shock, and are valid for any oblique shock. In the wedge solution we are interested in, the shock is straight and the flow behind it is uniform. We have then, for the wedge, the relation ·

(4.1.8)                         $\theta_b = \theta_s$,

and our equations are all interpretable with the inclination angle of the body surface $\theta_b$ in place of $\theta_s$. Note that for a symmetric wedge of half-angle $\theta_w$

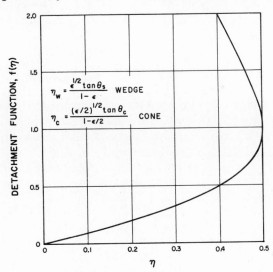

$$\eta_w = \frac{\epsilon^{1/2}\tan\theta_s}{1-\epsilon} \quad \text{WEDGE}$$

$$\eta_c = \frac{(\epsilon/2)^{1/2}\tan\theta_c}{1-\epsilon/2} \quad \text{CONE}$$

Fig. 4–2. Detachment function.

and angle of attack $\alpha$ the angle $\theta_b$ is equal to $\theta_w \pm \alpha$. The importance of the function $f(\eta)$ is that if $\epsilon$ is presumed known it gives the wedge solution explicitly in terms of the body angle. The upper sign in (4.1.6) corresponds to the weak solution relative to the detachment point, and the lower sign to the strong solution. This correspondence is precise if $\epsilon$ is constant, and only approximate otherwise. For small values of the argument $\eta$, the function $f$ may be approximated by

(4.1.9)        $f(\eta) \approx \eta(1 - \eta^2)(1 - 2\eta^2)^{-1} \approx \eta + \eta^3$

for the weak solution, and by the inverse of the expression given in (4.1.9) for the strong solution. Combining (4.1.7) and (4.1.9) gives the result

(4.1.10)        $\tan\sigma = \dfrac{\tan\theta_s}{1-\epsilon} + \dfrac{\epsilon\tan^3\theta_s}{(1-\epsilon)^3} + O\left[\dfrac{\epsilon^2\tan^5\theta_s}{(1-\epsilon)^5}\right],$

which in a shortened form was quoted earlier as (2.1.1).

With $\epsilon$ constant, (4.1.5) and (4.1.6) describe completely the detachment phenomenon. The body angle has a maximum value given by

$$(4.1.11) \qquad (\tan \theta_s)_{\text{det}} = \tfrac{1}{2}\epsilon^{-1/2}(1 - \epsilon),$$

beyond which no solution is possible. This detachment point is at a shock angle given by

$$(4.1.12) \qquad (\tan \sigma)_{\text{det}} = \epsilon^{-1/2}.$$

With $\epsilon$ very small, the angle of the body at detachment with respect to a normal to the flow direction is double that for the shock.

The pressure on the body may be expressed

$$(4.1.13) \qquad \tfrac{1}{2}C_{p_b} = \tfrac{1}{2}C_{p_s} = (1 - \epsilon) \sin^2 \sigma = \frac{\sin^2 \theta_b}{(1 - \epsilon) \cos^2 (\sigma - \theta_b)},$$

in which the factor $\cos^{-2} (\sigma - \theta_b)$ may be omitted if $\epsilon^{1/2} \tan \theta_b$ is small. This pressure, here obtained from the pressure jump across a shock (1.4.5b) with the aid of (4.1.3), may also be obtained from a mass and momentum balance in a coordinate system aligned with the body.

The mass per unit area in the infinitesimally thin shock layer of Newtonian theory was denoted $\rho_\infty m_1$. The Newtonian flow solution for the wedge is simple, and the quantity $m_1$ calculated from (3.2.10) is

$$(4.1.14) \qquad m_1 = R \tan \sigma,$$

where $R$ is the distance along the layer. If we wish to apply this Newtonian solution to the case of a wedge with the density $\epsilon^{-1}\rho_\infty$ very large but not infinite, we must identify the mass per unit area in the shock layer as this high density times the thickness $\Delta$ of the shock layer. But $\Delta$ is simply $R$ times the small angle $\sigma - \theta_b$ of the shock layer itself. Thus we must identify $m_1$ as

$$(4.1.15) \qquad m_1 = \epsilon^{-1}R \tan (\sigma - \theta_b).$$

We note that (4.1.14) and (4.1.15), together with (4.1.8), are consistent with the basic relation (4.1.1). This consistency would not have been obtained had we identified the shock layer inclination angle of the Newtonian theory with the body angle $\theta_b$ rather than with the shock angle $\sigma$.

We conclude that as long as the shock layer may be regarded as thin, Newtonian theory gives us all the results that a general theory can, provided that the shock angle is used as the appropriate angle for the shock layer to be used in the Newtonian formulas. Included here are all the results for the detachment phenomenon. This exemplifies the general rule that Newtonian theory must be applied in terms of the shock angle rather than the body angle in order to enjoy its widest range of validity. We have implicitly taken account of this rule in our notation in the development of Newtonian theory.

We close with a look at the case of an almost-normal shock with $\epsilon$ small, for which $\tan \sigma$ is approximately $\sec \sigma$ and $(1 - \epsilon)$ is approximately 1. The basic equation for this case may be obtained directly from (4.1.2), and is

$$(4.1.16) \qquad\qquad \cos \sigma = \epsilon \tan \theta_s.$$

Note here that $\tan \theta_s$ may be of any order of magnitude with $\epsilon$ and $\cos \sigma$ both small. The Newtonian approach is valueless in this case even with $\epsilon$ very small, as the shock layer is not thin.

## 2. The cone

For the case of the right circular cone we introduce spherical coordinates, and seek a velocity potential with axial symmetry. With the shock wave at

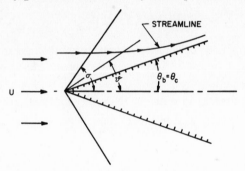

FIG. 4–3. Flow on a cone.

constant inclination the flow is isentropic, and therefore irrotational; thus we know a velocity potential exists. The coordinates are the spherical radius $R$ and the polar angle measured from the downstream axis $\vartheta$ (see Fig. 4–3). In place of $\vartheta$ we shall usually use in this section the quantity $\mu$, defined by

$$(4.2.1) \qquad\qquad \mu = \cos \vartheta.$$

The velocity potential is designated $U\phi$, and with the density constant and the flow axisymmetric $\phi$ satisfies the equation

$$(4.2.2) \qquad\qquad ((1 - \mu^2)\phi_\mu)_\mu + (R^2\phi_R)_R.$$

The subscripts $\mu$ and $R$ here indicate partial differentiation, and the radial and polar velocity components are $U\phi_R$ and $-UR^{-1}\sqrt{1 - \mu^2}\,\phi_\mu$, respectively.

A solution which is conical must have $\phi$ proportional to $R$, and $\phi$ must be of the general form

(4.2.3) $$\phi = R[AP_1(\mu) + BQ_1(\mu)],$$

where $P_1$ and $Q_1$ are Legendre functions. These functions are defined

(4.2.4a) $$P_1(\mu) = \mu,$$

(4.2.4b) $$Q_1(\mu) = \tfrac{1}{2}\mu \ln \frac{1+\mu}{1-\mu} - 1.$$

The function $Q_1$ may be related to its derivative and to the function $Q_0$ by the relation

(4.2.5) $$Q_1(\mu) = \mu Q_1'(\mu) - \frac{1}{1-\mu^2} = \mu Q_0 - 1,$$

where

(4.2.6) $$Q_0(\mu) = \tfrac{1}{2} \ln \frac{1+\mu}{1-\mu}.$$

The radial component of velocity is constant across the shock, and equals $U\mu_s$ there, where $\mu_s = \cos\sigma$. The polar component of velocity is normal to the shock, and equals $\epsilon U\sqrt{1-\mu_s^2}$ immediately behind the shock. These two conditions expressed in terms of the solution (4.2.3) give

(4.2.7a) $$A + B\mu_s^{-1}Q_1(\mu_s) = 1,$$

(4.2.7b) $$A + BQ_1'(\mu_s) = \epsilon.$$

We may evaluate the constants $A$ and $B$ to be

(4.2.8a) $$A = \epsilon + (1-\epsilon)\mu_s(1-\mu_s^2)Q_1'(\mu_s),$$

(4.2.8b) $$B = -(1-\epsilon)\mu_s(1-\mu_s^2).$$

The boundary condition on the body is that the polar component of velocity is zero, and gives us

(4.2.9) $$\frac{\epsilon}{1-\epsilon} = \mu_s(1-\mu_s^2)[Q_1'(\mu_c) - Q_1'(\mu_s)],$$

where $\mu_c = \cos\theta_c$. We use here the subscript $c$ in place of $b$ to indicate our results are for the right circular cone.

The pressure coefficient is a function of $\mu$ alone, and may be evaluated by a straightforward application of the form of Bernoulli's equation applicable to constant-density flows. In evaluating the difference in pressure from the pressure immediately behind the shock, we find no contribution from the part of $\phi$ involving $A$ alone, or no contribution in $A^2$. The terms in $AB$ and

$B^2$ may be simplified through the use of (4.2.5), so that only the function $Q_0$ appears. The result may be expressed

$$(4.2.10) \quad \tfrac{1}{2}C_p - \tfrac{1}{2}C_{p_s} = -\epsilon^{-1}AB[Q_0(\mu) - Q_0(\mu_s)]$$

$$+ \tfrac{1}{2}\epsilon^{-1}B^2\left[\frac{1}{1 - \mu_s^2} - \frac{1}{1 - \mu^2} + Q_0^2(\mu_s) - Q_0^2(\mu)\right],$$

where

$$(4.2.11) \qquad \tfrac{1}{2}C_{p_s} = (1 - \epsilon)\sin^2\sigma = (1 - \epsilon)(1 - \mu_s^2)$$

is the pressure coefficient behind the shock. Of perhaps more interest to us is the pressure gradient, which may be expressed

$$(4.2.12) \qquad \frac{d\tfrac{1}{2}C_p}{d\mu} = -\frac{\epsilon^{-1}B}{1 - \mu^2}[A + BQ_1'(\mu)]$$

or with relation (4.2.9) and the values of $A$ and $B$ from (4.2.8),

$$(4.2.13) \qquad \frac{d\tfrac{1}{2}C_p}{d\mu} = \frac{(1 - \epsilon)^2\mu_s^2(1 - \mu_s^2)^2}{\epsilon(1 - \mu^2)}[Q_1'(\mu_c) - Q_1'(\mu)].$$

It may be noted that the pressure gradient vanishes on the body.

The general analysis just given is based upon the assumption that the density in the flow field behind the shock is constant. This assumption is approximately valid only if the density ratio $\epsilon$ is sufficiently small, in which case the shock layer is thin unless the shock is almost normal. If the shock layer is thin we may expand the difference between the two values of $Q_1'$ which appears in (4.2.9) and (4.2.13) in a Taylor series about $\mu = \mu_s$. The result may be expressed

$$(4.2.14a) \qquad \mu_s(1 - \mu_s^2)[Q_1'(\mu) - Q_1'(\mu_s)] = 2\bar{\xi} + 4\bar{\xi}^2 + O(\bar{\xi}^3)$$

$$(4.2.14b) \qquad\qquad\qquad\qquad\qquad = 2\xi + \xi^2 + O(\xi^3),$$

where

$$(4.2.15) \qquad \bar{\xi} = \mu_s(1 - \mu_s^2)^{-1}(\mu - \mu_s),$$

and

$$(4.2.16) \qquad \xi = \frac{\cos^2\sigma(\tan\sigma - \tan\vartheta)}{\tan\vartheta} = \frac{\cos\sigma\sin(\sigma - \vartheta)}{\sin\vartheta}.$$

On the body the variable $\xi$ has the same form as that appearing in (4.1.2). The limitations of the constant-density approximation require that $\xi$ remain small and restrict us to only one valid term in the series which appear in (4.2.14), provided $\mu_s$ is not small. Allowing an error in the second term of an expansion in $\xi_c$ we may satisfy the boundary condition (4.2.9) with the approximate expression

$$(4.2.17) \qquad \frac{\epsilon}{1 - \epsilon} = \frac{2\xi_c}{1 - \xi_c},$$

which is equivalent to

$$(4.2.18) \qquad \frac{\frac{1}{2}\epsilon}{1 - \frac{1}{2}\epsilon} = \xi_c.$$

Comparison of this result with (4.1.2) shows that, within the approximation used, the geometric relation between shock angle and body angle in the solution on a cone is the same as that on a wedge with $\epsilon$ reduced by the factor $\frac{1}{2}$. To be more accurate we should replace $\epsilon$ by $\frac{1}{2}\epsilon(1 + \frac{1}{4}\epsilon)$, but we may not justifiably keep the higher-order term within the limits of our approximation. A similar factor of $\frac{1}{2}$ connects the corrections to the tangent-wedge and tangent-cone pressure results if $\epsilon$ is small; cf. (7.3.7) and (7.3.9). Thus we may write in place of (4.1.7), for example,

$$(4.2.19a) \qquad \tan \sigma = (\tfrac{1}{2}\epsilon)^{-1/2} f(\eta_c)$$

with

$$(4.2.19b) \qquad \eta_c = (\tfrac{1}{2}\epsilon)^{1/2}(1 - \tfrac{1}{2}\epsilon)^{-1} \tan \theta_c.$$

The structure of the solution is different for the two cases, of course. In place of (4.1.8) we have the approximate relation

$$(4.2.20) \qquad \sigma - \theta_c = \tfrac{1}{2}(\sigma - \theta_s) = \tfrac{1}{2}\epsilon \tan \sigma.$$

If we re-express (4.2.13) in terms of the polar angle $\vartheta$, we obtain

$$(4.2.21) \qquad \frac{d\tfrac{1}{2}C_p}{d\vartheta} = - \frac{(1 - \epsilon)^2 \cos \sigma \sin^2 \sigma}{\epsilon \sin \vartheta} [2(\xi_c - \xi) + O(\xi_c^2 - \xi^2)],$$

or to the accuracy of our constant-density theory,

$$(4.2.22) \qquad \frac{d\tfrac{1}{2}C_p}{d\vartheta} = -2\epsilon^{-1} \cos^2 \sigma(\vartheta - \theta_c).$$

This expression we may integrate to obtain

$$(4.2.23) \qquad \tfrac{1}{2}C_p = (1 - \epsilon) \sin^2 \sigma + \epsilon^{-1} \cos^2 \sigma(\sigma - \vartheta)(\sigma + \vartheta - 2\theta_c).$$

On the body we may use (4.2.20) to express the pressure

$$(4.2.24) \qquad \tfrac{1}{2}C_{p_b} = (1 - \tfrac{3}{4}\epsilon) \sin^2 \sigma.$$

The formula for the cone which is analogous to (4.1.3) is

$$(4.2.25) \qquad \sin \theta_c = (1 - \tfrac{1}{2}\epsilon) \sin \sigma \cos (\sigma - \theta_c),$$

and the use of this permits us to rewrite (4.2.24) as

$$(4.2.26) \qquad \tfrac{1}{2}C_{p_b} = \frac{\sin^2 \theta_c}{(1 - \tfrac{1}{4}\epsilon) \cos^2 (\sigma - \theta_c)}$$

within the accuracy of our approximation. The result may be compared with (4.1.13) for the wedge, and we note again that the factor in cos $(\sigma - \theta_c)$ may be dropped if $\epsilon^{1/2} \tan \theta_c$ is small.

Following an alternate approach used earlier by Hayes [3], we could start with the assumption that the shock layer on the cone is thin, obtain an approximate picture of the structure of the layer on the basis of continuity arguments, and derive the equivalents of the approximate relations (4.2.19), (4.2.20), (4.2.24), and (4.2.26). This analysis is much simpler than that given in terms of Legendre functions, and leads to results of equal validity except for the isolated case of the almost-normal shock considered below. We have followed the approach with Legendre functions in order to include this special case and in order to follow the philosophy expressed in the fourth paragraph of Section 4.1 of exhibiting the most general constant-density solution.

Either the analysis we have given or the alternate approach just mentioned leads to a simple geometric picture of the streamline pattern. Analogous to (4.2.20) we may obtain the approximate relation

$$(4.2.27) \qquad\qquad \theta_c - \theta = \vartheta - \theta_c,$$

where $\theta$ is the local streamline inclination angle. This relation states that the slope of a streamline with respect to the body surface is equal to minus the distance from the body surface divided by the distance from the vertex. Such streamlines are hyperbolas with the body surface as asymptote. The velocity component parallel to the body surface is approximately constant, while that normal to the surface varies approximately linearly with distance from the surface. The linear variation of the pressure gradient in (4.2.22) is consistent with this picture. As in the case of the wedge, the pressure relations may be obtained on the basis of a mass and momentum balance.

Feldman [3] has independently developed a constant-density theory for the cone which uses Legendre functions and which is essentially equivalent to that given here. He compares results of his theory with calculated results according to the exact theory of Taylor and Maccoll [1] for a number of cases of cones at high flight speeds at an altitude of 100,000 feet. He obtains excellent agreement for those cases in which $\epsilon$ is about $\frac{1}{10}$ or less. He does not make any approximation beyond that of assuming constant density; thus with given shock angle he uses his equivalent to (4.2.9) to calculate the cone angle $\theta_c$, and his equivalent of (4.2.10) to calculate the pressure coefficient on the body. As we have pointed out, the validity of the constant-density approach implies the validity of our additional assumptions. With the additional assumptions and the attendant simplification we may use the simpler formulas (4.2.20) and (4.2.24) in place of their counterparts (4.2.9) and (4.2.10) of the full constant-density theory. The errors are generally of the same order of magnitude. And with $\theta_c$ given and $\epsilon$ known approximately (4.2.19) and (4.2.26) are available for the calculation of shock angle and pressure coefficient on the cone.

Hord [1] and Zienkiewicz [1] have given theories for the cone in a perfect gas of constant $\gamma$, based upon the assumptions of constant density in addition to other assumptions. Hord obtains an approximate formula for the relation between shock angle and cone angle, and compares the predictions of his approximate theory with various approximations and the exact results of Kopal [1]. Our relation (4.2.20) for small $\epsilon$ may be deduced from Hord's approximate result, but his approximation breaks down in the detachment region and may not be used to predict detachment. Hord also makes the remark that the complete constant-density solution of the form (4.2.3) had been recognized independently by several persons as being a good approximation. But he gives no indication that he or any of these several unnamed persons has exploited this approach.

Zienkiewicz [1] takes the constant-density form of the Taylor-Maccoll equation (essentially our 4.2.2), and drops one of the terms. His approximation is valid as long as $\epsilon$ is small and the shock layer is thin, and represents an intermediate point between the approximation of the complete constant-density theory and the simplest equally valid approximation. Within the limits of validity of constant-density theory a number of almost equivalent approximations of slightly different form are equally valid except in the case of the almost-normal shock. Zienkiewicz derives no geometrical or pressure relationships based upon his approximation, but compares a few numerically calculated examples with the results of Kopal [1]. Some results for cones in air at high temperatures obtained from the exact Taylor-Maccoll equations have been reported by Romig [2].

The result from Newtonian flow analogous to (4.1.14) is

$$(4.2.28) \qquad\qquad m_1 = \tfrac{1}{2} R \tan \sigma$$

for the cone. Following the same approach that we used for the wedge we obtain the conical analogue of (4.1.1) with $\tfrac{1}{2}\epsilon$ in place of $\epsilon$ and $\theta_c$ in place of $\theta_s$. For the geometry of the cone solution with a thin shock layer the Newtonian theory is again adequate, provided that the shock angle is used for the shock layer angle. However, the Newtonian theory cannot give us any information about the structure of the shock layer in terms of the polar velocity component or of the pressure difference between the shock and the body.

We next look at the one special case for which the expansion of (4.2.14) and the approximation of (4.2.18) may not be applied even if $\epsilon$ is very small. This is the case of the almost-normal shock, with $\sin \sigma$ very close to one. As long as $\epsilon$ is small the constant-density assumption is still valid in this case even though the shock layer may be anything but thin. This is true because the Mach number of the subsonic flow behind the almost-normal shock is of order $\epsilon^{1/2}$ (see Section 1.7) and its square is small. From (4.2.9) we obtain the relation

$$(4.2.29) \qquad \cos \sigma = \frac{\epsilon}{Q_1'(\mu_c)},$$

which is analogous to (4.1.16). Here we have a realistic physical problem for which our complete theory involving Legendre functions is essential.

We turn now to an estimation of the effects of the variations in the density upon our approximate results. In so doing we shall seek a correction to the thickness of the shock layer, and shall base a formula for this correction upon a simple argument. The actual solution is assumed to be at almost constant density and at constant $\epsilon$, and is considered to be almost the same as the constant-density solution with the same shock shape and the same value of $\epsilon$. The two solutions have the same pressures immediately behind the shock and approximately the same pressure distributions at corresponding points in the flow field. Corresponding points are defined as points at the same distance along the shock layer which have the same entering stream-line. With these pressure distributions extremely close the mass flow relations in the two compared solutions must be extremely close, and we should be able to approximately set the Howarth-Dorodnitsyn variable $\int_0 \rho \, dy$ ($y$ is here distance from the body) equal at corresponding points in the two flows.

With the assumption that the Howarth-Dorodnitsyn variable, or its equivalent $\rho_\infty m$ used in Newtonian theory, is unchanged, we may write an expression for the correction to the shock layer thickness

$$(4.2.30) \qquad \frac{\Delta}{\Delta_{CD}} = 1 - \chi = \frac{1}{\Delta_{CD}} \int_0^{\Delta_{CD}} \frac{\rho_s \, dy}{\rho} .$$

Here the subscript $CD$ indicates the constant-density result, and the density $\rho_s$ is the assumed constant density $\epsilon^{-1}\rho_\infty$ of the constant-density solution. The quantity $\chi$ defined in (4.2.30) is a measure of the decrease in thickness of the shock layer due to an increase in density from compressibility. Defining $\gamma_s$ as the value of $\gamma_e$ defined in (1.4.22) immediately behind the shock, and assuming that the speed of sound is approximately constant in the shock layer, we may replace the integrand $\rho_s/\rho$ of (4.2.30) by

$$(4.2.31) \qquad \frac{\rho_s}{\rho} = 1 - \frac{\rho - \rho_s}{\rho_s} = 1 - \frac{p - p_s}{\gamma_s p_s}$$

within the accuracy of our approximation. We obtain for $\chi$ the expression

$$(4.2.32) \qquad \chi = \frac{1}{\gamma_s} \int_0^1 \left( \frac{p - p_s}{p_s} \right) d\left( \frac{y}{\Delta_{CD}} \right),$$

and shall use this expression in this and the two succeeding sections. This gives a correction on the constant-density solution of the same $\epsilon$ and the same shock shape; hence the correction gives us a change in the body shape.

In the case of the cone, we may use (4.2.23) to obtain an expression

$$(4.2.33) \qquad \frac{p - p_s}{p_s} = \frac{\epsilon}{4} \left[ 1 - \left( \frac{y}{\Delta_{CD}} \right)^2 \right],$$

whence we obtain immediately

$$(4.2.34) \qquad \chi = \frac{\epsilon}{6\gamma_s}.$$

Using $\frac{1}{2}\epsilon(1 + \frac{1}{4}\epsilon)$ in place of $\epsilon$ in the equivalent of (4.1.1) for the cone, we obtain with the density correction

$$(4.2.35) \qquad \sigma - \theta_c = \frac{1}{2}\epsilon[1 + \frac{1}{4}\epsilon - \chi + O(\epsilon^2)] \tan \sigma.$$

in place of (4.2.20). If we may take $\gamma_s - 1$ to be of order $\epsilon$ or less we obtain the somewhat simpler result

$$(4.2.36) \qquad \sigma - \theta_c = \frac{1}{2}\epsilon[1 + \frac{1}{12}\epsilon + O(\epsilon^2)] \tan \sigma.$$

For a perfect gas $\gamma_s - 1$ is of order $\epsilon$. We may note that if $0 < \gamma_s^{-1} < \frac{3}{2}$ the result of (4.2.35) lies between our approximate result (4.2.20) and that of the complete constant-density theory, and that if $\gamma_s < \frac{4}{3}$, our approximate result (4.2.20) should be more accurate than that of the complete constant-density theory.

## 3. Circular cylinder

Our general solution with constant density for a circular cylinder was suggested by the analogous solution of Lighthill for a sphere, which will be presented later. For the cylinder we take two-dimensional polar coordinates $R$ and $\vartheta$, with the axis $\vartheta = 0$ directed upstream. We assume that the shock wave is in the shape of a circular cylinder of radius $R_s$, that the density ratio $\epsilon$ is constant, and that the flow behind the shock is at constant density (see Fig. 4–4). We define $\psi$ as before as the stream function for the flow, with the properties that the outward radial component of the mass flow may be expressed

$$(4.3.1) \qquad (\rho U v) = -R^{-1} \psi_\vartheta$$

and the angular or tangential component expressed

(4.3.2)    $$(\rho U u) = \psi_R,$$

with the subscripts $R$ and $\vartheta$ indicating partial differentiation. The stream function immediately behind the shock equals that immediately in front of it, and we have the condition that

(4.3.3)    $$\psi_s = \rho_\infty U R_s \sin \vartheta.$$

The vorticity immediately behind the shock may be obtained from (1.5.12), and is

(4.3.4)    $$\zeta_s = - \frac{U(1 - \epsilon)^2 \sin \vartheta}{\epsilon R_s} .$$

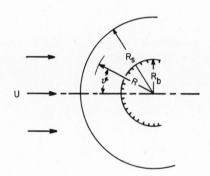

FIG. 4–4. Constant-density flow on a cylinder or sphere.

Since in a steady two-dimensional flow with constant density the vorticity is a function of the stream function alone, we may write

(4.3.5)    $$\zeta = - \frac{(1 - \epsilon)^2}{\epsilon \rho_\infty R_s^2} \psi ,$$

which is a relation obtained from (4.3.3) and (4.3.4) on the shock and which is valid over the entire field. Note that the vorticity $\zeta$ must be zero if $\psi$ is zero, and will necessarily be zero at the surface of the body.

The stream function $\psi$ satisfies the equation

(4.3.6)    $$\psi_{RR} + \frac{1}{R} \psi_R + \frac{1}{R^2} \psi_{\vartheta\vartheta} = -\epsilon^{-1} \rho_\infty \zeta = \frac{(1 - \epsilon)^2}{\epsilon^2 R_s^2} \psi$$

(see Milne-Thomson [1, §4.41]). We may see from (4.3.3) that $\psi$ should be of the form of $\sin \vartheta$ times a function of $R$. A general solution to (4.3.6) which is of this form does exist and may be expressed

(4.3.7)    $$\psi = \epsilon^{-1} \rho_\infty U R_s \sin \vartheta [A I_1(\kappa R) + B K_1(\kappa R)],$$

where the parameter $\kappa$ is defined

$$(4.3.8) \qquad \kappa = \frac{1-\epsilon}{\epsilon R_s},$$

and $I_1$ and $K_1$ are modified Bessel functions of order one. The boundary condition on the velocity component normal to the shock is equivalent to (4.3.3), and the condition on the tangential component (4.3.2) is

$$(4.3.9) \qquad \psi_{R_s} = \epsilon^{-1} \rho_\infty U \sin \vartheta.$$

The two boundary conditions (4.3.3) and (4.3.9) are expressed

$$(4.3.10a) \qquad AI_1(\kappa R_s) + BK_1(\kappa R_s) = \epsilon,$$

$$(4.3.10b) \qquad AI_1'(\kappa R_s) + BK_1'(\kappa R_s) = \frac{\epsilon}{1-\epsilon},$$

from which the constants $A$ and $B$ may be evaluated. From the theory of Bessel functions we take the evaluation of the Wronskian of the modified Bessel functions and write the identity

$$(4.3.11) \qquad K_1(\kappa R)I_1'(\kappa R) - I_1(\kappa R)K_1'(\kappa R) = \frac{1}{\kappa R}.$$

The constants $A$ and $B$ are calculated from (4.3.10) and (4.3.11) as

$$(4.3.12a) \qquad A = K_1\left(\frac{1-\epsilon}{\epsilon}\right) - (1-\epsilon)K_1'\left(\frac{1-\epsilon}{\epsilon}\right),$$

$$(4.3.12b) \qquad B = (1-\epsilon)I_1'\left(\frac{1-\epsilon}{\epsilon}\right) - I_1\left(\frac{1-\epsilon}{\epsilon}\right).$$

The boundary condition from which the body shape is determined is that $\psi = 0$ on the body. From (4.3.7) we see that $\psi = 0$ on the splitting streamline and on a cylindrical body of radius $R_b$, where

$$(4.3.13) \qquad AI_1(\kappa R_b) + BK_1(\kappa R_b) = 0.$$

The general solution of this equation for $R_b$ may not be obtained in closed form. An approximate solution with $\epsilon$ small obtainable from the asymptotic expansions of the Bessel functions is

$$(4.3.14a) \qquad \Delta = R_s - R_b = \tfrac{1}{2}\epsilon R_s\left[\ln\frac{4}{3\epsilon} + \epsilon\ln\frac{4}{3\epsilon} + O\left(\epsilon^2\ln\frac{1}{\epsilon}\right)\right],$$

which is in agreement to the lowest-order term with the results of Chester [1] and Freeman [1]. Chester's result is for a parabolic shock in a perfect gas of constant $\gamma$, and may be expressed for comparison as

$$(4.3.14b) \qquad \Delta_0 = \tfrac{1}{2}\epsilon R_s\left[\ln\frac{4}{3\epsilon} + \tfrac{1}{2}\epsilon\left(\ln\frac{4}{3\epsilon} - \frac{3}{2} - \frac{4}{M_\infty^2\epsilon}\right) + O\left(\epsilon^2\ln\frac{1}{\epsilon}\right)\right].$$

The subscript 0 here indicates a result taken on the axis. The density ratio $\epsilon$ in Chester's problem is not a constant, and the value for $\epsilon$ intended in (4.3.14b) is that valid on the axis, with the shock normal and (1.4.19) applicable. The presence of the term involving $M_\infty$ in (4.3.14b) is an indication of the effect of nonconstancy of $\epsilon$. We shall discuss the two results (4.3.14) further when we consider the approximate density correction.

The pressure coefficient in our constant-density solution may be obtained by the application of Bernoulli's equation, and is

$$(4.3.15) \quad \tfrac{1}{2}C_p = (1 - \tfrac{1}{2}\epsilon) + \frac{(1-\epsilon)^2}{2\epsilon\rho_\infty^2 U^2 R_s^2}\,\psi^2 - \frac{\epsilon}{2\rho_\infty^2 U^2}\left(\psi_R^2 + \frac{1}{R^2}\,\psi_\vartheta^2\right).$$

On the body we may re-express (4.3.15)

$$(4.3.16) \quad \tfrac{1}{2}C_{p_b} = (1 - \tfrac{1}{2}\epsilon) - \frac{(1-\epsilon)^2}{2\epsilon^3}\,[AI_1'(\kappa R_b) + BK_1'(\kappa R_b)]^2 \sin^2\vartheta.$$

With $\sin\vartheta$ sufficiently large, the pressure coefficient is negative on and near the body, regardless of the value of $\epsilon$. For small $\epsilon$, W. B. Bush (private communication) and N. H. Kemp (private communication) have found an approximate expression for (4.3.16) from the Bessel function asymptotic expansion

$$(4.3.17) \quad \tfrac{1}{2}C_{p_b} = (1 - \tfrac{1}{2}\epsilon) - \tfrac{3}{2}\sin^2\vartheta\left[1 + \tfrac{1}{2}\epsilon\left(\ln\frac{4}{3\epsilon} - 1\right) + O\left(\epsilon^2\ln\frac{1}{\epsilon}\right)\right].$$

Whitham [1] has obtained essentially the same constant-density solution we have presented above from (4.3.1) to (4.3.15), expressed in somewhat different terms. His method is different in one respect, in that he uses the vorticity equation obtained by taking the curl of the vector momentum equation instead of using the known law of dependence of the vorticity on $\psi$ (and on $R\sin\vartheta$ for the Lighthill solution of the next section). Our solution was obtained independently of Whitham's and at about the same time.

As with the cone, the foregoing general analysis is not valid for a hypersonic flow unless $\epsilon$ is very small. Even with $\epsilon$ small, the validity is limited by the large pressure changes to a local region in the vicinity of the stagnation point. However, the analysis is instructive and provides a valuable check on results obtained by other methods. But it must be strongly emphasized that only the lowest-order term on the right-hand side of (4.3.14a) may be justifiably retained.

We turn now to a quite different approach to the problem, in which only a local solution near the stagnation point is sought. No real restriction is imposed, however, as only such a local solution is valid anyway with the assumption of constant density. Within the limits of validity obtainable from a constant-density theory we have a great deal of freedom in making approximations in this analysis. We choose the coordinate $x$ as distance along the layer from the stagnation point, and approximate $\sin \sigma$ by one within the region of interest except in calculating the pressure (see Fig. 4–5). The quantity $x$ is thus identical with the stream function $\psi$ of the free stream flow divided by $\rho_\infty U$. We first neglect the fact that the normal component of velocity is nonzero within the layer, and calculate a correction to the Newtonian velocity distribution using the constant density $\epsilon^{-1} \rho_\infty$ in Bernoulli's equation and the Newtonian pressure distribution. We next calculate

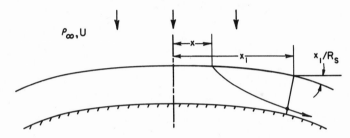

FIG. 4–5. Coordinate system for stagnation region.

on the basis of continuity the corrected vertical scale corresponding to the Newtonian $m$ scale. Finally we calculate the distributions of both velocity components with respect to this scale and obtain an improved pressure distribution. Our reasons for carrying out this alternate analysis are two, first to show how we may obtain results of the same validity as those of the Bessel function analysis starting from our Newtonian results, and second to develop an approach applicable to a more general problem, such as that treated in Section 4.5.

The Newtonian pressure is obtained from the variant of (3.2.7) analogous to (3.5.19), with the aid of (3.3.3) with $n = 2$ and (3.5.6). The result in terms of the pressure coefficient is

$$(4.3.18) \qquad \tfrac{1}{2} C_p = 1 - \frac{x_1^2}{R_s^2} - \frac{1}{2R_s^2} (x_1^2 - x^2),$$

with $\psi$ replaced by $\rho_\infty U x$. The quantity $x_1$ is the $x$ coordinate of the point being investigated, and the quantity $x$ is the coordinate at entry into the shock layer of the streamline passing through the point being investigated. The velocity given by (3.5.7) is an initial velocity upon entry, assumed within the Newtonian approximation to be purely tangential with respect to the shock layer. We denote this velocity as $Uu$ (essentially the same $u$ as in (4.3.2)) and neglect, for the moment, the normal component of velocity. With the assumed constant density $\epsilon^{-1} \rho_\infty$, and with the initial value of $u$

equal to $x/R_s$, we may apply Bernoulli's equation to calculate $u$. We obtain first the equation

(4.3.19)
$$\frac{1}{2\epsilon}\left(u^2 - \frac{x^2}{R_s^2}\right) = \frac{3}{2R_s^2}(x_1^2 - x^2),$$

and may then calculate $u$

(4.3.20)
$$u = \frac{1}{R_s}\sqrt{x^2 + 3\epsilon(x_1^2 - x^2)}.$$

We now use this corrected velocity distribution to obtain the distance $y$ measured normal to the body. The method we use is based on continuity, analogous to that used to obtain $m$ in Newtonian theory. The quantity $y$ is equivalent to $\epsilon m$, and is

(4.3.21)
$$y = \epsilon \int_0^{} \frac{dx}{u} = \frac{\epsilon R_s}{\sqrt{1 - 3\epsilon}} \sinh^{-1}\left(\sqrt{\frac{1 - 3\epsilon}{3\epsilon}}\frac{x}{x_1}\right).$$

We obtain also the result

(4.3.22)
$$\Delta_0 = \frac{\epsilon R_s}{\sqrt{1 - 3\epsilon}} \sinh^{-1}\sqrt{\frac{1 - 3\epsilon}{3\epsilon}} = \frac{\epsilon R_s}{\sqrt{1 - 3\epsilon}} \cosh^{-1}\frac{1}{\sqrt{3\epsilon}}$$

for the stand-off or stagnation point detachment distance. By expanding the function $\cosh^{-1}$ this result may be also expressed

(4.3.23)
$$\Delta_0 = \tfrac{1}{2}\epsilon R_s\left[\ln\frac{4}{3\epsilon} + \tfrac{3}{2}\epsilon\left(\ln\frac{4}{3\epsilon} - 1\right) + O\left(\epsilon^2\ln\frac{1}{\epsilon}\right)\right],$$

in agreement with (4.3.14) to the term of lowest order, which again is the only term which may justifiably be retained. The second term, the one in $R_s\epsilon^2\ln(1/\epsilon)$, is affected by the additional assumptions we have made in our approximate analysis, and is in error for the constant-density theory.

The distribution of the tangential component of the velocity $Uu$ is given by

(4.3.24)
$$u = \frac{\sqrt{3\epsilon}\,x_1}{R_s}\cosh\left(\frac{\sqrt{1 - 3\epsilon}\,y}{\epsilon R_s}\right),$$

in terms of $y$, and the corresponding distribution of outward normal velocity $Uv$ (essentially the same $v$ as in (4.3.1)) calculated to satisfy the cartesian continuity equation in $x$ and $y$ is

(4.3.25)
$$v = -\epsilon\sqrt{\frac{3\epsilon}{1 - 3\epsilon}}\sinh\left(\frac{\sqrt{1 - 3\epsilon}\,y}{\epsilon R_s}\right) = -\epsilon\frac{x}{x_1}.$$

From (4.3.24), the velocity gradient on the body is simply $\sqrt{3\epsilon}\,R_s^{-1}U$. The pressure distribution from Bernoulli's equation corresponding to this velocity distribution is

$$(4.3.26) \qquad \tfrac{1}{2}C_p = 1 - \tfrac{1}{2}\epsilon \left(1 + \frac{x^2}{x_1^2}\right) - \frac{x_1^2}{2R_s^2}\left(3 - \frac{x^2}{x_1^2}\right),$$

with a term in $\epsilon x^2/R_s^2$ dropped, where

$$(4.3.27) \qquad \frac{x^2}{x_1^2} = \frac{3\epsilon}{1 - 3\epsilon}\,\sinh^2\frac{\sqrt{1 - 3\epsilon}\,y}{\epsilon R_s}\,.$$

It may be shown that the pressure given by (4.3.26) satisfies the dynamic equations approximately, with best agreement near the shock wave. On the body (4.3.26) gives simply the Newtonian pressure plus an appropriate correction to give the correct stagnation pressure, and is consistent with (4.3.17).

A simplified analysis similar to that above was first given by Hayes [3], neglecting the centrifugal correction to the Newtonian pressure distribution. In this analysis the number 2 appeared wherever 3 appears in equations (4.3.19) through (4.3.25). Hayes' results were rederived by Li and Geiger [1] using a different approach. Li and Geiger assumed local similarity of the type evident in (4.3.24) and (4.3.25) and calculated the appropriate stream function in a coordinate system similar to ours. The centrifugal corrections to the pressure have an effect on the results which may not be neglected within the degree of approximation desired, and these earlier analyses which neglect this effect must be considered to be in error on this point. The correct factor 3 appeared first in the results of Chester [1] and Freeman [1].

The stand-off distance $\Delta$ as given by (4.3.22) or (4.3.23) is independent of $x_1$ and thus constant along the body. This would correspond to a radius of curvature $R_b$ for the body simply equal to $R_s - \Delta_0$. However, the theory cannot yield a value for the second derivative of $\Delta$ with respect to $x_1$ accurately, and the body radius $R_b$ is actually undetermined in this approximation. Here we have another example of our principle that Newtonian theory should be used with the shock shape rather than with the body shape. In our present problem the shock shape is the prime determiner of the principal features of the solution, of the velocity distributions and of the pressure field.

At this point we list the principal effects in a hypersonic flow on a blunt body which are not taken into account in a constant-density analysis such as those we have given:

1. The effect of the compressibility of the fluid.
2. The effect of variation of the density ratio $\epsilon$ along the shock.
3. The effect of the departure of the shock shape from circular.

For our local analysis we should add the geometrical effect of the curvature of the coordinate system we have used—the dynamical effect of this curvature has been included approximately. The point of view we have taken here is that the shock shape is specified; with this point of view the ratio of body curvature to shock curvature is a result of the analysis and not a quantity which we may specify a priori.

Unpublished investigations of Mr. W. B. Bush and the solution of Chester [1] indicate that the inclusion of all these effects does not change our results as far as the leading terms. Thus (4.3.14) and (4.3.23) are correct insofar as they agree, to terms of order $\epsilon R_s \ln (1/\epsilon)$. Of the effects neglected that of compressibility appears to be more important than the others.

It is possible to use an approach based upon local similarity near the stagnation point to solve certain different types of problems of flow on blunt two-dimensional and axisymmetric bodies with a thin shock layer, using an assumed form of the stream function. One such problem is that of hypersonic flow on a blunt body in a relaxing fluid, with the assumption that the density of a fluid parcel is a single known function of the time elapsed after the parcel has passed through the shock. Another is the viscous hypersonic flow on a blunt body treated in Section 10.2. Another is the magnetohydrodynamic flow on an axisymmetric blunt body studied by Bush [1] and Kemp [1].

To obtain the density correction we use (4.2.32), together with (4.3.26) for the pressure on the axis. Within the accuracy of this correction we may replace (4.3.27) by its limiting form for small $\epsilon$

$$(4.3.28) \qquad \frac{x^2}{x_1^2} = \tfrac{3}{4}\epsilon \exp \left( \frac{y}{\Delta_{CD}} \ln \frac{4}{3\epsilon} \right).$$

The integrand of (4.2.32) may now be expressed

$$(4.3.29) \qquad \frac{p - p_s}{p_s} = \tfrac{1}{2}\epsilon \left[ 1 - \tfrac{3}{4}\epsilon \exp \left( \frac{y}{\Delta_{CD}} \ln \frac{4}{3\epsilon} \right) \right],$$

from which the quantity $\chi$ is evaluated as

$$(4.3.30) \qquad \chi = \frac{\epsilon}{2\gamma_s} \left[ 1 - \frac{1}{\ln \dfrac{4}{3\epsilon}} + O(\epsilon) \right].$$

If we now take $\gamma_s - 1$ to be of the order $\epsilon$ or less and apply the correction to the full constant-density result (4.3.14a) for $\Delta$, we obtain the corrected expression

$$(4.3.31) \qquad \Delta_0 = \tfrac{1}{2}\epsilon R_s \left[ \ln \frac{4}{3\epsilon} + \tfrac{1}{2}\epsilon \left( \ln \frac{4}{3\epsilon} + 1 \right) + O \left( \epsilon^2 \ln \frac{1}{\epsilon} \right) \right].$$

In comparing this result with that of Chester (4.3.14b) we note that the density correction has given us agreement in the term of order $R_s\epsilon^2 \ln (1/\epsilon)$ but that a difference remains in the term of order $R_s\epsilon^2$. We infer that the result of (4.3.14b) or (4.3.31) should be a general result for all rounded blunt two-dimensional bodies when expressed only to the term in $R_s\epsilon^2 \ln (1/\epsilon)$ as long as $\gamma_s - 1$ is of order $\epsilon$ or less, or

$$(4.3.32) \qquad \Delta_0 = \tfrac{1}{2}\epsilon R_s \left[ (1 + \tfrac{1}{2}\epsilon) \ln \frac{4}{3\epsilon} + O(\epsilon) \right].$$

The term of order $R_s\epsilon^2$ is affected both by variation in $\epsilon$ along the shock and by nonsphericity of the shock (fourth-order terms in an expansion describing the shock shape).

## 4. The sphere

The analytical solution for the constant-density flow on a sphere is due to Lighthill [3], and is closely connected with Hill's classical solution for a spherical vortex (see Milne-Thomson [1, § 18.50 and § 18.51]). We use spherical coordinates analogous to those we used for the circular cylinder, with $\vartheta$ the polar angle from the upstream axis, and $R$ the spherical radius. We use the Stokes stream function $\psi$ defined as before, with the outward radial component of the mass flow

$$(4.4.1) \qquad (\rho U v) = -(R^2 \sin \vartheta)^{-1} \psi_\vartheta,$$

and the polar or tangential component

$$(4.4.2) \qquad (\rho U u) = (R \sin \vartheta)^{-1} \psi_R ;$$

the subscripts again denote partial differentiation. The stream function immediately behind the shock equals that immediately in front of it, and we have the condition that

$$(4.4.3) \qquad \psi_s = \tfrac{1}{2}\rho_\infty U R_s^2 \sin^2 \vartheta,$$

which may be compared with the two-dimensional value given in (4.3.3). The vorticity immediately behind the shock is given again by (4.3.4), but in axisymmetric constant-density flow the vorticity is proportional to the cylindrical radius $R \sin \vartheta$. In place of (4.3.5) we have

$$(4.4.4) \qquad \zeta = - \frac{U(1 - \epsilon)^2}{\epsilon R_s^2} R \sin \vartheta$$

for the vorticity in the flow field, independent of $\psi$. Note that the vorticity $\zeta$ is never zero except on the axis $\vartheta = 0$, and hence is nonzero at the surface of the body. The stream function satisfies the equation

$$(4.4.5) \qquad \psi_{RR} + \frac{\sin \vartheta}{R^2} \left( \frac{1}{\sin \vartheta} \psi_\vartheta \right)_\vartheta = \frac{(1 - \epsilon)^2 \rho_\infty U}{\epsilon^2 R_s^2} R^2 \sin^2 \vartheta.$$

From (4.4.3) we note that $\psi$ should be of the form of $\sin^2 \vartheta$ times a function of $R$, and we find that the general solution of (4.4.5) of this form exists and may be expressed

$$(4.4.6) \qquad \psi = \frac{\rho_\infty U R_s^2 \sin^2 \vartheta}{30\epsilon^2} \left[ 3(1 - \epsilon)^2 \left(\frac{R}{R_s}\right)^4 + A \left(\frac{R}{R_s}\right)^2 + B \left(\frac{R_s}{R}\right) \right].$$

Evaluation of the constants $A$ and $B$ using (4.4.3) and the condition that the tangential component of velocity $U \sin \vartheta$ is continuous across the shock gives

$$(4.4.7a) \qquad\qquad A = -5(1 - 4\epsilon),$$

$$(4.4.7b) \qquad\qquad B = 2(1 - \epsilon)(1 - 6\epsilon).$$

The boundary condition which determines the location of the body is that $\psi = 0$, and this yields a spherical body of radius $R_b$, with

$$(4.4.8) \quad 3(1 - \epsilon)^2 \left(\frac{R_b}{R_s}\right)^4 - 5(1 - 4\epsilon) \left(\frac{R_b}{R_s}\right)^2 + 2(1 - \epsilon)(1 - 6\epsilon) \left(\frac{R_s}{R_b}\right) = 0.$$

This equation is a quintic in $R_b/R_s$ for which a closed form solution is not available; a numerical solution is given in Fig. 6–10. Equation (4.4.8) is a quadratic equation for $\epsilon$, and so may be solved explicitly for $\epsilon$ in terms of $R_b/R_s$. An approximate solution with $\epsilon$ small is

$$(4.4.9) \qquad \Delta = R_s - R_b = \epsilon R_s \left[ 1 - \sqrt{\frac{8\epsilon}{3}} + 3\epsilon + O(\epsilon^{3/2}) \right],$$

which agrees with the result of Chester [2] to the first two terms; Chester obtains 2.6 for the coefficient of the third term. As with the cylinder, we shall compare these solutions after obtaining the density correction. The Newtonian solution (3.5.3) gives us the first term in (4.4.9), but no more. The pressure may be expressed in an equation analogous to (4.3.15) as

$$(4.4.10) \quad \tfrac{1}{2} C_p = (1 - \tfrac{1}{2}\epsilon) + \frac{(1 - \epsilon)^2}{\epsilon \rho_\infty U R_s^2} \psi - \frac{\epsilon}{2\rho_\infty^2 U^2 R^2 \sin^2 \vartheta} \left( \psi_R^2 + \frac{1}{R^2} \psi_\vartheta^2 \right).$$

On the body W. B. Bush (private communication) and N. H. Kemp (private communication) obtain the approximate result

$$(4.4.11) \quad \tfrac{1}{2} C_{p_b} = (1 - \tfrac{1}{2}\epsilon) - \tfrac{4}{3} \sin^2 \vartheta \left[ 1 + \tfrac{1}{4}\epsilon - \tfrac{2}{3} \sqrt{\frac{8}{3}} \, \epsilon^{3/2} + O(\epsilon^2) \right]$$

by a suitable but laborious expansion. Regardless of the value of $\epsilon$, with $\sin \vartheta$ sufficiently large, the pressure coefficient is negative on and near the body.

As with the analogous solution for the circular cylinder, this solution of

Lighthill is only valid with $\epsilon$ small and for a local region in the vicinity of the stagnation point. Only the first two terms (to order $R_s \epsilon^{3/2}$) in (4.4.9) may be justifiably retained. As with the cylinder, the solution is instructive and has intrinsic interest. We turn now to the local solution of the type obtained for the circular cylinder. The same coordinate system is used, except that now the Stokes stream function is replaced by the quantity $\frac{1}{2}\rho_\infty U x^2$. The quantity $x$ is essentially the same as $R_s \sin \vartheta$ of (4.4.3).

The Newtonian pressure is again obtained from the variant of (3.2.7) analogous to (3.5.19), with the aid of (3.3.3) and (3.5.1), and is

$$(4.4.12) \qquad \tfrac{1}{2}C_p = 1 - \frac{x_1^2}{R_s^2} - \frac{1}{3x_1 R_s^2}(x_1^3 - x^3).$$

Again, $x_1$ is the coordinate of the point being investigated and $x$ is the coordinate at entry of the streamline of interest. It can be shown that the term $x^3$ in (4.4.12) may be replaced by $x_1 x^2$ or may be dropped without affecting the principal results and with but a small error in terms of higher order. We choose to replace $x^3$ by $x_1 x^2$ to simplify the form of the expressions for $u$ and $v$, and obtain in place of (4.4.12)

$$(4.4.13) \qquad \tfrac{1}{2}C_p = 1 - \frac{x_1^2}{R_s^2} - \frac{1}{3R_s^2}(x_1^2 - x^2)$$

in a form similar to (4.3.18). Application of Bernoulli's equation as before gives us for the tangential velocity component $Uu$ (essentially the same $u$ as in (4.4.2)) the result

$$(4.4.14) \qquad u = \frac{1}{R_s}\sqrt{x^2 + \frac{8\epsilon}{3}(x_1^2 - x^2)}$$

in place of (4.3.20). The vertical scale may now be calculated, with the result

$$(4.4.15) \quad y = \epsilon \int_0^{} \frac{x\,dx}{x_1 u} = \frac{\epsilon R_s}{x_1\left(1 - \dfrac{8\epsilon}{3}\right)}\left[\sqrt{x^2 + \frac{8\epsilon}{3}(x_1^2 - x^2)} - \sqrt{\frac{8\epsilon}{3}}\,x_1\right],$$

analogous to (4.3.21). The stand-off distance is the value of $y$ at $x = x_1$, or

$$(4.4.16) \qquad \Delta_0 = \frac{\epsilon R_s}{1 + \sqrt{\dfrac{8\epsilon}{3}}},$$

analogous to (4.3.22). If we expand $\Delta_0$ in a power series in $\epsilon^{1/2}$, we obtain

$$(4.4.17) \qquad \Delta_0 = \epsilon R_s\left[1 - \sqrt{\frac{8\epsilon}{3}} + \frac{8}{3}\epsilon + O(\epsilon^{3/2})\right],$$

which may be compared with (4.4.9) and is analogous to (4.3.23). The third term, the one in $R_s \epsilon^2$, is in error for two reasons. First, it is in error because of the approximations involved in our simplified coordinate system, and second, because of the approximation made in getting (4.4.13). This term cannot be justifiably retained anyway in a constant-density analysis.

The distribution of $u$ is given by

$$(4.4.18) \qquad u = \sqrt{\frac{8\epsilon}{3}} \frac{x_1}{R_s} \left[ \frac{\kappa y}{\epsilon R_s} + 1 \right],$$

where

$$(4.4.19) \qquad \kappa = \frac{1 - \dfrac{8\epsilon}{3}}{\sqrt{\dfrac{8\epsilon}{3}}},$$

and the velocity gradient on the body is $\sqrt{8\epsilon/3}\, R_s^{-1} U$. The corresponding distribution of the normal velocity component $Uv$ (essentially the same $v$ as in (4.4.1)) is obtained through a cylindrical continuity equation in $x$ and $y$, and is

$$(4.4.20) \qquad v = -\sqrt{\frac{8\epsilon}{3}} \frac{y}{R_s} \left[ \frac{\kappa y}{\epsilon R_s} + 2 \right] = -\epsilon \frac{x^2}{x_1^2}.$$

The pressure distribution is

$$(4.4.21) \qquad \tfrac{1}{2} C_p = 1 - \tfrac{1}{2}\epsilon \left( 1 + \frac{x^4}{x_1^4} \right) - \frac{x_1^2}{3R_s^2} \left( 4 - \frac{x^3}{x_1^3} \right),$$

with $x/x_1$ obtainable as a function of $y$ from (4.4.20). Again, (4.4.21) satisfies the dynamic equations approximately, and is consistent with (4.4.11).

An approximate analysis similar to that given above was given by Hayes [2], neglecting the centrifugal correction to the Newtonian pressure distribution, and the results of Hayes were rederived by Li and Geiger [1] using a different approach, the one mentioned in the last section using a stream function. In these analyses the number 4 appeared wherever 3 does in equations (4.4.14) through (4.4.20). As with the circular cylinder, the centrifugal corrections to the pressure should not be neglected and these earlier analyses are in error on this point. The correct factor 3 appeared first in the results of Chester [2].

In general, the same comments that we made on the extent of validity of the results for the circular cylinder apply with equal force for the sphere. However, we should point out an essential difference between the two-dimensional and the axisymmetric blunt body problems. In the two-dimensional case the Newtonian solution was divergent, and we obtained a reasonable solution for shock layer structure and stand-off distance only in our constant-density solution in which the fluid acceleration is taken into account. In the axisymmetric case the Newtonian solution gives a first approximation to the structure of the shock layer, and a stand-off distance corresponding to the first term in (4.4.9) or (4.4.17). The meaning of this distinction will be discussed further in Section 5.4.

Again, unpublished results of Bush and the solution of Chester [2] indicate that the results of (4.4.9) and (4.4.17) are generally correct to two terms, including the effect of compressibility, of nonconstant $\epsilon$, and of nonsphericity of the shock. The third term is influenced by the density correction.

For the density correction to the stand-off distance we again use (4.2.32), and calculate the pressure on the axis from (4.4.21). However, instead of using $x^2/x_1^2$ directly from (4.4.20) we first carry out a limiting process $\epsilon \to 0$ and obtain from (4.4.20)

$$(4.4.22) \qquad \frac{x^2}{x_1^2} = \left(\frac{y}{\Delta_{CD}}\right)^2.$$

An analysis based on (4.4.20) as it stands gives us the same leading term in $\chi$, which is the only one of interest to us. The integrand of (4.2.32) is then

$$(4.4.23) \qquad \frac{p - p_s}{p_s} = \tfrac{1}{2}\epsilon\left[1 - \left(\frac{y}{\Delta_{CD}}\right)^4\right],$$

and $\chi$ is evaluated as

$$(4.4.24) \qquad \chi = \frac{2\epsilon}{5\gamma_s}.$$

Applying the correction $1 - \chi$ to the complete constant-density result (4.4.9) with $\gamma_s - 1$ assumed to be of order $\epsilon$, we obtain

$$(4.4.25) \qquad \Delta_0 = \epsilon R_s\left[1 - \sqrt{\frac{8\epsilon}{3}} + 2.6\epsilon + O(\epsilon^{3/2})\right],$$

in complete agreement with Chester to terms of order $\epsilon^2$. We infer that (4.4.25) should be a general result for all rounded blunt axisymmetric bodies, provided $\gamma_s - 1$ is of order $\epsilon^{1/2}$ or less. The terms of higher order are affected both by variations in the density ratio $\epsilon$ along the shock and by nonsphericity of the shock.

## 5. Solutions with cross flow

Within the limitations inherent in the constant-density approximation, we may seek for constant-density solutions for problems with cross flow. The approach we need is very like the approach we used for Newtonian solutions with cross flow. However, we must now include the influence of the pressure field on the trajectory as well as on the velocity of a fluid particle. Following the alternate approximate constant-density approach used in the last two sections, we use the pressure distribution from the Newtonian theory for this purpose. The additional complexity prevents us from finding analytical solutions in closed form except in trivial cases, but the procedures involved are straightforward and we can readily obtain a number of solutions with numerical quadratures.

To exemplify the method we present here the constant-density solution for a general stagnation point flow, for which we have already obtained the Newtonian solution. We shall take advantage of the fact that the Newtonian pressure we shall use, (3.6.34) and (3.6.35), is the sum of a function of $x$ and a function of $y$. Since the value of $u = q_x$ upon entry from (3.6.26) and the pressure gradient in the $x$ direction are independent of $y$, $u$ will remain independent of $y$, and we can calculate $u$ from a one-dimensional Bernoulli equation. The result obtained, analogous to (4.3.20) and (4.4.14), is

$$(4.5.1) \qquad u = K_1\sqrt{x^2 + 2\epsilon(1 + \pi_1)(x_1^2 - x^2)},$$

with $x_1$ the coordinate of the point investigated and $x$ the coordinate at entry of a streamline. In a similar way we may obtain an expression for the other dimensionless tangential velocity component $v = q_y$,

$$(4.5.2) \qquad v = K_2\sqrt{y^2 + 2\epsilon(1 + \pi_2)(y_1^2 - y^2)}.$$

The quantities $\pi_1$ and $\pi_2$ are pressure correction terms from the Newtonian analysis. The accuracy of these expressions is about the same as that of (4.4.14) for our approximate solution for a blunt body of revolution. The quantities $K_1$ and $K_2$ are the principal curvatures of the shock, and are not generally the same as those of the body.

The particle trajectories are the integral curves of the equation

$$(4.5.3) \qquad \frac{dx_1}{u} = \frac{dy_1}{v},$$

with the coordinates $x$ and $y$ of the point of entry kept fixed. The result of this integration is the equation for the particle trajectories,

$$(4.5.4) \qquad \frac{1}{K_1\sqrt{2\epsilon(1 + \pi_1)}}\left[\sinh^{-1}\frac{\alpha_1 x_1}{x} - \sinh^{-1}\alpha_1\right] =$$

$$\frac{1}{K_2\sqrt{2\epsilon(1 + \pi_2)}}\left[\sinh^{-1}\frac{\alpha_2 y_1}{y} - \sinh^{-1}\alpha_2\right],$$

where the parameters $\alpha_1$ and $\alpha_2$ are defined as

$$(4.5.5a) \qquad \alpha_1 = \sqrt{\frac{2\epsilon(1 + \pi_1)}{1 - 2\epsilon(1 + \pi_1)}},$$

$$(4.5.5b) \qquad \alpha_2 = \sqrt{\frac{2\epsilon(1 + \pi_2)}{1 - 2\epsilon(1 + \pi_2)}}.$$

As in the Newtonian theory the locus of entering streamlines for a point is given by (4.5.4) with $x_1$ and $y_1$ fixed and $x$ and $y$ considered the variables.

The quantity $m$ of Newtonian theory is replaced by $\epsilon^{-1}z$ in our constant-density theory, with $z$ distance normal to the body in this case. Using the same reasoning as for the Newtonian analysis and in complete analogy with (4.3.21) and (4.4.15), we obtain

$$(4.5.6) \qquad \epsilon^{-1}z = \int_0^{} \frac{y\,dx}{y_1 u} = \int_0^{} \frac{x\,dy}{x_1 v}.$$

The derivative of this expression may be looked upon as a differential equation for the locus of entering streamlines, and (4.5.4) can be obtained with this alternate approach. To calculate the stand-off distance, we must carry out the integral (4.5.6) over the entire range of integration, for example from $x = 0$ to $x = x_1$ in the first integral. The result is

$$(4.5.7) \qquad \Delta_0 =$$

$$\frac{\epsilon \alpha_2}{K_1 \sqrt{1 - 2\epsilon(1 + \pi_1)}} \int_{x=0}^{x=x_1} \frac{d \sinh^{-1}\left(\dfrac{x}{\alpha_1 x_1}\right)}{\sinh\left(\sinh^{-1} \alpha_2 + \mathscr{K} \sinh^{-1}\dfrac{\alpha_1 x_1}{x} - \mathscr{K} \sinh^{-1} \alpha_1\right)}$$

expressed as a Stieltjes integral, where the parameter $\mathscr{K}$

$$(4.5.8) \qquad \mathscr{K} = \frac{K_2 \sqrt{1 + \pi_2}}{K_1 \sqrt{1 + \pi_1}} = \frac{\sqrt{1 + \pi_2}}{\kappa \sqrt{1 + \pi_1}}$$

is a function of the parameter $\kappa$ of the Newtonian analysis alone. A transformation of variables changes the integral of (4.5.7) to

$$(4.5.9) \qquad \Delta_0 =$$

$$\frac{\epsilon \alpha_2}{K_1 \sqrt{1 - 2\epsilon(1 + \pi_1)}} \int_{\sinh^{-1}\alpha_1}^{\infty} \frac{d\xi}{\sinh \xi \sinh (\sinh^{-1} \alpha_2 + \mathscr{K}\xi - \mathscr{K} \sinh^{-1} \alpha_1)}.$$

Except for the special cases already considered we must obtain $\Delta_0$ from (4.5.7) or (4.5.9) through a numerical quadrature. The evaluation of the corresponding indefinite integral is necessary for the establishment of a vertical scale. For example, we may integrate (4.5.7) from $x = 0$ only to $x$ to obtain the quantity $z(x, x_1)$. This function inverted gives $x(z, x_1)$. The velocity $u$ of (4.5.1) may then be expressed as $u(z, x_1)$, as a velocity profile. We may do the same with $v(z, y_1)$, calculate $\partial w/\partial z$ from the equation of continuity, and obtain the normal velocity profile $w(z)$ by a quadrature.

In general, the comments we have made for the corresponding two-dimensional and axisymmetric constant-density solutions for stagnation point regions apply for the solution we have just obtained. The second derivatives of $\Delta$ are undetermined and the body curvature is unspecified within this approximate theory. In fact, unless the body is suitably symmetric, we have no assurance that even the principal axes of curvature are the same for the body surface as for the shock. The most important limitation in the accuracy of the results probably lies in the effect of compressibility. And the remarks we made at the end of Section 4.3 on other types of stagnation point solutions also apply here; it is clear that the calculational difficulties in some of these problems may be formidable.

Before a calculation of the density correction would be worthwhile, it would be necessary for us to improve our constant-density analysis to take account of the errors inherent in our approximate analysis. The sources of error include the approximations made in the simplified coordinate system and the approximations made in establishing the equations for the velocity components (4.5.1) and (4.5.2).

# CHAPTER V

# THE THEORY OF THIN SHOCK LAYERS

## 1. Basic concepts

The methods given in the last two sections are generally inadequate for the calculation of a sufficiently good approximation to the flow field in the shock layer on a blunt body. Although the Newtonian theory gives us a valuable conceptual picture of phenomena in a thin shock layer, its estimate of velocities and pressures is too rough to be satisfactory in engineering practice, and its anomalies are unrealistic and also unacceptable in practice. The improvement afforded by the constant-density solutions is limited in scope and validity, and an improvement of Newtonian theory adequate for most purposes cannot be based upon the assumption of constant density.

In order to utilize the information gained from the other methods, however, we must assume that the shock layer is thin and take advantage of this assumption in our analysis. With the shock layer thin the shape of the shock wave cannot be greatly different from the shape of the body; and the pressure on the body is determined primarily by the shock shape. In order that the shock layer be thin we must be able to make assumption D, that the density ratio $\epsilon$ across the shock be small compared with one. This assumption on the behavior of the fluid is appreciably weaker than the assumption required for Newtonian theory, but still puts some limitation on the validity of the resulting development.

Some investigators who have based their work on a shock layer which is thin have used the assumption that the fluid is a perfect gas with constant ratio of specific heats $\gamma$ which is close to one. In practice reasonably small values of the density ratio $\epsilon$ are only obtainable with gases which depart significantly from the perfect gas laws, and it is preferable to postulate a fluid obeying a general equation of state. The greater generality that we gain thereby in our development is at little or no expense in conceptual or analytical simplicity.

Although the concepts of the theory of thin shock layers apply to steady flows with cross flow and to unsteady flows with a direct extension of the methods of the last two sections, it does not appear worth while to attempt here the development of such a general theory. The difficulties in such a generalization are more calculational than conceptual, provided we may accept as understood the corresponding concepts in Newtonian theory with

166

the modifications needed for constant-density solutions. We shall limit our attention here to steady two-dimensional and axisymmetric flows, and concentrate on the new concepts which arise in a study of these relatively simpler flows.

The basic problem considered may be one of several types, of which we shall list three. Our attention will be focused principally on the first two types, termed the "inverse problem" and the "direct problem." But we include the "pressure problem" primarily to make it clear that the problems of interest are not necessarily limited to those of the first two types. The problem types considered are:

*Inverse Problem* (*Shock Given*). The shape of the shock wave is given, and it is required to find the corresponding shape of the body and the pressures on this body.

*Direct Problem* (*Body Given*). The shape of the body is given, and it is required to find the shape of the shock wave and the pressures on the body.

*Pressure Problem* (*Pressure Given*). The pressure on the body is given as a function of distance from the stagnation point, and it is required to find the corresponding body shape and shock shape.

In any of these problems information about the structure of the shock layer (pressures, densities, and velocities) may or may not be required, but is normally available as part of the results of the problem solution. The direct problem may be considered the problem normally met with in practice, while the pressure problem may arise when it is desirable to control the behavior of the viscous boundary layer in some manner. The inverse problem does not appear directly as a design problem, but has a physical simplicity which the others do not have. If the shock shape is given, so also are all components of the velocity and the thermodynamic state of the fluid behind the shock. In fact, certain mathematical difficulties appear in the inverse problem because the quantities behind the shock are so completely specified (see Section 6.5).

With the shock layer very thin, there is a close correspondence between the shock shape and the body shape, and in the Newtonian limit the two shapes coincide in an unseparated flow. With the shock layer not so thin, we find that a relatively large change of small wavelength in the body shape corresponds to a small change in the shock shape. This insensitiveness of the shock shape to changes in the body shape, discussed in more detail in Section 6.5, is related to the fact that the shock shape in front of a body in a hypersonic flow (or supersonic) flow may not be chosen arbitrarily, but must satisfy certain restrictions. Qualitatively speaking, the shock shape must be smooth. It is probably necessary that the shock shape be analytic except at special singular points, if the pertinent equations of state of the fluid are analytic.

The coordinate system used in an investigation of the hypersonic flow around a blunt body may be cartesian or cylindrical. Various authors have used these straightforward systems with success. Our principle of taking advantage of the thinness of the shock layer leads naturally to a different type of coordinate system, generally designated as of the boundary layer type. In a coordinate system of this type, the two coordinates are chosen to correspond to distances along the layer and across the layer, respectively. Fig. 5–1 depicts the coordinate system we shall use.

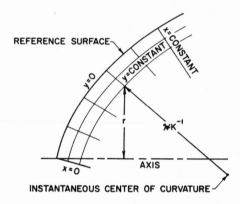

FIG. 5–1. Coordinate system of the boundary layer type.

To serve as a basis for our coordinate system a reference surface is chosen, generally either the shock surface or the body surface. This surface must be smooth, by which we mean that the surface must have a finite curvature at every point except perhaps at a leading edge, and that this curvature must be continuous. The coordinate $x$ is defined on the surface as distance on the surface from the leading edge or stagnation point for the portion of the shock layer investigated. For the coordinate system as a whole we set $x$ constant on the straight lines normal to the surface. The coordinate $y$ is distance from the surface along one of these normals, defined as positive in the direction toward the body from the shock (the purpose of this choice of direction is to make the corresponding velocity components positive at the shock). The surfaces of constant $y$ form with the reference surface a family of parallel surfaces (or geodesic parallels) as defined in standard texts on differential geometry. The curvature of the reference surface is denoted $K(x)$, defined as positive when the surface is concave on the side of positive $y$. The curvature of any of the other surfaces of constant $y$ is $\mathscr{H}^{-1}K$, where

(5.1.1)                    $$\mathscr{H} = 1 - Ky.$$

The domain within which we may use the coordinate system is limited by the requirement that $\mathscr{H}$ be always positive (see Fig. 5–1).

We now have a coordinate system which is orthogonal and generally left-handed, and for which the metric is

$$(5.1.2) \qquad ds^2 = \mathscr{H}^2 \, dx^2 + dy^2.$$

Thus $x$ corresponds to distance only at the reference surface, for which $\mathscr{H} = 1$. For axisymmetric problems we need also the distance from the axis $r(x, y)$. If the angle of incidence of the surface is $\sigma(x)$ (if the reference surface is the shock surface), the quantity $r$ has the form

$$(5.1.3) \qquad r(x, y) = \int \sin \sigma \, dx - y \cos \sigma.$$

The curvature in this case is given by

$$(5.1.4) \qquad K(x) = - \frac{d\sigma}{dx},$$

and $r$ from (5.1.3) satisfies the equation

$$(5.1.5) \qquad dr = \sin \sigma \mathscr{H} \, dx - \cos \sigma \, dy.$$

If the surface is the body surface, (5.1.3) to (5.1.5) are still valid with $\theta_b$ in place of $\sigma$.

The component of the velocity in the $x$ direction is denoted $u$, and the component in the $y$ direction is denoted $v$. The equations of motion in our coordinate system are

$$(5.1.6a) \qquad \frac{\partial r^j \rho u}{\partial x} + \frac{\partial \mathscr{H} r^j \rho v}{\partial y} = 0,$$

$$(5.1.6b) \qquad u \frac{\partial u}{\partial x} + \mathscr{H} v \frac{\partial u}{\partial y} - Kuv + \frac{1}{\rho} \frac{\partial p}{\partial x} = 0,$$

$$(5.1.6c) \qquad u \frac{\partial v}{\partial x} + \mathscr{H} v \frac{\partial v}{\partial y} + Ku^2 + \frac{\mathscr{H}}{\rho} \frac{\partial p}{\partial y} = 0,$$

$$(5.1.7) \qquad u \frac{\partial S}{\partial x} + \mathscr{H} v \frac{\partial S}{\partial y} = 0,$$

in which the entropy equation (5.1.7) is used in place of the energy equation.

A transformation which is convenient for many purposes replaces the normal coordinate $y$ by a stream function $\psi$ but does not change the dependent variables. Such a transformation is called a von Mises transformation after the well known transformation of boundary layer theory. We define $\psi$ in terms of its partial derivatives

$$(5.1.8a) \qquad \psi_x = \mathscr{H} r^j \rho v,$$

$$(5.1.8b) \qquad \psi_y = -r^j \rho u;$$

the existence of such a quantity is ensured by the continuity equation (5.1.6a). In changing to the new coordinate system $(x, \psi)$ there is no possibility of confusion in partial derivatives with respect to $y$ or $\psi$, as they are both taken with $x$ constant. In order to distinguish clearly between partial derivatives with respect to $x$ taken with $y$ constant and with $\psi$ constant, we shall reserve the usual notation for the former and introduce the notation

$$(5.1.9) \qquad \frac{D}{Dx} = \left(\frac{\partial}{\partial x}\right)_{\psi} = \frac{\partial}{\partial x} + \mathscr{H}\frac{v}{u}\frac{\partial}{\partial y}$$

for the latter.

In the new coordinate system with the variable $y$ eliminated, (5.1.7) and a suitable combination of (5.1.6b) and (5.1.6c) become (assuming $u$ not equal to zero)

$$(5.1.10) \qquad \frac{DS}{Dx} = 0,$$

$$(5.1.11) \qquad \frac{D}{Dx}\left[\tfrac{1}{2}(u^2 + v^2)\right] + \frac{1}{\rho}\frac{Dp}{Dx} = \frac{D}{Dx}\left(h + \tfrac{1}{2}q^2\right) = 0.$$

These two equations are immediately recognizable as stating that the entropy and total enthalpy are constant along streamlines. Since the total enthalpy is constant across the shock and thus across the entire flow field we shall use that fact in place of (5.1.11). And (5.1.10) will be automatically taken care of by requiring the entropy to be a function $S(\psi)$ of the stream function alone.

Equation (5.1.6c) becomes

$$(5.1.12) \qquad \mathscr{H}r^j\frac{\partial p}{\partial \psi} = \frac{Dv}{Dx} + Ku,$$

which gives pressure changes across streamlines. Equation (5.1.6a) may be put into alternative forms

$$(5.1.13a) \qquad \mathscr{H}\frac{\partial\left(\dfrac{v}{u}\right)}{\partial \psi} + \frac{D\left(\dfrac{1}{r^j\rho u}\right)}{Dx} + \left(\frac{1}{r^j\rho u}\right)\left(\frac{v}{u}\right)K = 0,$$

$$(5.1.13b) \qquad \frac{\partial\left(\mathscr{H}r^j\dfrac{v}{u}\right)}{\partial \psi} + \frac{D\left(\dfrac{1}{\rho u}\right)}{Dx} - j\mathscr{H}\sin\,\sigma\left(\frac{1}{r}\right)\left(\frac{1}{\rho u}\right) = 0,$$

in which the $\sigma$ in the third term of (5.1.13b) indicates that the reference surface is the shock, and is to be replaced by $\theta_b$ if the body surface is used. The quantity $(r^j\rho u)^{-1}$ is proportional to the width of a streamtube measured on an $x = constant$ section, while $v/u$ is the tangent of the inclination angle of a streamline relative to the coordinate system. Equations (5.1.13) express a geometric relation between these quantities.

Provided the shock layer is very thin and the reference surface is suitably chosen we may expect that the velocity component $v$ should be much smaller than $u$ over most of the range of the solution. However, in certain regions this is not true, particularly in the immediate neighborhood of a stagnation point. Where it is true, we may note that $Dv/Dx$ in (5.1.12) is of smaller order of magnitude than is $Ku$, and the quantity $v/u$ in (5.1.13) is small compared with one. This result, that certain quantities are small, is one of the reasons for choosing a coordinate system of the boundary layer type.

So far, we have said little about the choice of reference surface. The only choices considered will be the two obvious ones, the shock surface and the body surface. A coordinate system of the boundary layer type with the reference surface on the shock wave is termed a "shock-oriented" coordinate system. Analogously a system with the reference surface on the body surface is termed a "body-oriented" coordinate system.

It is clear that there is a natural relation between the problem set the investigator and the choice of coordinate system. With the inverse problem (shock given), for example, the shock-oriented coordinate system does not depend upon the solution to the problem. With the pressure problem (pressure given), of course, neither coordinate system may be fixed beforehand.

There is an undisputable advantage in being able to fix the coordinate system for a problem before solving the problem. However, it is not necessary to do so, and we may attack the inverse problem with a body-oriented coordinate system or the direct problem with a shock-oriented coordinate system. If we put this factor aside, we may note that, intrinsically, a shock-oriented system has certain advantages over a body-oriented system. Probably the principal one of these is that the shock surface is smoother than is the body surface, as we have noted above in discussing the insensitiveness of the shock shape to small changes in the body shape. In addition, certain of the equations involved may appear in simpler form with shock orientation. In the case of the direct problem, these intrinsic advantages of shock orientation may outweigh the one of being able to fix the coordinate system in advance. Alternatively, we could choose a system which roughly approximates the shock shape, but is fixed. Thereby, we would have a fixed coordinate system with some of the intrinsic advantages of a shock-oriented system.

In attacking the inverse problem a direct "marching-ahead" method is available; this approach and its intrinsic difficulties are considered in Section 6.5. The general approach for the problems of interest which we shall consider here is that of successive approximations. Successive approximation schemes may be of many types, ranging from relaxation methods applied to the differential equations of motion to integral methods employing integral relations analogous to those well known in boundary layer theory or employing direct quadratures as part of the scheme. Successive approximation schemes are considered in the following section, and other related methods are reported in Chapter VI.

We close this section with a brief discussion of the physical nature of the direct problem, with the body shape given. The shock surface, the location of which is unknown, is a free surface in a sense closely analogous to that of classical water-wave or channel-flow theory. The existence of such a free surface suggests an analogy between our hypersonic blunt-body problem and

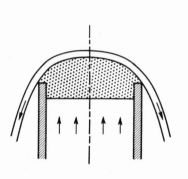

FIG. 5–2. Artesian-well analogy.        FIG. 5–3. Shower-bath analogy.

the general hydraulic problem of an inviscid constant-density fluid under gravity with a free surface. We note that with the density ratio very small, the density outside the free surface in the hypersonic case is negligible compared to that inside the surface, as is the case in the usual hydraulic problem. And in both problems there is a continuous supply of unidirectional momentum to the fluid, from the free stream in the hypersonic case and from gravity in the hydraulic case.

The correctness of this analogy stops with the similarities mentioned above. The momentum flux per unit area in the hydraulic case is proportional to the depth of the layer rather than constant, and is distributed to the fluid uniformly through the layer instead of being concentrated at a shock surface. Also, the hypersonic flow is rotational and is not strictly at constant density. Nevertheless, an analogy does exist which has a limited qualitative correctness, and which is useful conceptually.

In hydraulic shallow-water theory there is a critical velocity equal to $\sqrt{gh}$, where $h$ is the depth of the fluid and $g$ the acceleration due to gravity, which corresponds to the propagation velocity of weak disturbances. In the elementary theory given in Section 5.3 for blunt bodies of revolution there is a critical point at which the (steady) velocity of the flow in the thin shock layer immediately behind the shock is $\sqrt{\epsilon}U$. It may be noted that in both cases the square of the critical velocity times the fluid density is equal to the momentum flux per unit area. In either problem, the critical velocity disappears as a fundamental phenomenon in a more accurate theory.

Two figures are given to illustrate the analogy. Figure 5–2 depicts the "Artesian-well" analogy, in which the water flow under gravity over a blunt shape is likened to a hypersonic flow. The water is considered to come from a pipe through a porous block of appropriate shape. Figure 5–3 depicts the "Shower-bath" analogy, which differs from the analogy discussed before in several respects. The water is supplied from a unidirectional flow of small droplets from a shower head, and the principal part of the momentum can come from this flow. This second analogy would avoid several of the weaknesses of the direct hydraulic or artesian-well analogy. Certain practical difficulties may arise in setting up laboratory models for these analogies, principally that of finding a suitable porous material and that of avoiding excessive splashing in the shower bath.

## 2. Successive approximation schemes

The small-density-ratio assumption (D) is not essential for the application of a successive approximation scheme to the calculation of a hypersonic flow (see Sections 6.2 to 6.4). However, the Newtonian theory gives in most cases a solution for zero density ratio which may be used as a zeroth approximation, and an attack based upon improvement of the Newtonian results appears logical and attractive if the density ratio is small. A number of authors have obtained a first approximation according to a successive approximation scheme, including Hayes [3; 4], Chester [1; 2], Freeman [1], Fraenkel [1], Chernyi [1], and Cole [1]. It is of interest to note that the investigations of each of the authors mentioned were carried out independently and apparently without knowledge of the work of the others.

All these authors considered both two-dimensional and axisymmetric flow, and all except Chester considered the direct problem (body given) with a general body shape. The shapes considered by Fraenkel and Chernyi are restricted to those with shock waves attached on a leading edge, while Cole's analysis is devoted to slender bodies for which the small-disturbance theory discussed in Chapter II is available. Chester considered a special case of the inverse problem with a shock of parabolic shape, and carried out the analytic solution to a high order of approximation. All the authors except Hayes and Freeman limited their investigations to a perfect gas. Chester and Cole used cartesian and cylindrical coordinate systems, while the others used systems of the boundary layer type.  Freeman, Fraenkel, and Chernyi used body orientation, while Hayes considered both types of orientation.  Chester, Freeman, Fraenkel, and Chernyi used the von Mises transformation in their analyses.

We shall not attempt to present individually the methods of these authors, or of later ones such as Maslen and Moeckel [1] (Integral Method).  Instead we shall outline a general successive approximation scheme which combines various features of all these contributions, which is a representative composite emphasizing the philosophy of the general approach.  Five basic relations besides the shock relations are needed.  One of these is the constancy of total enthalpy (5.1.11), restated as

$$(5.2.1) \qquad\qquad h + \tfrac{1}{2}q^2 = h_\infty + \tfrac{1}{2}U^2 = H.$$

The second is the constancy of entropy along a streamline (5.1.10) indicated by its functional form

$$(5.2.2) \qquad\qquad S = S(\psi).$$

The third is an equation for the pressure gradient across streamlines, for which we may use (5.1.12).  The fourth is an equation derived from the continuity equation which relates the streamline inclination with a measure of the mass flow.  Such an equation is either of (5.1.13), with $v/u$ describing the streamline inclination and $\rho u$ the mass flow.  The fifth is the equation of state of the fluid material, which we need in the form

$$(5.2.3) \qquad\qquad h = h(p, S).$$

The density of the fluid is also needed, and may be obtained from (5.2.3) by the relation

$$(5.2.4) \qquad\qquad \frac{1}{\rho} = \left(\frac{\partial h}{\partial p}\right)_S.$$

A number of subsidiary relations are needed, including (5.1.1), (5.1.4), and (5.1.8), and, with axisymmetric problems, (5.1.3) and (5.1.5).  The pressure, entropy, and streamline inclination as a function of a shock angle $\sigma$ must be available, and are obtainable from the shock relations given in Chapter I and the equation of state.

We shall divide our successive approximation scheme into two principal stages, with the first stage starting with a given shock shape.  In the inverse problem (shock given) this shock shape is the correct one and with its associated shock-oriented coordinate system is the same for all approximations.  In the direct problem (body given) the shock shape is an approximate one based on the last approximation and, with the coordinate system if shock orientation is used, is different for each approximation as long as a correct solution has not been reached. With this distinction between the two problem types in mind, we may consider them together.

For the first stage, the quantities shock wave inclination $\sigma(x)$ and pressure difference from pressure behind the shock $p(x, \psi) - p_s(x)$ are given; these have been estimated from an earlier approximation. On the shock wave $\psi(x)$ is known, in fact is simply

$$(5.2.5) \qquad \psi_s = \frac{\rho_\infty r^{1+j}}{1+j},$$

where $r$ is the lateral cartesian coordinate in the two-dimensional case. From $\sigma(x)$ and the shock relations $p_s(x)$ and $S(\psi)$ are obtained. The quantity $p_s$ is added to the pressure difference $p(x, \psi) - p_s(x)$ to give the pressure

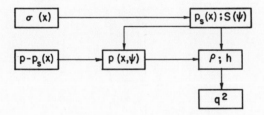

Fig. 5–4. First stage of successive approximation scheme.

$p(x, \psi)$. From the equation of state (5.2.3) are obtained $h(x, \psi)$ and $\rho(x, \psi)$. Finally $q^2(x, \psi) = u^2 + v^2$ is obtained from (5.2.1). This completes the first stage. A block diagram of this stage is shown in Fig. 5–4, in which the steps just described are shown as directed lines.

The second stage starts with the approximate functions $\rho(x, \psi)$ and $q^2(x, \psi)$ from the first stage, an approximation for $v(x, \psi)$ or $v/u$, and for axisymmetric flow an approximation for $r(x, \psi)$. The values of $v$ or $v/u$ are used to obtain $u(x, \psi)$ by the relation

$$(5.2.6) \qquad u = \sqrt{q^2 - v^2} = q\sqrt{1 - (v/u)^2}.$$

An equation for streamline inclination (5.1.13), which uses the quantities $\rho$, $u$, and $r^j$, is used to check the approximation given for $v$ or $v/u$ or to give new approximate values for the next approximation.

The quadrature of (5.1.8b)

$$(5.2.7) \qquad y = \int^{\psi_s} \frac{d\psi}{r^j \rho u}$$

on an $x = constant$ line then gives new approximate values for $r(x, \psi)$ in the axisymmetric case, and carried out across the whole layer gives the shock layer thickness

$$(5.2.8) \qquad \Delta = \int_0^{\psi_s} \frac{d\psi}{r^j \rho u} = y(x, 0).$$

This second stage has the property of generating the quantities needed for starting it, apart from $\rho$ and $q^2$. It may thus be repeated without an intervening application of the first stage in an attempt to obtain the flow

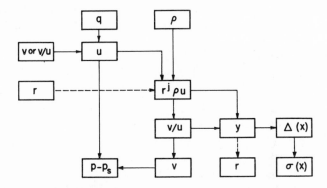

FIG. 5–5. Second stage of successive approximation scheme.

geometry consistent with the given functions $\rho(x, \psi)$ and $q^2(x, \psi)$. Finally, (5.1.12) is used to obtain a new approximation for the pressure difference $p(x, \psi) - p_s(x)$. This second stage is diagrammed in Fig. 5–5. Note that $v/u$ and $y$ are connected by the relation

$$(5.2.9) \qquad \frac{v}{u} = \frac{1}{\mathscr{H}} \left( \frac{\partial y}{\partial x} \right)_\psi = \frac{1}{\mathscr{H}} \frac{Dy}{Dx}.$$

The dashed lines in Fig. 5–5 indicate steps needed only in axisymmetric problems ($j = 1$).

In the inverse problem the resulting shock layer thickness $\Delta(x)$ gives the desired shape of the body. In the direct problem, with the body shape known, $\Delta(x)$ gives the shape of the shock, which in turn yields the function $\sigma(x)$ to be used in the next application of the first stage. The objective of the second stage is to determine the geometry corresponding to a given distribution of $\rho$ and $q^2$ as functions of $x$ and $\psi$. The interplay between the two stages has the objective of determining the pressure field and, in the direct problem, the shock shape.

If the body is blunt so that the shock is detached, there is a stagnation point on the body. In the immediate vicinity of this stagnation point lies a region of the shock layer within which our assumptions of orders of magnitude do not hold. In particular, not only is $v/u$ not much smaller than one here, but may be much larger than one in part of this stagnation region. We have no positive assurance that a successive approximation scheme of the type outlined above converges, and in the stagnation region the scheme as stated above undoubtedly diverges. A modification of the scheme is needed to take care of this region. Of the authors mentioned who considered problems with stagnation regions, Hayes depended on the constant-density solutions and on anticipated improvements on them for this region; Chester chose as dependent variables quantities for which his Newtonian zeroth approximation was a uniformly valid one as $\psi \to 0$; and Freeman obtained a first approximation without considering the stagnation region, then checked that his solution was consistent within this region.

The root of the difficulty lies in the problem character which is exploited by the boundary layer approach. This approach assumes that, with the solution established for smaller values of $x$ the solution may be continued along the layer to larger values of $x$. Away from the stagnation region the problem does indeed have such a quasiparabolic character if the shock layer is thin. But in the stagnation region the problem is fundamentally elliptic in character and not amenable to boundary layer treatment. With the shock shape given (the inverse problem), the solution may be obtained directly by the "marching-ahead" process discussed in Section 6.5. Thus Chester [1; 2] has no difficulty, in principle, in computing higher approximations for the inverse problems which he solves. A minor difficulty, existent but unimportant in Chester's problems, is that the coordinate system after the von Mises transformation is singular along the dividing streamline; this difficulty may be readily circumvented if necessary by using a different coordinate system locally.

With the direct problem (body given), the difficulty is more fundamental. The most obvious attack is to guess the shock shape, calculate by a "marching-ahead" process, find the corresponding body shape, and use the error in body shape as a guide in guessing a new shock shape. Another approach is to set up a scheme similar to that described above but based upon different assumptions as to what quantities are small. Account must be taken of the essential elliptic nature of the problem, with both components of the pressure gradient of equivalent importance, and with upstream influence in the shock layer important. An approach used by W. B. Bush (unpublished) uses the vorticity equation obtained by taking the curl of the momentum equation to obtain improvements over the constant-density solutions for this region.

An additional difficulty arises in the vicinity of the Newtonian separation point, the point at which the pressure on the body according to the Newtonian theory drops to zero. As this point is approached in a shock layer of finite thickness the layer thickens markedly and the boundary layer approach becomes invalid. This difficulty was noted and discussed by Freeman [1], who found that his successive approximation procedure diverged strongly near this singular point. In his first approximation the expression for the shock layer thickness approached infinity as this point was approached. This difficulty must be circumvented by abandoning the boundary layer approach and, as with the stagnation region, by shifting to an appropriate field approach. In the Newtonian separation region, however, the problem is generally hyperbolic rather than elliptic, and the appropriate approach is with the method of characteristics.

The flow in the shock layer of a blunt body is actually transonic, with a sonic line dividing subsonic and supersonic domains. Of the upstream-running characteristics leaving the sonic line there is a last one, termed the limiting characteristic. This divides the supersonic hyperbolic region into a region which is properly hyperbolic and one which is "transonic" or pseudo-elliptic, in which a disturbance has an influence in the elliptic region of the flow (see also Section 6.1). All the classical difficulties associated with rotational transonic flow thus appear here in principle. However, if the shock layer is very thin the influence of the free surface in a direct problem is predominant and more important than the influence of the sonic line. It is likely that the early approximations following a successive approximation scheme of the boundary layer type are not affected by any peculiar transonic behavior, but difficulty on this point may appear in higher approximations. It is not known whether such a scheme may be expected to converge or not in a transonic region.

So far we have said little about how to start our successive approximation scheme, about what we should use as our lowest-order approximation in a direct problem. The obvious choice with a thin shock layer is the Newtonian solution, with the shock shape the same as the body shape. The Newtonian theory gives $p(x, \psi)$ directly, with $v = 0$. This choice of a starting approximation is the one used by most authors. There are certain body shapes, however, for which the Newtonian solution is inappropriate for a lowest-order approximation. One such is a flat-faced strip or disc, for which no steady solution is obtainable from Newtonian theory. Another is a shape with a blunt wedge or conical nose such that the actual solution involves a detached shock wave. In such cases the approximate theories of the next two sections may be used to obtain a lowest-order approximation, or, alternatively, we may depend upon an "educated guess." Of course, the procedure of the next two sections may be used to obtain a starting approximation for a successive approximation procedure when the Newtonian approximation could have been used.

With the pressure problem (pressure given), the procedure is not much different from that used with the direct problem (body given). The second stage described above is used to obtain the quantity

$$(5.2.10) \qquad p_b - p_s = p(x, 0) - p_s(x),$$

which with the given value of $p_b$ gives a new value for $p_s(x)$. The relation between shock angle and pressure is applied backwards to obtain the new $\sigma(x)$ and, by integration, the shock shape if desired. The information needed to recommence the first stage is then available.

To illustrate the successive approximation approach let us consider the flow of a perfect gas with $\gamma - 1$ small on a body with a pointed nose at $M_\infty = \infty$. With the pointed nose we avoid the difficulties of the stagnation region, and with $M_\infty = \infty$ the quantity $\epsilon$ is constant. This example is a simplification of those treated by Freeman [1], Fraenkel [1], and Chernyi [1]. With this approach based on small $\epsilon$ the shock and body shapes are treated as identical for the first approximation, and no distinction between the direct and indirect problems appears until the second approximation is considered. We assume also that we do not have a shape which would lead to a detached free layer in the Newtonian theory within the region of interest.

The shock shape is assumed to be known (approximately the same as the body shape in the direct problem), and is specified in terms of the quantity $\cos \sigma$ as a function of the stream function $\psi$. In the lowest-order approximation $\epsilon$ is considered to be zero and the density in the shock layer infinite. Consistent with the assumption of infinite density the enthalpy $h$ is considered a function of the entropy $S$ alone, and hence $q$ is constant along each streamline. With these considerations the first stage is complete in this lowest-order approximation.

With infinite density the shock layer is infinitesimally thin and $v$ is zero everywhere. Thus we obtain the result $q = u$. The quantity $\Delta$ from (5.2.8) is zero because of the assumed infinite density. The pressure difference $p - p_s$ is given directly by the Newtonian theory. With this result the second stage is complete in the lowest-order approximation.

We thus start what we shall call the first approximation with the results of the Newtonian theory at our disposal. In calculating successive approximations we have a choice in procedure. We may at each stage use the complete equation of state in calculating $\rho$ and $h$, or we may use approximate expressions consistent with the level of approximation involved. The principal danger in the latter course lies in the stagnation or Newtonian separation regions, in which too coarse an approximation may preclude a convergent result. In addition, too coarse an approximation for the equation of state may unnecessarily slow down the convergence of the successive approximation scheme.

The pressure immediately behind the shock is expressed

(5.2.11) $$p_s = \rho_\infty U^2 \sin^2 \sigma,$$

with the factor $1 - \epsilon$ dropped. The pressure within the shock layer is given by the Newton-Busemann pressure law (3.2.7) as

(5.2.12) $$p = \rho_\infty U^2 \left[ \sin^2 \sigma_1 - \left( \frac{d \cos \sigma}{d\psi} \right)_1 \int_\psi^{\psi_1} \cos \sigma \, d\psi \right],$$

with the integral a function of its lower limit $\psi$ and with the subscript 1 used as in Chapters III and IV.

The density immediately behind the shock is $\rho_s = \rho_\infty/\epsilon$, where $\epsilon$ is given by (1.4.18) and is constant. The density within the layer is determined by the condition of constant entropy along a streamline, and may be expressed in terms of $p_s$ and $\rho_s$ for the same value of $\psi$ as

(5.2.13) $$\rho = \rho_s \left( \frac{p}{p_s} \right)^{\frac{1}{\gamma}} \approx \frac{\rho_s}{p_s} p \left( 1 - \frac{\gamma - 1}{\gamma} \ln \frac{p}{p_s} \right) \approx \frac{\rho_s}{p_s} p.$$

These approximate expressions are based on the assumption that $\gamma - 1$ is small. Which of the expressions is used depends upon the choice of the person carrying out the approximation.

The velocity $u$ is considered equal to $q$ and is determined by the constancy of total enthalpy. Thus we have

(5.2.14) $$u^2 = q^2 = u_s^2 + \frac{2\gamma}{\gamma - 1} \frac{p_s}{\rho_s} \left[ 1 - \left( \frac{p}{p_s} \right)^{\frac{\gamma-1}{\gamma}} \right] \approx u_s^2 + 2 \frac{p_s}{\rho_s} \ln \frac{p}{p_s} \approx u_s^2,$$

in terms of conditions at the point of entry of the streamline being considered. Again, there is a freedom of choice in the expression used.

With shock orientation we may calculate $y$ from (5.2.7) using (5.2.12) and the simplest expressions of (5.2.13) and (5.2.14). The result is the same as that of Freeman [1, p. 376]

(5.2.15) $$y(x, \psi) = \frac{\epsilon}{\rho_\infty U r_1^j} \int_\psi^{\psi_1} \frac{\sin^2 \sigma \sec \sigma \, d\psi}{\sin^2 \sigma_1 - \left( \dfrac{d \cos \sigma}{d\psi} \right)_1 \int_\psi^{\psi_1} \cos \sigma \, d\psi},$$

with the integrals again functions of their lower limits $\psi$. The shock layer thickness is given by (5.2.8). The result (5.2.15) may be improved without repeating the entire procedure by using the more complete expressions for $\rho$ and $u$ from (5.2.13) and (5.2.14). Of particular importance is the improvement afforded by using a more accurate expression for the velocity from (5.2.14) instead of simply $u = u_s$. Freeman obtained convergence in the stagnation region of a two-dimensional blunt body only with this improvement, obtaining the first term of (4.3.14) or (4.3.23). Thus an appreciably better result may be obtained by replacing the term sec $\sigma$ representing $U/u$ in (5.2.15) by the quantity $U/u$ obtained from

$$(5.2.16) \qquad \frac{u^2}{U^2} = \cos^2 \sigma + \epsilon \sin^2 \sigma \ln \frac{p}{p_s},$$

with $p$ and $p_s$ given by (5.2.12) and (5.2.11).

For a second approximation the pressure distribution $p - p_s$ should be recomputed on the basis of the first approximation, the shock shape should be corrected if the problem is a direct one, and the quantities $p_s(x)$, $p(x, \psi)$, $\rho(x, \psi)$, and $q^2(x, \psi)$ should be obtained as before to complete the first stage. The streamline slope according to (5.2.9) may be calculated from (5.2.15) and used to compute $u$. Finally $\rho$ and $u$ are used in (5.2.7) to recalculate $y$. Examples of calculations for the second approximation may be found in the cited references.

### 3. Constant-streamtube-area approximation

In this section we shall present an approximate theory due to Hayes [4] for the hypersonic flow on a given blunt body of revolution. The analysis is based on the assumption that $\epsilon^{1/2}$ is small (assumption D-strong), and thus has a limited validity. The results have less accuracy than do the results of the constant-density theory, as is indicated by the fact that in the analogue of (4.4.16) the factor $1 + \sqrt{8\epsilon/3}$ is not obtained. What this theory does do is to permit a straightforward solution of the direct problem in which the body shape is given and the shock shape is unknown, to give this shape on the blunt part of the body by a simple and direct procedure. The theory thus provides an improvement in obtaining shock shapes over Newtonian theory which is of a different type than the improvement offered by the constant-density solutions; the constant-density solutions give us no information on the relation between shock and body shape. In particular, solutions are obtained for problems for which there is no Newtonian solution. Although the part of the shock layer to which the theory may apply is limited, its extent is larger by the order of $\epsilon^{-1/2}$ than that of the stagnation region discussed in the previous section. The constant-density solutions are limited in validity to the stagnation region.

The primary purpose of this theory is to obtain the shock shape as a function of the distance $x$ along the body. For the blunt shapes we are considering the shock angle $\sigma$ is close to $\pi/2$ over the range of interest and is equal to $\pi/2$ on the axis of symmetry if the shock is detached. We shall use the tangent of $\pi/2 - \sigma$ as the principal independent variable describing the shock shape, or cot $\sigma$. Similarly, we shall use cot $\theta_b$ considered as a known function of $x$ as the quantity describing the body shape. This choice of variables is partly dictated by the fact that our formulation is to serve in the following section as well, for a theory valid over a somewhat wider range of $\sigma$.

The theory leads to a differential equation for $\cot \sigma$ considered as a function of $x$, once the body shape is given. The solution to the problem of determining the shock shape is a solution to this differential equation. Thus we shall be primarily concerned with the nature of the solutions to this differential equation, with a study of its singular points, and with interpretations of its mathematical behavior in terms of physical solutions.

Certain simplifying assumptions are now introduced for the purposes of this section and the following one. We assume that the thickness of the layer $\Delta$ is small enough so that $K\Delta$ may be neglected, and hence that $\mathscr{H}$ defined in (5.1.1) may be set equal to one. Similarly, we neglect the dependence of $r$ on $y$ in (5.1.3) and take $r$ to be a function of $x$ alone. And we assume that for a given value of $x$, the quantity $\sigma - \theta_b$ is small even though it may be the quantity of direct interest to us. With these assumptions we may integrate (5.1.13b) to obtain

$$(5.3.1) \qquad \left(\frac{v}{u}\right)_s - \left(\frac{v}{u}\right)_b = \frac{j \sin \sigma}{r}\Delta + \mathscr{D},$$

where

$$(5.3.2) \qquad \mathscr{D} = \int_0^\Delta \frac{1}{\rho u}\frac{D\rho u}{Dx}\, dy.$$

In these equations (5.1.8b) has been used to replace the stream function $\psi$ by $y$. Shock orientation has been assumed here; with body orientation $\sin \theta_b$ would appear in (5.3.1) in place of $\sin \sigma$, and the limits in the integral of (5.3.2) would be $-\Delta$ and $0$ in place of $0$ and $\Delta$. Regardless of the choice of orientation we may write

$$(5.3.3) \qquad \frac{d\Delta}{dx} = \tan(\sigma - \theta_b) = \frac{\cot \theta_b - \cot \sigma}{1 + \cot \sigma \cot \theta_b}.$$

With our assumption that $\sigma - \theta_b$ is small, we may replace $\tan(\sigma - \theta_b)$ in (5.3.3) by $\sin(\sigma - \theta_b)$ and obtain

$$(5.3.4) \qquad \Delta = \Delta_0 - \int_0^{} \sin \theta_b \sin \sigma\, (\cot \sigma - \cot \theta_b)\, dx.$$

With shock orientation we may evaluate the left side of (5.3.1) with the aid of (1.5.4) to give

$$(5.3.5) \qquad \left(\frac{v}{u}\right)_s - \left(\frac{v}{u}\right)_b = \tan(\sigma - \theta_s) - \tan(\sigma - \theta_b)$$

$$= \epsilon \tan \sigma - \tan(\sigma - \theta_b).$$

Combining this result with (5.3.1) we obtain

$$(5.3.6) \qquad \frac{\cot \theta_b - \cot \sigma}{1 + \cot \sigma \cot \theta_b} = \frac{\epsilon}{\cot \sigma} - \frac{j \sin \sigma}{r} \Delta - \mathscr{D},$$

which with $\sigma - \theta_b$ small and $1 - \epsilon$ replaced with 1 may be rewritten

$$(5.3.7) \qquad \cot \sigma + \frac{\epsilon}{\cot \sigma} = \cot \theta_b + \frac{j \Delta}{r \sin \theta_b} + \frac{\mathscr{D}}{\sin^2 \sigma}.$$

With body orientation we have, in place of (5.3.5),

$$(5.3.8) \qquad \left(\frac{v}{u}\right)_s - \left(\frac{v}{u}\right)_b = \left(\frac{v}{u}\right)_s = \tan(\theta_b - \theta_s)$$

$$= \frac{\epsilon \tan \sigma - \tan(\sigma - \theta_b)}{1 + \epsilon \tan \sigma \tan(\sigma - \theta_b)}.$$

For the class of problems we are considering, the quantity $\tan \sigma \tan (\sigma - \theta_b)$ remains of the order of one or smaller; this fact may be checked later by examining extreme examples. Thus, the denominator in the right side of (5.3.8) is $1 + O(\epsilon)$ and may be dropped as a factor. We conclude that (5.3.8) is the same as (5.3.5) within our order of approximation, and thus that there is no important difference between shock orientation and body orientation. Equations (5.3.4) and (5.3.7) are the basic ones for this section and the following one.

We now turn to a somewhat cruder approximation applicable only to blunt bodies of revolution with $\epsilon^{1/2} \ll 1$ and limited to a region on the body within which $\cot \sigma$ is also very small. With the restriction that $\cot \sigma$ is small we set $j = 1$, replace $\sin \theta_b$ and $\sin \sigma$ in (5.3.4) and (5.3.7) by one, and replace $r$ by $x$. On the right side of (5.3.7) are left the terms $\Delta/x$ and $\mathscr{D}$.

We may interpret (5.3.7) as an equation expressing the effects which tend to make the shock layer become thicker or thinner with increasing $x$. The mass flow fed into the shock layer across the shock tends to make it thicker, an increase in the mass flow per unit area $\rho u$ tends to make it thinner (the influence of the term in $\mathscr{D}$), and in an axisymmetric flow the radial geometrical effect tends to make it thinner (the influence of the term in $j\Delta/r$). With our approximations for a blunt body of revolution the quantity $\mathscr{D}$ is smaller than $\Delta/x$ by a factor which is of the order of $\epsilon^{1/2}$, so that with $\epsilon^{1/2}$ small the quantity $\Delta/x$ predominates. This conclusion is based on estimates of the relative order of magnitude of the two terms.

The approximation of this section is based on dropping this $\mathscr{D}$ term, on assuming that we may set

$$(5.3.9) \qquad \mathscr{D} = 0$$

approximately. Such an approximation is not available to us in two-dimensional flow. Combining (5.3.4) and (5.3.7) we obtain finally

$$(5.3.10) \qquad x\left(\cot \sigma + \frac{\epsilon}{\cot \sigma}\right) = x \cot \theta_b + \Delta_0 - \int_0^x (\cot \sigma - \cot \theta_b)\, dx.$$

Since the quantity $\mathscr{D}$ corresponds to changes in the cross-sectional areas of the streamtubes in the flow, this approximation is termed the constant-streamtube-area approximation. One result may be noted immediately, that

$$(5.3.11) \qquad \Delta_0 = \lim_{x \to 0} \left(\frac{\epsilon x}{\cot \sigma}\right) = \epsilon_0 R_s$$

in agreement with the lowest-order approximation of (4.4.9) or (4.4.17). This result is obtainable from the Newtonian theory, in which, however, there is no fundamental distinction between shock and body radii.

Equation (5.3.10) is an integral equation for the unknown function $\cot \sigma$ determining the shock shape in terms of the known function $\cot \theta_b$ describing the body shape. Although for some purposes we might wish to use the integral equation proper, a differential equation is generally preferable in this problem. This is obtained directly by differentiating (5.3.10), and is

$$(5.3.12) \qquad \left(1 - \frac{\epsilon}{\cot^2 \sigma} + \frac{1}{\cot \sigma} \frac{d\epsilon}{d \cot \sigma}\right) x \frac{d \cot \sigma}{dx} + 2 \cot \sigma + \frac{\epsilon}{\cot \sigma} = f(x),$$

where $f(x)$ is given by

$$(5.3.13) \qquad f(x) = 2 \cot \theta_b + x \frac{d \cot \theta_b}{dx} = \frac{d\, x^2 \cot \theta_b}{x\, dx}.$$

The term involving the derivative of $\epsilon$ appearing in (5.3.12) may be evaluated in terms of quantities evaluated from the Hugoniot curve for the fluid. With $\rho^{-1}$ the specific volume of the fluid, we may obtain the dimensionless quantity $\chi$ defined by

$$(5.3.14) \qquad \frac{\chi}{1 - \chi} = \frac{p_s - p_\infty}{\rho_\infty^{-1} - \rho_s^{-1}} \frac{d\rho_s^{-1}}{dp_s} = \frac{p_s - p_\infty}{1 - \epsilon} \frac{d\epsilon}{dp_s}$$

from the Hugoniot curve. Differentiation of the relation (1.4.5b) for $p_s$ in terms of $\epsilon$ and $\sigma$ yields

$$(5.3.15) \qquad dp_s = 2\rho_\infty U^2(1 - \epsilon) \sin \sigma \cos \sigma\, d\sigma - \rho_\infty U^2 \sin^2 \sigma\, d\epsilon.$$

A combination of the last two equations gives the expression

$$(5.3.16) \qquad \frac{1}{\cot \sigma} \frac{d\epsilon}{d \cot \sigma} = -\frac{2(1 - \epsilon)\chi}{1 + \cot^2 \sigma}.$$

Within the accuracy of our approximations, we may replace (5.3.16) by

·(5.3.17)
$$\frac{1}{\cot \sigma} \frac{d\epsilon}{d \cot \sigma} = -2\chi.$$

The quantity $\chi$ is generally small if $\epsilon$ is small, and is negative and of smaller order than $\epsilon$ for a perfect gas. However, it could be large in particular cases of a general fluid, and may be of either sign.

The basic differential equation (5.3.12) has a singular point where $\cot \sigma + \epsilon/\cot \sigma$ has a minimum value, where the parenthesis of (5.3.12) vanishes. This point is termed the "critical" point, and occurs for a shock angle given by

(5.3.18)
$$\cot^2 \sigma_{cr} = \frac{\epsilon_{cr}}{1 - 2\chi_{cr}}.$$

In order that a solution of (5.3.12) pass through the critical point, it is necessary that $f(x) - 2 \cot \sigma - \epsilon/\cot \sigma$ be zero there, or that

(5.3.19)
$$f(x_{cr}) = (3 - 2\chi_{cr}) \cot \sigma_{cr} = \frac{\sqrt{\epsilon_{cr}}(3 - 2\chi_{cr})}{\sqrt{1 - 2\chi_{cr}}}.$$

If $\epsilon$ is constant so that $\chi$ is zero, (5.3.18) and (5.3.19) become accordingly simpler in form. In any case, the quantity $x_{cr}$ is independent of the solution for the shock shape. The stand-off or detachment distance at the critical point is given from (5.3.10) and (5.3.4) as

(5.3.20)
$$\Delta_{cr} = x_{cr}[2(1 - \chi_{cr}) \cot \sigma_{cr} - \cot \theta_{b_{cr}}].$$

In order to exhibit some sample solutions we could take $\epsilon$ to be constant. The case in which $\chi$ is taken to be constant (instead of zero) involves but little more complexity; we shall consider this case as an example which includes effects of variations in $\epsilon$. The case $\chi = 0$ is simpler in form, of course. With $\chi$ constant we may integrate (5.3.17) to obtain

(5.3.21)
$$\epsilon = \epsilon_0 - \chi \cot^2 \sigma.$$

We may now rewrite the basic differential equation (5.3.12) as

(5.3.22)
$$\left(1 - \chi - \frac{\epsilon_0}{\cot^2 \sigma}\right) x \frac{d \cot \sigma}{dx} + (2 - \chi) \cot \sigma + \frac{\epsilon_0}{\cot \sigma} = f(x).$$

We next introduce a new variable $z$ defined by

(5.3.23)
$$z = \epsilon_0^{-1/2} \sqrt{1 - \chi} \cot \sigma,$$

in terms of which (5.3.22) may be rewritten

(5.3.24)
$$\left(1 - \frac{1}{z^2}\right) \frac{x}{z} \frac{dz}{dx} + 1 + \frac{1}{z^2} = \frac{f(x)}{\epsilon_0^{1/2}(1 - \chi)^{1/2}z} - \frac{1}{1 - \chi}.$$

The quantity $z$ is equal to one at the critical point.

A particular family of solutions to (5.3.24) which are of interest appears if the body shape function $f(x)$ is so chosen that a constant times $f(x)$ is a solution for $z$. Solutions for the sphere and for the axisymmetric flat-nosed body are included in this family. To investigate these solutions we set the right side of (5.3.24) equal to a constant, say to $1 - a$. In this case the solution of interest may be expressed in the form

$$(5.3.25) \qquad x = \epsilon_0^{1/2}(1 - \chi)^{-1/2}R_s z(1 + az^2)^{-\frac{1+a}{2a}},$$

in which the arbitrary multiplicative constant has been evaluated in terms of the shock radius at the nose $R_s$. For this solution $f(x)$ must satisfy the relation

$$(5.3.26) \qquad f(x) = \cot \sigma[(1 - \chi)(1 - a) + 1].$$

It will be observed that (5.3.26) is apparently clearly inconsistent with (5.3.19) except in the case $a = -1$. In this special case (5.3.25) tells us that $\cot \sigma$ is proportional to $x$, corresponding to a spherical or parabolic nose shape. If $\chi \neq 0$ we obtain a result for the body radius of curvature different from that of the shock. With the definition (5.3.13) for $f(x)$ and the relation (5.3.26) with $a = -1$ we obtain the result

$$(5.3.27) \qquad \frac{R_s}{R_b} = 1 - \tfrac{2}{3}\chi$$

for the ratio of these radii of curvature at the nose. The term in $\chi$ may justifiably be retained only if $\chi$ is of larger order of magnitude than $\epsilon_0$. With $\chi = 0$ the shock and body radii are the same for this particular solution.

For the other solutions with $a \neq -1$, we first must impose the condition $a > -1$. The apparent inconsistency between (5.3.19) and (5.3.26) is resolved by the observation that $f(x)$ may be a discontinuous function, with $\theta_b$ continuous and $d\theta_b/dx$ discontinuous. The critical point may then be determined as the point at which $f(x)$ jumps across the value given by (5.3.19). In such a case the critical point on the body is determined by the presence of a shoulder at which a choking phenomenon occurs. This shoulder is at a given value of $x$ at which $f(x)$ jumps from a value consistent with (5.3.26) to a value greater than that given by (5.3.19). Thus the solution is determined by the given value of $x$ at the shoulder set equal to $x_{\mathrm{cr}}$, which from (5.3.25) must be related to $R_s$ by the relation

$$(5.3.28) \qquad x_{\mathrm{cr}} = \epsilon_0^{1/2}(1 - \chi)^{-1/2}R_s(1 + a)^{-\frac{1+a}{2a}}.$$

Of particular interest is the case of a flat-nosed body, with $f(x) = 0$ for all $x < x_{\mathrm{cr}}$. In this case $a = (2 - \chi)/(1 - \chi)$ or, if $\chi = 0$, $a = 2$. With $\chi = 0$ and $\epsilon$ constant, the stand-off or detachment distance on the axis is given by

$$(5.3.29) \qquad \Delta_0 = \epsilon_0 R_s = 3^{3/4}\epsilon^{1/2}x_{\mathrm{cr}}$$

from (5.3.28). The detachment distance at the shoulder is

$$(5.3.30) \qquad \Delta_{cr} = 2\epsilon^{1/2}x_{cr}$$

from (5.3.20). These particular results were obtained by an alternative method by Hayes [3], in which constant velocity along streamlines was assumed in a constant-density approach.

Within the approximation of this section there is a definite relation between the deviation of the shock shape from spherical and the relative radii of curvature of the shock and the body. With the body shape given locally by

$$(5.3.31) \qquad \cot \theta_b = \frac{x}{R_b} + O(x^3)$$

the shock shape must have the form

$$(5.3.32) \qquad \cot \sigma = \frac{x}{R_s} + \frac{3x^3}{2\epsilon R_s^2}\left(\frac{1 - \frac{2}{3}\chi}{R_s} - \frac{1}{R_b}\right) + O(x^5),$$

in which $\epsilon$ and $\chi$ are evaluated at $x = 0$. This result may be obtained directly from (5.3.22) by substituting and equating like powers of $x$, and is important because it shows that the shock radius is not determined by the body radius on the axis alone.

A distinctive feature of the constant-streamtube-area approximation is the possibility of a jump in the value of $\cot \sigma$. This possibility is most readily seen from (5.3.10), in which the quantity $\cot \sigma + \epsilon/\cot \sigma$ appears. A value of $\cot \sigma + \epsilon/\cot \sigma$ above its minimum or critical value corresponds to two possible values of $\cot \sigma$ (barring an exceptional case in which more than two might be possible), of which one is greater than $\cot \sigma_{cr}$ and the other less. As none of the other terms appearing in (5.3.10) are affected, a jump from one of the two corresponding values of $\cot \sigma$ to the other is permitted. Such a jump is analogous to the hydraulic jump of classical free-surface hydraulic theory, and gives a jump in the pressure. The apparently anomalous fact that there is no jump in the thickness of the shock layer is consistent with our basic assumption $\mathscr{D} = 0$, whereby all changes in streamtube area are neglected. We may expect that such a jump should be considered possible only in one direction, in the direction of decreasing $\cot \sigma$ from a supercritical value ($\cot \sigma > \cot \sigma_{cr}$) to a subcritical value ($\cot \sigma < \cot \sigma_{cr}$). Although we cannot prove this is the case without going to a more refined approximation, this restriction appears physically reasonable and we shall adopt it. This jump does not generally appear in problems for which $f(x)$ is monotonic increasing, as the solution of interest with supercritical downstream conditions never passes from the supercritical to the subcritical domain.

A plot of $\cot \sigma$ versus $x$ is instructive in the study of solutions of (5.3.12).

Such a plot is shown for a typical blunt body in Fig. 5–6. The mathematical solutions having shock angle $\sigma$ equal to $\pi/2$ at $x = 0$ form a one-parameter family of integral curves, each of which passes through the origin on the $(x, \cot \sigma)$ plot. The slope of each of these curves corresponds to the shock curvature. The critical point $(x_{cr}, \cot \sigma_{cr})$ is a saddle point, and the solution A which passes through this point is the one of physical interest. If the initial shock curvature had been chosen too large, as in solution B, the

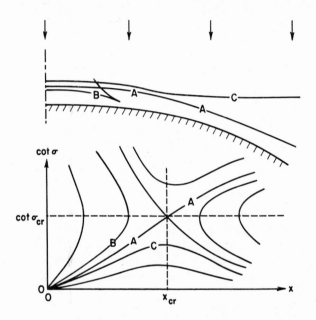

FIG. 5–6. Constant-streamtube-area solution for a blunt axisymmetric body.

solution reverses onto a different Riemann sheet for the variable $x$ and is not physically interpretable through this reversal point. If the initial shock curvature had been chosen too small, as in solution C, the solution remains subcritical and approaches the solution $\cot \sigma = 0$ for a normal shock. In this case the solution does have a direct physical interpretation and is rejected only because it is not the solution desired. In general, we have a one-parameter family of initially possible solutions; of these solutions only a single one passes from the subcritical region into the supercritical region and is the desired solution. In addition, there is a one-parameter family of solutions following solution A through the critical point into the super-critical region, jumping discontinuously to a subcritical solution, and approaching a solution for a normal shock. As with solution C, a solution of this type is rejected as not representing the solution desired.

So far we have implicitly assumed that $f(x)$ is a monotonic increasing function (not necessarily a continuous one) and that the body is initially blunt with a finite curvature. In order to generalize our study of the basic equation (5.3.12) we may take one of a number of directions. A fruitful and instructive direction is toward the study of attached shock waves on blunt ogival bodies, for which the initial value of $\cot \theta_b$ is not zero. On such bodies we find an analogue of the Crocco point, a detachment point, and detached as well as attached solutions.

The shape of an ogival body of revolution may be expressed in terms of the Taylor series for the function $f(x)$ under the assumption that this shape is analytic. Thus we have

$$(5.3.33) \qquad f(x) = f_0 + f_0' x + \tfrac{1}{2} f_0'' x^2 + \cdots .$$

In order to simplify our analysis we shall assume generally that $\epsilon$ is constant and hence that $\chi$ is zero. A similar analysis would hold with $\chi$ constant or with $\chi$ analytic in $\cot^2 \sigma$, but no significant additional features appear in such a more general analysis. The coefficients appearing in (5.3.33) may be evaluated in terms of $\cot \theta_b$ as

$$(5.3.34a) \qquad f_0 = 2 \, (\cot \theta_b)_0,$$

$$(5.3.34b) \qquad f_0' = 3 \left( \frac{d \cot \theta_b}{dx} \right)_0 ,$$

$$(5.3.34c) \qquad f_0'' = 4 \left( \frac{d^2 \cot \theta_b}{dx^2} \right)_0 .$$

We are interested primarily in attached solutions, for which we may assume $\cot \sigma$ finite and $d \cot \sigma / dx$ of smaller order than $x^{-1}$ near the origin. From (5.3.12) and (5.3.34a) we obtain

$$(5.3.35) \qquad (\cot \theta_b)_0 = \cot \sigma_0 + \frac{\epsilon_0}{2 \cot \sigma_0} .$$

In order that an attached solution may exist, it is necessary that $(\cot \theta_b)_0$ be greater than a minimum value determined by the minimum of the right side of (5.3.35), its value at the detachment point (cf. Section 4.2). At this detachment point for which $(\cot \theta_b)_0$ takes on its minimum value from (5.3.35), the shock angle is determined by the condition

$$(5.3.36) \qquad \cot^2 \sigma_{\det} = \frac{\epsilon_{\det}}{2(1 - \chi_{\det})} ,$$

and the initial body slope has the value

$$(5.3.37) \qquad (\cot \theta_b)_{\det} = (2 - \chi_{\det}) \cot \sigma_{\det}.$$

We assume in the treatment below that an attached solution exists, i.e. that $(\cot \theta_b)_0$ is greater than $(\cot \theta_b)_{\det}$. The possible solutions in the vicinity of the origin are divided into three principal classes, into detached solutions, "strong" attached solutions for which $\cot \sigma < \cot \sigma_{\text{det}}$, and "weak" attached solutions for which $\cot \sigma > \cot \sigma_{\text{det}}$. At least one solution of each class exists. A weak attached solution is generally of one of three types, determined by whether $(\cot \theta_b)_0$ is greater or less than two reference values corresponding to the Crocco point (defined below; cf. Crocco [1]) and to the critical point. A weak solution may thus be classed as a weak sub-Crocco solution, as a subcritical super-Crocco solution, or as a supercritical solution.

The Crocco point is an intermediate point between the critical point and the detachment point. It is defined as a point for which the second term obtained by expanding the left side of (5.3.12) in a Taylor's series in $x$ vanishes. This second term is $x(d \cot \sigma/dx)_0$ times $3 - 4\chi - 2\epsilon/\cot^2 \sigma$ evaluated at $x = 0$, and the Crocco point is accordingly defined by the relation

$$(5.3.38) \qquad \cot^2 \sigma_{\text{crocco}} = \frac{2\epsilon_{\text{crocco}}}{3 - 4\chi_{\text{crocco}}}.$$

From (5.3.35) we see that this corresponds to an initial body slope of

$$(5.3.39) \qquad (\cot \theta_b)_{\text{crocco}} = (\tfrac{7}{4} - \chi_{\text{crocco}}) \cot \sigma_{\text{crocco}}.$$

The critical point is defined by (5.3.18) applied at $x = 0$ and the corresponding initial body slope obtained from (5.3.19) or (5.3.35) is

$$(5.3.40) \qquad (\cot \theta_b)_{\text{cr}} = (\tfrac{3}{2} - \chi_{\text{cr}}) \cot \sigma_{\text{cr}}.$$

We now set $\chi = 0$ and $\cot \sigma = \cot \sigma_0 + \delta \cot \sigma$, so that $\delta \cot \sigma$ is the change in $\cot \sigma$ from its value at $x = 0$. Equation (5.3.12) is now expanded with $\delta \cot \sigma$ as the dependent variable, giving

$$(5.3.41) \qquad \left(1 - \frac{\epsilon}{\cot^2 \sigma_0} + \frac{2\epsilon \, \delta \cot \sigma}{\cot^3 \sigma_0}\right) x \frac{d \, \delta \cot \sigma}{dx}$$
$$+ \left(2 - \frac{\epsilon}{\cot^2 \sigma_0} + \frac{\epsilon \, \delta \cot \sigma}{\cot^3 \sigma_0}\right) \delta \cot \sigma = f_0' x + \tfrac{1}{2} f_0'' x^2 + \cdots$$

with terms of order $(\delta \cot \sigma)^3$ dropped. With terms of order $(\delta \cot \sigma)^2$ dropped, (5.3.41) is linear and has the general solution

$$(5.3.42) \qquad \delta \cot \sigma = A x^\alpha - \frac{f_0' x}{\dfrac{2\epsilon}{\cot^2 \sigma_0} - 3} - \frac{\tfrac{1}{2} f_0'' x^2}{\dfrac{3\epsilon}{\cot^2 \sigma_0} - 4} - \cdots,$$

where the exponent $\alpha$ is given by

$$(5.3.43) \qquad \alpha = \frac{2 - \dfrac{\epsilon}{\cot^2 \sigma_0}}{\dfrac{\epsilon}{\cot^2 \sigma_0} - 1}$$

and $A$ is an arbitrary constant. This solution is invalid at the critical point, for which $\cot^2 \sigma_0 = \epsilon$, at the detachment point, for which $\cot^2 \sigma_0 = \frac{1}{2}\epsilon$, at the Crocco point, for which $\cot^2 \sigma_0 = \frac{2}{3}\epsilon$, or at any point for which $\cot^2 \sigma_0 = n\epsilon/(n + 1)$ with $n$ a positive integer. With $n$ larger than 2 the solution (5.3.42) is still correct in its leading terms.

The behavior of the solution (5.3.42) depends critically on the value of $\alpha$. For a strong solution, one for which $\cot^2 \sigma_0 < \frac{1}{2}\epsilon$, we have $0 > \alpha > -1$. With $\alpha$ thus negative the local singularity is a saddle point and only a single integral curve is possible with $(\delta \cot \sigma)_0 = 0$, that for which the constant $A$ is zero. Since in general we need a one-parameter family of solutions from which to choose the one which can go from a subcritical state to a supercritical state, we must reject such a strong solution as not being of general physical interest. The remaining solutions are either weak or detached.

If the weak solution is supercritical, with $\cot^2 \sigma_0 > \epsilon$, we have $-2 > \alpha > -\infty$. Again $\alpha$ is negative, the singularity is a saddle point, and only a single integral curve is possible. In this case, however, the solution is initially supercritical and the multiplicity of initial solutions is not needed. If $f(x)$ is monotonic increasing from its initial value we are assured that the entire solution will remain supercritical.

If the initial solution is weak and subcritical, so that $\frac{1}{2}\epsilon < \cot^2 \sigma_0 < \epsilon$, then $0 < \alpha < \infty$ and we always have a one-parameter family of solutions, with the singularity a node. The Crocco point divides this range into a range for which $\frac{2}{3}\epsilon < \cot^2 \sigma_0 < \epsilon$ and $1 < \alpha < \infty$, designated as super-Crocco, and a range for which $\frac{1}{2}\epsilon < \cot^2 \sigma_0 < \frac{2}{3}\epsilon$ and $0 < \alpha < 1$, designated as sub-Crocco. In the super-Crocco range with $\alpha > 1$ the leading term is the one in $f_0'$ and all integral curves have the same finite slope at the origin (shock curvature) given by

$$(5.3.44) \qquad \left(\frac{d \cot \sigma}{dx}\right)_0 = \frac{f_0' \cot^2 \sigma_0}{3 \cot^2 \sigma_0 - 2\epsilon}.$$

In the sub-Crocco range with $\alpha < 1$ the leading term is the one in $x^\alpha$, and the only integral curve of finite slope corresponding to (5.3.44) is the one with $A = 0$. All the other integral curves have infinite slope at the origin, corresponding to infinite shock curvatures. It is interesting to note that these results correspond completely with the analogous results for supersonic flow on a two-dimensional ogive. See, for example, Ferri [2, Art. H,10].

In order to illustrate the solutions of the type just discussed, we present in Fig. 5–7 the integral curves for an ogive in the sub-Crocco range for which the shock is attached. The solution of interest is solution A and passes through the critical point into the supercritical region. Solution B reverses itself and is to be rejected. Solutions C, D, and E approach solutions for normal shocks. All the attached weak solutions have infinite shock curvature at the nose except the single solution C. There is a single strong solution **D**. And there is a one-parameter family of detached solutions such as solution E for which $(\cot \sigma)_0 = 0$.

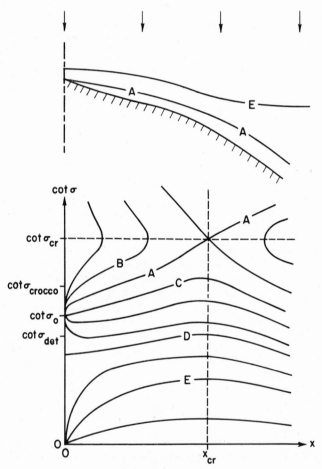

Fig. 5–7. Solution for an ogive of revolution in the sub-Crocco range.

The solution (5.3.42) is invalid at the various special points, and special solutions are needed for these cases. If the initial point is the Crocco point the solution may be expressed

$$(5.3.45) \qquad \delta \cot \sigma = Ax - 2f_0'x \ln x - f_0''x^2 + \cdots.$$

For the other special points other than the detachment or critical points (5.3.42) needs only a modification involving a logarithmic term in $x^\alpha \ln x$.

If the initial point is the detachment point the term in $\delta \cot \sigma$ in the second parenthesis of (5.3.41) must be retained, with the approximate solution

$$(5.3.46) \qquad \delta \cot \sigma = \frac{\cot \sigma_{\det}}{2(A - \ln x)} - f_0' x + \cdots .$$

The solutions (5.3.46) all start at the detachment point and form a one-parameter family.

The case in which the initial point is the critical point is a little more involved. The term in $\delta \cot \sigma$ in the first parenthesis of (5.3.41) must necessarily be retained, and the resulting nonlinear equation has no general approximate solution. If $f_0' \neq 0$ and $\delta \cot \sigma - f_0' x$ is small compared with $f_0' x$ we can obtain the approximate solution for small $x$

$$(5.3.47) \qquad \delta \cot \sigma \approx f_0' x + \tfrac{1}{2} f_0'' x^2 - \frac{3 f_0'^2 x^2}{\cot \sigma_{\mathrm{cr}}} + A \exp \left( \frac{\cot \sigma_{\mathrm{cr}}}{2 f_0' x} \right) + O(x^3),$$

with $A$ an arbitrary constant. If $f_0' \neq 0$ and $\delta \cot \sigma$ is small compared with $f_0' x$ we can obtain

$$(5.3.48) \qquad \delta \cot \sigma \approx \pm \sqrt{f_0' \cot \sigma_{\mathrm{cr}} (x - a)},$$

where $a$ is an arbitrary constant. A study of these two approximate solutions indicates that if $f_0' > 0$ there is but a single initially critical solution and that this solution is supercritical for $x > 0$. If $f_0' < 0$ there is a one-parameter family of solutions which are initially critical, all of which are subcritical for $x$ small enough but nonzero. Thus we have here another example of the principle that the solutions of interest should form a one-parameter family in the subcritical region but should not have this multiplicity in the supercritical region.

As one final example, we show in Fig. 5–8 a solution with the initial angle supercritical, but for which $f(x)$ decreases to a subcritical value and subsequently increases and returns into the supercritical region. The singularity at a critical point may be shown to be always a saddle point if $f'(x_{\mathrm{cr}}) > 0$ and to be either a node or a focus (spiral) if $f'(x_{\mathrm{cr}}) < 0$. In Fig. 5–8 the first critical point, with $f(x)$ decreasing, is shown as a focus. The initial part of the solution lies on a single integral curve in the supercritical region. The locus of points in the subcritical region to which points on this integral curve may jump is termed the "image" locus and is shown as a dotted curve in Fig. 5–8. If the value of $\cot \sigma$ on this image locus is denoted $\cot \sigma_*$, the jump condition reads

$$(5.3.49) \qquad \cot \sigma + \frac{\epsilon}{\cot \sigma} = \cot \sigma_* + \frac{\epsilon_*}{\cot \sigma_*} .$$

It may be shown that $\cot \sigma_*$ satisfies a differential equation of exactly the same form as (5.3.12), but with $f(x) - (\cot \sigma - \cot \sigma_*)$ on the right-hand side in place of $f(x)$. Since if $\cot \sigma_*$ is in the subcritical regime $\cot \sigma - \cot \sigma_*$ is positive and the coefficient of $d \cot \sigma_*/dx$ is negative, we may conclude that $d \cot \sigma_*/dx$ is always greater than the slope of the local integral curves passing through the same point. In the case of Fig. 5–8, this ensures that there is a one-parameter family of subcritical integral curves leaving the region bounded by the image locus and the critical line in the direction of increasing $x$. With the possibility of a jump from supercritical to subcritical

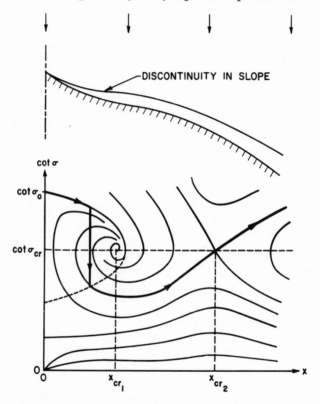

FIG. 5–8. Solution for an ogive of revolution with a jump in the shock slope.

permitted, the single supercritical integral curve jumps to a one-parameter family of subcritical integral curves. The one of these which is of physical interest is the one which traverses the saddle point at the second critical point. Thus, for the case shown in Fig. 5–8, the presence of a supercritical-to-subcritical jump has given us a single solution which is unique.

In assessing the constant-streamtube-area approximation we have presented, we must emphasize the limitations inherent in the assumptions.

The theory should be valid in an asymptotic sense as $\epsilon \to 0$, in the same sense in which the Newtonian theory is valid. What the theory does accomplish is that it does give nontrivial solutions to the direct problem, in which the shock shape is initially unknown and in which the initial approximation that the shock and body shapes are the same may be fundamentally incorrect. The existence of such an elementary theory in the axisymmetric case and not in the two-dimensional case points out again the important differences between these two cases. It should be noted that the concept of the speed of sound or of the compressibility of the gas has no place in the constant-streamtube-area approximation.

Serbin [1] carried out an analysis for the sphere and for the flat-faced circular disk which is essentially equivalent to that presented here, and he notes the agreement of his shock shapes with those of Hayes [3]. However, Serbin does not use relations such as (5.3.11) or (5.3.20) to determine the shock layer thickness. Instead he uses a condition of uniform sonic flow at the critical point, analogous to the useful semi-empirical condition introduced by Moeckel [1]. The use of this condition gives Serbin good agreement with experimental results but destroys completely the internal consistency of his theory. An alteration of his theory to maintain consistency leads to results for the shock layer thickness consistent with (5.3.11) and (5.3.20).

Maslen and Moeckel [1] (Integral Method) obtained the basic equations of the constant-streamtube-area approximation as the lowest-order approximation of their theory, and obtained approximate solutions for the case in which $\cot \theta_b$ is proportional to $x$.

## 4. Variable-streamtube-area approximations

The analysis of the previous section is strongly limited in its applicability by the basic assumption made therein, the assumption that the term $\mathscr{D}$ defined in (5.3.2) could be neglected in the basic equation (5.3.7) for the shock shape. The underlying requirement that $\epsilon^{1/2}$ is small can rarely, if ever, be considered to be satisfied in practice. For a more realistic theory for bodies of revolution or for any theory at all for two-dimensional bodies the term $\mathscr{D}$ must be taken into account. One obvious possibility is an iteration scheme in which the previous approximation is used to obtain an estimate of the shock layer structure and thence of $\mathscr{D}$, which estimate is then used in (5.3.7) in calculating the shock shape.

In this section we follow an alternative approach, in which the quantity $\mathscr{D}$ is estimated in such a way that it will be estimated reasonably accurately near the stagnation point and at the same time be of relatively simple form. We shall estimate $\mathscr{D}$ in terms of functions of the shock layer structure which do not involve a differentiation with respect to $x$. Note that in the definition (5.3.2) of $\mathscr{D}$ there is a differentiation with respect to $x$. Our principal purpose is to gain insight into the effect of the term $\mathscr{D}$ and to obtain a simple procedure for obtaining better approximate solutions than those given by the constant-streamtube-area approximation. The approach is the same as that of Hayes [4], modified to include a centrifugal pressure term.

A direct evaluation of $\mathscr{D}$ using the definition of $a^2$ and (5.1.6b) yields the alternative form

$$(5.4.1) \qquad \mathscr{D} = - \int_0^\Delta \left( \frac{1}{\rho u^2} \frac{\partial p}{\partial x} - \frac{1}{\rho a^2} \frac{Dp}{Dx} - K \frac{v}{u} \right) dy.$$

Of the three terms in the integrand of (5.4.1) the third is small compared with the first. The second term in $Dp/Dx$ may be divided into a term in $\partial p/\partial x$ and one in $\partial p/\partial y$. The latter is small compared with at least one of the other terms. We now approximate $\mathscr{D}$ by an expression of the form

$$(5.4.2) \qquad \mathscr{D} \approx - \left( \frac{\partial p}{\partial x} \right)_{\mathrm{av}} \int_0^\Delta \left( \frac{1}{u^2} - \frac{1}{a^2} \right) \frac{dy}{\rho} \,,$$

with the question of how the average value $(\partial p/\partial x)_{\mathrm{av}}$ of the pressure gradient should be defined left open.

With a sharp-nosed body the distribution of $\rho u^2$ across the shock layer may be expected to be roughly uniform even if $\epsilon$ is very small, and an appropriate choice of $(\partial p/\partial x)_{\mathrm{av}}$ would be the arithmetic mean of $dp_s/dx$ and $(Dp/Dx)_b$. In the stagnation region of a blunt body the quantity $1/\rho u^2$ is appreciably larger near the wall (by a factor of $0(\epsilon^{-1})$), than elsewhere and $1/\rho a^2$ is relatively small; see the velocity profiles of (4.3.24) and (4.4.18). The material nearest the wall has passed through a normal shock. In this case the choice $(\partial p/\partial x)_{\mathrm{av}} = (Dp/Dx)_b$ appears more appropriate. We shall make this latter choice, but should recognize that with other than a blunt body another course may be preferable.

The difference in pressure between shock and body may be expressed from (5.1.6c) approximately as

$$(5.4.3a) \qquad p_s - p_b \approx K \int_0^\Delta \rho u^2 \, dy = K \rho_s u_s^2 \, \Delta \, \alpha(x),$$

where

$$(5.4.3b) \qquad \alpha(x) = \int_0^1 \frac{\rho u^2}{\rho_s u_s^2} \, d \left( \frac{y}{\Delta} \right)$$

is a dimensionless variable. We may evaluate $p_b$ approximately as

$$(5.4.4) \qquad p_b \approx p_\infty + \rho_\infty U^2 \left[ \frac{1 - \epsilon}{1 + \cot^2 \sigma} - \frac{\alpha \cot^2 \sigma}{(1 + \cot^2 \sigma)^2} \left( \frac{\Delta}{\epsilon} \frac{d \cot \sigma}{dx} \right) \right],$$

in which we have expressed the shock angle in terms of cot $\sigma$. In differentiating this expression we shall neglect the derivatives of all the factors in the term containing $\alpha$ coming from (5.4.3) except the factor $\cot^2 \sigma$ in the numerator. Terms coming from the other derivatives are small compared with the one kept if the body is blunt, and the simplifying assumption that we may drop them is consistent with the degree of approximation used in the other steps. With the factor $1 - \epsilon$ in (5.3.16) dropped we obtain

$$(5.4.5) \quad \left(\frac{\partial p}{\partial x}\right)_{av} \approx \left(\frac{Dp}{Dx}\right)_b \approx -\frac{2\rho_\infty U^2 \cot \sigma}{(1 + \cot^2 \sigma)^2}\left[1 - \chi + \alpha \left(\frac{\Delta}{\epsilon}\frac{d \cot \sigma}{dx}\right)\right]\frac{d \cot \sigma}{dx}.$$

We express the integral appearing in (5.4.2) as

$$(5.4.6) \quad \int_0^\Delta \left(\frac{1}{u^2} - \frac{1}{a^2}\right)\frac{dy}{\rho} = \frac{\Delta}{\rho_s u_s^2}\beta(x)$$

where

$$(5.4.7) \quad \beta(x) = \int_0^1 \frac{\rho_s u_s^2}{\rho u^2}\left(1 - \frac{u^2}{a^2}\right)d\left(\frac{y}{\Delta}\right).$$

Substituting (5.4.5) and (5.4.6) into (5.4.2) gives the approximate expression for $\mathscr{D}$

$$(5.4.8) \quad \mathscr{D} \approx \sin^2 \sigma \frac{\mathscr{B}(x) \Delta}{\cot \sigma}\frac{d \cot \sigma}{dx},$$

with the quantity $\mathscr{B}(x)$ defined as

$$(5.4.9) \quad \mathscr{B}(x) = 2\epsilon\beta \left[1 - \chi + \alpha \left(\frac{\Delta}{\epsilon}\frac{d \cot \sigma}{dx}\right)\right].$$

With the approximation of (5.4.8) for $\mathscr{D}$ we may rewrite (5.3.7) as

$$(5.4.10) \quad \cot \sigma + \frac{\epsilon}{\cot \sigma} = \cot \theta_b + \frac{j\Delta}{r \sin \theta_b} + \frac{\Delta \mathscr{B}(x)}{\cot \sigma}\frac{d \cot \sigma}{dx}.$$

The quantity $\Delta$ is given by (5.3.4) or its equivalent, and (5.4.10) is an integro-differential equation. It may be reduced to a second-order differential equation, but only at the expense of algebraic complication.

From (5.4.10) we may immediately write the result analogous to (5.3.11) for the detachment distance on the axis of a blunt body

$$(5.4.11) \quad \Delta_0 = \frac{\epsilon_0 R_s}{j + \mathscr{B}_0},$$

where $\mathscr{B}_0 = \mathscr{B}(0)$. To check this result against the results already obtained in Chapter IV, we note first that the bracket of (5.4.9) is simply the pressure factor of (3.3.4), equal to $1 + 1/(2 + j)$. In the two-dimensional case the velocity profile (4.3.24) yields the approximate result $\beta_0 = R_s/3\Delta_0$ which with $\mathscr{B}_0 = 3\epsilon\beta_0$ is consistent with (5.4.11). In the axisymmetric case the velocity profile (4.4.18) yields the approximate result $\beta_0 = (8\epsilon/3)^{-1/2}$ which in turn yields $\mathscr{B}_0 = (8\epsilon/3)^{1/2}$. In this case (5.4.11) is consistent with (4.4.16). Note that all we have done is to check (5.4.11) against the constant-density solutions for consistency. It would be impossible to compute $\Delta_0$ from (5.4.11) without an approximation for the velocity profiles.

The critical point which appears in the analysis of the previous section has lost most of its importance in the approach used in this section. In its place is a "singular" point, defined by the condition

$$(5.4.12) \qquad \beta(x_{\text{sing}}) = 0; \qquad \mathscr{B}(x_{\text{sing}}) = 0.$$

At this point the shock layer is sonic in an appropriate average sense. In analogy with the criteria we used in the last section the solution of interest must pass from a subsingular condition ($\mathscr{B} > 0$) to a supersingular condition ($\mathscr{B} < 0$) in the direction of increasing $x$. On a plot of $\cot \sigma$ versus $x$ the singular point is generally a saddle point, and the solution of interest must pass through this saddle point.

In the method of the last section no trial and error is involved in a numerical solution. The solution may be carried out in the direction of decreasing $x$ from the known critical point. In the approach of this section we must assume either $\mathscr{B}(x)$ or both $\alpha(x)$ and $\beta(x)$ to be known functions of $x$ or of $\cot \sigma$ in order to have a well posed problem. Even with this assumption the location of the singular point on a ($\cot \sigma$, $x$) plot is not known at the outset. The problem must be solved by assuming a series of initial values of $\Delta_0$, solving (5.4.10) for each choice of $\Delta_0$, and selecting by interpolation that solution which passes through the singular point. Thus the numerical approach is necessarily a trial-and-error approach, except in the case of a flat-nosed body considered below.

If $\mathscr{B}$ is considered to be negligibly small, (5.4.10) reduces to its analogue of the last section, for which a discontinuity in $\cot \sigma$ was permitted. We can obtain a rough picture of the structure of such a discontinuity by assuming in (5.4.10) that $\epsilon$ is constant and $\mathscr{B}$ is small and approximately constant. We rewrite (5.4.10) in the form

$$(5.4.13) \qquad \mathscr{B}\Delta \frac{d \cot \sigma}{dx} = \cot^2 \sigma - \left( \cot \theta_b + \frac{j\Delta}{r \sin \theta_b} \right) \cot \sigma + \epsilon$$

$$= -(\cot \sigma_1 - \cot \sigma)(\cot \sigma - \cot \sigma_2),$$

with $\sigma_1$ and $\sigma_2$ the values of $\sigma$ on the two sides of the discontinuity. The change in the quantity $\Delta$ is infinitesimal if $\mathscr{B}$ is small. The desired solution of (5.4.13) is

$$(5.4.14) \qquad \cot \sigma = \frac{\cot \sigma_1 + \cot \sigma_2}{2}$$
$$- \frac{\cot \sigma_1 - \cot \sigma_2}{2} \tanh \left[ \frac{\cot \sigma_1 - \cot \sigma_2}{2 \mathscr{B} \Delta} (x - x_c) \right],$$

where $x_c$ is the value of $x$ at the center of the discontinuity. This solution is analogous to that for the structure of a weak shock wave. This result supports our conjecture of the previous section that a jump should be possible only in the direction of decreasing $\cot \sigma$. But we see also that this conjecture necessarily applies only in the subsingular range and would be reversed in the supersingular range. Because of the weakness of the approximation that $\mathscr{B}$ is constant (see (5.4.9)) this anomaly should not be considered meaningful.

We turn finally to the problem of the flat-nosed body, with an attempt to obtain an approximate solution for the shock shape which is more realistic than that of (5.3.25) and (5.3.29). With $\epsilon$ assumed constant, $\chi = 0$. We reintroduce $z = \epsilon^{-1/2} \cot \sigma$ as in (5.3.23), and with $\cot \theta_b = 0$ we obtain

$$(5.4.15) \qquad z + \frac{1}{z} = \frac{j(\Delta/\Delta_0)}{\xi} + \frac{\mathscr{B}(\Delta/\Delta_0)}{z} \frac{dz}{d\xi},$$

where

$$(5.4.16) \qquad \xi = \frac{\epsilon^{1/2} x}{\Delta_0}.$$

The quantity $\Delta/\Delta_0$ appearing in (5.4.15) may be expressed from (5.3.4) as

$$(5.4.17) \qquad \frac{\Delta}{\Delta_0} = 1 - \int_0^\cdot z \, d\xi.$$

We estimate $\mathscr{B}$ as a function of $z$ roughly as

$$(5.4.18) \qquad \mathscr{B} = \mathscr{B}_0 (1 - z^2).$$

This approximation puts the singular point at the critical point. This approximation is a completely arbitrary one which does not take into account the fact that a derivative appears in the definition (5.4.9), but which does take into account the fact that $\mathscr{B}$ must be an even function of $\xi$ and should decrease as $z$ increases. The choice of (5.4.18) was made because of its mathematical simplicity. A number of other equally suitable arbitrary choices could have been made with equal justification, probably with but little change in numerical results.

If $j = 0$ (two-dimensional case) and $\mathscr{B}$ is considered to be a function of $z$ alone, the solution of (5.4.15) and (5.4.17) may be reduced to two successive quadratures. For the approximation of (5.4.18) for $\mathscr{B}$ the first integral with $j = 0$ (communicated to us by D. Roger Willis) is

(5.4.19)
$$\frac{\Delta}{\Delta_0} = \left[\frac{\exp \frac{1}{2}z^2}{1 + z^2}\right]^{\mathscr{B}_0}.$$

With $\Delta/\Delta_0$ given by (5.4.19) the quantity $\xi$ is obtained from the quadrature of

(5.4.20)
$$\frac{d\xi}{dz} = \mathscr{B}_0 \frac{1 - z^2}{1 + z^2}\left(\frac{\Delta}{\Delta_0}\right).$$

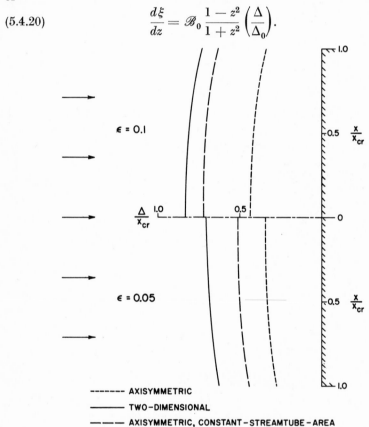

------- AXISYMMETRIC

———— TWO-DIMENSIONAL

—·—·— AXISYMMETRIC, CONSTANT-STREAMTUBE-AREA

Fig. 5–9. Shock wave shapes on flat-nosed bodies at $\epsilon = 0.1$ and $\epsilon = 0.05$.

The results of calculations based on the approximation of (5.4.18) are presented in Fig. 5–9, for $\epsilon = 0.1$ and $\epsilon = 0.05$. The quantity $\mathscr{B}_0$ was calculated from $\epsilon$ from the formulas

(5.4.21)
$$\mathscr{B}_0 = \frac{\sqrt{1 - 3\epsilon}}{\cosh^{-1}\dfrac{1}{\sqrt{3\epsilon}}}$$

in the two-dimensional case, and

$$(5.4.22) \qquad \mathcal{B}_0 = \sqrt{\frac{8\epsilon}{3}}$$

in the axisymmetric case. Compare (5.4.11) with (4.3.22) and (4.4.16). Also presented in Fig. 5–9 are the corresponding axisymmetric results from the constant-streamtube-area theory, corresponding to $\mathcal{B}_0 = 0$. In Table 5–1 are presented the numerical results for the detachment distance on the axis in terms of $\Delta_0/x_{cr}$, where $x_{cr}$ is the half-width of the two-dimensional flat-nosed body or the radius of the axisymmetric flat-nosed body.

The important quantitative difference between the detachment distance on a two-dimensional and on an axisymmetric body is evident in Fig. 5–9 or Table 5–1. It may also be noted from Fig. 5–9 that for a given value of $\epsilon$ all the shock curves shown differ but slightly in contour, and differ primarily in the separation of the curve from the body. The very significant difference in detachment distance on an axisymmetric body between that given by

TABLE 5–1

*Detachment distance on axis for flat-nosed bodies with $\mathcal{B} = \mathcal{B}_0(1 - z^2)$*

| | Two-dimensional | | Axisymmetric | | | |
| | (5.4.20) | | (5.4.15) | | Constant-streamtube-area | |
| $\epsilon$ | 0.1 | 0.05 | 0.1 | 0.05 | 0.1 | 0.05 |
| $\mathcal{B}_0$ | 0.692 | 0.576 | 0.516 | 0.365 | 0 | 0 |
| $\Delta_0/x_{cr}$ | 0.834 | 0.704 | 0.433 | 0.341 | 0.721 | 0.510 |

the constant-streamtube-area approximation and that given by the variable-streamtube-area approximation is an indication of the limitation of the former approximation. In the cases shown the quantity $\epsilon^{1/2}$ or the equivalent quantity $\mathcal{B}_0$ from (5.4.22) is not small. It may be noticed, however, that this difference in detachment distance is relatively less with $\epsilon = 0.05$ than with $\epsilon = 0.1$.

# CHAPTER VI

# OTHER METHODS FOR BLUNT-BODY FLOWS

## 1. Nature of the problem

In our work so far we have examined approximate solutions for the inviscid hypersonic flow over blunt bodies based on the assumption of constant density in the shock layer or on the assumption of a very thin shock layer. It seems natural for us to inquire into alternative methods of obtaining approximate solutions and also to investigate the possibility of computing such flows exactly.

In spite of the amount of effort that has gone into this problem in recent years, at present no single method has been agreed on as being the best for calculating the hypersonic flow past general blunt shapes. It is to be emphasized that this situation exists for the relatively simple cases of symmetric two-dimensional or axisymmetric flows, which are the only cases we shall consider in this chapter.

The problem which can be considered to be the important one met in practice is what we term the direct problem (cf. Section 5.1), in which the shape of the body is given and the details of the flow field are unknown. We shall also consider in Section 6.5 the inverse problem, in which the shock shape is given and the shape of the body and the pressure on it are unknown. We take the attitude that the direct problem is more important than the inverse problem, and we shall accordingly emphasize the direct problem. This point of view was also taken in Chapter V. There is some possibility of using methods developed for the inverse problem for an attack on the more difficult direct problem by a successive approximation scheme. However, such an approach would seem to involve procedures of trial and error, in which it is not necessarily clear how a solution which gives an approximation to the desired body is to be improved.

The difficulty in solving the mathematical problem of determining the detached shock wave and the flow field behind the shock for a given body (direct problem) lies principally in the fact that the flow around the body is a nonlinear mixed subsonic-supersonic flow, with a free boundary which is not known a priori. This free boundary is the bow shock wave in front of the body. Also unknown is the location of what we shall term the "limiting characteristic", which generally intersects the sonic line at one point (see Fig. 6–1). The limiting characteristic in an accelerating flow may be defined as the locus of points each of which has only one point of the sonic line in its zone of action. The transonic or pseudoelliptic character of the supersonic flow in the region between the sonic line and the limiting characteristic must be taken into account; a disturbance in this region would affect the shape of the sonic line and hence also the subsonic flow field upstream. This particular supersonic region will be referred to in this chapter as the "transonic zone". In Fig. 6–1 we have shown the structure of this region schematically

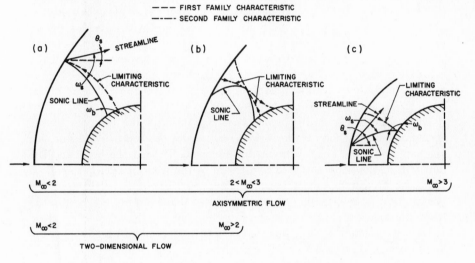

FIG. 6–1. Sketch of sonic line and limiting characteristic shapes for a sphere and a circular cylinder with $\gamma \approx 1.4$. Values of $M_\infty$ are approximate.

for three different Mach number ranges, for the flow of air past a hemispherical nose and a circular cylinder normal to the stream direction. We shall justify the details of the diagrams below. We note that in the moderate $M_\infty$ case shown in Fig. 6–1(b) the limiting characteristic is divided by the point of tangency with the sonic line into two characteristics of different families.

The supersonic domain downstream of the limiting characteristic can always be handled by the method of characteristics (see Section 7.1) once the sonic line or limiting characteristic shape and flow conditions on this shape are known. However, it is not the solution in this purely supersonic downstream region which is of the greatest importance to our problem, but rather that in the initially undetermined subsonic region and the transonic zone.

In order to illustrate in the simplest manner possible how one arrives at the limiting characteristic shapes which are sketched in Fig. 6–1, let us examine some of the geometrical characteristics of the sonic line for super-sonic and hypersonic flows past blunt bodies (cf. Probstein [5]). Such con-siderations can help us to obtain a better appreciation of how a body in hypersonic flow influences the upstream flow in the shock layer, and how this influence is different from that ordinarily associated with detached shock waves at low and moderate supersonic speeds. For most of these considera-tions we shall use the assumption of a perfect gas of constant $\gamma$. We may expect that the conclusions which we reach should hold for most general fluids which do not have some anomalous behavior. It is possible to obtain most of the same primary results for a general fluid with some additional labor and a judicious choice of assumptions on the behavior of the material.

Our method will be to estimate the location of the sonic point and the inclination angle of the sonic line both on the body and on the shock. With this information we shall be able to obtain a picture of the geometry of the sonic line and of the limiting characteristic.

The geometrical quantity which best characterizes the behavior of the sonic line near the body is the angle it makes with the body. We define this angle $\omega_b$ to be the angle between the sonic line leaving the body and the direction of the body surface downstream of the sonic point. We shall be primarily interested in whether this angle is acute or obtuse, as this question is important in determining whether the body shape has an influence in the transonic zone.

The angle that the sonic line makes with a streamline (in this case the body surface) is given for a perfect gas by

$$(6.1.1) \qquad \tan \omega = - \frac{\partial q}{\partial s} \Big/ \frac{\partial q}{\partial n} ,$$

where $q$ is the total velocity and $s$ and $n$ are intrinsic coordinates (see Fig. 7–1). These intrinsic coordinates are discussed in detail in Section 7.1. The $s$-axis here lies in the flow direction at the intersection of the streamline and sonic line. The relation (6.1.1) follows directly from the fact that along the sonic line $dq = 0$ for an isoenergetic flow.

To determine $(\partial q/\partial n)_b$ we utilize the expression for the vorticity in intrinsic coordinates

$$(6.1.2) \qquad \frac{\partial q}{\partial n} = -\zeta - \frac{q}{R} ,$$

where $\zeta$ is the vorticity, and $R$ is the local radius of curvature of the stream-line equal to $-ds/d\theta$. The quantity $R$ is positive at the surface of a convex body. In a two-dimensional flow on a blunt body the entropy gradient at the body surface is zero, and Crocco's vorticity law (see Section 1.5) gives us the result that the vorticity there is zero (cf. Section 4.3). From (6.1.2) we see that in two-dimensional flow on a blunt convex body $(\partial q/\partial n)_b < 0$, regardless of the value of the Mach number of the flow. Since $(\partial q/\partial s)_b$ is positive, it follows from (6.1.1) that in two-dimensional flow the sonic line is always inclined at an acute angle to the surface, as shown in Figs. 6–1(a) and 6–1(b). In axisymmetric flow the vorticity at the body surface is finite, and we shall find that whether the angle $\omega_b$ is acute or obtuse depends strongly on the density ratio $\epsilon$ and on the shape of the body. We shall next obtain an expression for the vorticity at the body surface in an axisymmetric flow.

In the vicinity of the axis of a detached shock we may approximate sin $\sigma$ by 1, and both $-dr_s/d\sigma$ and $r_s/\cos \sigma$ by the shock radius of curvature $R_s$. The quantity $r$ here is the cylindrical radius in our axisymmetric problem. From (1.5.9) we obtain the local result

$$(6.1.3) \qquad \frac{dS}{d\psi} = -\frac{(1-\epsilon)^2 U}{\rho_\infty T_s R_s^2},$$

for axisymmetric flow. This result is obtained in terms of conditions immediately behind the shock, but since $S$ is a function of $\psi$ alone the result is valid everywhere for the streamtube nearest the body surface. Using Crocco's vorticity law we may calculate the vorticity at a point on the body

$$(6.1.4) \qquad \zeta_b = \frac{T_b}{q_b}\left(\frac{\partial S}{\partial n}\right)_b = -\frac{(1-\epsilon)^2}{\epsilon}\left(\frac{\rho_b T_b}{\rho_s T_s}\right)\left(\frac{r_b U}{R_s^2}\right).$$

We have made the assumption that the gas is a perfect one in (6.1.1), and we now express $(\partial q/\partial n)_b$ at the sonic point from (6.1.2) with this assumption as

$$(6.1.5) \qquad \left(\frac{\partial q}{\partial n}\right)_{b,\text{son}} = \left(\frac{q_b}{R_b}\right)_{\text{son}}\left[\frac{p_b}{p_s}\left(\frac{R_b r_b}{R_s^2}\right)\left(\frac{(1-\epsilon)^2}{\epsilon}\frac{U}{q_b}\right) - 1\right]_{\text{son}}.$$

It should be kept in mind that the subscript $s$ in (6.1.3) to (6.1.5) refers to conditions immediately behind the shock on the axis of the body. The particular characteristic of the quantity expressed in (6.1.5) which is of interest to us is its sign. From (6.1.1) and the fact that $(\partial q/\partial s)_b$ is positive, this sign determines whether $\omega_b$ is greater or less than $\frac{1}{2}\pi$. The quantity $p_b/p_s$ is about $\frac{1}{2}$ at the sonic point if $\epsilon$ is reasonably small (say less than $\frac{1}{2}$). The quantity $R_b r_b/R_s^2$ is also of the order of $\frac{1}{2}$ for a sphere if $\epsilon$ is small enough (say less than $\frac{1}{5}$), but may be much less than one if $\epsilon$ is close to one.

The remaining factor in the first term in the bracket of (6.1.5) is very small at low values of $M_\infty$, for which $1 - \epsilon$ is small. Thus, with $M_\infty - 1$ sufficiently small, $\omega_b$ is less than $\frac{1}{2}\pi$ and the angle of interest to us is acute. At very high values of $M_\infty$, $q_b/U$ is of the order of magnitude $\epsilon^{1/2}$ at the sonic point, $\epsilon$ may be approximated by $\epsilon_{\lim}$, and the first term in the bracket of (6.1.5) may be greater than 1 if $\epsilon_{\lim}$ is sufficiently small.

For our perfect gas of constant $\gamma$ we may derive the formula

$$(6.1.6) \qquad \frac{(1 - \epsilon)^2}{\epsilon} \frac{U}{q_{b,\mathrm{son}}} = \sqrt{\frac{2}{\gamma + 1}} \frac{(M_\infty^2 - 1)^2}{M_\infty \left(1 + \dfrac{\gamma - 1}{2} M_\infty^2\right)^{3/2}},$$

and we note that this approaches $4\epsilon_{\lim}^{-3/2}/(\gamma + 1)^2$ in the limit as $M_\infty \to \infty$. With helium this limiting value is 4.5, with a diatomic perfect gas it is 10.2, while with a perfect gas with $\gamma = 1.2$ it is 30.2.

The quantity $R_b r_b/R_s^2$ depends critically on the geometry of the body, and also on the value of $\epsilon$. For a sphere it is of the order of $\frac{1}{2}$ with $\epsilon$ small, but is probably less than $\frac{1}{4}$ for $\epsilon = \frac{1}{4}$. Thus, on a sphere we may conclude that the angle $\omega_b$ is always acute in helium even in the limit $M_\infty \to \infty$, and that it is obtuse in air ($\gamma = 1.4$) if $M_\infty$ is greater than about 2.5 or 3.0. On a body with a flattened face and a rounded corner the quantity $R_b r_b/R_s^2$ will be very small and the angle $\omega_b$ may remain acute even in a perfect gas with $\gamma - 1$ small. And it is possible to find a body shape such as a blunted ogive for which $R_s$ is small, $R_b$ at the sonic point is large, and the factor $R_b r_b/R_s^2$ is very large. On such a body the angle would be obtuse even at moderate values of $M_\infty$ in helium.

In this chapter we shall be considering mostly bodies such as spheres and cylinders for which the radius of curvature of the body does not vary greatly over the front of the body. For bodies of this character the location of the body sonic point does not depend greatly on either the Mach number or the gas properties. The critical pressure ratio $p_{\mathrm{son}}/p_0$ varies for a perfect gas only from 0.59 at $\gamma = 1.1$ to 0.49 at $\gamma = 5/3$. Here the subscript 0 refers to stagnation conditions. The pressure on the body divided by the stagnation pressure varies roughly as $\sin^2 \theta_b$ ("modified Newtonian"), and is somewhat less than this if $\gamma$ is small. Thus at hypersonic speeds the body sonic point will occur somewhat farther downstream for a gas with a higher value of $\gamma$ because of the lower pressure required. Nevertheless, the sonic point movement will not be very large (compare for example the experiments of Oliver [1] in air and those of Vas, Bogdonoff, and Hammitt [1] in helium). This fact regarding the sonic point location is significant in determining the structure of the transonic zone.

The distance from the axis to the sonic point on the shock is roughly proportional to the radius of curvature of the shock at the axis $R_s$ times $\cos \sigma_{\mathrm{son}}$. As the Mach number increases, both of these quantities decrease and the shock sonic point moves toward the axis. The limiting value of $\cos \sigma_{\mathrm{son}}$ as $M_\infty \to \infty$ is $\sqrt{(\gamma - 1)/2\gamma}$, and this limit varies from $63\frac{1}{2}°$ for $\gamma = 5/3$ to $90°$ for $\gamma = 1$.

One of the final quantities to be determined is the angle the sonic line makes with the flow direction at the shock wave. To do this we again use (6.1.1) and evaluate the velocity derivatives from the oblique shock relations. The result for plane flow was obtained by Hasimoto [1], Drebinger [1], Belotserkovskii [1], and others. This result is independent of the shock curvature and may be expressed in terms of the shock angle and flow deflection angle as

$$(6.1.7) \qquad \tan \omega_s = \frac{\tan^3 (\sigma - \theta_s)[3(\gamma + 1) \tan^2 (\sigma - \theta_s) + 5 - \gamma]}{[1 - \tan^2 (\sigma - \theta_s)][(\gamma + 1) \tan^2 (\sigma - \theta_s) + 2]},$$

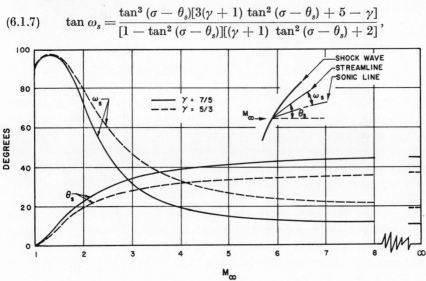

FIG. 6–2. Sonic line and streamline inclination behind a shock wave in two-dimensional flow.

where $\omega_s$ is negative when measured clockwise from the streamline direction (see Fig. 6–1). The angle $\omega_s$ is the angle between the streamline direction and the direction of the sonic line leaving the shock, and is thus the negative of the $\omega$ in (6.1.1) evaluated at the shock. In Fig. 6–2 we have plotted both the sonic line angle at the shock and the flow deflection angle behind the shock as a function of Mach number for $\gamma = 7/5$ and $5/3$. We note for $\gamma = 7/5$ above a Mach number of about 3 the sonic line always has a positive inclination angle with respect to the free stream direction. This inclination increases with increasing Mach number until at about $M_\infty = 8$ it has almost reached its asymptotic value for $M_\infty = \infty$. This rapid approach to an asymptotic value is characteristic of the behavior of a perfect gas of constant $\gamma$. It is not difficult to show, for the type of body we are considering, that this same general type of behavior also holds for axisymmetric flow, although in this case the angle does depend on the ratio of the radius of curvature of the shock to the distance from the axis of symmetry (see e.g. Drebinger [1]).

On the basis of the considerations above and of general experimental evidence we now have a picture as to the location of the sonic point and the inclination of the sonic line on the body surface and on the shock. We make the plausible assumption that the sonic line is a reasonably smooth curve between its intersections with the shock and the body surface. For most cases on bodies of approximately circular cross-section, the inclination angles of the sonic line indicate that the sonic line is concave with respect to the upstream subsonic region. We must emphasize that for bodies of widely varying shape and with general fluids of different thermodynamic behavior it is impossible to make such a general statement.

In a diatomic gas ($\gamma = 1.4$) on an almost-spherical body we may conclude that the geometry of the sonic line and transonic zone will be as shown in Fig. 6–1(c) at high Mach numbers ($M_\infty > 3$). At low Mach numbers (say, $M_\infty < 2$) this geometry will be as shown in Fig. 6–1(a) for either almost-spherical or almost-cylindrical bodies. At intermediate Mach numbers on an almost-spherical body and at intermediate and high Mach numbers on an almost-cylindrical body the geometry is intermediate in character, as shown in Fig. 6–1(b). The flow pattern shown in Fig. 6–1(c) is a characteristic one, and we may refer to the sonic line in this case as a "hypersonic axisymmetric sonic line".

In the low Mach number case on a body of almost-circular cross section the limiting characteristic intersects the sonic line at the shock. On the other hand, in the high Mach number case on an almost-spherical body ($\gamma$ about 1.4 or less) the limiting characteristic intersects the sonic line at the body. In this case no disturbance propagated by the first family (left-running) Mach waves from the body can make its influence felt in the subsonic region of the flow field, although first family Mach waves from the sonic line can carry disturbances from the sonic line to the shock wave. Between the sonic line and the limiting characteristic (of the second family, or right-running) is the transonic zone, from a point in which a disturbance will affect the sonic line and hence the entire subsonic flow field.

Except with this characteristic hypersonic axisymmetric sonic line there will be a portion of the body downstream of the sonic point from which a disturbance will affect the subsonic region. At low speeds this portion is appreciable in extent, as indicated in Fig. 6–1(a). In two-dimensional flow this portion of the body always exists, but at very high Mach numbers its extent becomes very small.

In the discussion above we have assumed that the value of $\gamma$ is of the order of 1.4 or less. The way in which the value of $\gamma$ influences the flow field lies primarily in its influence upon $\epsilon$, although a number of other influences are important. The primary effect of an increase in $\gamma$ is thus equivalent to a decrease in $M_\infty$. Thus, in this special sense a flow at $M_\infty = \infty$

and $\gamma = 5/3$ is roughly equivalent in a gas of $\gamma = 7/5$ to a flow with the same value of $\epsilon$, or to a flow with $M_\infty$ about 3.

With all the ideas we have discussed in mind, we may now inquire what simplifications, if any, are possible in the techniques for obtaining exact numerical solutions as a result of the limiting nature of the hypersonic flow. From all of our discussion it would still appear that the one basic characteristic which can be utilized either to simplify the method of solution, or at least to permit somewhat different techniques, is the fact that the shock lies very close to the body surface. In the present chapter we therefore envisage employing this fact to allow the use of mathematical techniques which might prove to be impractical or inapplicable when applied to flows with large shock layer thicknesses, but with appreciably weaker limitations than were required in Chapter V.

One complication introduced by considering the flow of air at hypersonic speed over a blunt body is the variation in gas properties from those of a perfect gas resulting from the high stagnation temperature. Although we will briefly indicate in this chapter how such variable fluid properties can be accounted for in an equilibrium flow, we will reserve our main discussion for Section 7.1, where the method of characteristics is examined. The reason for this is that in the purely supersonic region the general method of solution is clearer as well as simpler, and the introduction of the variable fluid properties only adds somewhat to the computational effort involved. In principle, however, any of the methods given in this chapter may be applied to flows in a fluid with general thermodynamic properties, provided we may assume the flow to be in equilibrium.

Of the various methods of attack available to us for the direct problem of a given body, we shall consider first a streamtube-continuity technique in which the streamline patterns are assumed and corrections to this pattern are carried out by satisfying mass flow and vorticity criteria. We shall examine next a numerical scheme based on dividing the shock layer into strips and assuming that the values of the hydrodynamic variables within these strips are expressible by appropriate interpolation polynomials. By this means the hydrodynamic equations are reduced to a finite system of simultaneous first-order nonlinear ordinary differential equations which can be solved numerically as a two point boundary value problem starting from the stagnation streamline and passing through a critical region near the sonic line. Finally, for the direct problem we shall propose a relaxation technique for determining the purely subsonic or elliptic region, combined with a trial-and-error method for calculating the mixed flow domain in the neighborhood of the sonic line. For the inverse problem of determining the body shape associated with a given shock shape we shall describe two methods, one of which operates in the complex plane. Both methods start at the known shock wave and have the sonic line and body as undetermined boundaries.

Although all of the schemes to be discussed hold certain promise, no one scheme has in general been shown to be clearly better than another. We shall therefore consider it one of our primary purposes to indicate the limitations of the methods and in some cases to offer suggestions for improvement.

## 2. Streamtube-continuity methods

For hypersonic flow past a blunt body the shock wave lies close enough to the surface that the streamlines are roughly parallel to the body except in a small region near the stagnation point. Such a fact immediately suggests the possibility of utilizing an assumed streamline pattern and shock shape as the parameters for calculating the flow over the nose of a blunt body in a high speed stream. Presumably a method could then be worked out in which these initial assumptions are corrected by an iterative procedure employing mass flow and vorticity considerations. In this manner the flow field variables could be determined, while at the same time many of the difficulties associated with the transonic character of the flow in the neighborhood of the sonic line could be minimized. The general philosophy of such an iterative approach has been discussed in Section 5.2. However, the applications discussed there have been based directly on the assumption of a thin shock layer.

Two such iteration schemes have been reported in the literature, one by Maslen and Moeckel [1] (Streamtube Method), the other by Uchida and Yasuhara [1]. The first of these, although simple to apply since it only requires iteration of the shock shape, is nevertheless a very rough approximation and requires as a starting point of the calculation a knowledge of the surface pressure distribution. As a result, the method lacks an essential necessary feature since this pressure distribution is unknown and is usually what we would like to find out in most problems of interest. On the other hand, the method of Uchida and Yasuhara, although very laborious since it requires iterating both the shock shape and streamline pattern, is nevertheless exact in principle. This method provides a way of completely computing the flows under consideration, provided no difficulty in convergence is experienced.

In the procedure of Maslen and Moeckel (Streamtube Method), both the pressure distribution on the entire body and the shock shape and stand-off or detachment distance in the stagnation region must be presumed known. Starting with the streamtube nearest the body and an approximate shock shape, a picture of the streamline pattern is built up on the basis of the mass flow calculated from the known entropy distribution $S(\psi)$ and the presumably known pressure. The pressure at a distance from the body is estimated from the pressure on the body through an equation for the pressure gradient normal to the streamlines. The shock location is determined by a continuity condition of equal mass flows, and if the shock location disagrees with the original approximate shock shape a new approximate shock shape is chosen and the procedure is repeated.

That this method is an unsatisfactory one is immediately evident from the fact that the quantities which would generally be considered the principal answers to the problem have had to be assumed as being accurately known before the problem is started. In the details of the method, the stream function describing the mass flow is correctly matched immediately behind the shock, but there is no way of ensuring that the pressure from the analysis matches the pressure from the oblique shock relations immediately behind the shock. It is clearly possible to repair this aspect of the method by providing for an adjustment of the pressure distribution on the body. We would then be led to a procedure following the general lines described in Section 5.2.

In the scheme given by Uchida and Yasuhara, although the computations are laborious, no fixed assumptions are required regarding values of the flow variables either at the surface or in the flow field. The method starts by assuming an approximation for both the shock shape and distribution of streamlines, and a double iteration technique is carried out whereby both the streamlines and the shock are readjusted until a consistent solution is obtained. The philosophy of this procedure is very like that given in Section 5.2, although the details are different.

In the first step of the procedure, an assumed approximate pattern for the streamlines around the body is chosen. Such a streamline pattern can be obtained from one of the more approximate theories which we have discussed previously. In addition to assuming the streamlines, an approximation for the location and shape of the shock wave is also assumed, and this too may also be obtained from an approximate solution.

In the first step, the streamline deflection $\theta$ will in general not coincide with the flow deflection angle immediately behind the shock $\theta_s$ obtained from the oblique shock relations for the assumed shock angle. In fact, the ratio of the maximum value of these two flow deflections is the parameter which is used to define the incompleteness of the solution at the shock boundary for a fixed detachment distance. For example, for the assumed shock and streamlines, we can plot both $\theta$ and $\theta_s$ at the shock as a function of the radial coordinate $y$ or $r$ (see Fig. 6–3) or of the stream function $\psi$. If we then assume that $\theta_s = \theta/Q$, where

(6.2.1)
$$Q = \frac{\theta_{\max}}{\theta_{s,\max}},$$

we can in turn recalculate $\theta_s$ and draw in a new shock corresponding to this flow deflection. This process is then repeated until the shock shape does not change. In general, $Q$ should be close to but not equal to one when this occurs. Only if both the streamline pattern and the shock shape are correct is the quantity $Q$ necessarily equal to one.

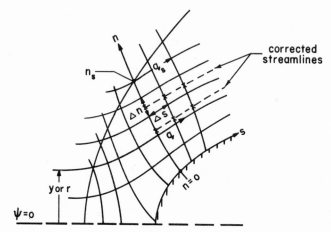

FIG. 6–3. Coordinate system for streamtube-continuity analysis of Uchida and Yasuhara [1].

With the shock shape and streamlines thus assumed, the procedure is to readjust the streamlines by means of a calculation which is carried out in intrinsic or natural coordinates (see Section 7.1). In order to do this we introduce the stream function defined by the relation

$$(6.2.2) \qquad \psi = \int_0^r \rho q y^j \, dn,$$

where $j = 0$ for two-dimensional flow and $j = 1$ for axisymmetric flow. When $j = 1$ the coordinate $y$ is to be read as $r$, the radial distance from the $x$ axis. For the assumed shock shape the stream function at the shock is given by

$$(6.2.3) \qquad \psi_s = \frac{\rho_\infty U y_s^{1+j}}{1 + j} .$$

To redetermine the distribution of $\psi$ in the field along any given orthogonal trajectory to the streamline, we numerically integrate (6.2.2)—a process which can be carried out once the distribution of $\rho q$ is determined along these orthogonal trajectories.

To calculate $\rho q$ we must first find $q$ itself, which is derivable from the expression for the vorticity

$$(6.2.4) \qquad \zeta = q \frac{\partial \theta}{\partial s} - \frac{\partial q}{\partial n},$$

and from the Crocco vorticity law

$$(6.2.5) \qquad \zeta = \frac{T}{q} \frac{\partial S}{\partial n}.$$

For simplicity we shall assume a perfect gas with constant specific heats, for which the isoenergetic relation may be written as $c_p T + \frac{1}{2} q^2 = c_p T_0$. Then under the assumed streamline curvature and the entropy distribution $S(\psi)$ obtained from the assumed shock shape, we obtain a differential equation for $q$ by equating (6.2.4) and (6.2.5). This equation is

$$(6.2.6) \qquad \frac{\partial (q/a_0)^2}{\partial n} - 2 \left[ \frac{\partial \theta}{\partial s} + \frac{1}{2} \frac{\partial S/c_p}{\partial n} \right] \left( \frac{q}{a_0} \right)^2 = - \frac{2}{\gamma - 1} \frac{\partial S/c_p}{\partial n},$$

where $a_0$ is the stagnation speed of sound. If $\Delta s$ is the separation distance between two orthogonal trajectories which are close together (see Fig. 6-3), we may obtain the expression for the streamline curvature

$$(6.2.7) \qquad \frac{\partial \theta}{\partial s} = - \frac{d \ln \Delta s}{dn}.$$

Using (6.2.7) and substituting $\psi$ for $n$ in (6.2.6), the differential equation becomes

$$(6.2.8) \qquad \frac{\partial (q/a_0)^2}{\partial \psi} + \left[ \frac{\partial \ln (\Delta s)^2}{\partial \psi} - \frac{dS/c_p}{d\psi} \right] \left( \frac{q}{a_0} \right)^2 = - \frac{2}{\gamma - 1} \frac{dS/c_p}{d\psi}.$$

On integrating this equation from the shock to the point of interest we find that

$$(6.2.9) \qquad \left( \frac{q}{a_0} \right)^2 = \left( \frac{\Delta s}{\Delta s_s} \right)^2 \left\{ \left( \frac{q_s}{a_0} \right)^2 \exp \left( \frac{S - S_s}{c_p} \right) \right.$$

$$\left. - \frac{2}{\gamma - 1} \frac{1}{c_p} \exp \left( \frac{S}{c_p} \right) \int_{\psi_s} \left( \frac{\Delta s}{\Delta s_s} \right)^2 \exp \left( - \frac{S}{c_p} \right) \frac{dS}{d\psi} d\psi \right\}.$$

From the energy equation the mass flow is given by

$$(6.2.10) \qquad \frac{\rho q}{\rho_0 a_0} = \exp \left( - \frac{S - S_0}{\mathscr{R}} \right) \left( 1 - \frac{\gamma - 1}{2} \frac{q^2}{a_0^2} \right)^{\frac{1}{\gamma - 1}} \frac{q}{a_0},$$

where $\mathscr{R}$ is the gas constant. Thus with $q$ determined, $\rho q$ may be found and (6.2.2) can be integrated. With the new values of $\psi$ fixed on each orthogonal trajectory, the corrected streamlines are drawn in (see Fig. 6-3) by connecting corresponding points. In this manner the coordinate axes are set for the next approximation once the corresponding new orthogonal curves are also drawn. The shock detachment distance is then altered, and the shock shape is once again iterated by the method described previously. This complete procedure is carried through as many times as is necessary until the connection factor $Q$ is obtained equal to one for a given streamline distribution pattern. A certain amount of judgment on the part of the operator is necessary for the success of this procedure.

Uchida and Yasuhara have carried out such a calculation for the flow over a blunt-nosed cylinder at a Mach number of 2, and their results compare favorably with experiment both as to shock shape and pressure distribution. In addition, from their calculations they were able to draw in the sonic line and the limiting characteristic. The angle that the sonic line made with the streamline at the shock was found to be in good agreement with the local exact value shown in Fig. 6–2. Because only one calculation was carried out, all further discussion of its results will be reserved for Section 6.3, where a comparison with other exact calculations at higher Mach numbers can be made (see Figs. 6–4 and 6–5).

It is of interest to observe that in the $M_\infty = 2$ calculation six alterations of the streamline pattern in the flow fields were required, along with six to seven iterations of the shock shape for each streamline pattern determined. That such a large number of iterations was necessary, in spite of the fact that the initial guess regarding the shock shape and detachment distance was not too far off, is indicative of the amount of labor required by this scheme. It should be pointed out, however, that the problem is essentially more difficult at $M_\infty = 2$ than at higher values of the Mach number, and that the procedure should work better in the hypersonic range. Furthermore, it is probable that such a method could be programmed for automatic computation. Apart from the question of the stability and convergence of such an iteration scheme, which of course cannot readily be answered because of the nonlinear nature of the problem, it would appear that such a procedure does at least afford an exact numerical method for the calculation of inviscid flow fields of the type discussed.

### 3. Method of integral relations

Although the streamtube-continuity technique provides us with an exact formulation for computing the hypersonic flow over blunt bodies, it possesses the drawback of being somewhat difficult to program for electronic computation. A method which is well adaptable to machine computation would be highly desirable. At the Ninth International Congress of Applied Mechanics, in Brussels, Dorodnitsyn [2] submitted an abstract of a paper in which he proposed a general method of numerical solution for nonlinear hydrodynamic problems (see also Dorodnitsyn [3]). This interesting scheme is directly applicable to our blunt-body problem, and, though rather lengthy, does have the important advantage of being well suited for automatic digital computation.

The basic idea of Dorodnitsyn's scheme can be illustrated by considering the following system of partial differential equations in two independent variables

$$(6.3.1) \qquad \frac{\partial P_i(x, y;\ u_1, \cdots, u_n)}{\partial x} + \frac{\partial Q_i(x, y;\ u_1, \cdots, u_n)}{\partial y}$$
$$= L_i(x, y;\ u_1, \cdots, u_n).$$

Here $i = 1, 2, \cdots, n$, the $u_i$'s are unknown functions of $x$ and $y$, and $P_i, Q_i$, and $L_i$ are known functions of their arguments. To simplify the presentation we shall consider the solution of this system of equations in a rectangular domain bounded by the lines $x = 0$; $x = constant$, and $y = 0$; $y = 1$. The method of attack is first to divide this domain into $N$ strips by drawing equidistant lines on $y = y_k = constant$ $(0 \leqslant y \leqslant 1)$, and then to integrate the system of equations along an arbitrary line $x = constant$ from $y = 0$ to the boundary of each of the strips. Since we have $n$ equations and $N$ strips we will obtain $nN$ independent integral relations of the form

$$(6.3.2) \qquad (Q_i)_k + \frac{d}{dx} \int_0^{y_k} P_i\, dy = \int_0^{y_k} L_i\, dy + (Q_i)_{y=0}\,.$$

Here $k = 1, 2, \cdots, N$, and on the $k^{\text{th}}$ line $y = y_k = [N - (k - 1)]/N$, with the conditions at $y = 1$ denoted by $k = 1$.

Suppose now that we approximate the integrands in (6.3.2) by interpolation polynomials, for example $P_1$ by

$$(6.3.3) \qquad P_1 = \sum_{m=0}^{N} a_m(x)y^m,$$

where the $a_m(x)$ depend linearly on the values of the function $P_1$ on the strip boundaries. By substituting relations of the form of (6.3.3) into the integral relations and integrating, we obtain a system of $nN$ simultaneous ordinary differential equations, with the values of the functions $u_n$ at the interpolation points as the dependent variables. Applying the appropriate boundary conditions and numerically integrating this system from $x = 0$ to $x = constant$ will then give us the desired solution. The basic question of how large $N$ must be can be answered readily only by carrying out the solution for increasing values of $N$ until a satisfactory convergence of the result is achieved.

Although we have described Dorodnitsyn's technique for fixed boundaries, its extension to problems whose boundaries are initially unknown is quite straightforward. We shall illustrate this generalization in connection with our blunt-body study. Dorodnitsyn's method has been applied by Belotser-kovskii [1] in calculating the supersonic flow of a perfect gas past a circular cylinder. In our discussion we shall follow the approach of Belotserkovskii, although we shall present the method in a form which is also applicable to computing the flow past a sphere. It will become apparent to the reader that by utilizing the hydrodynamic equations in general orthogonal coordinates oriented with respect to the body, the technique can be generalized to flows around two-dimensional or axisymmetric blunt bodies of arbitrary shape. We shall restrict our attention to the case of the cylinder or sphere because of the relative simplicity of form afforded by polar coordinates.

As in our constant-density solutions for the cylinder and sphere, we utilize polar coordinates $R$ and $\vartheta$, where $R$ is the cylindrical or spherical radius measured from the center of the body and $\vartheta$ is the polar angle measured from the upstream axis (see Fig. 4–4). The equations of continuity and momentum in these coordinates are expressible as

$$(6.3.4) \qquad \frac{\partial \rho v R y^j}{\partial R} + \frac{\partial \rho u y^j}{\partial \vartheta} = 0 \,,$$

$$(6.3.5) \qquad v \frac{\partial v}{\partial R} + \frac{u}{R} \frac{\partial v}{\partial \vartheta} - \frac{u^2}{R} = -\frac{1}{\rho} \frac{\partial p}{\partial R} \,,$$

$$(6.3.6) \qquad v \frac{\partial u}{\partial R} + \frac{u}{R} \frac{\partial u}{\partial \vartheta} + \frac{uv}{R} = -\frac{1}{\rho R} \frac{\partial p}{\partial \vartheta} \,.$$

Here $y = R \sin \vartheta$ is the radius from the axis, with $j = 0$ for the cylinder and $j = 1$ for the sphere, while $u$ and $v$ are the velocity components along the $\vartheta$ and $R$ axes, respectively.

In order to recast the flow equations into Dorodnitsyn's divergence form, we first rewrite (6.3.5) so that a term $\partial(p + \rho v^2)/\partial R$ appears, then eliminate $\partial \rho v / \partial R$ by means of the continuity equation. The result is

$$(6.3.7) \qquad \frac{\partial R y^j (p + \rho v^2)}{\partial R} + \frac{\partial \rho u v y^j}{\partial \vartheta} - [(1 + j)p + \rho u^2] y^j = 0 \,.$$

By using the Bernoulli relation, only one of the momentum equations is required so that (6.3.7) is sufficient. At this point we make the restriction that the fluid is a perfect gas of constant $\gamma$. As with our restriction to polar coordinates this restriction is not a fundamental one and is made only to facilitate our presentation. Following Belotserkovskii we now rewrite (6.3.7) in non-dimensional form by referring the pressure and density to their free stream stagnation values ($\bar{p} = p/p_{0,\infty}$; $\bar{\rho} = \rho/\rho_{0,\infty}$) and all velocities to the maximum adiabatic velocity denoted by $q_{max}$ (e.g. $\bar{v} = v/q_{max}$). Note that $q_{max}^2 = 2a_0^2/(\gamma - 1)$. The dimensionless momentum equation becomes

$$(6.3.8) \qquad \frac{\partial \bar{R}\bar{y}^j P_v}{\partial \bar{R}} + \frac{\partial \bar{y}^j P_{uv}}{\partial \vartheta} - \bar{y}^j P_u = 0,$$

where

$$(6.3.9a) \qquad P_v = \frac{\gamma - 1}{2\gamma}\,\bar{p} + \bar{\rho}\bar{v}^2,$$

$$(6.3.9b) \qquad P_u = (1 + j)\frac{\gamma - 1}{2\gamma}\,\bar{p} + \bar{\rho}\bar{u}^2,$$

$$(6.3.9c) \qquad P_{uv} = \bar{\rho}\bar{u}\bar{v}.$$

Here the barred quantities denote the appropriate dimensionless variables, and $\bar{R} = R/R_b$ and $\bar{y} = y/R_b$.

Using the condition of the constancy of entropy along streamlines, the continuity equation can be written as

$$(6.3.10) \qquad \frac{\partial \bar{R}\bar{y}^j Q_v}{\partial \bar{R}} + \frac{\partial \bar{y}^j Q_u}{\partial \vartheta} = 0,$$

where

$$(6.3.11a) \qquad Q_v = (1 - \bar{q}^2)^{\frac{1}{\gamma-1}}\,\bar{v},$$

$$(6.3.11b) \qquad Q_u = (1 - \bar{q}^2)^{\frac{1}{\gamma-1}}\,\bar{u},$$

and $\bar{q}^2 = \bar{u}^2 + \bar{v}^2$.

Finally, we have the entropy equation for a perfect gas

$$(6.3.12) \qquad \bar{p} = E(\bar{\psi})\bar{\rho}^\gamma,$$

whence we obtain

$$(6.3.13) \qquad \bar{\rho} = [(1 - \bar{q}^2)/E]^{\frac{1}{\gamma-1}}.$$

The quantity $E$ is a function only of the stream function $\bar{\psi}$ and may be found from its value just behind the shock wave. The stream function $\bar{\psi}$ is defined by

$$(6.3.14) \qquad d\bar{\psi} = \bar{\rho}\bar{y}^j(\bar{u}\,d\bar{R} - \bar{v}\bar{R}\,d\vartheta).$$

We note that with this definition the velocity components are given by

$$(6.3.15) \qquad \bar{\rho}\bar{u}\bar{y}^j = \frac{\partial \bar{\psi}}{\partial \bar{R}},$$

$$(6.3.16) \qquad \bar{\rho}\bar{v}\bar{y}^j\bar{R} = -\frac{\partial \bar{\psi}}{\partial \vartheta}.$$

The equations (6.3.8) to (6.3.14) define our problem for the four unknowns $\bar{v}$, $\bar{u}$, $E$, and $\bar{\psi}$, and are in a form suitable for the application of the method of integral relations.

In order to complete the definition of our problem we must now specify the boundary conditions. On the body where $\bar{R} = 1$ this is quite straightforward, since

$$(6.3.17a) \qquad \bar{v}_b(\vartheta) = 0,$$

$$(6.3.17b) \qquad \bar{\psi}_b(\vartheta) = 0,$$

$$(6.3.17c) \qquad E(\bar{\psi}_b) = E_b(0) = \text{constant.}$$

On the shock wave, on the other hand, the boundary conditions must be specified in terms of two unknown parameters describing both the location and shape of the shock, namely the shock inclination angle $\sigma$ and the shock layer thickness. The shock is taken to be located at $\bar{R}_s(\vartheta) = 1 + \bar{\Delta}(\vartheta)$, where $\bar{\Delta}$ is the unknown shock layer thickness made dimensionless with respect to the body radius and measured from the body to the shock along a ray $\vartheta = constant$. From the geometry of the shock wave we obtain the relation

$$(6.3.18) \qquad \frac{d\bar{\Delta}}{d\vartheta} = -(1 + \bar{\Delta}) \cot(\vartheta + \sigma).$$

The stream function at the shock is given in terms of $\bar{\Delta}$ by

$$(6.3.19) \qquad \bar{\psi}_s = \frac{\bar{\rho}_\infty \bar{U} \bar{y}_s^{1+j}}{1 + j} = \frac{\bar{\rho}_\infty \bar{U} [(1 + \bar{\Delta}) \sin \vartheta]^{1+j}}{1 + j} .$$

The remaining boundary conditions can be found from the oblique shock relations and are

$$(6.3.20) \qquad \bar{p}_s = \frac{4\gamma}{\gamma^2 - 1} (1 - \bar{U}^2)^{\frac{\gamma}{\gamma-1}} \left[ \frac{\bar{U}^2 \sin^2 \sigma}{1 - \bar{U}^2} - \frac{(\gamma - 1)^2}{4\gamma} \right],$$

$$(6.3.21) \qquad E_s = \bar{p}_s (1 - \bar{U}^2)^{-\frac{\gamma}{\gamma-1}} \left(\frac{\gamma - 1}{\gamma + 1}\right)^\gamma \left(\frac{1 - \bar{U}^2 \cos^2 \sigma}{\bar{U}^2 \sin^2 \sigma}\right)^\gamma,$$

$$(6.3.22a) \qquad \bar{u}_s = W_1 \sin \vartheta + W_2 \cos \vartheta,$$

$$(6.3.22b) \qquad \bar{v}_s = W_2 \sin \vartheta - W_1 \cos \vartheta,$$

where

$$(6.3.23) \qquad (\gamma + 1) \bar{U} W_1 = \gamma - 1 + 2 \bar{U}^2 \cos^2 \sigma,$$

and

$$(6.3.24) \qquad (\gamma + 1) \bar{U} W_2 = \cot \sigma [\bar{U}^2 (\gamma + 1 - 2 \cos^2 \sigma) - (\gamma - 1)].$$

It is to be recalled that $\bar{U} = U/q_{max}$ is related to the free stream Mach number by the equation

$$(6.3.25) \qquad \bar{U}^2 = \frac{\dfrac{\gamma - 1}{2} M_\infty^2}{1 + \dfrac{\gamma - 1}{2} M_\infty^2}.$$

With the problem thus formulated, the method of solution is quite straightforward. In order, however, to carry out Dorodnitsyn's scheme with an unknown shock boundary we introduce the dimensionless variable

$$(6.3.26) \qquad \zeta = \frac{\bar{R} - 1}{\bar{\Delta}}; \quad 0 \leqslant \zeta \leqslant 1.$$

In terms of this variable the shock layer can be broken up into $N$ strips by drawing equidistant lines $\zeta_k = constant$ between the wave and the body. Of course, at this stage of the calculation the actual shock layer thickness is still unknown. As before, let us denote all quantities on the body where $\zeta = 0$ by the subscript $b$. For the remaining strip boundaries we will adopt Belotserkovskii's notation and denote all quantities on the $k$-th line where $\zeta = \zeta_k = [N - (k - 1)]/N$ by the subscript $k$, and on the wave where $\zeta_s = \zeta_1 = 1$ by the subscript 1.

According to the method described at the outset, we must now integrate our partial differential equations (6.3.8) and (6.3.10) along an arbitrary ray $\vartheta = constant$ from the body surface to the boundary of each of the strips. Carrying out these integrations and applying the appropriate boundary conditions at the body surface ($\bar{R} = 1$), we obtain the following $2N$ independent relations:

$$(6.3.27) \quad (P_v)_k \bar{R}_k (\bar{R}_k \sin \vartheta)^j - (P_v)_b (\sin \vartheta)^j + \frac{d}{d\vartheta} (\sin \vartheta)^j \int_1^{1+\zeta_k \bar{\Delta}} P_{uv} \bar{R}^j \, d\bar{R}$$

$$- (P_{uv})_k \zeta_k (\bar{R}_k \sin \vartheta)^j \frac{d\bar{\Delta}}{d\vartheta} - (\sin \vartheta)^j \int_1^{1+\zeta_k \bar{\Delta}} P_u \bar{R}^j \, d\bar{R} = 0,$$

$$(6.3.28) \quad (Q_v)_k \bar{R}_k (\bar{R}_k \sin \vartheta)^j + \frac{d}{d\vartheta} (\sin \vartheta)^j \int_1^{1+\zeta_k \bar{\Delta}} Q_u \bar{R}^j \, d\bar{R}$$

$$- (Q_u)_k \zeta_k (\bar{R}_k \sin \vartheta)^j \frac{d\bar{\Delta}}{d\vartheta} = 0,$$

with $k = 1, 2, \cdots, N$. From the above equations it is apparent that the undetermined boundary enters through the additional unknown function $\bar{\Delta}(\vartheta)$.

Our next step is to reduce these integro-differential equations to ordinary differential equations by assuming that the $P$ and $Q$ functions can be represented by polynomials in $\zeta$. For example, we assume $P_u$ is of the form

$$(6.3.29) \qquad P_u(\bar{R}, \vartheta) = a_b(\vartheta) + \sum_{m=1}^{N} a_m(\vartheta)\zeta^m,$$

where $a_m(\vartheta)$ will depend linearly on the values of the function $P_u$ on the strip boundaries. For example, for $N = 2$ we would have with the subscript $u$ dropped $a_b = P_b$, $a_1 = 4P_2 - P_1 - 3P_b$, and $a_2 = 2(-2P_2 + P_1 + P_b)$. We remind the reader that the subscript 1 denotes conditions at the shock wave, subscript $b$ conditions on the body, and in this case the subscript 2 represents conditions along a line midway between the body and the shock.

If we substitute the appropriate relations of the form of (6.3.29) into our integral relations we obtain $2N$ ordinary differential equations. By writing (6.3.12) and (6.3.14) along each of the $N - 1$ lines $\zeta = \zeta_q$, where $q = 2, 3, \cdots$, $N$, we obtain $N - 1$ additional ordinary differential equations and $N - 1$ algebraic relations. The final relation to complete the system is the differential equation (6.3.18). This then gives us a total of $3N$ ordinary differential equations and $N - 1$ algebraic relations to determine the $4N - 1$ unknowns $\bar{u}_b$, $\bar{\Delta}$, $\sigma$, $\bar{u}_q$, $\bar{v}_q$, $E_q$, $\bar{\psi}_q$.

In order to find the desired solution, the approximating system of equations must now be integrated with respect to $\vartheta$ from the stagnation streamline ($\vartheta = 0$). An examination of the initial conditions at $\vartheta = 0$, namely $\bar{u}(\bar{R}, 0) = 0$, $\bar{\psi}(\bar{R}, 0) = 0$, $\sigma(0) = \frac{1}{2}\pi$, makes it clear that these conditions are by themselves insufficient to determine a unique solution to the problem. Physically, of course, it is obvious that if they were sufficient there would be no influence of the downstream flow on the upstream region. In point of fact, however, the upstream influence is manifested in the differential equations by a singular behavior somewhat analogous to that associated with the critical point or singular point in the thin shock layer theory of Chapter V. We shall term a singular point of this type in this theory a "sonic singular point". The reason for this terminology will appear later. To find that solution which properly traverses the sonic singular points it is necessary to add other requirements based on the nature of the solution near these singularities.

As a result of the imposition of the additional conditions at the sonic singular points the problem becomes a two point boundary value problem. We start with an assumed solution at the stagnation point, and require that it satisfy the imposed conditions in the critical region. If the conditions governing the singular behavior of the equations are not met, the stagnation point solution must be revised and the integration process repeated until all the requirements in the critical region are satisfied and a single unique solution is determined.

To illustrate the nature of the singularities and the computational technique, let us consider for either a sphere or cylinder the simple case in which we take $N = 1$ and thereby consider the shock layer as a single strip. Then the functions in (6.3.27) and (6.3.28) are linear functions of $\zeta$ determined by their values on the body and on the shock. For this example there are three simultaneous first-order differential equations to solve. These are (6.3.18), and two differential equations of the form

$$(6.3.30) \qquad \frac{d\sigma}{d\vartheta} + A\frac{d\bar{\Delta}}{d\vartheta} + B = 0,$$

$$(6.3.31) \qquad \left(\frac{\gamma - 1}{\gamma + 1} - \bar{u}_b^2\right)\frac{d\bar{u}_b}{d\vartheta} + C\frac{d\sigma}{d\vartheta} + D\frac{d\bar{\Delta}}{d\vartheta} + F = 0,$$

where $A$, $B$, $C$, $D$, and $F$ are known functions of $\bar{\Delta}$, $\sigma$, $\bar{u}_b$, and $\vartheta$. We note that the first of these equations comes from (6.3.27), and the second from the continuity relation (6.3.28).

The initial conditions at $\vartheta = 0$ for the integration of the differential equations are that $\sigma = \frac{1}{2}\pi$, $\bar{u}_b = 0$, and $\bar{\Delta} = \bar{\Delta}_0$, where $\bar{\Delta}_0$ is an assumed value of the stagnation point detachment distance. In order to start the integration process for each value of the parameter $\bar{\Delta}_0$ we also require the correct initial values of the quantity $d\sigma/d\vartheta$ (related to the curvature of the shock on the axis) and the quantity $d\bar{u}_b/d\vartheta$ (essentially the velocity gradient at the stagnation point). Once these have been determined from (6.3.30) and (6.3.31) for $\vartheta = 0$ and hence for $\sigma = \frac{1}{2}\pi$, we are prepared to initiate the integration in terms of the unknown but initially estimated stagnation point detachment distance.

From (6.3.31) it can be seen that $\bar{u}_b = \sqrt{(\gamma - 1)/(\gamma + 1)}$ is a singular point of the system and that, since $q_{max} = \sqrt{(\gamma + 1)/(\gamma - 1)}a_{son}$, this singularity corresponds to the sonic point on the body. By combining the three differential equations we can rewrite (6.3.31) as

$$(6.3.32) \qquad \frac{d\bar{u}_b}{d\vartheta} = \frac{J_b^{(1)}}{\left(\dfrac{\gamma - 1}{\gamma + 1} - \bar{u}_b^2\right)},$$

where $J_b^{(1)}$ is a function of $\bar{\Delta}_0$, $\bar{u}_b$, $\sigma$, and $\vartheta$. At this juncture we must now make a distinction between the types of bodies being considered. If the body shape is analytic and smooth so that there are no sharp corners at which the velocity must become sonic, then $\bar{u}_b$ is a continuous function cf $\vartheta$ and we require that $J_b^{(1)} = 0$ at $\bar{u}_b^2 = (\gamma - 1)/(\gamma + 1)$. In this case the solution is obtained by initially estimating the stagnation point detachment distance using one of the more approximate solutions, and then integrating the diffe-rential equations to $\bar{u}_b^2 = (\gamma - 1)/(\gamma + 1)$. If the condition $J_b^{(1)} = 0$ is not satisfied at that point, we must re-estimate $\bar{\Delta}_0$ and integrate again, repeating the process as many times as are necessary until the condition $J_b^{(1)} = 0$ at $\bar{u}_b^2 = (\gamma - 1)/(\gamma + 1)$ is satisfied.

Had one intermediate line been introduced in the problem of the sphere or cylinder, we observe that $N = 2$ and we should have obtained six simul-taneous ordinary differential equations and one algebraic relation. In this case three of the differential equations are of the same form as for the first approximation. The other three differential equations involve $d\bar{u}_2/d\vartheta$, $d\bar{v}_2/d\vartheta$, and $d\bar{\psi}_2/d\vartheta$, where the subscript 2 represents conditions along the line midway between the body and the shock. The two equations which come from the continuity relation (6.3.28) are singular and have the form

$$(6.3.33) \qquad \frac{d\bar{u}_b}{d\vartheta} = \frac{J_b^{(2)}}{\left(\dfrac{\gamma - 1}{\gamma + 1} - \bar{u}_b^2\right)},$$

$$(6.3.34) \qquad \frac{d\bar{u}_2}{d\vartheta} = \frac{J_2^{(2)}}{\dfrac{\gamma - 1 + 2\bar{v}_2^2}{\gamma + 1} - \bar{q}_2^2},$$

where $J_b^{(2)}$ and $J_2^{(2)}$ are known functions of $\vartheta$ and the dependent variables. We may note that $\bar{a}^2 = \frac{1}{2}(\gamma - 1)(1 - \bar{q}^2)$, and that the denominator on the right hand side of (6.3.34) may be expressed as $2/(\gamma + 1)$ times the quantity $\bar{a}_2^2 - \bar{u}_2^2$.

As with the case $N = 1$ the integration is again carried out from $\vartheta = 0$, where we apply the initial conditions $\bar{u}_b = \bar{u}_2 = 0$, $\bar{\psi}_2 = 0$, $\sigma = \frac{1}{2}\pi$. In this case, however, besides having to specify the parameter $\bar{\Delta}_0$ as an initial unknown, we must also specify $\bar{v}_2(0)$. Thus we see that in the second approxi-mation there are two unknown parameters to be determined by conditions in the critical region. Evidently, if we again require a continuous solution, then in addition to our requirement on $\bar{u}_b$, we also require that $J_2^{(2)} = 0$ when $\bar{u}_2^2 = \bar{a}_2^2$. In fact for each increase in $N$ by one, one parameter, $\bar{v}_k(0)$, and one condition, $J_k = 0$ for $\bar{u}_k^2 = \bar{a}_k^2$, are added. Hence the sonic singular points of the system will be located where the line

$$(6.3.35a) \qquad \bar{u}^2 = \bar{a}^2$$

intersects the strip boundaries. An examination of the topology of the differential equations indicates that these singularities are of a saddle type. Furthermore, since $q_{max}^2 = (\gamma + 1)q_{son}^2/(\gamma - 1)$, we note that the sonic singular points occur along the line

$$(6.3.35b) \qquad \bar{q}^2 = \left(1 + \frac{2}{\gamma - 1}\bar{v}^2\right)q_{son}^2.$$

Belotserkovskii's scheme is essentially a finite difference scheme, and it is well established that finite difference schemes in general have certain inherent limitations in solving partial differential equations. Thus, in the method of integral relations we should expect minor divergences in such problems as the precise determination of zones of action and of lines dividing elliptic and hyperbolic regions. With this minor limitation in mind we interpret the line of sonic singular points (6.3.35) directly as the sonic line. This interpretation is exact at the body and at any point for which $\bar{v}_k$ is zero, and is almost exact at other points because the quantity $2\bar{v}_k^2/(\gamma - 1)$ is generally small compared with one.

Because the functions $J_k$ depend upon all the dependent variables in general, we do have an analogue of the transonic zone in this analysis. The value of a function $u_k$ at a point past the sonic singular point for the strip $k = k_1$ may still have an effect on the solution at the same value of $\vartheta$ for $u_k$ at $k = k_2$ which is less than its singular value. A change in $u_k$ on this second strip has an upstream influence and would change the entire subsonic region. Let us define $\vartheta_{\lim}$ as the greatest value of $\vartheta$ for which a sonic singular point occurs. Only for $\vartheta > \vartheta_{\lim}$ is there no more upstream influence. The line $\vartheta = \vartheta_{\lim}$ is thus the analogue of the limiting characteristic in the method of integral relations. The roundabout manner by which a point in the transonic zone affects the subsonic region is completely analogous in the method of integral relations and in physical reality.

Belotserkovskii has carried out digital machine computations, using the method outlined, in order to determine the flow field around a circular cylinder for free stream Mach numbers of 3, 4, and 5 with $\gamma = 1.4$. For $M_\infty = 3, 4$, and 5 the calculations were carried out with $N = 2$ in the method, while for $M_\infty = 3$ the solution for $N = 3$ was also computed. The approximation with $N = 3$ was found to agree very closely with the results for $N = 2$. In Fig. 6–4 we have shown Belotserkovskii's results for the sonic line and shock shape, and, for purposes of comparison, Uchida and Yasuhara's [1] computation for $M_\infty = 2$.

In all cases, the angle the sonic line makes with the streamline behind the shock is in good agreement with the exact results shown in Fig. 6–2. In addition we note that, consistent with our previous approximate calculations, the sonic point on such a cylindrical body is practically independent of Mach number. We see also that the sonic line at the body always makes an acute angle with the surface, consistent with our observation in Section 6.1 for two-dimensional bodies. Furthermore, because the Mach number is also moderate, the sonic line is peaked well within the shock layer. In this case, then, the first family (left-running) characteristics from the body can make the influence of the body in the supersonic region felt on the subsonic part of the flow field (cf. Fig. 6–1(b)). From the results shown it is certainly clear that the actual region of body influence in the supersonic region is decreasing with increasing Mach number, as is to be expected.

In Fig. 6–5 we have shown the surface pressure distribution calculated by Uchida and Yasuhara for $M_\infty = 2$, and by Belotserkovskii for the approximation $N = 3$ at $M_\infty = 3$. Although not shown in this figure, the increase

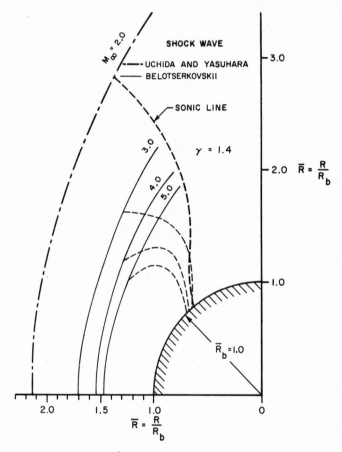

FIG. 6–4. Shock wave and sonic line shapes for a circular cylinder (Belotserkovskii [1]; Uchida and Yasuhara [1]).

in accuracy with increasing $N$ of Belotserkovskii's calculation is very rapid, with the approximation $N = 2$ giving the final result to what may be considered a desired practical accuracy. Both authors have compared their calculations with experiment; within experimental accuracy the agreement is exact, except for the last 15 degrees beyond the sonic point of Uchida and Yasuhara's calculations. Here the theoretical curve of Uchida and Yasuhara begins to fall below the experimental values, indicating an apparent loss in accuracy of the calculation. A comparison with Belotserkovskii's results would also seem to indicate that Uchida and Yasuhara's curve is slightly in error beyond the sonic point.

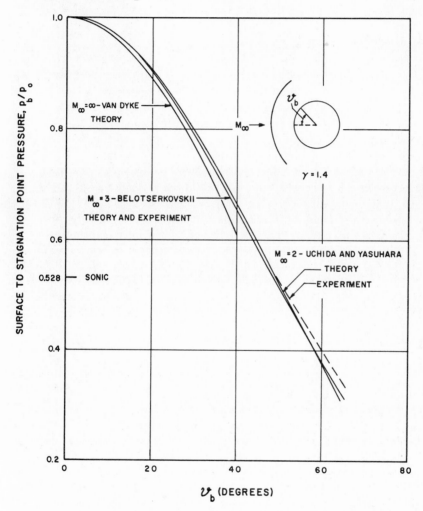

FIG. 6–5. Pressure distribution on a circular cylinder (Belotserkovskii [1]; Uchida and Yasuhara [1]; Van Dyke [6]).

In order to complete the picture of the flow past a circular cylinder we have also shown in Fig. 6–5 a numerical calculation of the pressure distribution for $\gamma = 1.4$ and $M_\infty = \infty$. This result was obtained by Van Dyke [6] using the inverse method to be discussed in Section 6.5. The interesting feature to be observed by comparing all the pressure distributions is the relative insensitivity to Mach number above about $M_\infty = 3$. This serves as a good example of how the Mach Number Independence Principle (Section 1.6) is operative at relatively low Mach numbers when the body is blunt.

## 4. Relaxation techniques

The last numerical approach we should like to discuss for the direct problem of finding the hypersonic flow field about a given blunt-nosed body is the relaxation method of Southwell. Although the technique is applicable to the problem at hand, it does have the disadvantages of being laborious, of being generally ill suited for machine computation, and of requiring judgment on the part of the computer. In spite of these drawbacks, it is still an alternative approach to a difficult problem.

Several authors have employed relaxation methods for determining the shock wave and inviscid field over blunt-nosed bodies at relatively low supersonic Mach numbers. The first of such investigations was carried out by Maccoll and Codd [1], who computed the supersonic flow past flat-nosed two-dimensional and axisymmetric bodies. Their initial estimations of the location and shape of the shock wave were obtained from experimental photographs. The accuracy of this study was strongly limited by their assumptions that the flow behind the shock was isentropic, and that the streamlines crossed the sonic line at right angles. Also, with these assumptions it is impossible to take into account the influence of the supersonic region in altering the sonic line shape and thereby in affecting the subsonic flow field.

Somewhat later, Drebinger [1], in his doctoral thesis, employed a relaxation technique to determine the flow over a blunt wedge behind a detached shock wave at a Mach number of 1.44. Although Drebinger was correct in taking the rotationality of the flow field into account, he also did not consider the upstream influence of the transonic zone between the sonic line and the limiting characteristic.

Proceeding one step still further, Mitchell [1] and Mitchell and McCall [1] again calculated the supersonic flow about flat-nosed two-dimensional and axisymmetric bodies. They automatically took into account the effect of the transonic zone on the upstream flow by carrying the relaxation calculation through to the purely supersonic region. In their calculations, no iteration on the shock shape was carried out, but instead the shock shape measured from an experimental photograph was taken as the shock shape in their solution. That this shock shape may not have been the correct one for their problem can be seen by examining their published results: the slope of the sonic line within and on the boundaries of the flow field and the shape of the streamlines in the sonic region appear to be inconsistent with exact calculations of local flow properties in the sonic region such as those discussed in Section 6.1.

We propose now to indicate a possible way of carrying out a relaxation solution for the blunt-body problem. Although this approach should apply for a general fluid, we shall again use the restriction to a perfect gas for simplicity. To arrive at the basic differential equation for the interior field let us again introduce the usual stream function through the relations

$$(6.4.1a) \qquad\qquad \rho u y^j = \frac{\partial \psi}{\partial y},$$

$$(6.4.1b) \qquad\qquad \rho v y^j = - \frac{\partial \psi}{\partial x},$$

where $x$ and $y$ are rectangular cartesian or cylindrical coordinates with origin at the stagnation point. From the definition of the vorticity $\zeta = \partial v/\partial x - \partial u/\partial y$, and the Crocco vorticity law (6.2.5) we may write the differential equation for the stream function in the form

$$(6.4.2) \quad \frac{\partial^2 \psi}{\partial x^2} + \frac{\partial^2 \psi}{\partial y^2} - \frac{\partial \psi}{\partial x}\frac{\partial \ln \rho}{\partial x} - \frac{\partial \psi}{\partial y}\frac{\partial \ln \rho}{\partial y} - \frac{j}{y}\frac{\partial \psi}{\partial y} + \frac{y^{2j} p \rho}{\mathscr{R}}\frac{dS}{d\psi} = 0,$$

where $\mathscr{R}$ is the gas constant in the perfect gas law. In addition, the pressure density, and entropy are connected by the relation

$$(6.4.3) \qquad\qquad \frac{p}{p_0} = \left(\frac{\rho}{\rho_0}\right)^\gamma \exp\left(\frac{S - S_0}{c_v}\right),$$

with the subscript 0 indicating stagnation conditions. The final relation required is supplied by the energy equation

$$(6.4.4) \qquad\qquad \frac{q^2}{2} + \frac{\gamma}{\gamma - 1}\frac{p}{\rho} = \frac{\gamma}{\gamma - 1}\frac{p_0}{\rho_0}.$$

By using (6.4.1) and (6.4.3) we may rewrite (6.4.4) as

$$(6.4.5) \qquad \frac{\gamma - 1}{2 a_0^2 \rho^2 y^{2j}}(\psi_x^2 + \psi_y^2) + \left(\frac{\rho}{\rho_0}\right)^{\gamma - 1} \exp\left(\frac{S - S_0}{c_v}\right) = 1,$$

with $a_0$ the stagnation speed of sound.

If we consider (6.4.2) as the basic differential equation for the stream function $\psi$, and (6.4.3) and (6.4.5) as auxiliary equations, we see that in the subsonic region behind the shock we have an elliptic partial differential equation for the stream function. As we have already observed, this problem is by no means a standard one since the location of the boundaries of the subsonic region, namely the shock and sonic line, are unknown.

The boundary conditions for this problem are as follows: at the shock wave the stream function and tangential velocity component are continuous across the shock. At the body and on the stagnation streamline $\psi = 0$, with the tangential velocity component being specified through the isentropic Bernoulli equation. Finally, the sonic line is determined by

$$(6.4.6) \qquad q^2 = a^2 = a_0^2 \left(\frac{\rho_{son}}{\rho_0}\right)^{\gamma - 1} \exp\left(\frac{S_{son} - S_0}{c_v}\right).$$

It might at first appear that we have overspecified the boundary conditions for the elliptic problem. However, this is not the case, since the fact that the boundary location is unknown requires the added information.

The general approach to the relaxation solution of (6.4.2) is to make an initial assumption as to the shock shape and location and the streamline distribution, based, say, on one of the more approximate theories discussed previously. Then (cf. Green and Southwell [1]) both the subsonic region and the supersonic region in the neighborhood of the sonic line are covered with a network of squares and the differential equations for $\psi$ are written in finite difference form. An assumed value of $\psi$ based on the approximate solution is assigned to each net point (making sure, of course, that the values of $\psi$ at both the shock boundary and the surface satisfy the appropriate boundary conditions). These values of $\psi$ are substituted in the difference equations, the terms of which will not in general add up to zero unless the assumed values are correct. This difference from zero at each net point is known as the residual, and the problem is to reduce the residuals to zero. The first step consists of obtaining a pattern relating a change in $\psi$ at each individual point to the changes in the neighboring residuals. Derivatives of $\psi$ can be computed from the assumed distribution of $\psi$. Since $S$ is a known function of $\psi$ for a given shock shape, $\ln \rho$ can then be determined from (6.4.5). Thus $\psi$, its derivatives, $\ln \rho$, $p$, and $dS/d\psi$ can be computed, and one can in turn determine the residual of (6.4.2).

Because the bow shock is curved, an interpolation technique such as discussed in Green and Southwell [1] or in Mitchell [1] is required at this boundary. A much more serious problem than this, however, is the break-down of the relaxation technique in the neighborhood of the sonic line because of the fact that small changes in $\psi$ cause relatively large variations in $\ln \rho$. Under such circumstances the relaxation pattern is no longer workable. Therefore, the main problems which we must consider are the devising of a method for carrying the relaxation calculation through the sonic region and somewhat beyond the limiting characteristic, and the establishment of certain consistency relations which are to serve as boundary conditions on the sonic line. These consistency relations can indicate how an incorrect shock shape should be adjusted so that the relaxation process can be repeated to obtain an improved solution.

One method of handling the flow pattern in the transonic zone is to approach the sonic line asymptotically from both the subsonic and supersonic regions by means of the relaxation technique, employing smaller and smaller squares as the sonic line is approached. Now the throat condition fixes $\rho$ exactly at the sonic line. The modification of the distribution of $\psi$ in the sonic region must be made subject to the mass flow requirement at $M = 1$, rather than with only the elimination of the residuals in mind. Therefore, a trial and error technique employing Bernoulli's equation and using first and second differences in $\rho$ can be used (because of the monotonic character of $\rho$) to extrapolate the location of the sonic line as the sonic line is approached. In this manner one may complete a tentative interior solution. In general, however, this solution will not be compatible with the conditions on the derivatives along the sonic line and along the shock, and the shock wave must be adjusted accordingly and another try made.

At this point any number of schemes are available for determining how the shock is to be altered. Perhaps the simplest of these is a method similar to the one described previously in conjunction with the streamtube-continuity technique. In this approach as many normal trajectories to the streamlines are drawn as are necessary to locate the shock. From the solution the new shock points $y_s$ are then computed by means of (6.2.2) and (6.2.3), which may be combined for a point on the shock in the form

$$(6.4.7) \qquad \frac{y_s^{1+j}}{1+j} = \int_{\psi=0}^{\psi=\psi_s} \frac{\rho q}{\rho_\infty U} y^j \, dn.$$

Of course one could also draw in the sonic line in the tentative solution, and a corresponding integral relation along this line could be obtained, in which the flow deflection angle, the angle the sonic line makes with the streamline, and $(\rho q)_{son}$ are the parameters (see Drebinger [1]). In any event, by this scheme or by one similar to it a new shock shape is determined in which the values of $\psi$ at the shock wave are altered, thereby causing a change in the residuals near the shock. A new interior solution must now be obtained by a repetition of the relaxation process. The shock shape must again be adjusted, and the cycle repeated until a consistent convergent solution is obtained.

Once such a solution is found we may check it by measuring the angles between the streamlines and constant velocity lines and then comparing these values with the corresponding angles which can be computed from the now known derivatives of $q$ and $\theta$. Of course, in two-dimensional flow the angles the streamlines make with the constant velocity lines such as the sonic line are known at the shock boundary independent of the shock curvature (cf. Fig. 6–2).

Although a scheme such as has been outlined appears to hold promise, there still remain questions as to its practicability. These questions will undoubtedly not be answered until a number of calculations are actually carried out.

## 5. The inverse problem

In the preceding sections of this chapter we have concerned ourselves with methods for finding exact numerical solutions for the direct problem, in which the shape of a blunt body in a uniform supersonic or hypersonic stream is given, and the shape and location of the detached bow shock and the flow in the shock layer are unknown. We turn now to what is termed the inverse problem (cf. Section 5.1), in which the shape of the shock is given and the shape of the body and the details of the flow in the shock layer are unknown. In this inverse problem, fundamental questions arise with respect to the uniqueness and existence of a solution and with respect to stability and convergence of calculation procedures.

The determination of the subsonic part of the flow field in this problem is governed by an elliptic partial differential equation, and is carried out as a Cauchy or initial value problem with Cauchy data (value of a function and of its normal derivative) specified along the shock wave; the boundaries of the subsonic region, namely the sonic line and the body, are unspecified. From the mathematical point of view a Cauchy problem for an elliptic differential equation is an improperly posed problem, and stringent restrictions must be placed on the boundary values in order that a solution exist. If a solution does exist, then the question of the uniqueness of the numerical solution to a given problem and the question of the stability of a calculation procedure for finding the solution are closely connected. The most important single feature of the inverse problem is the insensitiveness of the shock shape to local changes in body shape, and this feature leads to essential difficulties in the inverse problem. A minute local change in the shock shape will in general cause a large change in the body shape and may even preclude the existence of a solution.

Among the first to suggest the idea of approaching blunt-body flows as a Cauchy problem were Lin and Rubinov [1]. Their idea was simply that if the form of the detached shock wave were known precisely, the values of the flow variables behind the shock could be found from the oblique shock relations, while the first and higher derivatives of the flow quantities could be obtained from the equations of motion. The flow field is known to be analytic in a region immediately downstream of the shock if the shock shape is analytic. Lin and Rubinov pointed out that if the flow could be assumed to be analytic all the way to the body, then one could represent the flow between the shock wave and the body by an appropriate power series expansion. Lin and Shen [1], following these original ideas, carried out such an analysis for axisymmetric flow by means of a double power series expansion from an assumed parabolic shock. Their treatment was an essentially local one which was restricted to the stagnation region of the body.

Independently and at about the same time, Cabannes [1] performed a similar analysis for axisymmetric flow in which he assumed the shock wave to be described in rectangular cartesian coordinates by a power series of the form $x_s = \Sigma a_n y_s^n$. With this form of the shock wave he determined, for $\gamma = 1.4$ and arbitrary free stream Mach number, the coefficients in the double power series expansion for the flow variables to the $x^4$, $x^2 y^2$, and $y^4$ terms, and for the stream function to the $x^6$, $x^4 y^2$, $\cdots$ terms. Cabannes [2] later extended his calculations to terms of order two higher in the distance in the special case $M_\infty = 2$.

In both the work of Lin and Shen [1] and Cabannes [2] numerical calculations were made only for low supersonic Mach numbers. From unpublished calculations of Probstein which extended Lin and Shen's work to higher order terms, and from the calculations of Cabannes, the series expansions from the shock appear to be divergent in the region including the stagnation point. The existence of this apparent divergence was pointed out by Van Dyke [6] through a recasting of Cabannes' series into parabolic coordinates.

One possible reason for this state of affairs was suggested by Probstein [2] who pointed out that to a first approximation, when one is required to match just two geometrical parameters at the shock (e.g. flow deflection and rate of change of flow deflection), it is necessary to utilize third derivatives of the flow field velocity. In order to obtain a better approximation it is necessary to introduce still higher derivatives. Van Dyke [5; 6] suggested that the probable source of the divergence lies in the fact that the power series describes not only the flow downstream, but also its analytic continuation upstream. He points out that such a fictitious flow contains a limiting line at which the flow variables are nonanalytic. Therefore if the shock wave is closer to the limiting line than to the body, the power series will not include the body in its radius of convergence.

Actually for high Mach numbers and low $\epsilon$ where the shock layer is thin we might expect such methods to yield better results than for the lower Mach number cases, but even there the series-expansion techniques which have been developed are probably still not too satisfactory. It should be pointed out, however, that the divergence of the power series at the stagnation point does not exclude the possibility of the use of this method. As Lin and Shen observed, the justification of the method is really to be found in the idea of polynomial approximation. Therefore it seems reasonable that the method, if properly modified, might work just as the Kármán-Pohlhausen method works in boundary layer theory, where a series expansion of the Blasius equation diverges for large values of the independent variable. One reasonable modification might be to introduce in the scheme one (or more) integral relations, as for example an overall continuity condition, which would then serve to bring in the downstream influence on the upstream flow as well. Compare the Kármán-Pohlhausen approach of Maslen and Moeckel [1] (Integral Method).

Returning to the general inverse problem which we have set ourselves, we know that as far as elliptic differential equations are concerned, the initial value problem is improperly posed and leads to an unstable solution when treated by finite differences. If $\epsilon$ is small the shock layer is thin compared with the radius of curvature of the shock. In a "marching-ahead" procedure which starts with Cauchy data on the shock, only the relatively small thickness of the shock layer must be traversed. We may expect that there are fundamental singularities in the analytic continuation of the flow field past the body, and that these singularities are near the natural focii of the shock curve (e.g. at the center of a spherical shock). With a thin shock layer such singularities would be imbedded deeply within the body, far from the region in which the solution is to be obtained. The possibility presents itself of using a fundamentally unstable procedure to obtain a realistic solution. The idea here is that the essential instability is inescapable in the vicinity of one of these fundamental singularities, but that the instability may be circumvented in a narrow shock layer.

In order to better understand the nature of the instability which arises in an improperly set elliptic problem, let us briefly review the classic example of Hadamard [1, pp. 32–34] of solutions of Laplace's equation satisfying Cauchy conditions. Following Hadamard, let us consider Laplace's equation in rectangular cartesian coordinates

$$(6.5.1) \qquad\qquad \phi_{xx} + \phi_{yy} = 0,$$

subject to initial conditions on the $y$ axis

$$(6.5.2) \qquad \phi(0, y) = 0; \qquad \phi_x(0, y) = A_n \sin ny,$$

where $A_n$ is a function of $n$ equal to $n^{-q}$, where $q$ is a positive integer. The quantity $n$ is a parameter which may be very large.

We now note that the initial value of $\phi_x(0, y)$ can be made to differ as little as we like from zero by making $n$ sufficiently large. For any value of $A_n > 0$, the solution of Laplace's equation satisfying (6.5.2) is

$$(6.5.3) \qquad\qquad \phi(x, y) = n^{-1} A_n \sin ny \sinh nx.$$

Now on the other hand, suppose we were to have set $A_n = 0$ ($n$ arbitrarily large) in the initial conditions so that $\phi_x(0, y) = 0$. In this case we should have obtained the solution $\phi(x, y) = 0$. Clearly this result does not agree with

(6.5.3) in the limit $n \to \infty$ for any $x$ not equal to zero, since $|\phi(x, y)| \to \infty$ for $n \to \infty$; this is because $\sinh nx$ behaves like $\frac{1}{2}e^{nx}$ for large $n$. One interpretation of this from a practical point of view is that slight inaccuracies in the initial conditions can lead to large deviations in the solution. In fact, as Hadamard observed, the factor $\sin ny$ produces a fluting of the solution surface in this problem. This fluting, no matter how small in the immediate neighborhood of the $y$ axis, will "blow up" at any given distance away no matter how small this distance is, provided $n$ is sufficiently great. We should note that it is the high frequencies here which cause the instability.

In order to take care of the inherent instability associated with high frequencies in the hypersonic blunt-body problem, Zlotnick and Newman [1] consider the possibility of eliminating this magnification of errors. Such high frequencies are considered to be physically inadmissible in the blunt-body problem. We may expect this possibility to be realizable for smooth bodies at hypersonic speeds for which sudden large changes in shock or body curvature do not occur. These authors therefore propose to put an additional constraint on the solution wherein at every step of their marching-ahead process they filter out the high frequencies before proceeding by finite differences to the next step.

In order to estimate the error involved in such a filtering process, Zlotnick and Newman examined Laplace's equation subject to initial conditions of the type (6.5.2) on the $y$ axis, under the assumption that no frequencies higher than a given value, say $\lambda$, occur in the solution. They find that the absolute value of the error in calculating $\phi_{x_i}$, where $x_1 = x$ (for $i = 1$) and $x_2 = y$ (for $i = 2$), will be less than or equal to the quantity

$$(6.5.4) \quad \max|\text{error } \phi_{x_i}(x)| = e^{\lambda x} \left[ \sum_{j=1}^{2} \max|\text{error } \phi_{x_j}(0)| + \lambda^{-1}\delta \max|\phi_{x_i xx}| \right].$$

Here $\phi$ refers to the true solution of the problem, $\delta$ is the step length in the finite difference process, and $\max|\text{error } \phi_{x_j}(0)|$ is the maximum absolute value of the initial error in $\phi_{x_j}$. From this analysis we should have a good approximation as long as the step length, initial errors, and maximum allowable frequency are small. Although this estimation was carried out using Laplace's equation with a particular kind of smoothing process, we may reasonably assume that its validity would extend to the hypersonic blunt-body problem with other types of smoothing. We emphasize, however, that such an imposed constraint may by itself restrict the determinable bodies to smooth shapes with no sharp discontinuities or sudden changes in the curvature. Furthermore, such a smoothing process also raises the question of whether a small change in the shock shape would ever show up in an alteration of the body shape. The smoothing process gives us a spurious uniqueness to the problem, because we know that indistinguishably different shock shapes may correspond to radically different body shapes.

Many approaches are possible for solving the inverse problem numerically. We shall present the basic method of Zlotnick and Newman [1], Van Dyke [6], and Mangler and Evans [1], which is carried out in the real physical plane, and that of Garabedian [1] and Garabedian and Lieberstein [1], which is carried out in a complex three-dimensional space on planes that intersect the real physical plane. Mangler and Evans carried out the numerical calculation for the case with the shock wave a parabolic cylinder and $M_\infty = 7$ in a perfect gas of $\gamma = 1.4$. Zlotnick and Newman and Van Dyke compute several examples. No essential difference exists between the Zlotnick-Newman procedure, that of Van Dyke, and that of Mangler and Evans, all of which were developed independently. Zlotnick and Newman point out specifically that the basic instability in the subsonic region is suppressed by filtering out higher harmonics. A smoothing process is implicit in the procedure of Van Dyke. Both Lieberstein and Zlotnick have pointed out to the authors that in a finite difference method the use of differentiation schemes involving a large number of points is equivalent to applying a smoothing process. These procedures use shock-oriented coordinates; Van Dyke, who concerns himself specifically with shock waves described by conic sections, introduces a natural coordinate system appropriate to conic sections.

A subsequent development of the marching-ahead approach has been made by Vaglio-Laurin and Ferri [1], who also include a perturbation scheme for treating bodies of revolution at a small angle of incidence. These authors claim to have encountered no difficulty from instability. No specification of Mach number or gas was given for the numerical example whose results they present.

The method of Garabedian and Lieberstein differs from the other approach in that in it the initial data for a known analytic shock curve are first analytically continued into a fictitious three-dimensional space composed of the real value of one of the independent variables and a complex value of the other. In this manner the basic equation is transformed from elliptic to hyperbolic form, and thus the essential instability of the marching-ahead procedure is avoided through the stable numerical method of characteristics. The essential instability of the procedure appears in the analytic continuation step and is avoided by the choice of shock shapes expressed in terms of simple closed-form analytic functions. Although the method is mathematically rigorous it does possess the drawbacks of involving more computational effort than the other method mentioned and of being restricted in practice in the choice of shock shapes to those for which the required analytic continuation is feasible. However, the method does permit a control of the fundamental singularities mentioned above.

In presenting the inverse method in the real physical plane we shall follow the approach of Zlotnick and Newman in which the appropriate hydrodynamic equations are written in shock-oriented orthogonal curvilinear coordinates. These equations (5.1.1) and (5.1.6) have been discussed previously in Section 5.1 and are rewritten here for convenience:

$$(6.5.5\text{a}) \qquad uu_x + \mathcal{H}vu_y - Kuv = -\frac{p_x}{\rho},$$

$$(6.5.5\text{b}) \qquad uv_x + \mathcal{H}vv_y + Ku^2 = -\mathcal{H}\frac{p_y}{\rho},$$

$$(6.5.5\text{c}) \qquad (\rho ur^j)_x + (\mathcal{H}\rho vr^j)_y = 0,$$

where

$$(6.5.6) \qquad \mathcal{H} = 1 - Ky$$

and $K(x)$ is the curvature of the shock. In place of the entropy equation (5.1.7) we use the energy equation for a perfect gas

$$(6.5.7) \qquad \frac{\gamma}{\gamma-1}\frac{p}{\rho} + \frac{u^2+v^2}{2} = \frac{\gamma}{\gamma-1}\frac{p_0}{\rho_0}.$$

Here $x$ is the coordinate along the shock wave, $y$ is the coordinate at right angles to the shock wave and directed inward toward the center of curvature, and $u$ and $v$ are the respective velocity components.

By differentiating the energy equation with respect to $y$ and solving simultaneously for the $y$ derivatives of $u$, $v$, $p$, and $\rho$, we obtain

$$(6.5.8) \qquad u_y = -\frac{1}{\mathcal{H}v}\left(\frac{p_x}{\rho} + uu_x - Kuv\right),$$

$$(6.5.9) \qquad v_y = \frac{\dfrac{\gamma-1}{\gamma}\mathcal{H}uu_y - uv_x - Ku^2 + \dfrac{p(\rho ur^j)_x}{\rho^2 vr^j} + \dfrac{p(\mathcal{H}r^j)_y}{\rho r^j}}{\mathcal{H}\left(\dfrac{v}{\gamma} - \dfrac{p}{\rho v}\right)},$$

$$(6.5.10) \qquad \rho_y = -\frac{(\rho ur^j)_x + \mathcal{H}\rho v_y r^j + \rho v(\mathcal{H}r^j)_y}{\mathcal{H}vr^j},$$

$$(6.5.11) \qquad p_y = -\frac{\rho}{\mathcal{H}}(uv_x + \mathcal{H}vv_y + Ku^2).$$

These relations give us four equations for the determination of the four unknowns $u$, $v$, $\rho$, and $p$.

If we now start with a known shock shape the unknown functions $u$, $v$, $\rho$, and $p$ immediately behind the shock are determined by the oblique shock relations. With the functions known on this line $y = 0$ their $x$ derivatives are determined by differentiation. We may solve (6.5.8) to (6.5.11) successively for the values of the (normal) derivatives. Note that in (6.5.8) to (6.5.11) only $y$ derivatives determined in an earlier equation of the sequence are needed. The same procedure may be applied on any line $y = constant$ if the values of the functions are known. With the values of the unknown functions and their $y$ derivatives known as functions of $x$ at any value of $y$, say at $y_n$, the new values of the unknowns are determined in a finite difference scheme at $y_{n+1} = y_n + \delta y$ by taking $f(y_{n+1}) = f(y_n) + f_y(y_n)\delta y$, where $f$ is any one of the unknowns. Following Zlotnick and Newman's idea, the new value of the functions can be "appropriately smoothed". The process is then repeated until the unknown body is reached as determined by boundary conditions on the surface.

Zlotnick and Newman have performed automatic digital computations using the preceding scheme to determine the body shapes and shock layer profiles corresponding to a spherical shock for different values of the free stream Mach number and perfect gas specific heat ratio. They carried out the smoothing process by replacing the data at every forward step by new data obtained by fitting polynomials in $x$ to the old data. For their particular cases they found that a smooth fit of the data was necessary over an arc length no less than 0.16 of the shock radius of curvature in order to obtain a reasonably stable solution. The first step in determining the body shape was to note where the velocity on the stagnation streamline vanished, and thus to locate the stagnation point on the body. The body was then traced from the stagnation point along a line which was tangent to the streamline slope at each point, and for which the entropy had the same value as that of the stagnation streamline. In order to test the reasonableness of their calculated results, several streamlines were drawn in addition to the body streamline, and it was found that the two imposed requirements for a streamline were always fulfilled simultaneously: lines which passed through points of constant entropy were tangent to the streamline slopes.

Van Dyke, rather than using $u$, $v$, $\rho$, and $p$ as the independent variables, chose instead the density, a modified stream function, and its derivatives. He employed an 11-point differentiation scheme which had the effect of a smoothing process in the same manner as in Zlotnick and Newman's procedure. It appears that Van Dyke's numerical calculations were somewhat more accurate than those of Zlotnick and Newman. As we have mentioned Van Dyke's procedure is essentially equivalent to that we have presented, and we shall not discuss it separately.

In Mangler and Evans' procedure, the instability inherent in the marching-ahead procedure is overcome by using higher order differences in the marching direction, with values of the functions at three preceding points used at each step. The method has been programmed for digital computation and additional results will appear in later publications.

In Fig. 6–6 we have shown two computations of Zlotnick and Newman for the body and sonic line shape in axisymmetric flow, with a spherical shock in a flow at a free stream Mach number of 10 and with constant specific heat ratios $\gamma = \gamma_s = 1.2$ and 1.4. Although not shown, the results of the calculations for $M_\infty = 20$ and $M_\infty = \infty$ are very close to those for $M_\infty = 10$. We should point out that the derivative $r_y = \sin\vartheta$ in (6.5.9) and

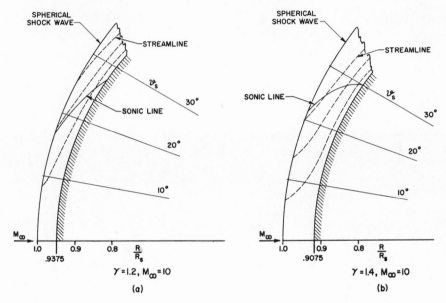

FIG. 6–6. Flow field and body for a spherical shock wave. (a) $\gamma = 1.2$, $M_\infty = 10$ (Zlotnick and Newman, unpublished). (b) $\gamma = 1.4$, $M_\infty = 10$ (Zlotnick and Newman [1]).

(6.5.10) was taken to be zero in the original calculations in order to simplify the calculations. This approximation appears in the results for $\gamma = 1.4$. It does not appear in the results for $\gamma = 1.2$ shown in Figs. 6–6 to 6–8, which are based on unpublished calculations of the same authors carried out without the approximation. The results for $\gamma = 1.2$ are very close to those calculated with $r_y = 0$.

From these calculations we observe the characteristic hypersonic axisymmetric sonic line associated with smooth bodies in hypersonic flows which we discussed in Section 6.1. Furthermore, as expected from our previous considerations, a comparison of the sonic line for $\gamma = 1.4$ and $\gamma = 1.2$ shows that for $\gamma = 1.4$ the sonic line approaches more closely the typical behavior at moderate Mach numbers. In addition we note the fact that the body is nearly parallel to the shock, which was indicated by the constant-density analysis of Section 4.4. Finally, the fact that the results for $M_\infty = 20$ and $M_\infty = \infty$ differ but slightly from the results for $M_\infty = 10$ points out the relative insensitiveness of the body shape to the Mach number at high Mach numbers for a constant $\gamma$. This is simply an inverse statement of the fact that the shock shape is relatively insensitive to the Mach number for a given body at a constant $\gamma$.

TABLE 6–1

*Comparison between Zlotnick-Newman and constant-density results for the stagnation point velocity gradient and the detachment distance for a spherical shock*

| $\gamma$ | | 1.2 | 1.4 |
|---|---|---|---|
| $M_\infty$ | | 10 | 10 |
| $\epsilon$ | | 0.100 | 0.175 |
| $\dfrac{R_s}{U}\left(\dfrac{du_b}{dx}\right)_0$ | Zlotnick-Newman numerical | 0.53 | 0.75 |
| | approximate constant-density $\sqrt{8\epsilon/3}$ | 0.52 | 0.68 |
| $\dfrac{\Delta_0}{R_s}$ | Zlotnick-Newman numerical | 0.063 | 0.092 |
| | approximate constant-density (4.4.16) | 0.066 | 0.104 |
| | complete constant-density (4.4.8) | 0.068 | 0.110 |

Other interesting conclusions can be obtained with regard to the stagnation point region from the same calculations. For example, in Table 6–1 we have shown the stagnation point detachment distance and velocity gradient obtained from the numerical integration, compared with the results of the constant-density analysis for a spherical shock. We have chosen to compare the results in this and what follows with the constant-density or Newtonian solutions because of the simple basis for comparison which they offer. In Table 6–1 the constant-density stagnation point detachment distance is obtained from the approximate relation (4.4.16) and from a numerical solution of (4.4.8) (see Lighthill [3] or Fig. 6–10). The velocity gradient is given approximately from (4.4.18) by $(du_b/dx)_0 = \sqrt{8\epsilon/3}(U/R_s)$. From the comparison it is certainly clear that the lower the density ratio, the closer is the agreement with the constant-density solution, and in fact for $\gamma = 1.2$ the agreement is seen to be moderately good.

Just how close the numerical solution approximates a constant-density flow is shown in Fig. 6–7, where we have plotted the profiles of pressure, density, and velocity components parallel and normal to the shock at two shock locations ($\vartheta_s = 5°$ and $32°$) for the case of $\gamma = 1.2$, $M_\infty = 10$. From these profiles we observe that near the stagnation point the assumption of constant density across the shock layer is indeed excellent. On the other hand, from the results at $\vartheta_s = 32°$ (somewhat beyond the sonic point on the body) it is equally clear that the constant-density assumption is beginning to break down. For example, according to the constant-density sphere solution the tangential velocity profile is approximately linear in $y$, and in fact from (4.4.18)

$$(6.5.12) \qquad \frac{u}{u_s} = \frac{\kappa(\Delta - y) + \epsilon R_s}{\kappa \Delta + \epsilon R_s},$$

with $\kappa = (1 - 8\epsilon/3)/\sqrt{8\epsilon/3}$. We remind the reader again that here $y$ is measured at right angles to the shock towards the body and equals zero on the shock. In Fig. 6–7(a) we have plotted for $\vartheta_s = 5°$ the constant-density result given by (6.5.12), using the value of $\Delta_0/R_s$ computed by Zlotnick and Newman. Clearly at $\vartheta_s = 5°$ the agreement is excellent. However, at $\vartheta_s = 32°$ we see that not only is $u/u_s$ no longer linear, but that it is appreciably different from its value at the stagnation point.

Figure 6–8 is a summary of the body surface distributions of pressure, velocity, Mach number, and of the detachment distance for $M_\infty = 10$ and $\gamma = 1.2$ and $1.4$, presented as a function of the shock angle. A comparison between the two cases again shows how the thin shock layer assumptions are more closely satisfied for $\gamma = 1.2$.

On the graphs of Fig. 6–8 we have also plotted the modified Newton-Busemann pressure distribution for a spherical shock in terms of the shock angle. This relation is a modification of (3.3.4) with $n = 3$, and is given by

$$(6.5.13) \qquad \frac{p_b}{p_0} = 1 - \tfrac{4}{3}\sin^2\vartheta_s.$$

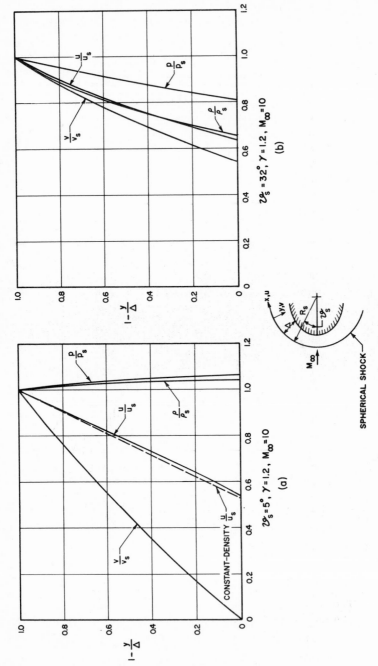

FIG. 6–7. Shock layer profiles for a spherical shock wave, $\gamma = 1.2$, $M_\infty = 10$ (Zlotnick and Newman, unpublished). (a) $\vartheta_s = 5°$. (b) $\vartheta_s = 32°$.

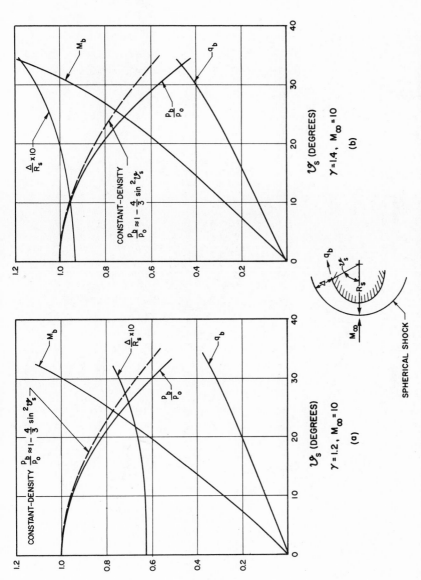

FIG. 6–8. Distribution of shock layer thickness and flow variables at body surface for a spherical shock wave. (a) $\gamma = 1.2$, $M_\infty = 10$ (Zlotnick and Newman, unpublished). (b) $\gamma = 1.4$, $M_\infty = 10$ (Zlotnick and Newman [1]).

As we have indicated in Section 3.1, the adjective "modified" always indicates division of the pressure by the correct stagnation pressure $p_0$ instead of by $\rho_\infty U^2$. This result is close to that obtained by Lighthill [3] from the constant-density analysis for a spherical shock and $\epsilon \ll 1$. Clearly, the agreement of the surface pressure distribution with (6.5.13) is better for $\gamma = 1.2$ than for $\gamma = 1.4$.

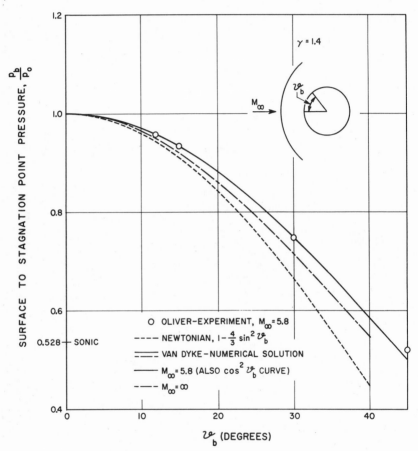

FIG. 6–9. Pressure distribution on a sphere (Van Dyke [6]) and comparison with experiment (Oliver [1]).

In Fig. 6–9 is shown the pressure distribution on a sphere as a function of the body angle for $\gamma = 1.4$ and $M_\infty = 5.8$ and $M_\infty = \infty$, as reported by Van Dyke from his numerical calculations. On the same figure we have shown the modified Newtonian pressure distributions both with and without the centrifugal correction, calculated in terms of the body angle. At $M_\infty = 5.8$

the agreement of Van Dyke's results with modified Newtonian (without the centrifugal correction) is good enough so that only one line need be drawn to describe both results. At $M_\infty = \infty$, the agreement with the modified Newtonian approximation is no better than with the modified Newton-Busemann relation up to about 30°. On this same figure is also shown for comparison the data of Oliver [1] for flow past a sphere in air at $M_\infty = 5.8$. The agreement with Van Dyke's calculation for the same case is seen to be excellent.

At this point we digress to discuss the Newtonian pressure laws which are commonly used for comparison purposes. The modification obtained by multiplying the pressure coefficient from one of these pressure laws by $p_0/\rho_\infty U^2$ to ensure agreement at the stagnation point is completely reasonable and appears in theories such as the constant-density theory of Chapter IV (cf. (4.3.17) and (4.4.11)). As we have pointed out in Section 3.1, only the Newton-Busemann pressure law has a rational basis and is a correct result in a limiting process. As we have also pointed out in Chapter IV, if the shock and the body surface are not strictly parallel any result of Newtonian theory is best interpreted in terms of shock angle. The Newtonian pressure law without the centrifugal correction applied in terms of the body angle is a purely empirical formula.

Many comparisons of experimental results and exact calculations show excellent agreement with the uncorrected modified Newtonian law expressed in terms of body angle, and relatively poorer agreement with the Newton-Busemann law, also in terms of body angle. The only rational comparison of the Newton-Busemann law with experiment must be in terms of shock angle and for flows with reasonably thin shock layers, although the law must approach correctness in terms of the body angle with $\epsilon$ extremely small. Such a rational comparison based on shock angle has been made in Fig. 6–8. The improvement of agreement with this law in terms of body angle with decreasing $\epsilon$ is indicated in Fig. 6–12. The agreement with the uncorrected law in terms of body angle clearly becomes worse as $\epsilon$ becomes smaller (cf. Fig. 6–12), and the agreement can be very poor for unusually shaped bodies. The excellency of the agreement depends upon $\epsilon$ being moderate and upon the bodies involved being roughly spherical or cylindrical at the nose.

We should look on the agreement with modified Newtonian as fortuitous; it is evident that the centrifugal pressure difference across the shock layer is approximately offset in many flows by the effect of the difference between shock angle and body angle. It should not be implied that the modified Newtonian pressure law is not a useful one in practice, as long as the user recognizes its empirical nature and its limitations.

To complete the picture for the flow past a sphere with $\gamma = 1.4$ we have shown in Fig. 6–10 the stagnation point detachment distance as computed by Van Dyke [6]. Also plotted on this graph are experimental points taken from a compilation in Van Dyke's paper, and also the constant-density result obtained from a numerical solution of (4.4.8). Van Dyke's results were obtained with his inverse method in which the body shape is unknown a priori, and it is not clear just how closely his bodies approximate spheres.

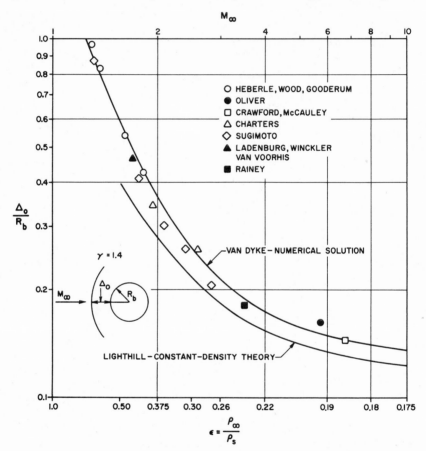

FIG. 6–10. Stagnation point detachment distance for a sphere (Van Dyke [6]), and comparison with constant-density result (Lighthill [3]) and experiment.

In order to plot the constant-density result on this graph $\epsilon$ was taken equal to the value of the density ratio across a normal shock corresponding to the Mach number indicated. Of course the constant-density solution has been extrapolated far beyond its limit of validity. In spite of this, it is seen to give a reasonable approximation over most of the range of supersonic Mach numbers. A more rational comparison with the constant-density theory would have been made on the basis of the shock shape rather than the body shape, plotting $\Delta/R_s$ instead of $\Delta/R_b$.

The last approach we discuss in connection with the inverse problem is the one developed by Garabedian [1] and Garabedian and Lieberstein [1]. Since an initial value problem is in general inappropriate to the elliptic system of equations governing the subsonic domain, they suggest introducing an analytic continuation into the complex domain by an alteration of one of the independent variables. This then transforms the elliptic system into a hyperbolic system, for which an initial value technique is proper.

The basic equation for the flow field in terms of the stream function and rectangular cartesian coordinates $x$ and $y$ (or cylindrical coordinates with $y$ read as $r$ for axisymmetric flow) is (6.4.2). This equation may be written in the form

$$(6.5.14) \qquad a\psi_{xx} + 2b\psi_{xy} + c\psi_{yy} + d = 0,$$

where $a$, $b$, $c$, and $d$ are known functions of $\psi$, $\psi_x$, $\psi_y$, and $y$. We note that this equation is elliptic for $b^2 - ac < 0$ and hyperbolic for $b^2 - ac > 0$. With the shock expressed as a known analytic curve $x = x(y)$, both $\psi$ and $\psi_x$ along the shock are also known analytic functions of the variable $y$ (from the shock relations), and the solution of (6.5.14) subject to these initial conditions constitutes a Cauchy problem for the determination of the stream function $\psi$.

To illustrate the Garabedian-Lieberstein method in the simplest manner possible, instead of dealing with (6.5.14) let us again consider the simpler Laplace equation (6.5.1) subject to the initial conditions

$$(6.5.15) \qquad \phi(0, y) = f(y); \qquad \phi_x(0, y) = g(y).$$

Following the idea used by these authors, we consider that we have obtained the analytic continuation of $f$ and $g$ with respect to the variable $y$ into the complex domain, leaving $x$ as a real parameter; we then confine our attention to purely imaginary changes in $y$, with the real part of $y$ held constant. We set $y = y_1 + iy_2$, then

$$(6.5.16a) \qquad \phi(0, y) = f(y) = f(y_1 + iy_2),$$

$$(6.5.16b) \qquad \phi_x(0, y) = g(y) = g(y_1 + iy_2).$$

In this case, for each value of $y_1$, $\phi(x, y)$ satisfies the wave equation

$$(6.5.17) \qquad \frac{\partial^2\phi}{\partial x^2} - \frac{\partial^2\phi}{\partial y_2^2} = 0 \,.$$

The function $\phi$ is therefore a complex-valued function $\phi(x, y_1 + iy_2)$ of three real arguments $x$, $y_1$, and $y_2$, which can be thought of as coordinates of a point in a cartesian three-dimensional space. In particular we are interested in the solution $\phi(x, y_1 + iy_2)$ for $y_2 = 0$ (that is, in the $(x, y_1)$ plane) satisfying the initial conditions (6.5.16). This solution can be found for each value of $y_1$ from the hyperbolic equation (6.5.17) in the $(x, y_2)$ plane rather than from the original elliptic equation (6.5.1) in the $(x, y_1)$ plane. Thus, although the solution is determined in a three-dimensional region, we are interested only in the portion of this region which intersects the plane $y_2 = 0$. Clearly, for every value of the parameter $y_1$ we are dealing only with an initial value problem in two independent variables. This same idea of solution can also be applied to the original equation (6.5.14); we must depend here on a mathematical equivalence of the elliptic equation (6.5.14) to an equation in which the second-derivative terms are in the form of a Laplacian.

From the above reasoning it appears that the instability of the original elliptic problem has been avoided by this scheme, since we deal with a hyperbolic equation which can always be treated in a stable manner by the numerical method of characteristics. As a natural reaction to this rather ingenious idea we may ask: can a simple change in variable alter an essential instability in a calculation procedure? The answer to this question is definitely no. But, as we shall see, the unstable step may be avoided if an analytic closed-form procedure can be substituted for the unstable part of the numerical procedure. In fact, any sound mathematical method of analytic continuation appropriate to the mathematical expression describing the given shock shape may be used.

To understand these previous statements somewhat better we note, as both Garabedian [1] and Lin [2] have pointed out, that a small change in the initial data in the real domain can result in a large change in this same initial data in the complex domain. This is because the latter is obtained by an analytic continuation of the former. As Lin observed, the analytic continuation of the initial conditions $f(y)$ and $g(y)$ (see (6.5.15)) from real values of $y$ into the complex domain is itself the solution of an initial value problem for Laplace's equation.

To show this, let us write

(6.5.18) $$g(y_1 + iy_2) = u(y_1, y_2) + iv(y_1, y_2).$$

In this case $u$ and $v$ each satisfy Laplace's equation with $y_1$ and $y_2$ as independent variables with the initial conditions

(6.5.19a) $$u(y_1, 0) = g(y_1), \qquad u_{y_2}(y_1, 0) = 0;$$

(6.5.19b) $$v(y_1, 0) = 0, \qquad v_{y_2}(y_1, 0) = g'(y_1).$$

Returning to Hadamard's example (6.5.2), for which $f(y) = 0$ and $g(y) = A_n \sin ny$, we find that analytic continuation of $g(y)$ gives

(6.5.20a) $$u(y_1, y_2) = A_n \sin ny_1 \cosh ny_2,$$

(6.5.20b) $$v(y_1, y_2) = A_n \cos ny_1 \sinh ny_2.$$

It is clear that the same instability as discussed previously with the original Laplace equation applies in the analytical continuation as well.

In our example using Laplace's equation this method has merely managed to substitute a new but essentially equivalent problem involving Laplace's equation again. In this instance there is no gain from the method. However, the essential feature of the Garabedian-Lieberstein method is that the original elliptic differential equation need not be Laplace's equation but may be a much more complicated one. The part of the problem involving analytic continuation is always equivalent to the much simpler Laplace's equation. We may thus transform a complicated elliptic Cauchy problem such as our blunt-body inverse problem into a simple elliptic problem equivalent to a Cauchy problem for Laplace's equation, plus a complicated hyperbolic problem. We may also investigate the fundamental singularities appearing in the analytic continuation or choose shock shapes yielding specified singularities. The question remains as to whether we can carry out the analytic continuation.

If we were to choose simple closed-form analytic shock shapes such as hyperbolas or parabolas for our hypersonic blunt-body problem, permitting the initial conditions to be continued *exactly* into the complex domain, the type of instability which we have illustrated would not occur. Nevertheless, our example does show clearly the manner in which small alterations in the shape of the shock in the physical plane can result in very large changes in the shape of the body as a result of the unstable process of analytic continuation if carried out numerically. This therefore places a restriction, as with any inverse scheme, on the general applicability of the method. However, the method of Garabedian and Lieberstein may be applied with initial data given numerically if some reasonable smoothing process such as we have discussed earlier is applied.

Garabedian and Lieberstein formulated their procedure for solving the detached shock problem by reducing the second-order equation (6.5.14) following a standard procedure to a system of five first-order partial differential equations, through the introduction of the characteristic coordinates

$$(6.5.21) \qquad \alpha = \frac{b + \sqrt{b^2 - ac}}{a}, \qquad \beta = \frac{b - \sqrt{b^2 - ac}}{a}.$$

Here $b^2 - ac < 0$ for the elliptic region, and $\alpha$ and $\beta$ are complex quantities. By making the additional transformation

$$(6.5.22) \qquad X = \frac{\alpha + \beta}{2}, \qquad Y = \frac{\alpha - \beta}{2i},$$

the system of differential equations in the $(X, Y)$ plane can then be written in the canonical matrix form

$$(6.5.23) \quad \begin{bmatrix} y_X \\ x_X \\ (\psi_y)_X \\ (\psi_x)_X \\ \psi_X \end{bmatrix} = \frac{1}{\sqrt{ac - b^2}} \begin{bmatrix} b & -a & 0 & 0 & 0 \\ c & -b & 0 & 0 & 0 \\ 0 & d & b & c & 0 \\ -d & 0 & -a & -b & 0 \\ b\psi_y + c\psi_x & -(a\psi_y + b\psi_x) & 0 & 0 & 0 \end{bmatrix} \begin{bmatrix} y_Y \\ x_Y \\ (\psi_y)_Y \\ (\psi_x)_Y \\ \psi_Y \end{bmatrix},$$

or in matrix notation

$$(6.5.24) \qquad\qquad J_X = B J_Y,$$

with $J$ denoting the column vector of the unknown functions. In this formulation real solutions generate real flows in the subsonic region $b^2 - ac < 0$.

These authors set up initial conditions for an analytic shock curve of the form

$$(6.5.25) \qquad\qquad (x_s + x_0)^2 = x_0^2 + g(y^2).$$

With $\psi_s = \rho_\infty U y_s^{1+j}/(1 + j)$ both $\psi_x$ and $\psi_y$ at the shock can be computed explicitly in terms of $y$ and $\psi$. These authors also choose the $Y$ axis as the initial curve in the $(X, Y)$ plane using the explicit relation

$$(6.5.26) \qquad y = F(Y) = E_1 Y + E_2 Y^3 + \frac{E_3 Y}{Y^2 + E_4}$$

between $y$ and $Y$, where the $E$'s are arbitrary real parameters which determine the shock shape.

In accordance with the scheme outlined previously we now let $Y = Y_1 + iY_2$, in which case (6.5.24) can be written as

$$(6.5.27) \qquad\qquad J_X = \frac{B}{i} J_{Y_2}.$$

The initial conditions are then imposed at $X = 0$, and analytically continued in closed form into the complex $Y$ plane. We now restrict our attention to the plane $Y_1 = constant$, in which $X$ and $Y_2$ are rectangular coordinates. In the $(X, Y_2)$ plane (6.5.27) is a hyperbolic system having the three families of characteristic curves $X + Y_2 = constant$, $X - Y_2 = constant$, and $Y_2 = constant$. In order to find the subsonic flow, the initial value problem (6.5.27) is solved, for a suitable set of values of the parameter $Y_1$, in a manner similar to that described for Laplace's equation. The solution of each initial value problem for a particular choice of the parameter $Y$ then yields values of $\psi$, $\psi_y$, and $\psi_x$ along a curve in the $(x, y)$ plane whose shape depends on the function $F(Y)$ in (6.5.26).

We may ask the general question as to how the sonic line and the supersonic part of the flow field are related to the subsonic part of the flow field treated by this method. The basic method breaks down near the sonic line because $b^2 - ac = 0$ there, but the location of the sonic line and flow properties there may be obtained by extrapolation. With a hypersonic axisymmetric sonic line (see Fig. 6–1(c)) the entire supersonic flow field and the sonic line can also be obtained by the method of characteristics with the original equations of motion. Lieberstein (private communication) has checked the location of the sonic line by these two procedures in the example shown in Fig. 6–11(b) and obtained excellent agreement. If a part of the body bounds a part of the transonic zone, as in Fig. 6–1(a) or Fig. 6–1(b), the solution in that part must be obtained starting with the sonic line determined by the solution in the subsonic region.

If the entire shock shape is an analytic shape its complete course is determined, including the part of the shock behind which the flow is supersonic. Implicit in this assumption that the shock shape is analytic is the fact that the entire flow field is determined, including the transonic zone. Therefore, no question arises as to the nature of the influence of the transonic zone on the subsonic flow. If the analytic shape is limited by the presence of a singularity or branch point, the situation may become much more complicated and has not yet been clarified.

Garabedian and Lieberstein, employing the method just described, have carried out machine calculations for several shock shapes in axisymmetric flow. In order to obtain different types of body shapes, the foci of the conic sections chosen to represent the shock were placed in different positions. Thus to obtain the flow past a flat-nosed body of revolution, an ellipse was chosen whose foci are located off the axis of symmetry near the points where the shoulder intersects the meridian plane. To obtain the flow past a blunt-nosed cone, a hyperbola was chosen for the shock with its focus just behind the stagnation point.

In Fig. 6–11 we have shown the body and sonic line shapes computed by these authors for two different hyperbolic shocks at $M_\infty = 5.8$ with $\gamma = 1.4$, and computed by Lieberstein and Garabedian (private communication) for a hyperbolic shock at $M_\infty = 20$ and $\gamma_s = 1.17$ ($\gamma = 1.4$). We have also indicated on these figures the ratio of the detachment distance at the stagnation point to the body radius of curvature at the vertex.

For all the bodies of Fig. 6–11 we again observe the hypersonic axisymmetric sonic line. The bodies obtained in Figs. 6–11(a) and (c) are roughly spherical, while that obtained in Fig. 6–11(b) approximates a blunt-nosed cone. An interesting result of the flow pattern in Fig. 6–11(b) is the shape of

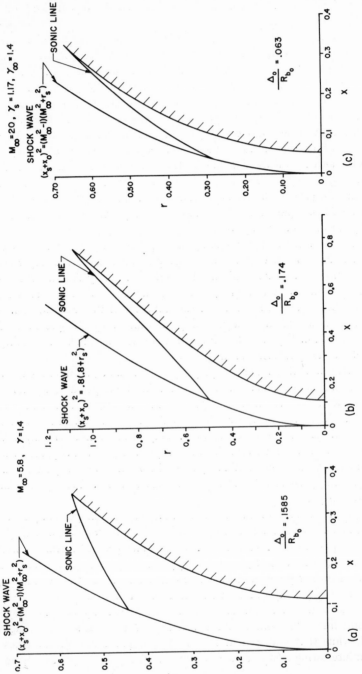

Fig. 6-11. Body and sonic line shapes for axisymmetric hyperbolic shock waves. (a) $(x_s + x_0)^2 = (5.8^2 - 1)(5.8^2 + r_s^2)$; $M_\infty = 5.8$, $\gamma = 1.4$ (Garabedian and Lieberstein [1]). (b) $(x_s + x_0)^2 = .8(.8 + r_s^2)$; $M_\infty = 5.8$, $\gamma = 1.4$ (Garabedian and Lieberstein [1]). (c) $(x_s + x_0)^2 = (20^2 - 1)(20^2 + r_s^2)$; $M_\infty = 20$, $\gamma_s = 1.17$ (Lieberstein and Garabedian, unpublished).

the sonic line, which is slightly convex with respect to the subsonic region.

Figure 6–12 shows the pressure distribution for the three bodies we have discussed, plotted against the angle of the body surface $\theta_b$. On the same graph we have also shown for comparison purposes the modified Newton-Busemann pressure distribution (with the centrifugal correction) based on body angle. The modified Newtonian pressure distribution without the

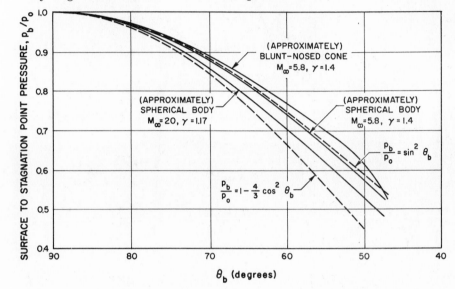

FIG. 6–12. Surface pressure distributions for bodies of Fig. 6–11 (Garabedian and Lieberstein [1]; Lieberstein and Garabedian, unpublished).

centrifugal correction is also shown, and falls very close to but somewhat above the numerical calculation for the approximately spherical body of Fig. 6–11(a). We note that with the much smaller value of $\epsilon$ for the body of Fig. 6–11(c) the pressure curve lies quite close to the modified Newton-Busemann curve, even though this is given in terms of the body angle.

A very interesting picture of the flow on a slightly concave truncated cylinder, which Garabedian and Lieberstein obtained by assuming an elliptic shock shape, is shown in Fig. 6–13. Here, we have indicated directly on the body the ratio of surface to stagnation point pressure. They have not presented the continuation of this solution into the supersonic region.

In summary, it would appear that the inverse methods described may afford a relatively simple way of finding exact numerical solutions to the hypersonic flow past blunt bodies, assuming the instability difficulty can be avoided. Before a more definitive statement can be made, however, it will be necessary to have more general solutions. Of course, the usual problem of interest is the direct problem, to which an inverse technique can only be applied through a method of trial and error. With the aid of modern automatic computing machines a "catalogue" of blunt-body solutions will

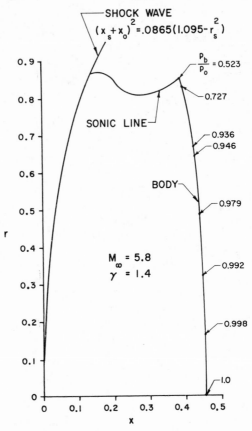

Fig. 6–13. Body and sonic line shape for oblate ellipsoidal shock wave (Garabedian and Lieberstein [1]).

undoubtedly be built up, and this will certainly be of some value. The point of view that such a catalogue of solutions can take the place of a suitable method for the direct problem represents a dangerous philosophy, one that has appreciably delayed scientific advances in the past in various fields of science, including aerodynamics.

# CHAPTER VII

# OTHER METHODS FOR LOCALLY SUPERSONIC FLOWS

## 1. Method of characteristics

In the preceding chapters we have discussed various means of obtaining approximate solutions to inviscid hypersonic flow problems. In addition we have presented various schemes for obtaining exact solutions for the flow past blunt bodies. We next turn to the problem in which the flow field is completely supersonic, still with the limitation to two-dimensional or axisymmetric flow. We can in this case carry out an exact numerical determination of the inviscid rotational supersonic flow by the well known method of characteristics, provided we are supplied with sufficient initial data. The problem involves the solution by finite differences of a system of first-order partial differential equations of hyperbolic type. In what follows, we shall assume that the reader is acquainted to some extent with the philosophy of this method or with the details of the method for a rotational supersonic gas flow in a perfect gas (see, for example, Ferri [1; 2], Isenberg and Lin [1] and Rockett and Hayes [1], or Meyer [1]). Our main purpose will be to point out those features which are characteristic of hypersonic flows.

The method of characteristics is well known and well established in the theory of supersonic flow. We treat the method of characteristics in this book for two reasons. The first is that we shall need the equations for the exact theory in order to describe and to evaluate the approximate methods given later in this chapter. The second is that the method of characteristics as usually presented in the literature includes the unnecessary restriction to a perfect gas of constant $\gamma$, and greater generality is desired.

Since any result of characteristic theory must be able to serve as an exact solution with which we may compare approximate theories (e.g. those of Chapter II or of the other sections in this chapter), we cannot properly utilize any of the simplifying hypersonic flow assumptions discussed in Section 1.3. This being the case, the essential new feature which arises in a hypersonic characteristics calculation is the marked deviation in gas properties from those of a perfect gas resulting from the high stagnation temperatures associated with extreme flight speeds.

For simplicity, our considerations will be restricted to the two limiting cases in which the flow is either frozen or in thermodynamic equilibrium.

For treatments of the method of characteristics with finite relaxation times we refer the reader to the papers of Chu [2], Resler [1], and Wood and Kirkwood [1]. In general, for a frozen flow the gas is taken to have a composition appropriate to the equilibrium composition at some specified state on the downstream side of the attached or detached shock wave. In our definition of a frozen flow we require that the characteristic chemical reaction times (the inverse of the rates) involving all the species of interest to be very large compared with a characteristic transit time for a fluid particle. We

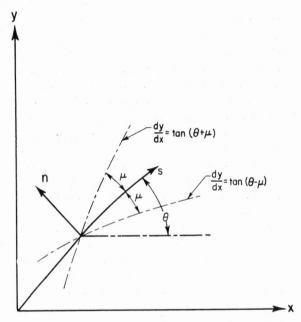

FIG. 7–1. Intrinsic coordinates.

may, however, define more than one type of frozen flow. On the other hand, for thermodynamic equilibrium both the characteristic reaction times and mechanical relaxation times are taken to be very small compared to a characteristic transit time.

In the present development of the method of characteristics we shall treat only two-dimensional and axisymmetric supersonic flows. The problem of the method of characteristics in three dimensions is an important one, but outside the scope of this book. Treatments of the method of characteristics for steady rotational supersonic flows in three dimensions are to be found, for example, in Lock and Tomlinson [1], Holt [1], and Coburn [1].

To derive the characteristic equations for either two-dimensional or axisymmetric flow it is convenient to write the hydrodynamic equations again in terms of the intrinsic or natural orthogonal coordinates defined by the streamlines and their normals. We let $s$ denote distance measured along a streamline and $n$ denote distance measured perpendicular to it (see Fig. 7–1). It must be emphasized that such intrinsic coordinates do not form a co-ordinate system in the usual sense. Streamlines are not curves for which a quantity $n$ is constant, and their orthogonal trajectories are not curves for which a quantity $s$ is constant. The quantities $s$ and $n$ are not independent variables in their own right, but are used only in terms of their differentials, which are not perfect ones. We may not take second derivatives with respect to intrinsic coordinates without the introduction of additional terms involving the streamline geometry. Any result obtained in terms of intrinsic coordi-nates can equally be expressed in terms of a curvilinear orthogonal coordinate system aligned with the streamlines, in terms of a metric which is necessarily unknown if the streamline geometry is unknown. We use intrinsic coordinates in this chapter and in Sections 6.1 and 6.2 primarily because of the simplicity of form which they afford.

The local relation between intrinsic coordinates and fixed rectangular cartesian coordinates is expressed by the differentiation formulas

$$(7.1.1a) \qquad \frac{\partial}{\partial s} = \cos\theta \, \frac{\partial}{\partial x} + \sin\theta \, \frac{\partial}{\partial y} \,,$$

$$(7.1.1b) \qquad \frac{\partial}{\partial n} = -\sin\theta \, \frac{\partial}{\partial x} + \cos\theta \, \frac{\partial}{\partial y} \,,$$

where $\theta$ denotes the angle between the streamlines and the free stream direction $x$ (see Fig. 7–1). As before, for the case of axisymmetric flow $y$ is the radial cylindrical coordinate, read as $r$.

The continuity equation in intrinsic coordinates assumes the form

$$(7.1.2) \qquad \frac{\partial \rho q y^j}{\partial s} + \rho q y^j \, \frac{\partial \theta}{\partial n} = 0 \,,$$

while the corresponding momentum equations along and normal to the streamlines are

$$(7.1.3) \qquad \rho q \, \frac{\partial q}{\partial s} + \frac{\partial p}{\partial s} = 0 \,,$$

$$(7.1.4) \qquad \rho q^2 \, \frac{\partial \theta}{\partial s} + \frac{\partial p}{\partial n} = 0 \,.$$

The assumption of an inviscid adiabatic flow which is in thermodynamic equilibrium (or frozen) leads to the condition of constancy of entropy along a streamline

$$(7.1.5) \qquad \frac{\partial S}{\partial s} = 0 \,.$$

The above relations are supplemented by the equation of state (1.4.3), in which the pressure may be expressed as a function of density and entropy. Finally, since we will consider only problems in which the total enthalpy is a constant throughout the flow, we have

$$(7.1.6) \qquad H = h + \tfrac{1}{2}q^2 = h_\infty + \tfrac{1}{2}U^2.$$

A characteristic is a line in the field for which an ordinary differential equation may be written. Such an equation must be written as a relation connecting total differentials and in which partial derivatives do not appear. One such characteristic line which we may obtain immediately is the streamline, for which $dn = 0$. For this characteristic (7.1.3) and (7.1.5) are already in characteristic form, as no partial derivatives normal to the streamline appear. Since we are treating isoenergetic flow, we use (7.1.3) in its integrated form (7.1.6) rather than as a characteristic equation. But our entire development would hold essentially without change for flows which are not isoenergetic. From (7.1.5) we obtain the essential characteristic equation

$$(7.1.7) \qquad dS = 0, \quad \text{on} \quad dn = 0.$$

We next eliminate $\partial q/\partial s$ from (7.1.2) by use of (7.1.3), substitute $\sin\theta$ for $\partial y/\partial s$, substitute $a^{-2}\partial p/\partial s$ for $\partial\rho/\partial s$, and replace $q/a$ by $M$. The result is an altered form of the continuity equation,

$$(7.1.8) \qquad \frac{M^2 - 1}{\rho q^2}\frac{\partial p}{\partial s} + \frac{\partial\theta}{\partial n} = -\frac{j}{y}\sin\theta.$$

Since we wish to obtain relations involving total differentials, we write the expressions for $dp$ and $d\theta$

$$(7.1.9\text{a}) \qquad dp = \frac{\partial p}{\partial s}\,ds + \frac{\partial p}{\partial n}\,dn,$$

$$(7.1.9\text{b}) \qquad d\theta = \frac{\partial\theta}{\partial s}\,ds + \frac{\partial\theta}{\partial n}\,dn.$$

We now have four equations (7.1.4), (7.1.8), and (7.1.9) which involve the four partial derivatives of $p$ and $\theta$ with respect to $s$ and $n$. A characteristic equation must be completely independent of these partial derivatives, and the determinant of the coefficients of the partial derivatives in our four equations must vanish. This condition determines two characteristic directions, besides the one already found. Since the four equations are not homogeneous in the partial derivatives another condition must be satisfied in order that solutions to the system may exist. This condition gives us two characteristic equations, each corresponding to one of the characteristic directions. These characteristic equations are found to be

$$(7.1.10) \qquad dp \pm \frac{\rho q^2}{\sqrt{M^2 - 1}}\, d\theta + \frac{j\rho q^2 \sin\theta}{M^2 - 1}\, \frac{ds}{y} = 0,$$

$$\text{on} \quad \frac{dn}{ds} = \pm \frac{1}{\sqrt{M^2 - 1}}\, .$$

Transforming the characteristic equations and directions (7.1.7) and (7.1.10) to rectangular cartesian coordinates, we obtain

$$(7.1.11) \qquad dS = 0\,, \quad \text{on} \quad \frac{dy}{dx} = \tan\theta,$$

and

$$(7.1.12) \qquad \frac{dp}{\rho q^2 \tan\mu} \pm d\theta + \frac{j\sin\theta\sin\mu}{\sin(\theta \pm \mu)}\, \frac{dy}{y} = 0,$$

$$\text{on} \quad \frac{dy}{dx} = \tan(\theta \pm \mu),$$

where $\mu$ is the local Mach angle $\sin^{-1}(1/M)$ (see Fig. 7–1). Thus the characteristic directions are the streamlines and Mach lines in the flow field. We note that (7.1.12) has exactly the same form as in potential flow, for which the pressure is a function of the velocity alone. However, in a general rotational flow it is necessary to determine the relation between pressure and velocity at each point through the equation of state, the isoenergetic relation (7.1.6), and the condition of constancy of entropy along a streamline (7.1.7).

If the flow is two-dimensional and isentropic (irrotational) an explicit integral may be obtained for both characteristic equations (7.1.10) or (7.1.12). If the flow is axisymmetric or rotational such an integral may not be obtained, and a stepwise numerical integration procedure is required to obtain the solution.

There are many developments of the method of characteristics in the literature and in standard texts (e.g. in the references cited at the beginning of this section). We do not consider it worthwhile in this book to repeat the details of various numerical procedures, and the reader is referred to the works cited for such details. A few points should be emphasized, however. In a general fluid the thermodynamic behavior of the one-dimensional steady isentropic flow along each streamline must be known. Since the flow is assumed to be isocompositional and isoenergetic these one-dimensional flows form a one-parameter family, with the entropy as the parameter. The simplicity of form of the characteristic equations as expressed in terms of $dp$ and $d\theta$ is also to be emphasized. If another variable is introduced in place of $p$ the characteristic equations become significantly more complicated. That the quantities $p$ and $\theta$ should be considered as the basic variables is related to the fact that it is these quantities which must be matched across a contact discontinuity or slipstream.

In a calculation it may be more convenient to replace the quantity $dp/\rho q^2$ appearing in the first term of (7.1.12) by $dp/\gamma_e M^2 p$, where $\gamma_e$ is defined in (1.4.22). A chart of $\gamma_e$ for air is available in Moeckel [2] or in Hansen [2, Fig. 5].

The explicit integral available for two-dimensional isentropic flow is equivalent to the integral describing Prandtl-Meyer flow in a general fluid. We shall devote the remainder of this section to Prandtl-Meyer flow, the results for which are used in the shock-expansion method of the next section. It is possible for hypersonic flow problems to arise in which the flow is approximately or strictly two-dimensional and isentropic, and in such a problem the explicit integral may be used directly. If the flow is isentropic, then $dS = 0$ throughout the flow field, and the Bernoulli relation $q\,dq = -dp/\rho$ is valid in any direction. From (7.1.12) we then obtain the usual form of the characteristic relations for two-dimensional, isentropic, supersonic flow:

$$(7.1.13) \qquad d\nu \mp d\theta = 0; \quad \nu \mp \theta = \text{constant},$$

$$\text{on} \quad \frac{dy}{dx} = \tan(\theta \pm \mu),$$

where $\nu$ is the Prandtl-Meyer turning angle defined by

$$(7.1.14) \qquad d\nu = \cot\mu\,\frac{dq}{q} = \sqrt{M^2 - 1}\,\frac{dq}{q}.$$

We define $\nu$ to be zero at $M = 1$. With this convention $\nu$ is a function $\nu(H, S, p)$ of the total enthalpy and the thermodynamic state.

It is at this point that the problem in a general fluid differs from the conventional perfect gas treatment. In a general fluid no simple explicit relation exists for the speed of sound as a function of the velocity. Instead this relation is an implicit one expressed through the equation of state and the isoenergetic relation (7.1.6). Thus with the aid of (7.1.6), we have from (7.1.14)

$$(7.1.15) \qquad \nu = \frac{1}{2}\int\left[\frac{2(H - h)}{a^2} - 1\right]^{1/2}\frac{d(H - h)}{H - h},$$

with the integration constant chosen by convention so that $\nu = 0$ at $M = \sqrt{2(H-h)}/a^2 = 1$. It is to be emphasized that this integration is taken along an isentrope. To integrate (7.1.15) it is necessary to specify the equation of state, to obtain the function $a^2(h, S)$.

Let us now first consider the case of an equilibrium flow for which the state relation is defined by a Mollier diagram such as is shown in Fig. 1–4, or given in the charts of Feldman [1] or Korobkin and Hastings [1]. Before carrying out the integration, however, it is also necessary to specify both the total enthalpy and the entropy. Under such circumstances, it is evident that a characteristics diagram, such as is employed for a perfect gas, can be constructed for a general fluid only for a given choice of total enthalpy and the entropy. For a given fluid, the characteristic diagrams form a two-parameter family.

Although (7.1.15) is in a convenient form for numerical integration, since values of the speed of sound are available from charts or may be obtained from the equation of state, it does not permit a simple interpretation of how a Prandtl-Meyer flow in a general fluid differs from the usual perfect gas solution. We present here two alternative formulations of Prandtl-Meyer flow which show clearly such an interpretation. In order to do so we must use quantities involving an isentropic derivative of $a^2$, even though such a derivative does not appear in (7.1.15).

We turn our attention from $\nu$ to the quantity $\nu + \frac{1}{2}\pi - \mu$, with $\mu$ the Mach angle $\sin^{-1}(1/M)$. This quantity is also zero at $M = q/a = 1$, and its differential may be expressed as

$$(7.1.16) \qquad d\nu - d\mu = \frac{1}{\sqrt{M^2-1}}\left[(M^2-1)\frac{dq}{q} + \frac{dq}{q} - \frac{da}{a}\right]$$

$$= \frac{q\,dq - a\,da}{a\sqrt{q^2-a^2}}.$$

Since the process involved is always isentropic we may write partial derivatives as ratios of differentials, and using (7.1.6) may write

$$(7.1.17) \qquad \frac{da}{a} = a_h\frac{dh}{a} = -aa_hM^2\frac{dq}{q},$$

with $a_h = (\partial a/\partial h)_S$. We then obtain

$$(7.1.18) \qquad \frac{dM}{M(1 + aa_hM^2)} = \frac{dq}{q} = \frac{dM}{M} + \frac{da}{a},$$

and may substitute this expression for $dq$ and for $da$ into (7.1.16). The resulting equation may be put in the form

$$(7.1.19) \qquad \nu + \tfrac{1}{2}\pi - \mu = \int \left( \frac{1 + aa_h}{1 + aa_h M^2} \right) \frac{M \, dM}{\sqrt{M^2 - 1}} \, ,$$

with the integral defined to be zero at $M = 1$. Noting that $\tfrac{1}{2}\pi - \mu = \cos^{-1}(1/M) = \tan^{-1}\sqrt{M^2 - 1}$, we can arrive at the following formally simple expression for the turning angle

$$(7.1.20) \qquad \nu = \int_0^{} \frac{d\beta}{1 + (F_* \beta)^2} - \tan^{-1}\beta \, ,$$

where $\beta = \sqrt{M^2 - 1}$,   and

$$(7.1.21) \qquad F_*^2 = \frac{aa_h}{1 + aa_h} = \frac{\left( \dfrac{\partial a^2}{\partial h} \right)_S}{2 + \left( \dfrac{\partial a^2}{\partial h} \right)_S} \, .$$

The significance of the function $F_*$ is made clearer by recognizing that it may be expressed in terms of the quantity $\gamma_*$ defined in (1.4.24). The quantity $\gamma_*$ may be re-expressed as

$$(7.1.22) \qquad \gamma_* = 1 + \left( \frac{\partial a^2}{\partial h} \right)_S \, ,$$

and we obtain immediately

$$(7.1.23) \qquad F_*^2 = \frac{\gamma_* - 1}{\gamma_* + 1} \, .$$

For a perfect gas of constant $\gamma$, $a^2 = (\gamma - 1)h$, $\gamma = \gamma_*$, and $F_*^2 = (\gamma - 1)/(\gamma + 1)$. In this case (7.1.20) may be integrated directly to give the conventional form of the Prandtl-Meyer relation,

$$(7.1.24) \qquad \nu = F^{-1} \tan^{-1}(\beta F) - \tan^{-1}\beta,$$

in which the subscript $*$ on $F$ has been dropped.

The second formulation for the Prandtl-Meyer flow is due to Heims [1]. T.e formulation just presented and that of Heims were developed independently, and we have slightly changed Heims' analysis to fit the development of this section. Heims defines a quantity $\eta$, which we here replace by its inverse

$$(7.1.25) \qquad F_e = \frac{a}{\sqrt{a^2 + 2h}} \, .$$

It must be noted that this quantity requires the assignment of a reference value of the enthalpy before it is uniquely defined. Although any assignment of reference enthalpy will serve, an arbitrary assignment may lead to complex values of $F_e$ or to a zero value of $F_e$ at absolute zero temperature. To avoid such mathematical behavior and to provide the most significant interpretation of the results, we must assign to the enthalpy $h$ the value zero at absolute zero temperature.

With the enthalpy zero at absolute zero temperature the total enthalpy of the stream $H$ is equal to $\frac{1}{2}q_{max}^2$, where $q_{max}$ is the maximum velocity of the steady flow. The energy equation then takes the form

$$(7.1.26) \qquad q^2 = q_{max}^2 - 2h.$$

We may now rewrite (7.1.16) in the form

$$(7.1.27) \qquad dv - d\mu = - \frac{a\,da + dh}{F_e\sqrt{q_{max}^2 - a^2 - 2h}\,\sqrt{a^2 + 2h}}$$
$$= F_e^{-1}\,d\cos^{-1}\left(\frac{a}{q_{max}F_e}\right).$$

Next we introduce the angle $\varphi$ (in Heims' notation $\psi$), defined by the relation

$$(7.1.28) \qquad \varphi = \cos^{-1}\left(\frac{a}{q_{max}F_e}\right),$$

which takes the value zero at $M = 1$. We may now express the Prandtl-Meyer turning angle $v$ as

$$(7.1.29) \qquad v = \int_0^{\varphi} F_e^{-1}\,d\varphi - \cos^{-1}(1/M),$$

in terms of what is essentially a Stieltje's integral.

The radial component of velocity in a Prandtl-Meyer flow is $\sqrt{q^2 - a^2}$, and is expressed in terms of $\varphi$ as

$$(7.1.30) \qquad \sqrt{q^2 - a^2} = q_{max}\sin\varphi.$$

The velocity of sound is simply

$$(7.1.31) \qquad a = F_e\,q_{max}\cos\varphi,$$

and the quantity $\beta = \sqrt{M^2 - 1}$ is

$$(7.1.32) \qquad \beta = F_e^{-1}\tan\varphi.$$

In a perfect gas of constant $\gamma$, we have $F_e^2 = (\gamma - 1)/(\gamma + 1)$ is constant, and we again obtain (7.1.24) with the subscript $e$ dropped. The quantity $F_e^2$

is expressible in general in terms of the $\gamma_\epsilon$ and $\gamma_e$ defined in (1.4.20) and (1.4.22) as

(7.1.33)
$$F_e^2 = \frac{\gamma_e(\gamma_\epsilon - 1)}{\gamma_\epsilon\gamma_e + 2\gamma_\epsilon - \gamma_e}.$$

In comparing these two formulations we find no tremendous distinction. Both involve derivatives of the speed of sound $a$, in the definition of $\gamma_*$ in the first, and in the differential of $\varphi$ in (7.1.29) in the second. Both require a calculation of $M$ as a function of thermodynamic state along the isentrope. The first formulation is closer in form to the usual one for a perfect gas, and is expressed in terms of the quantity $\beta = \sqrt{M^2 - 1}$. It is perhaps somewhat more closely related to our characteristics calculation. The second formulation shows more clearly the relation between the velocity components and the maximum velocity $q_{\max}$, provided the correct zero point has been assigned to $h$.

In general it is not possible to carry out the quadrature (7.1.20) or (7.1.29) in closed form. Charts or tables of $F_*$ or of $F_e$ are needed, and should be prepared for air under conditions of practical interest. Information on the quantity $F_e$ would be needed more accurately than on the quantity $F_*$, as $F_e$ is differentiated in the process of obtaining the quadrature (7.1.29). One empirical approximation would be to take $F_*$ or $F_e$ equal to some constant average value, corresponding to some fictitious perfect gas of constant $\gamma$. Another would be to replace $F_*$ by $(\gamma_e - 1)/(\gamma_e + 1)$. Results of two sample calculations using this latter empirical approximation are given in Fig. 7–2, and compared with the results for a perfect gas and with one exact calculation according to (7.1.15). The empirical approximation $\gamma_* = \gamma_e$ appears to be reasonably accurate for air at moderate altitudes.

We now discuss the case of frozen equilibrium, in which the gas is assumed to have a fixed composition corresponding to a specified reference state. In contrast to the case of thermodynamic equilibrium, this kind of flow can be treated with relative simplicity. To show this, we first write the usual equation of state for the pressure in terms of the "compressibility factor" $Z(p, T)$ as

(7.1.34)
$$p = \rho\mathscr{R}TZ,$$

where $\mathscr{R}$ is the undissociated perfect gas constant.

We concern ourselves with air, which when undissociated is essentially entirely composed of diatomic molecules, and let $\alpha$ be the fraction of original molecules dissociated. Since $\alpha$ moles of molecules dissociate into $2\alpha$ moles of atoms, there must be $1 + \alpha$ moles of mixture for each original mole of molecules. It follows that $Z = 1 + \alpha$, and the gas law may be written as

(7.1.35)
$$p = \rho(1 + \alpha)\mathscr{R}T = \rho\mathscr{R}_f T,$$

where $\mathscr{R}_f$ is the gas constant for the frozen state. With this form of the gas law, we can express all the frozen flow relationships in the same form as for a perfect gas by the use of the modified $\mathscr{R}_f$ instead of $\mathscr{R}$, and an effective $\gamma_f$ instead of $\gamma$. All of the quantities for a frozen state are then functions of $\alpha$, which is assumed constant during the frozen flow process.

Two frozen states would appear to be of particular interest. The first is one in which both any chemical reaction rates involved are sufficiently slow

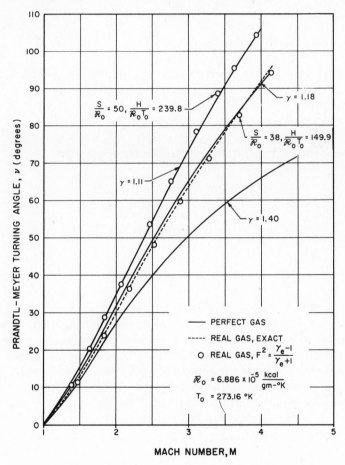

FIG. 7–2. Prandtl-Meyer turning angle.

that no change in composition occurs in the process, and the vibrational relaxation times are sufficiently long that no change in the vibrational energy levels occurs. In this frozen state we assume that the rotational energy of the molecules is always in equilibrium. From the fact that the specific heat at constant pressure equals $7\mathscr{R}/2$ for a diatomic gas and $5\mathscr{R}/2$ for a monatomic gas, we may calculate

(7.1.36) $$c_{p_f} = \frac{7 + 3\alpha}{2}\,\mathscr{R} = \frac{7 + 3\alpha}{2(1 + \alpha)}\,\mathscr{R}_f.$$

But with $\mathscr{R}_f = c_{p_f} - c_{v_f}$ and $\gamma_f = c_{p_f}/c_{v_f}$, we have

(7.1.37) $$\gamma_f = \frac{7 + 3\alpha}{5 + \alpha}.$$

The isentropic exponent for the frozen state $\gamma_f$ varies from $7/5$ at $\alpha = 0$ to $5/3$ at $\alpha = 1$ for an originally diatomic gas.

We define the other frozen state of interest as one in which the relaxation time for chemical recombination is assumed to be much longer than the relaxation time for the vibrational degrees of freedom. If the temperatures are sufficiently high in a diatomic gas that the vibrational mode is fully excited, it contributes the classical amount $\mathscr{R}T$ to the heat capacities. It follows that for a frozen state with vibrational equilibrium

(7.1.38) $$c_{p_f} = \frac{9 + \alpha}{2}\,\mathscr{R} = \frac{9 + \alpha}{2(1 + \alpha)}\,\mathscr{R}_f,$$

and

(7.1.39) $$\gamma_f = \frac{9 + \alpha}{7 - \alpha}.$$

Here $\gamma_f$ varies from $9/7$ at $\alpha = 0$ to $5/3$ at $\alpha = 1$ for an originally diatomic gas. Clearly, there are other frozen states which can be defined, and a fuller discussion of this point is given by Feldman [2].

From the preceding discussion it can be seen that the usual form of the Prandtl-Meyer relation (7.1.24) is valid for the frozen case provided the correct effective value of $\gamma$ is utilized. In order to know just which value to employ, we need to know the appropriate relaxation times for the gas. Once the frozen state is specified, however, it is only necessary to determine $\alpha$ from a Mollier diagram to complete the problem. For air at high temperatures the effective value of $\gamma_f$ lies between the limits $9/7 \leqslant \gamma_f \leqslant 5/3$.

In using the Prandtl-Meyer relation it is often useful to have it in inverted form, in terms of the function $M(\nu)$. In the general case this inversion must be done numerically, but for a perfect gas with $\gamma = 5/4$ or $5/3$ it may be done analytically (see Probstein [4]). If $\gamma = 5/3$ the inverted relation is

(7.1.40) $$M = \frac{1 + (\tan \nu/2)^{2/3}}{1 - (\tan \nu/2)^{2/3}}.$$

The inverted relation for $\gamma = 5/4$ is much more complicated in form.

## 2. Shock-expansion theory

Although the method of characteristics serves to supply an exact scheme for computing a supersonic flow field, the lengthiness of such a calculation makes its application to hypersonic flows quite onerous. One fairly accurate technique for finding simple approximate hypersonic flow solutions for two-dimensional sharp-nosed airfoils, for which the shock is attached at the leading edge and the flow behind the shock is supersonic, is the shock-expansion method first used by Epstein [1]. Epstein considered principally polygonal profiles for which the reflected waves neglected in the shock-expansion method do not hit the body. In the shock-expansion method, the airfoil characteristics are computed by assuming that the flow behind the leading edge shock is the same as an isentropic Prandtl-Meyer expansion, with only a single family of characteristics taken into account. The obvious calculational advantage of the method is that while it does take into account the change in entropy through the strong leading edge shock, it yields a result for the pressure on the body which is dependent only upon the flow inclination angle. In addition, none of the basic hypersonic assumptions discussed in Section 1.3 need be applied. But we must examine with care the inherent limitations on the accuracy of the method.

The concept introduced by Epstein for the calculation of surface pressures was extended by Eggers and Syvertson [1] in their "generalized shock-expansion method" (see also, Eggers, Syvertson, and Kraus [1]) to include an approximate determination of the shock shape and of the entire flow field. In this procedure we still only consider a single family of principal characteristics, with reflections from the shock wave and from the vortex lines in the flow neglected. The field is not taken to be isentropic, however, and the Mach lines are not taken to be straight as in a Prandtl-Meyer flow. This allows the development of a procedure similar to the method of characteristics but much simpler than it. The scheme is illustrated in Fig. 7–3, in which no reflected characteristics are shown. We use the established condition that the entropy is constant along streamlines downstream of the shock wave. An additional assumption is now needed to permit a calculation of the flow field. We may, for example, assume that the pressure is constant along the principal characteristics, and thereby calculate the corresponding deflection angle $\theta$, the Mach angle $\mu$, and the location of the principal characteristics and streamlines in the field. An alternative assumption would be that the flow deflection angle $\theta$ is constant along principal characteristics, with the pressure and the Mach angle calculated in the flow field. The reader will observe that the method as thus proposed has a large degree of arbitrariness. Since it is assumed that there are no reflected waves, the pressure on the body is not affected by the choice of method used for the flow field. It was pointed out by Eggers, Syvertson, and Kraus [1] that the choice of method affects the primary geometry of the flow field but slightly. But the arbitrariness prevents any rational estimate of the change in pressure along a principal characteristic. This deficiency can be partially corrected

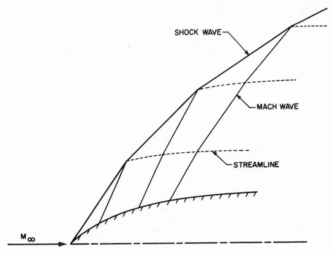

FIG. 7–3.  Sketch of flow field in shock-expansion method.

and a closer approximation to the true flow geometry obtained by simply averaging the shock wave angle determined by assuming constant flow deflection with that obtained by assuming constant pressure.

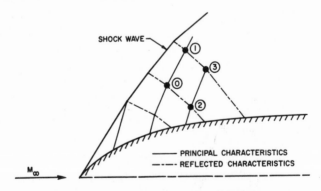

FIG. 7–4.  Interaction of principal and reflected characteristics.

We present a rough analysis to justify this averaging procedure in two-dimensional flow. Referring to Fig. 7–4, the characteristic equations (with

$j = 0$) applied along the principal characteristics with a difference scheme give

(7.2.1a) $$p_1 - p_0 = -\Gamma_0 p_0(\theta_1 - \theta_0),$$

(7.2.1b) $$p_3 - p_2 = -\Gamma_0 p_0(\theta_3 - \theta_2),$$

in which $\Gamma p$ is used for $\rho q^2 \tan \mu$ in (7.1.12) and

(7.2.2) $$\Gamma = \frac{\gamma_e M^2}{\sqrt{M^2 - 1}}.$$

The differences appearing in (7.2.1) are small, and the change in $\Gamma p$ is neglected. The characteristic equations applied along the reflected characteristics give

(7.2.3a) $$p_2 - p_0 = \Gamma_0 p_0(\theta_2 - \theta_0),$$

(7.2.3b) $$p_3 - p_1 = \Gamma_0 p_0(\theta_3 - \theta_1) + \delta(\Gamma p)(\theta_2 - \theta_0),$$

in which the change in $\Gamma p$ between point 1 and point 0 is designated $\delta(\Gamma p)$. In the shock-expansion method (7.2.1) is not used but is replaced by an assumed relation.

If we now assume constant pressure along principal characteristics, we obtain

(7.2.4a) $$p_3 - p_2 = p_1 - p_0 = 0,$$

(7.2.4b) $$\Gamma_0 p_0(\theta_3 - \theta_2) = \Gamma_0 p_0(\theta_1 - \theta_0) - \delta(\Gamma p)(\theta_2 - \theta_0).$$

If, on the other hand, we assume constant flow deflection, we obtain

(7.2.5a) $$p_3 - p_2 = p_1 - p_0 + \delta(\Gamma p)(\theta_2 - \theta_0),$$

(7.2.5b) $$\Gamma_0 p_0(\theta_3 - \theta_2) = \Gamma_0 p_0(\theta_1 - \theta_0) = 0.$$

By using both sets of characteristic equations (7.2.1) and (7.2.3) we can obtain without further assumption the results

(7.2.6a) $$p_3 - p_2 = p_1 - p_0 + \tfrac{1}{2}\delta(\Gamma p)(\theta_2 - \theta_0),$$

(7.2.6b) $$\Gamma_0 p_0(\theta_3 - \theta_2) = \Gamma_0 p_0(\theta_1 - \theta_0) - \tfrac{1}{2}\delta(\Gamma p)(\theta_2 - \theta_0).$$

If we now assume that the strength of the reflected wave is zero along the first principal characteristic and that $p_1 = p_0$ and $\theta_1 = \theta_0$ we see that the complete result may be obtained by taking the arithmetic mean of the constant pressure result and the constant deflection result.If we had assumed that both $p$ and $\theta$ were constant along the principal characteristic preceding (0-1), so that $p_1 - p_0$ and $\theta_1 - \theta_0$ could be obtained by the averaging process, the same is again true of $p_3 - p_2$ and $\theta_3 - \theta_2$. Thus the argument may be continued by induction along the reflected characteristic.

This argument is based on the assumption that we may take $p$ and $\theta$ both constant along a first principal characteristic (negligible reflection from the shock), and on the assumption that the strength of the reflected waves remains small compared with that of the principal waves (negligible reflection from the vorticity). These assumptions are examined below. In any case the choice of the arithmetic mean of the constant pressure procedure and the constant deflection procedure is not irrational and removes the arbitrariness of the method.

From the description of the shock-expansion method we see that it depends

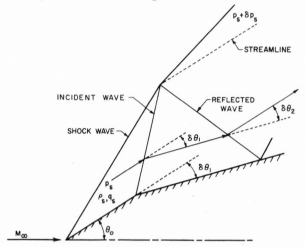

FIG. 7–5. Wave reflection from a shock wave.

upon two basic assumptions: First, the reflections of the Mach waves from the curved shock are weak, and second, the reflections of the Mach waves from the streamlines are also weak.

Let us consider first the problem of determining the strength of the Mach waves reflected from the shock. The problem of the ratio of shock curvature to body curvature at the nose of a two-dimensional ogive is a closely related problem, treated by Crocco [1] and others (see references in Kraus [1]). Munk and Prim [1] carried out calculations of the ratio of the exact surface pressure gradient to that obtained by the use of shock-expansion over a range of free stream Mach numbers and leading edge deflection angles in a perfect gas.

The calculation for the strength of a wave reflected from a shock front in terms of the incident wave has been carried out by Lighthill [1], Chu [1], Eggers and Syvertson [1], Eggers, Savin, and Syvertson [1], and Waldman and Probstein [1].

To compute the value of this reflection coefficient, let us consider the incidence of an expansion wave on an oblique shock (see Fig. 7–5). If we denote the change in pressure across the incident wave as $\delta p_1$ and that across the reflected wave as $\delta p_2$, then from the characteristic relations for a simple wave flow we have

$$(7.2.7) \qquad \delta p_1 = \rho_s q_s^2 \tan \mu_s \, \delta\theta_1,$$

$$(7.2.8) \qquad \delta p_1 + \delta p_2 = \rho_s q_s^2 \tan \mu_s(\delta\theta_1 - \delta\theta_2).$$

Here we neglect the change in the reference quantity $\rho_s q_s^2 \tan \mu_s$, as this change is itself of the order of $\delta\theta_1$. On the other hand, from the oblique shock relations we may formally write the change in pressure associated with a small change in deflection angle as

$$(7.2.9) \qquad \delta p_s = \rho_s q_s^2 \tan \varphi \, \delta\theta_s = \rho_s q_s^2 \tan \varphi(\delta\theta_1 + \delta\theta_2),$$

where $\tan \varphi$ is some function of the free stream conditions and the shock strength. Since the pressure in the region separated from the shock by the slipstream must equal the pressure directly behind the shock, we find on equating (7.2.8) and (7.2.9) that

$$(7.2.10) \qquad \delta\theta_2 = \left[\frac{\tan \mu_s - \tan \varphi}{\tan \mu_s + \tan \varphi}\right] \delta\theta_1.$$

If a reflection coefficient $\Re_s$ is now defined as the change in pressure across the reflected wave divided by the change in pressure across the incident wave, we obtain

$$(7.2.11) \qquad \Re_s = \frac{\tan \varphi - \tan \mu_s}{\tan \varphi + \tan \mu_s}.$$

This is the form given for this quantity by both Lighthill and Chu.

In principle, one can now calculate the change in the pressure behind the shock associated with a small change in deflection, and in this manner determine $\tan \varphi$. By way of example, we consider the special case in which we may make the assumption that $\epsilon$ is constant along the shock, and that the shock inclination angle $\sigma$ is small. These assumptions are the same as those underlying the similar solutions of Section 2.6. From the oblique shock relation (1.4.5b) the pressure jump across the shock is

$$(7.2.12) \qquad p_s - p_\infty = \rho_\infty U^2 \sin^2 \sigma(1 - \epsilon).$$

From (1.5.1) and (1.5.2a) we obtain

$$(7.2.13) \qquad q_s^2 = U^2(\cos^2 \sigma + \epsilon^2 \sin^2 \sigma) \approx U^2.$$

Differentiation of (7.2.12) gives the result

$$(7.2.14) \qquad \frac{\delta p_s}{\rho_s q_s^2} = 2\epsilon(1 - \epsilon)\sigma \, \delta\sigma,$$

in which $\sin \sigma$ has been replaced by $\sigma$ and $\cos \sigma$ by one. We now only need to differentiate the relation

$$(7.2.15) \qquad\qquad \theta_s = \sigma(1 - \epsilon)$$

obtainable from (4.1.2), in order to obtain $\delta\sigma$ as a function of $\delta\theta_s$. Then, from the definition of $\tan \varphi$ in (7.2.9) we obtain immediately

$$(7.2.16) \qquad\qquad \tan \varphi = \frac{2\epsilon}{1 - \epsilon} \, \theta_s.$$

The local Mach angle behind the shock can be found by employing the formula $a_s^2 = \gamma_s p_s / \rho_s$ from (1.4.22), with the effective $\gamma_s$ taking either a frozen or equilibrium value. Thus, with the strong shock assumption ($p_\infty = 0$) and (7.2.12) we find

$$(7.2.17) \qquad\qquad M_s^2 = \frac{1 - \epsilon}{\gamma_s \epsilon \theta_s^2} .$$

Since $\tan \mu_s \approx 1/M_s$, from (7.2.16) and (7.2.17) the result for this limiting value of the reflection coefficient is

$$(7.2.18) \qquad\qquad \Re_s = \frac{2\sqrt{\epsilon} - \sqrt{\gamma_s(1 - \epsilon)}}{2\sqrt{\epsilon} + \sqrt{\gamma_s(1 - \epsilon)}} .$$

One of the most interesting features of this result is that the limiting value of the reflection coefficient is independent of the deflection angle and dependent only on the state of the gas behind the shock. In fact, when expressed in terms of $\Re_s$, the calculations of Eggers, Syvertson, and Kraus[1] (see Waldman and Probstein[1]) show this conclusion to be quite generally accurate, practically up to the detachment point angle. Furthermore, we see from (7.2.18) that as $\epsilon \rightarrow 0$, the reflection coefficient approaches $-1$.

TABLE 7–1

*Reflection coefficient at shock for $M_\infty = \infty$ in a perfect gas*

| $\gamma$ | 1.4 | 1.3 | 1.2 | 1.1 | 1.05 | 1 |
|---|---|---|---|---|---|---|
| $\Re_s$ | $-0.14$ | $-0.19$ | $-0.27$ | $-0.40$ | $-0.53$ | $-1.0$ |

In this extreme case an expansion wave will reflect from the shock as a compression wave of undiminished strength.

In order to give some idea of the magnitude of the reflection, we have presented in Table 7–1, for different values of $\gamma$, the limiting value of the reflection coefficient in a perfect gas. Even in this extreme limiting case of $M_\infty \rightarrow \infty$, except for $\epsilon$ very close to zero, and except near the detachment point, the absolute value of the reflection coefficient is never large. This implies that the disturbances are absorbed to a great extent by the shock wave and are only weakly reflected.

As we have pointed out, the reflection coefficient is not the entire story, because of the interactions which take place between the waves from the airfoil surface and the vorticity or entropy layers in the flow. An estimate of the magnitude of this effect can be found by calculating the reflection of a simple wave from an idealized supersonic shear layer (see Fig. 7-6). By using the form of the characteristic relations as given by (7.2.7) and (7.2.8),

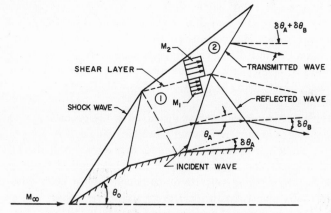

FIG. 7-6. Wave reflection from a shear layer.

with the pressure and flow deflection on both sides of the shear layer taken to be constant, one can show that the ratio of the pressure rise across the reflected wave to that across the incident wave is given by

$$(7.2.19) \qquad \Re_v = \frac{\Gamma_2 - \Gamma_1}{\Gamma_2 + \Gamma_1}$$

where the quantity $\Gamma$ is the same as the one defined by (7.2.2).

When the shear layer is very weak, $M_2 \to M_1$ and $\Gamma_2 \to \Gamma_1$, with the result that the strength of the reflected wave tends to zero. Let us consider on the other hand the case of a strong shear layer with the conditions $M_2 \gg M_1$ and $M_1$ not too close to unity $[(M_1^2 - 1)^{-1/2} \ll M_2]$. It follows in this case that $\Gamma_2 \gg \Gamma_1$ and $\Re_v \approx 1$. In such a case, the change in pressure across the reflected wave is almost equal to the change in pressure across the incident wave, so that a wave reflects from the shear layer as if from a solid wall. Therefore, if such a shear layer were present in the flow field the shock-expansion method could not be applied. This extreme example points out that vorticity reflections may be equally important to or more important than the reflections from the shock.

In considering the applicability of the shock-expansion method, we must not be misled into treating the influence on surface pressure of either of the reflection processes which we have discussed as if it by itself necessarily characterized the accuracy of the method. An important feature of these processes is a tendency for them to cancel each other in their effect on the surface pressure. Thus, an expansion wave reflects from a shear layer as an expansion, but reflects from the shock as a compression. This annulment would tend to make the shock-expansion method more accurate for the surface pressure distribution than a consideration of either one of the two inherent sources of error would indicate. A similar conclusion has been reached by Mahony [1], and Mahony and Skeat [1] through a somewhat different approach. The conclusion that these reflections tend to cancel depends upon $\Re_s$ and $\Re_v$ having opposite signs, in particular on $\Re_s$ being negative and $\Re_v$ being positive. Changes of sign can appear in either quantity, such as near the detachment point and at low Mach numbers (see Waldman and Probstein [1]).

A factor which we have not yet discussed is the geometry of the streamlines and Mach waves. In Epstein's original studies for polygonal bodies the first outgoing wave starts at a shoulder of the body well aft of the leading edge, and its reflection from the shock may be assumed to miss the body completely at hypersonic velocities. In general, on a body with a wedge-shaped forebody shock-expansion theory should be either very accurate or should be exact in giving the pressure on the body. On the other hand, on a body with large curvatures very near the nose or with a blunted nose there will be a strong concentration of vorticity in the streamlines very near the body (the entropy layer discussed in Section 1.2), and the shock-expansion method is subject to serious inaccuracy. Thus the shape of the forebody is extremely important, particularly at hypersonic speeds.

Stocker [1] has made a careful analysis of shock-expansion theory for a perfect gas. He points out that considerable error may arise in a region if the body curvature is small compared with the body curvature at the nose, and emphasizes the role of the parameter $\gamma$. If $\gamma = 1.4$ shock-expansion theory can yield a good estimate, while at $\gamma = 1.2$ the accuracy is already appreciably reduced.

Figure 7–7(a) presents the results of calculations by Eggers, Syvertson, and Kraus [1] of the shock wave shape and surface pressure distribution by the characteristics method and by the generalized shock-expansion method in a perfect gas with $\gamma = 1.4$ and $M_{\cdot\infty} = \infty$. The body shown is a 10 per cent thick parabolic arc biconvex airfoil at zero incidence. In Fig. 7–7(b) surface pressure distribution calculations are shown for the same body in the same flow but with $\gamma = 1.05$. Although shock-expansion checks well with the characteristics result for $\gamma = 1.4$ and would be even better for a lower Mach number, its accuracy is seen to be considerably reduced for $\gamma = 1.05$ (see Eggers, Syvertson, and Kraus [1]).

Following the development of Mahony [1] and Mahony and Skeat [1], Meyer [2] formulated the generalized shock-expansion method analytically by using the stream function and flow deflection angle as independent variables. In principle, by this method the solution can be built up in a simple rectangular network in the plane of the independent variables. The determination of the shock shape in this approach is based on matching the flow deflection for the generalized simple wave with the flow deflection given by the shock equation. The result given for the shape of the shock is expressed in an integral form which can be evaluated by quadrature. In Section 7.4 we shall consider improvements such as those carried out by Mahony [1], Mahony and Skeat [1], and Waldman and Probstein [1] which can be made by using the shock-expansion method as a first approximation to the flow field. A recent analysis of the shock-expansion method has been made by Guiraud [1]. He notes that the principal characteristics must make a relatively small angle with the shock wave if the method is to be valid.

In the light of the practical success of this method in treating two-dimensional hypersonic flows with the isentropic exponent $\gamma$ not too close to one, it is reasonable to inquire whether such an approach could be adopted in three-dimensional problems even though there is no simple general solution analogous to the Prandtl-Meyer flow. It appears reasonable that such a scheme could be applied to slender bodies at high local Mach numbers, since if the local Mach number is high the concepts of strip theory apply (see Section 2.4) and the flow may be considered to be approximately two-dimensional locally. One may then anticipate that for values of the hypersonic similarity parameter $K = M_\infty \tau > 1$ the pressure distribution can be calculated approximately on bodies of revolution by assuming a conical shock wave at the nose followed by a two-dimensional Prandtl-Meyer expansion.

For axisymmetric flow we can justify such an approach by considering the behavior of the axisymmetric term in the characteristic equations (7.1.12). This term can be expressed as $r^{-1} \sin \theta \sin \mu \, dC_{1,2}$, where $dC_{1,2}$ are elements of length along the first and second family characteristics respectively. Since $\sin \mu = 1/M$, we can write the coefficient of $dC_{1,2}$ for small deflections as $\theta^2/r(M\theta)$. We see then that the axisymmetric term will indeed be small away from the axis in comparison with the other terms in the characteristic equations if $\theta$ is small and $M\theta$ is of the order of one or greater. With $\theta$ fixed, the larger the value of the local similarity parameter $M\theta$, the better will be the approximation of neglecting the axisymmetric contribution.

Following Eggers and Savin [1; 2] (see also Eggers, Savin, and Syvertson [1]), these considerations can be extended to general three-dimensional flows

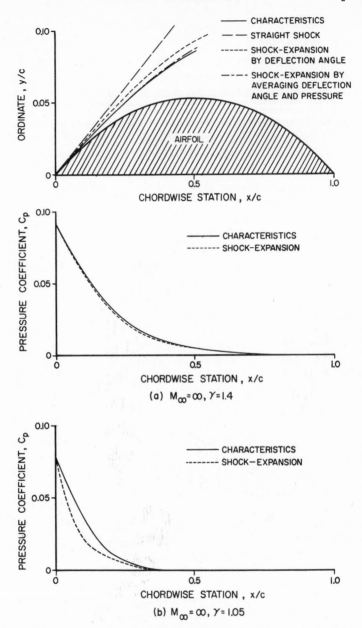

FIG. 7-7. Comparison of shock-expansion method and characteristics theory for a 10 per cent thick biconvex airfoil (Eggers, Syvertson, and Kraus [1]). (a) Pressure distribution and shock shape, $M_\infty = \infty$, $\gamma = 1.4$. (b) Pressure distribution, $M_\infty = \infty$, $\gamma = 1.05$.

past slender bodies by noting that at high local Mach numbers the shock layer is quite thin, so that we may confine our attention to the neighborhood of the surface. Such an assumption is the basic one employed in the strip theory similitude of Section 2.4.

Justifications of the application of the shock-expansion method to axisymmetric and other three-dimensional flows have appeared in the references cited. If the flow inclination angles are small and the local Mach numbers are large a justification is afforded by the arguments of Section 2.4. In axisymmetric flow where these conditions are not met a correction (described below) may be used to reduce the errors inherent in such a direct application. For other three-dimensional bodies such as yawed bodies of revolution the justifications are somewhat clouded and we should consider the application of the direct shock-expansion method as primarily empirically based.

In Fig. 7–8 taken from Eggers, Savin, and Syvertson [1] the surface pressure distributions computed by shock-expansion for an unyawed ogive of fineness ratio 3 are compared with results obtained by the method of characteristics and experiment. The good agreement for values of the hypersonic similarity parameter $K$ greater than one is clearly evident, although for $K$ of the order of one the comparison is somewhat less favorable.

We have seen that the application of the shock-expansion method to the three-dimensional case requires the use of two-dimensional techniques in a three-dimensional flow, so that the continuity equation is only approximately satisfied. Syvertson and Dennis [1] have attempted to increase the accuracy of the method for the axisymmetric case by adjusting the stream tube thickness to satisfy the continuity requirement.

In the approach of Syvertson and Dennis, their correction to the shock-expansion method for axisymmetric flow is based on representing the body of arbitrary contour by a series of tangents. The surface pressure distribution around the corners of the tangent-body is then found by the Prandtl-Meyer relation. The problem is to determine the change in surface pressure along the straight line elements, for which no pressure change is predicted by shock-expansion.

On the basis of a quasi-rational argument based on continuity the authors conclude that the pressure on such a straight line element should have an approximate behavior given by

$$(7.2.20) \qquad\qquad p = b + ce^{-as},$$

where $s$ is distance along the element taken from the corner and $a$, $b$, and $c$ are constants. The pressure immediately behind the corner is $b + c$ and is obtained from the local Prandtl-Meyer expansion. The pressure gradient immediately behind the corner $\partial p/\partial s$ is needed, and gives the quantity $ac$. If the line element were extended to infinity the pressure should approach

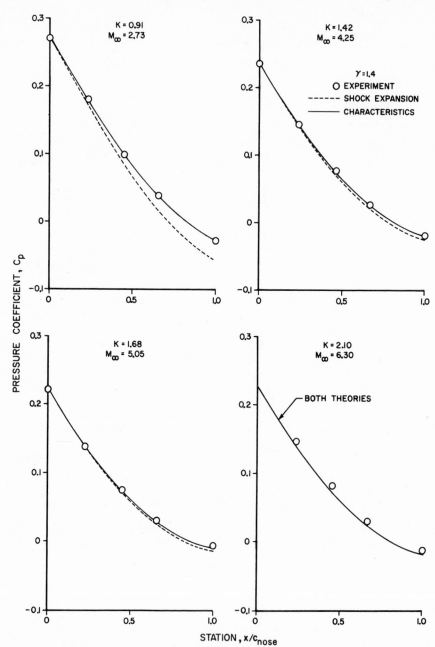

FIG. 7-8. Pressure distributions on an ogive of fineness ratio 3 at zero incidence (Eggers, Savin, and Syvertson [1]).

asymptotically the value on a cone of the same inclination angle, and this fact is used as a condition to evaluate $b$. It is difficult to see how the surface pressure of (7.2.20) could be far wrong, since it has the correct initial value and initial derivative and approaches a correct limit. However, we must consider this result as primarily empirically based.

The evaluation of the pressure gradient on a straight line element immediately after a Prandtl-Meyer expansion is needed in the evaluation of the constants in (7.2.20). Determinations of the exact value of this pressure gradient for a perfect gas have been given by Johannsen and Meyer [1] and Ferrari [1], with numerical calculations carried out for $\gamma = 1.4$. An approximate evaluation of this pressure gradient has been made by Syvertson and Dennis [1], who calculated the streamtube areas by a one-dimensional analysis, and obtained a simplified analytical result. We refer the reader to the original references for detailed results.

It is evident that an approximate distribution for the surface pressure along the tangent-body can be determined by a step-by-step process using (7.2.20). Calculations of Syvertson and Dennis which are shown in Fig. 7–9 illustrate for $K = 1$ the improved accuracy which can be obtained for unyawed bodies of revolution with this correction. Other numerical results by these same authors indicate equally good comparisons for $K$ as low as 0.4, while for $K > 1.5$ their calculations show that the correction becomes small, and the results of this method approach those of the generalized shock-expansion method, as they should. Syvertson and Dennis have extended this technique to the evaluation of normal-force derivatives and to the location of centers of pressure at zero angle of attack.

## 3. Tangent-wedge and tangent-cone

Two other approximate inviscid methods for obtaining surface pressure distributions on moderately slender bodies at hypersonic speeds are the "tangent-wedge" approximation for two-dimensional bodies and the "tangent-cone" approximation for bodies of revolution. Although these empirical methods are extremely simple to apply, they give no information on the structure of the shock layer and they neglect centrifugal effects. Yet because of the simple relation they afford between surface pressure and local streamline inclination, we feel that some discussion of them is warranted, even though they must be considered as empirically based in the range in which they are usually used.

In the tangent-wedge approximation for two-dimensional flow the surface pressure at any point on a body at an arbitrary angle of attack is taken to be equal to the pressure on a wedge whose half-angle equals the local inclination angle of the streamline with respect to the flight direction. Physically the approximation relies on the fact that at hypersonic speeds the shock layer is sufficiently thin that there is little change in either flow inclination or pressure along a normal to the airfoil. Hence the surface values are approximately the same as those at the shock.

The extreme simplicity of the tangent-wedge approximation lies in the

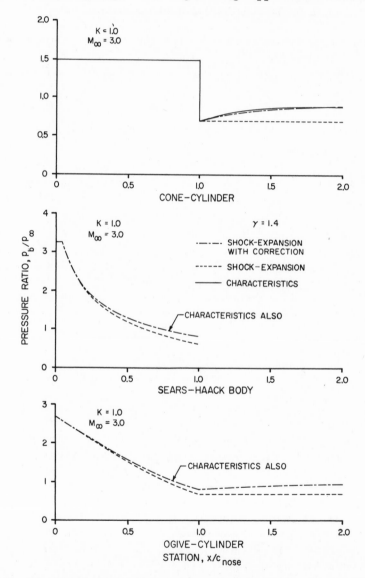

FIG. 7–9. Pressure distributions on axisymmetric bodies (Syvertson and Dennis [1]).

fact that a single function of body angle is used to estimate the pressure. With such simplicity it is evident that in general the tangent-wedge approximation should be less accurate than the result of the shock-expansion method. However, for $\epsilon$ very small it should be better. We shall present the pressure law given by the tangent-wedge approximation in some special cases and shall present a method for improving it if $\epsilon$ is very small.

In the special case of a slender body in a hypersonic flow of a perfect gas with constant $\gamma$ we have available the result of Linnell [1] given in (2.5.2). It is convenient to rewrite (2.5.2) in a different form, in which $K = M_\infty \theta_b$ is used to replace $\theta_b$. In this form the result for the pressure may be expressed

$$(7.3.1) \qquad \frac{p_b}{p_\infty} = 1 + \gamma K^2 \left[ \sqrt{\left( \frac{\gamma + 1}{4} \right)^2 + \frac{1}{K^2}} + \frac{\gamma + 1}{4} \right].$$

For $K$ small this result may be rewritten as a power series in $K$,

$$(7.3.2) \qquad \frac{p_b}{p_\infty} = 1 + \gamma K + \frac{\gamma(\gamma + 1)}{4} K^2 + \frac{\gamma(\gamma + 1)^2}{32} K^3 + O(K^5),$$

which represents the hypersonic limit of the well known Busemann expansion for the pressure behind an oblique shock (cf. (2.7.1) for an isentropic flow).

Another special case is that of a gas which is a perfect gas behind the shock of fixed $\gamma_e = \gamma_s$, with $\epsilon_{\lim} = (\gamma_s - 1)/(\gamma_s + 1)$, but for which $\gamma_s \neq \gamma$. Here we assume not only that the body is a slender one in a hypersonic flow but that $K$ is large. We take the approximation afforded by (1.4.14) and (1.5.4), and obtain

$$(7.3.3) \qquad \frac{\sigma - \theta_b}{\sigma} = \epsilon = \epsilon_{\lim} \left[ 1 + \frac{\epsilon_\infty^{-1} - \epsilon_{\lim}}{1 - \epsilon_{\lim}} \frac{1}{\gamma M_\infty^2 \sigma^2} \right].$$

Solving this equation for $\sigma/\theta_b$ yields for $p_b/p_\infty$ from (1.4.12) or (4.1.13) the result

$$(7.3.4) \qquad \frac{p_b}{p_\infty} = 1 + \gamma K^2 \left( \frac{\sigma}{\theta_b} \right) = 1 + \frac{\gamma K^2}{1 - \epsilon_{\lim}} \left[ 1 + \frac{\epsilon_{\lim}(\epsilon_\infty^{-1} - \epsilon_{\lim})}{\gamma K^2} \right],$$

with terms of higher order in $K^{-2}$ dropped because terms of order $K^{-4}$ have been neglected in (7.3.3). Since (7.3.4) is only valid for large $K$, no expansion analogous to (7.3.2) may be made.

As was pointed out by Lees [3], the tangent-wedge approximation is based on the constancy of both pressure and flow inclination angle across the shock layer (along the same path), and will be in error for at least two reasons. First, centrifugal force effects arising from the curvature of the body cause a pressure gradient across the shock layer. Second, the pressure gradient along the shock layer causes a divergence or convergence of the streamlines, and the flow inclination angle has a gradient across the shock layer. The only completely rational theory for a correction of these errors must be made for $\epsilon$ very small. With $\epsilon$ very small the correction for the change in flow inclination angle is small in comparison with the correction from the centrifugal effects, and must be neglected within the accuracy to which we are able to estimate the latter. Within this order of accuracy the correction for the centrifugal effects is the same as that appearing in the Newtonian theory treated in Chapter III.

Within hypersonic slender body theory the pressure immediately behind the shock is given by (1.4.12) or (4.1.13) as

$$(7.3.5) \qquad \frac{p_s - p_\infty}{\gamma p_\infty M_\infty^2} = (1 - \epsilon)\sigma^2 = \frac{\theta_s^2}{1 - \epsilon}.$$

The centrifugal pressure correction across the shock layer with $\epsilon$ small may be approximated from (7.1.4) with $d\theta/ds = -1/R_b$ and $\rho(y_s - y_b) \approx \rho_\infty y_b$ by

$$(7.3.6) \qquad p_s - p_b = \rho U^2 \left(\frac{y_s - y_b}{R_b}\right) = \gamma p_\infty M_\infty^2 \left(\frac{y_b}{R_b}\right).$$

As before $R_b$ is the radius of curvature of the body, taken positive for a convex body.

Taking $\theta_b = \theta_s$, we obtain for the corrected pressure on the body

$$(7.3.7) \qquad \frac{p_b}{p_\infty} = 1 + \frac{\gamma K^2}{1 - \epsilon} - \gamma M_\infty^2 \frac{y_b}{R_b}.$$

The third term on the right hand side of (7.3.7) is the centrifugal pressure correction. Since we have assumed that $\epsilon$ is small in calculating the pressure correction, we should ask whether the factor $(1 - \epsilon)^{-1}$ in the second term should not also consistently be dropped. If the quantity $y_b/R_b\theta_b^2$ is of order 1 this question should be answered yes, and we are left simply with the result of Newtonian theory for a slender body. In order for the result (7.3.7) to give us something new, we must assume that $y_b/R_b\theta_b^2$ is small compared with one. We may apply a similar centrifugal correction if $\theta_b$ is finite instead of small, provided $\cos \theta_b$ is not small and provided the other conditions discussed above are met.

One problem to which this correction may be immediately applied is to the calculation of the initial pressure gradient on a two-dimensional ogive. Here we must take the Newtonian limit in order to retain consistency. We take $d\theta_b/ds = -1/R_b$ and $dy_b/ds = \theta_b$, where $s$ is distance along the body surface, and obtain

$$(7.3.8) \qquad \frac{dC_{p_b}}{ds} = -6 \frac{\theta_b}{R_b}.$$

This result is consistent with the Newtonian result shown on Fig. 2–5. Had we omitted the correction we would have obtained the same result with the incorrect factor 4 in place of 6.

The centrifugal pressure correction which appears in (7.3.7) was suggested and calculated for a perfect gas by Lees [3]. In addition to calculating this correction he also included a correction for the change in flow deflection angle across the shock layer. However, as we have pointed out, the order of magnitude of this deflection angle correction is of the same order of magnitude as that of the error in estimating the centrifugal pressure correction.

The corresponding procedure for bodies of revolution is the so-called tangent-cone method which has been applied to the calculation of surface pressure distributions (e.g., Fowler and French [1]). According to this approximation, the pressure at any point on the surface of a slender body of revolution at arbitrary angles of pitch and yaw is identical with the Taylor-Maccoll value at the same Mach number on a semi-infinite unyawed circular cone of half-angle equal to the local inclination of the streamline with respect to the flight direction. Of course, this method will be in error for the same reasons as those given in the two-dimensional case.

We can in a very simple manner carry out a correction for the body of revolution similar to the one which was made for two-dimensional flow, with the same assumptions and under the same conditions as those for the tangent-wedge correction.

For the cone, (7.3.6) is repeated but with a factor $\frac{1}{2}$ arising from the relation $\rho(r_s - r_b) \approx \frac{1}{2}\rho_\infty r_b$, and the analogue of (7.3.5) may be obtained from (4.2.26). The final result for the pressure on a slender body is

$$(7.3.9) \qquad \frac{p_b}{p_\infty} = 1 + \frac{\gamma K^2}{1 - \frac{1}{4}\epsilon} - \frac{\gamma M_\infty^2}{2}\frac{r_b}{R_b}.$$

In order to justifiably keep the factor $1 - \frac{1}{4}\epsilon$ above we must again impose the condition that $r_b/R_b\theta_b^2$ is small, and again a similar correction for axisymmetric flow may be applied if $\theta_b$ is finite under the suitable restrictions discussed previously. In calculating the initial pressure gradient on an ogive of revolution (7.3.8) is again obtained, but with a factor 5 instead of 6, consistent with Fig. 2–9. Had the correction been omitted, the incorrect factor 4 would have appeared.

Despite the lack of an unassailable theoretical justification, the tangent-wedge and tangent-cone approximations are useful, particularly when other approximate theories such as shock-expansion break down. Thus, the tangent-wedge approximation might be especially valuable for an estimate of the pressure on a blunted wedge or on a two-dimensional ogive highly curved near the nose. We shall use the tangent-wedge approximation in Chapter IX when we treat boundary layer interactions.

## 4. Successive approximation schemes

As we have seen, various schemes have been proposed for the calculation of rotational hypersonic flows over sharp-nosed airfoils, most of which are based to some extent on empirical considerations. In this section we describe briefly several perturbation techniques which take as a starting point an approximate solution which is known to be reasonably accurate. The advantage of such an approach is that it can offer a mathematically consistent treatment of the flow problem and at the same time be capable of providing general analytic results and an indication as to when the simple approximate scheme breaks down.

Mahony [1], for example, seeks to improve on and investigate the accuracy of the shock-expansion method in a perfect gas. His method is to solve the unsteady one-dimensional piston problem through an iteration technique starting with the isentropic shock-expansion solution. He carries his results over to steady two-dimensional flow by using the equivalence principle described in Section 2.1. Recognizing the dominant role played by the principal characteristics in contrast to the secondary role of the reflected characteristics, he introduces two new independent variables. One is a parameter which is defined so that it is constant along reflected characteristics, and which serves as a coordinate. The other is the characteristic parameter for the principal characteristics, which would be constant along principal characteristics only if the flow were isentropic. Using these variables he establishes an approximate basic solution including a curved shock and straight principal characteristics. He then applies an iterative procedure in which the independent variables are held fixed, but an entropy distribution appears at the shock and is made to propagate along the streamlines. This then permits the corrected pressure distribution at the airfoil to be obtained by integrating back along the reflected characteristics from the shock. His results show, as we have already seen, that for $\gamma = 7/5$ and $\gamma = 5/3$ the predictions of shock-expansion theory are very accurate in the hypersonic similarity range. Mahony makes the observation that this is partly due to a tendency of the inherent errors to cancel, an observation which we made in Section 7.2 on the basis of general considerations of the wave reflection process. He also finds, in agreement with our previous discussion, that the pressure distribution predictions for $\gamma = 1$ are in great error, and that the shock-expansion method is completely unsatisfactory with $\gamma$ near one.

One of the difficulties in the analysis of Mahony is that it applies only to the region of hypersonic similarity and hence to slender bodies in hypersonic flow. Mahony and Skeat [1] and Waldman and Probstein [1] extended the approach of Mahony to general supersonic two-dimensional flows in a perfect gas, without the restrictions inherent in using the equivalence principle. The analysis of Mahony and Skeat followed the original analysis of Mahony very closely. Waldman and Probstein obtain subsequent approximations beyond the lowest isentropic one by expanding in powers of the shock reflection coefficient $\mathfrak{R}_s$ discussed in Section 7.2. Through this technique they find a general expression to second order for the pressure distribution on two-dimensional airfoils in rotational flow, valid for relatively thick bodies. Evidently, these techniques can always be continued to any order desired, although beyond a first correction to shock-expansion the algebra becomes rather extensive. The results of such second-order calculations, however, are found to be in excellent agreement with characteristic calculations.

Another method which is of interest is that of Kogan [1; 3], who developed a successive approximation scheme using the Crocco stream function as the dependent variable. Since the vorticity which enters in the equation for the stream function depends on the form of the shock wave, which is initially unknown, Kogan takes as the zeroth-order approximation the flow behind a plane shock wave. The shock wave profile which is obtained in each step of the iteration is then used to determine the differential equations and boundary conditions for the following iteration. Using his first-order solution for the flow near the leading edge of a two-dimensional ogive, he calculates the shock curvature and pressure gradient on the body at the leading edge for a perfect gas with $\gamma = 1.4$. These results are found to be identical with the calculations of Kraus [1] based upon the complete equations of motion. The second approximation yields expressions for the derivative of the shock curvature and the second derivative of the pressure coefficient at the leading edge. The second approximation for the pressure and shock shape gives results near the leading edge which are in very good agreement with the pressure distribution and shock profiles determined by characteristic calculations, even considerably downstream of the leading edge.

Kogan [1; 2] also carried out a similar calculation for a first-order approximation to the axisymmetric flow past an ogive of revolution. He uses the conical flow solution corresponding to the nose angle as the zeroth-order solution, and obtains the appropriate expansions for the shock wave profile in terms of the ogive profile. In this work he shows that the mathematical singularity of the first approximation near the surface of the ogive, which caused difficulties in other methods of treatment, is avoided by the use of the Crocco stream function.

Although all of these methods are of interest they are all expressed for a perfect gas of constant $\gamma$, and we feel that their extension to general fluids would enhance their usefulness considerably for hypersonic flow calculations.

# CHAPTER VIII

# VISCOUS FLOWS

## 1. Hypersonic viscous effects

We now turn from the problems of inviscid continuum flow to those real-fluid effects which are termed "viscous". Within the broad definition of the term viscous adopted in Section 1.7 we include not only viscosity and heat conduction but also relaxation, diffusion, and chemical reaction. Within this general concept, viscous phenomena are restricted to phenomena for which the fluid may be considered to be in thermodynamic quasi-equilibrium. Accordingly, our attention in this and the following chapter will be restricted to those flows where the local mean free path is sufficiently small in comparison with a dimension or boundary layer thickness characteristic of the velocity, temperature, and concentration gradients in the flow field.

In a low speed flow of air around a body at normal densities, the processes of viscous dissipation and heat conduction are restricted to a relatively thin boundary layer near the surface of the body. This boundary layer may be considered as an entity distinct from the outer or external inviscid flow. The boundary layer may be laminar or turbulent, or it may be in an intermediate or transitional state. And as we have seen in Section 1.7, for either blunt or slender bodies at hypersonic speeds, the shock wave can be considered infinitesimally thin as long as the boundary layer thickness is small compared to the shock layer thickness.

At hypersonic speeds the deceleration of the fluid by a shock wave or by viscous processes in a boundary layer generally produces very high temperatures. One result of these high temperatures is an increase in the thickness of the boundary layer over the thicknesses encountered at the same free stream Reynolds number at lower speeds. Another result is the appearance of various physical phenomena comprised in the subject of high temperature gasdynamics (see Section 1.1). These phenomena cause the gas to depart from a perfect gas behavior. They include dissociation and ionization proceeding at finite rates, diffusion of atoms and ions, and recombination processes. Certainly these two types of effects are not mutually independent, but in a broad sense we can consider them as giving rise to two different types of hypersonic viscous problems.

The increased thickness of the boundary layer contributes to two types of interaction of the boundary layer with the inviscid flow field. In the first of these types the interaction of the boundary layer is with the external supersonic flow. The outward streamline deflection induced by the layer as it grows along the surface amounts to a significant change in the "effective" shape of the body. Thus as a result of the large induced pressures transmitted into the external inviscid field along Mach lines, the boundary layer itself generates an inviscid hypersonic shock layer from the nose or leading edge of the body. These pressures in turn govern the growth of the boundary layer. In this case we would have a "Mach wave" interaction or what we shall term a "pressure" interaction. In general this phenomenon is only important for slender bodies, since on blunt bodies the shock is detached and the flow velocities are subsonic or only moderately supersonic.

The second type of interaction associated with large boundary layer thicknesses occurs when the vorticity in the external inviscid flow is sufficiently large that the boundary layer structure is affected not only by the external velocity distribution but also by the inviscid vorticity distribution. Such a "streamline" interaction or what we shall term a "vorticity" interaction becomes important when the vorticity in the inviscid layer due to the curved shock wave becomes of the same order as the average vorticity in the boundary layer due to the shear stress.

This vorticity interaction can enter in the hypersonic flow past both blunt and slender bodies. As long as the boundary layer thickness is small in comparison with the shock layer thickness, however, this effect will generally not be important. On the other hand, under conditions where there is a strong highly curved shock and the boundary layer thickness is of the order of the shock layer thickness, vorticity interaction may have to be taken into account.

These two types of interaction phenomena are primarily of a hydrodynamic nature and do not necessarily involve questions of high temperature gasdynamics. Chapter IX is devoted to the study of these interactions.

In the phenomena involving high temperature gasdynamics we are concerned with those gas effects connected with hypersonic flight which are primarily of a physical-chemical nature. For these problems we use the original Prandtl boundary layer concept that the external inviscid flow is not influenced by the boundary layer, and that the principal features of the external flow field which determine the growth and nature of the boundary layer may be calculated as though the boundary layer were not present.

Because such processes as dissociation, ionization, and their reverse recombination reactions proceed at finite rates, thermodynamic equilibrium is not necessarily achieved in the hypersonic boundary layer. As in our analysis of inviscid flow we shall treat the two limiting cases of thermodynamic equilibrium and frozen flow equilibrium in order to obtain an understanding of the physical mechanisms involved. For boundary layer problems with finite recombination rates see, for example, Fay and Riddell [1].

For thermodynamic equilibrium we assume that the reaction rates are fast in comparison with analogous rates for convection along streamlines or for diffusion across streamlines. Under these circumstances chemical equilibrium prevails throughout and either the temperature or the concentration distribution along with the pressure is sufficient to describe the thermodynamic state of the boundary layer. Of course, the fluid cannot be in strict thermodynamic equilibrium, for with finite reaction rate constants no reaction can take place in a material which is at equilibrium. For large enough reaction rate constants, however, the fluid will be very close to equilibrium, in what we have referred to as quasi-equilibrium.

For sufficiently slow recombination rates, on the other hand, the flow may be considered to be in frozen equilibrium. The phenomenon of frozen equilibrium has been discussed in Sections 1.4 and 7.1. For this case, it turns out that the temperature and concentration distributions are practically independent.

The most important practical question involving viscous effects at hypersonic speeds is usually the magnitude of the heat transfer to the body. The magnitude of the skin friction drag is also of extreme importance for slender bodies, particularly in low-density flows such as would be encountered at very high flight altitudes.

Despite the fact that the distributions of atoms in the two limiting cases of frozen and equilibrium flow are quite different, so that the thermodynamic state of the flow field depends on the type of process, it turns out that the actual effect of the difference in these distributions on the surface heat transfer rate and the skin friction is small. In addition, the local skin friction and heat transfer rate are not markedly different from what one would compute for a perfect gas with the same free stream enthalpy. The basic principle here is that the heat transfer depends primarily on the enthalpy difference across the layer. This conclusion, later substantiated by numerical calculations, was reached by many authors (see, for example, Fay and Riddell [1], Lees [4], Kantrowitz [1] and Kuo [2]) through elementary considerations of the heat transfer process in a dissociating gas.

In order to illustrate the manner in which heat is transferred in a dissociating gas, let us neglect convection and consider the heat flow that takes place between a hot and a cold surface in a fluid at rest with a temperature and concentration gradient. The arguments that we will use apply equally well either to a laminar flow or to a turbulent flow defined in terms of the appropriate mean quantities. The energy transfer rate across any plane normal to the direction of the gradient is given approximately by

$$(8.1.1) \qquad -\dot{q} = k\,\frac{dT}{dy} + D_A \rho\, h_A^0\, \frac{dc_A}{dy},$$

where $k$ is the thermal conductivity (frozen), $h_A^0$ is the dissociation energy per unit mass of atomic products, $D_A$ is the atomic diffusion coefficient, and $c_A$ is the atom mass fraction. In writing down this expression we have considered the fluid to be a binary mixture of atoms and molecules in which the specific heats at constant pressure of the atoms and of the corresponding molecules are assumed to be substantially equal. For air in the high temperature region in which the atom concentration becomes significant this is a very good approximation.

The approximate expression for energy flux given by (8.1.1) may be expressed in terms of enthalpy as

$$(8.1.2) \qquad -\dot{q} = \frac{k}{\bar{c}_p}\left[\frac{d(h_{p\text{-}g} + h_A^0 c_A)}{dy} + (Le - 1)\frac{dh_A^0 c_A}{dy}\right],$$

where $\bar{c}_p$ is the mean (frozen) specific heat ratio of the mixture, and $Le = \bar{c}_p D_A \rho/k$ is the Lewis-Semenov number, and the subscript $p\text{-}g$ indicates a perfect gas value defined to be zero at $T = 0$. The quantity $h_{p\text{-}g} + h_A^0 c_A$ is the specific enthalpy of the mixture. From kinetic theory estimates the Lewis-Semenov number is of the order of one (see, for example, Hirschfelder, Curtiss, and Bird [1]). If we make the approximation that it is exactly one, then the energy flux is directly proportional to the enthalpy gradient. If any atoms striking the cold surface recombine immediately there (catalytic recombination), the heat transfer is the same as the energy transfer and is determined primarily by the difference in enthalpy between the hot surface and the cold surface, and is approximately independent of the mechanism of heat transfer. Thus it makes no essential difference whether the atoms recombine in the boundary layer or on the wall, since the energy is transported at approximately the same rate whether it is carried as internal or translational energy by a molecule or as energy of dissociation by an atom. On the other hand we must use the actual values of the Lewis-Semenov number, the variation in heat capacities, the variation in transport properties, etc., if the heat transfer and other relevant quantities are to be known more exactly.

From (8.1.1) it can also be seen that when the gas temperatures are sufficiently low that no dissociation occurs, or when the gas is frozen in such a way that $c_A$ is constant across the boundary layer (and no recombination occurs at the surface), then just as for the case $Le = 1$, the surface heat transfer rate is given by

$$(8.1.3) \qquad -\dot{q} = \left(\frac{k}{\bar{c}_p}\frac{dh_{p\text{-}g}}{dy}\right)_b.$$

We shall be interested in the heat transfer only at the wall, and shall henceforth consider the subscript $b$ understood on the quantity $-\dot{q}$.

If the wall could be made noncatalytic to recombination, so that recombination only takes place in the fluid, only the heat transfer term $k \, dT/dy$ in (8.1.1) comes into the expression for heat transfer at the body surface. In general, the heat transfer from a hot dissociating gas flow to a cold body may be greatly reduced if the wall could be made noncatalytic to recombination.

## 2. Boundary layer equations

Making the usual assumptions that the boundary layer thickness is small compared to the body radius of curvature and that centrifugal forces are negligible, we can derive the boundary layer equations suitable for the laminar flow of a dissociating gas from the general hydrodynamic equations (for these equations see, for example, Hirschfelder, Curtiss, and Bird [1] or Penner [1]). In order to simplify the problem somewhat, we restrict our considerations to two-dimensional or axisymmetric flow and treat the gas in the boundary layer as a binary mixture of atoms of one species and molecules of one species, at least as far as diffusion is concerned. Such an assumption holds quite well for air, because of the close similarity of the transport properties and atomic weights of oxygen and nitrogen. In particular, this approximation permits us to deal with a single bimolecular atom-molecule diffusion coefficient which is practically independent of composition. In the analysis to follow we will account for the actual differences between oxygen and nitrogen through the use of suitable average properties. It should be emphasized that this last statement does not constitute a restrictive assumption since it is only used to simplify the calculation of the diffusion effect. As we shall see, this effect does not usually by itself have a large influence on such quantities as the heat transfer rate.

Under the preceding approximations we can write the basic equations for laminar boundary layer flow (see e.g. Fay and Riddell [1]) as follows. The overall continuity equation for the mixture is

$$(8.2.1) \qquad \frac{\partial \rho u r^j}{\partial x} + \frac{\partial \rho v r^j}{\partial y} = 0,$$

where again $j = 0$ for two-dimensional flow and $j = 1$ for axisymmetric flow. Here the coordinate $x$ is measured along the body surface from the nose or leading edge, the coordinate $y$ is measured along the outward normal from the body surface, and $r$ is the cylindrical radius from the axis of symmetry to any point in the boundary layer. In our discussion we will at first assume that the boundary layer thickness is small in comparison with the radius of the body cross section so that for axisymmetric flow we may replace $r$ by $r_b(x)$. That is, we will neglect transverse curvature effects. In Chapter IX we will briefly consider modifications which include the influence of transverse curvature. Note that in this and the following chapter the directions of $v$ and $y$ are reversed with respect to the boundary layer type of coordinate system used in Chapter V and VI. The usage in this and the following chapter is more conventional and is better adapted to boundary layer problems.

The corresponding continuity equation for each species is

$$(8.2.2) \qquad \rho u \frac{\partial c_i}{\partial x} + \rho v \frac{\partial c_i}{\partial y} = \frac{\partial}{\partial y} \left( \rho D_{12} \frac{\partial c_i}{\partial y} \right) + w_i,$$

with $c_i$ the mass fraction of the $i^{\text{th}}$ component (with $\Sigma c_i = 1$), $w_i$ the mass rate of formation of the $i^{\text{th}}$ species per unit volume and time, and $D_{12}$ the binary diffusion coefficient. In order that mass be conserved in any chemical change we require $\Sigma w_i = 0$. We have neglected thermal diffusion in writing the continuity equation in this form. The effect of thermal diffusion is unimportant in air for stagnation temperatures less than $10,000°\text{K}$, at least for an equilibrium flow (see Fay and Riddell [1]). Furthermore we have not considered pressure diffusion, which turns out to be even less important (because the pressure is approximately constant across a boundary layer).

The momentum equation is unchanged by the fact that the gas may be in a dissociated state; it is written in the usual form

$$(8.2.3) \qquad \rho u \frac{\partial u}{\partial x} + \rho v \frac{\partial u}{\partial y} = -\frac{\partial p}{\partial x} + \frac{\partial}{\partial y} \left( \mu \frac{\partial u}{\partial y} \right).$$

The fact that the gas is partly dissociated does however have an important effect upon the values of the viscosity coefficient $\mu$.

In our treatment we assume that each component of the fluid behaves as a perfect gas in contributing to the total pressure. Consequently $p_i = \rho_i \mathscr{R}_i T$ and we have for the mixture

$$(8.2.4) \qquad p = \rho \bar{\mathscr{R}} T,$$

where

$$(8.2.5) \qquad \bar{\mathscr{R}} = \sum c_i \mathscr{R}_i.$$

Finally we express the energy equation in terms of the total enthalpy

$$(8.2.6) \qquad H = h + \tfrac{1}{2} u^2 = \sum c_i (h_i - h_i^0) + \tfrac{1}{2} u^2,$$

where $h_i^0$ is the heat liberated in the formation of the $i^{\text{th}}$ component at $0°\text{K}$. By convention, we define $h_i^0$ to be zero for the molecules and to be minus the heat of dissociation for the atoms. The energy equation is given by

$$(8.2.7) \quad \rho u \frac{\partial H}{\partial x} + \rho v \frac{\partial H}{\partial y} = \frac{\partial}{\partial y} \left( \frac{\mu}{Pr} \frac{\partial H}{\partial y} \right) + \frac{\partial}{\partial y} \left[ \mu \left( 1 - \frac{1}{Pr} \right) \frac{\partial}{\partial y} \left( \frac{u^2}{2} \right) \right]$$
$$+ \frac{\partial}{\partial y} \left[ \rho D_{12} \left( 1 - \frac{1}{Le} \right) \sum (h_i - h_i^0) \frac{\partial c_i}{\partial y} \right],$$

with $Pr = \bar{c}_p \mu / k$. Here we have defined the Prandtl number $Pr$ and Lewis-Semenov number $Le$ in terms of the mean specific heat of the mixture

$$(8.2.8) \qquad \bar{c}_p = \sum c_i \frac{dh_i}{dT} = \sum c_i c_{p_i}.$$

As for the simple one-dimensional model discussed in the preceding section, it can be seen that the energy equation takes the familar form for a one-component gas when either $Le = 1$ or $c_i = constant$ across the boundary layer.

In order to simplify the problem of the solution of this system of partial differential equations, we shall first investigate similar solutions for which this system may be reduced to a set of ordinary differential equations. Before proceeding to the investigation of such possible similar solutions we shall find it convenient to rewrite our differential equations in terms of more appropriate variables. Stewartson [1] and Illingworth [1] introduced transformations which reduced the compressible boundary layer equations to incompressible form, and suggested similar solutions as analogues of the Falkner-Skan solutions. Their transformation is equivalent to the relation (8.3.29) of the approach presented here. They assumed $Pr = 1$, a perfect gas and a linear variation of viscosity with temperature.

The transformation of coordinates which we introduce includes the usual Mangler (see, for example, Young [1]) and Howarth-Dorodnitsyn transformations (see Howarth [1] and Dorodnitsyn [1]). It was proposed by Levy [1] for two-dimensional flow in the case where the specific heat of the gas was taken to be constant, and it was generalized to the present form by Lees [4], who included the effects of axial symmetry and variable specific heats. Using the subscript $b$ to denote conditions at the body surface (often referred to as the wall) and the subscript $\delta$ to denote conditions at the edge of the boundary layer, we may write the transformation as

$$(8.2.9a) \qquad \xi(x) = \int_0^{} \rho_b \mu_b u_\delta r_b^{2j}\, dx, \qquad \eta(x, y) = \frac{u_\delta r_b^j}{\sqrt{2\xi}} \int_0^{} \rho\, dy,$$

from which

$$(8.2.9b) \qquad \frac{d\xi}{dx} = \rho_b \mu_b u_\delta r_b^{2j}, \qquad \frac{\partial \eta}{\partial y} = \frac{\rho u_\delta r_b^j}{\sqrt{2\xi}}.$$

We also define as dependent variables the following dimensionless quantities:

$$(8.2.10a) \qquad f = \int_0^{} \frac{u}{u_\delta}\, d\eta, \qquad \frac{\partial f}{\partial \eta} = \frac{u}{u_\delta},$$

$$(8.2.10b) \qquad g = \frac{H}{H_\delta}, \qquad z_i = \frac{c_i}{c_{i\delta}}.$$

Through the use of (8.2.9) we may transform from the coordinates $(x, y)$ to the coordinates $(\xi, \eta)$ by employing the transformed continuity equation

$$(8.2.11a) \qquad \rho v = -r_b^{-j}\left(\frac{d\xi}{dx}\frac{\partial\sqrt{2\xi}f}{\partial\xi} + \sqrt{2\xi}\frac{\partial\eta}{\partial x}\frac{\partial f}{\partial\eta}\right)$$

and the transformed convective operator

$$(8.2.11b) \qquad \rho u\frac{\partial}{\partial x} + \rho v\frac{\partial}{\partial y} = \frac{\rho u_\delta}{2\xi}\frac{d\xi}{dx}\left[2\xi\left(\frac{\partial f}{\partial\eta}\frac{\partial}{\partial\xi} - \frac{\partial f}{\partial\xi}\frac{\partial}{\partial\eta}\right) - f\frac{\partial}{\partial\eta}\right].$$

With the aid of (8.2.11), we obtain for the continuity of species the relation

$$(8.2.12) \qquad \frac{\partial}{\partial\eta}\left(\frac{NLe}{Pr}\frac{\partial z_i}{\partial\eta}\right) + f\frac{\partial z_i}{\partial\eta} - 2z_i\frac{\partial f}{\partial\eta}\frac{d\ln c_{i\delta}}{d\ln\xi} + \frac{2\xi}{\rho u_\delta}\frac{dx}{d\xi}\frac{w_i}{c_{i\delta}}$$
$$= 2\xi\left(\frac{\partial f}{\partial\eta}\frac{\partial z_i}{\partial\xi} - \frac{\partial f}{\partial\xi}\frac{\partial z_i}{\partial\eta}\right),$$

where

$$(8.2.13) \qquad N = \frac{\rho\mu}{\rho_b\mu_b}.$$

The corresponding momentum equation is

$$(8.2.14) \qquad \frac{\partial}{\partial\eta}\left(N\frac{\partial^2 f}{\partial\eta^2}\right) + f\frac{\partial^2 f}{\partial\eta^2} + 2\frac{d\ln u_\delta}{d\ln\xi}\left[\frac{\rho_\delta}{\rho} - \left(\frac{\partial f}{\partial\eta}\right)^2\right]$$
$$= 2\xi\left(\frac{\partial f}{\partial\eta}\frac{\partial^2 f}{\partial\eta\partial\xi} - \frac{\partial f}{\partial\xi}\frac{\partial^2 f}{\partial\eta^2}\right),$$

while we have for the energy equation

$$(8.2.15) \qquad \frac{\partial}{\partial\eta}\left(\frac{N}{Pr}\frac{\partial g}{\partial\eta}\right) + f\frac{\partial g}{\partial\eta} + \frac{\partial}{\partial\eta}\left[\frac{N(Le-1)}{Pr}\sum c_{i\delta}\frac{(h_i - h_i^0)}{H_\delta}\frac{\partial z_i}{\partial\eta}\right]$$
$$+ \frac{u_\delta^2}{H_\delta}\frac{\partial}{\partial\eta}\left[N\left(1 - \frac{1}{Pr}\right)\frac{\partial f}{\partial\eta}\frac{\partial^2 f}{\partial\eta^2}\right] = 2\xi\left(\frac{\partial f}{\partial\eta}\frac{\partial g}{\partial\xi} - \frac{\partial f}{\partial\xi}\frac{\partial g}{\partial\eta}\right).$$

The overall continuity relation is not required since it is automatically satisfied by the transformation.

The parameter $u_\delta^2/H_\delta$ appearing in (8.2.15) is closely related to the Mach number $M_\delta$ in the external flow; it is small if $M_\delta \ll 1$ compared with one, and is close to 2 if $M_\delta \gg 1$. For a perfect gas of constant $\gamma$ we may write

$$(8.2.16) \qquad \frac{u_\delta^2}{H_\delta} = 2\left(1 + \frac{2}{\gamma - 1}M_\delta^{-2}\right)^{-1}.$$

### 3. Similar laminar boundary layer solutions

With the boundary layer equations in the form (8.2.12) to (8.2.15) we may seek those similar or $\xi$-independent solutions in which the dependent variables are functions of $\eta$ alone. In order to limit our considerations we will at first restrict our discussion to the equilibrium case of a binary mixture of atoms and molecules in which the recombination rates are assumed so fast that the concentration of each species is uniquely determined by any two independent thermodynamic variables such as pressure and temperature. For this case the continuity of species equation (8.2.12) is superfluous, and we need only examine the momentum and energy equations.

We now inquire what the requisite conditions are for the existence of similar solutions of (8.2.14) and (8.2.15) under the boundary conditions

$$(8.3.1a) \quad f(0) = 0, \qquad f_\eta(0) = 0, \qquad g(0) = g_b(\xi) \quad \text{or} \quad g_\eta(0) = 0,$$

$$(8.3.1b) \qquad\qquad f_\eta \to 1, \qquad g \to 1, \quad \text{as} \quad \eta \to \infty.$$

The subscript $\eta$ is used here to indicate partial differentiation with respect to $\eta$. Of the boundary conditions on $g$ in (8.3.1a), the first is for the case of a given wall temperature distribution and the second is for the case of an insulated wall. With these boundary conditions it can be seen from the differential equations that, for an isoenergetic flow outside the boundary layer where $H_\delta = constant$, the similarity criteria become

(1) $$N = \text{function of } \eta;$$

(2) $$\frac{d \ln u_\delta}{d \ln \xi} \left( \frac{\rho_\delta}{\rho} - f_\eta^2 \right) = \text{function of } \eta;$$

(3) Either (a) $Pr = 1$, or

    (b) $Pr = \text{function of } \eta$    and    $\dfrac{u_\delta^2}{H_\delta} = \text{constant};$

(4) Either (a) $Le = 1$, or

    (b) $Le = \text{function of } \eta$    and

$$\sum c_{i_\delta}(h_i - h_i^0) z_{i_\eta} = \text{function of } \eta;$$

(5) $$g_b(\xi) = \text{constant}.$$

These conditions are mathematical conditions only. In general, not all of these conditions may be satisfied simultaneously, and we must determine under what physical conditions the similarity is either exact or is approximately correct. In a dissociating gas we must be able to check that similarity holds also for the equation of continuity of species (8.2.12).

There are only two physical situations in which we may expect similarity to hold for a general fluid in equilibrium. One situation is that in which $u_\delta$ and $p_\delta$ are constant along the boundary layer, with the solutions termed "constant-pressure" solutions. Included in this category are the attached flow on a wedge or on a cone. The other situation is that in which there is a stagnation point for the inviscid flow and the boundary layer we are interested in lies on the body within the stagnation region. We term these solutions "stagnation point" solutions. In this case the requirement of equilibrium is not needed, but the similar solution breaks down outside the stagnation region where $u_\delta^2/H_\delta$ and $(p_0 - p_\delta)/p_0$ are not negligibly small. Another important physical case is the hypersonic case, in which $M_\delta$ is very large and $u_\delta^2/H_\delta$ is close to 2. In this hypersonic case, similarity may be obtained only if the fluid has certain self-similar properties. A nondissociating perfect gas is such a self-similar fluid, and this is the case we consider here. With the fluid a perfect gas and $u_\delta^2/H_\delta = 2$, the requirement for a similar solution is that the pressure be proportional to $\bar{x}^n$, where $\bar{x} = \int r_b^{2j}\, dx$. These solutions will be termed "hypersonic" solutions. With $Pr = 1$ in such a self-similar fluid, similar solutions may also be found.

In addition to these physically obtainable similar solutions, we here consider certain mathematical solutions to the ordinary differential equations for similar solutions which may not be physically obtainable in a strict sense. We shall term these solutions "locally similar" solutions with reference to the way in which they will be used in Section 8.4.

Before going into the details of these solutions let us quote two simple exact results in closed form obtainable in compressible boundary layer theory for a flow in thermodynamic equilibrium. The first of these is the solution with $Pr = 1$ and $Le = 1$ of a boundary layer with arbitrary pressure gradient and an insulated wall. Busemann's general result for this problem is

$$(8.3.2) \qquad\qquad g = 1.$$

The boundary layer does not have to be similar, and the gas may have any number of components with chemical reaction.

The other solution again requires that $Pr = 1$ and $Le = 1$, and also that the pressure gradient be zero. In this case the solution must be a similar one, but the wall need not be insulated. Crocco's result for this problem is

$$(8.3.3) \qquad\qquad g = g_b + f'(1 - g_b),$$

with $g_b$ required to be constant and with the prime denoting differentiation with respect to $\eta$. Again, this solution is of great generality; for example the variation of $\rho\mu$ with respect to $\eta$ may be arbitrary.

We digress here to mention two exact results analogous to (8.3.3) obtainable in frozen flow. We consider the equation for the continuity of species (8.2.12) for a frozen flow ($w_i = 0$), with a similar solution for $f$ and $g$ and the requirement that $z_{i_b}$ is constant. With either a stagnation solution or a constant-pressure solution the quantity $d \ln c_{i\delta}/d \ln \xi$ is zero. With a stagnation solution we require that $Le = 1$ and note that (8.2.12) for $z_i$ and (8.2.15) for $g$ are the same equation. Hence $z_i$ and $g$ must be connected by the relation

$$(8.3.4) \qquad\qquad z_i = z_{i_b} + \frac{g - g_b}{1 - g_b}(1 - z_{i_b}).$$

For the other result we must have a constant-pressure solution, and require that the Schmidt number $Pr/Le = 1$. In this case (8.2.12) for $z_i$ and (8.2.14) for $f_\eta$ are the same equation. Accordingly, $z_i$ may be expressed

$$(8.3.5) \qquad\qquad z_i = z_{i_b} + f'(1 - z_{i_b}).$$

We return now to the equilibrium similar solutions. We shall consider separately the categories A. constant-pressure solutions, B. stagnation point solutions, C. hypersonic solutions, and D. solutions with $Pr = 1$ and locally similar solutions. Most of the solutions which have been obtained have been with diffusion not considered and the gas undissociated. Finally, after considering these equilibrium solutions, we shall consider the category E. frozen solutions.

**A. Constant-pressure solutions.** For a uniform free stream and a constant surface temperature, no simple integrals of the momentum and energy equations exist when the Prandtl number is not unity, even for $Le = 1$. In this case, a solution can be determined only by a simultaneous numerical integration of the following two ordinary differential equations derived from (8.2.14) and (8.2.15):

$$(8.3.6) \qquad\qquad (Nf'')' + ff'' = 0,$$

$$(8.3.7) \qquad \left(\frac{N}{Pr}g'\right)' + fg' + \frac{u_\delta^2}{H_\delta}\left[N\left(1 - \frac{1}{Pr}\right)f'f''\right]' = 0.$$

These equations (or equivalent forms) have been the subject of numerous investigations, and we can classify their solutions by reference to the type of fluid property variations which has been assumed.

In the first category we have the non-dissociated perfect gas case ($c_i = 0$) in which the Prandtl number and the specific heat have been assumed constant but the $\rho\mu$ ratio $N$ has been considered variable with temperature. Examples of such numerical solutions are those of Crocco [2] and Van Driest [1], who followed Crocco's scheme. In these calculations, the equations were employed in a form in which the enthalpy and shear stress were used as the dependent variables and the velocity was used as the independent variable. The dependence of viscosity on the temperature was assumed to follow Sutherland's law.

These calculations were later extended for air to include variations of the Prandtl number and of the specific heat with temperature, although the undissociated form of the perfect gas law was still used. Examples of such computations are those of: Young and Janssen [1], who employed variables similar to those of Crocco but in the manner suggested by Hantzsche and Wendt [1]; Klunker and McLean [1], who integrated equations similar to ours but with the stream function divided by $x^{1/2}$ as the independent variable; and Van Driest [2], who extended the Crocco method to this case. All of these authors made their calculations for air using the best information on its thermal properties available at the time. One of the most interesting results of this work is the excellent agreement of the skin friction coefficients and of the heat transfer rates obtained with variable Prandtl number, specific heat, and $\rho\mu$ ratio with the values computed for constant specific heat and Prandtl number but a variable $\rho\mu$ ratio. These results indicate that, apart from the enthalpy difference between the free stream and the wall, it is primarily the variation in $\rho\mu$ across the boundary layer which governs the skin friction and the heat transfer rate, at least for the undissociated cases which were treated.

The first complete numerical solution of (8.3.6) and (8.3.7) which considered the actual dissociated state of the equilibrium air was that of Moore [1]. Hansen [1] pointed out that Moore miscalculated the Prandtl number for dissociated air, and later an analysis similar to Moore's, with a corrected Prandtl number variation, was carried out by Romig and Dore [1]. These computations were done on a differential analyzer using Hantzsche and Wendt's form of the differential equations. Unfortunately the authors employed equilibrium air properties based on the older incorrect value of the dissociation energy of nitrogen; yet in spite of this their general results are of interest. We must re-emphasize that all the solutions of which we have spoken are only valid under the approximation that the Lewis-Semenov number is exactly one, and there is no way in which the results can be extrapolated to the case where the Lewis-Semenov number is different from one. This follows from the fact that with $Le \neq 1$ the heat transfer is no longer simply proportional to the enthalpy difference across the layer but also involves the extent to which the energy of the flow contained in energy of dissociation is transferred.

One of the most pertinent results which Romig and Dore found was that their skin friction coefficient and heat transfer rate agreed within a maximum error of 15 percent with the perfect gas solutions (e.g. Van Driest [1]) if the temperature dependent properties in these solutions were based on free stream enthalpy instead of free stream temperature. Thus we have a demonstration of the principle that when $Le = 1$, the heat transfer is determined by the total enthalpy of the air outside the boundary layer, regardless of how the energy is distributed among its various forms.

A summary of the results of Romig and Dore can be given by noting that all their numerical solutions for the skin friction could be correlated within 3 percent, and the heat transfer rate within 6 percent, by the empirical reference enthalpy method of Eckert [1; 2]. This correlation covered an extensive range of free stream conditions, with values of $u_\delta^2/H_\delta$ from about $\frac{1}{4}$ to almost 2 ($u_\delta = 1000$–23,000 ft/sec and $T_\delta = 800$–12,000°R), wall temperatures from 500 to 5000°R, and pressures of 0.1, 1, and 10 atmospheres (most of their calculations were for 1 atmosphere).

The reference enthalpy method employed in their correlation is based on the assumption that both the heat transfer and the skin friction can be calculated with incompressible flow relations, provided all temperature dependent air properties are evaluated at an appropriate reference enthalpy $h^*$ which lies somewhere between the extremes encountered in the boundary layer. The technique is purely empirical; it was adopted from the reference temperature scheme of Rubesin and Johnson [1], in which the reference temperature is selected so as to cause the variation of friction factor with Mach number and Reynolds number to vanish in the solutions for a perfect gas with constant specific heat but variable $\rho\mu$.

The reference value of the enthalpy at which reference values of all the pertinent temperature-dependent quantities such as $\rho\mu$ and $Pr$ are evaluated must first be found. The skin friction and the heat transfer are then expressed in terms of these reference values. Since the method is purely empirical it cannot be trusted outside a range in which it has been tested. We present this method and other empirical formulas only to give the reader some idea of the dependence of the numerical results on the parameters involved. The reference enthalpy as given by Eckert is

$$(8.3.8) \qquad h^* = 0.5(h_\delta + h_b) + 0.22(h_r - h_\delta),$$

where an empirical expression for the recovery enthalpy $h_r$ is

$$(8.3.9) \qquad h_r = h_\delta + \tfrac{1}{2}\sqrt{Pr^*}u_\delta^2.$$

The skin friction coefficient defined by the relation

$$(8.3.10) \qquad C_f = \frac{2}{\rho_\delta u_\delta^2}\left(\mu\frac{\partial u}{\partial y}\right)_b$$

is expressed by this method as

$$(8.3.11) \qquad C_f\sqrt{Re_x} = 0.664\sqrt{\frac{\rho^*\mu^*}{\rho_\delta\mu_\delta}},$$

with the Reynolds number $Re_x = u_\delta \rho_\delta x / \mu_\delta$. The heat transfer is given in terms of the Stanton number $St$ as

$$(8.3.12) \qquad St = \frac{-\dot{q}}{\rho_\delta u_\delta (h_r - h_b)} = \tfrac{1}{2} C_f (Pr^*)^{-2/3},$$

with $h_r$ again the recovery enthalpy, or in terms of the Nusselt number $Nu = St\, Re_x\, Pr = -\dot{q}\, c_{p_\delta} x / k_\delta (h_r - h_b)$ as

$$(8.3.13) \qquad \frac{Nu}{\sqrt{Re_x}} = 0.332 \sqrt{\frac{\rho^* \mu^*}{\rho_\delta \mu_\delta}} \, (Pr^*)^{1/3}.$$

For conical flows the right-hand sides of (8.3.11) to (8.3.13) are multiplied by the Mangler factor $\sqrt{3}$. From the correlating equations (8.3.11) to (8.3.13) we observe again that the variation of $\rho\mu$ across the boundary layer is the important parameter in determining the detailed values of the skin friction and heat transfer, even in a dissociated flow.

Additional uniform flow similarity solutions for dissociated air have been obtained by Kemp, Rose, and Detra [1] by solving (8.3.6) and (8.3.7) on a digital computer. In their calculations they employed a constant Prandtl number of 0.71 and Sutherland's viscosity law. The use of these transport properties was based on unpublished estimates of Penner and Litvak (see Fay and Riddell [1]) that the viscosity of equilibrium air, determined from the average molecular weight and various interaction parameters, does not vary more than ten percent from Sutherland's formula below 9000°K, and that the Prandtl number does not change appreciably in this range from its low temperature value. In addition they employed thermal properties of air (see, for example, Feldman [1]) which were calculated using the recent corrected value for the dissociation energy of nitrogen.

In Fig. 8–1 we have shown the mean density and $\rho\mu$ used in their computations plotted as functions of the enthalpy, with all variables except the density made dimensionless with respect to standard conditions. In order to eliminate the pressure dependence of density from these curves (at least to within a few percent in the range of 0.1 to 10 atmospheres), the standard reference density has been defined in terms of the local pressure by means of the relation $\rho_{ref} = p_\delta / \mathcal{R} T_{ref}$. Their calculations were carried out with values of $\tfrac{1}{4}$, and $\tfrac{1}{2}$, and $\tfrac{3}{2}$ for $u_\delta^2 / H_\delta$, covering a range from 0.17 to 1 for $N_\delta = \rho_\delta \mu_\delta / \rho_b \mu_b$. On examining their results we find, by using the fluid properties they employed, that the correlation of (8.3.8) to (8.3.13) also holds within a few percent for the cases calculated.

At the present time no systematic equilibrium boundary layer calculations

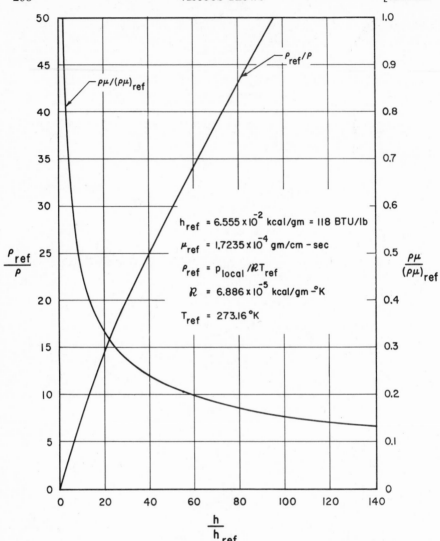

$$h_{ref} = 6.555 \times 10^{-2} \text{ kcal/gm} = 118 \text{ BTU/lb}$$

$$\mu_{ref} = 1.7235 \times 10^{-4} \text{ gm/cm} - \text{sec}$$

$$\rho_{ref} = p_{local} / \mathcal{R} T_{ref}$$

$$\mathcal{R} = 6.886 \times 10^{-5} \text{ kcal/gm} - {}^\circ\text{K}$$

$$T_{ref} = 273.16 \,{}^\circ\text{K}$$

FIG. 8–1. Mean density and $\rho\mu$ as a function of enthalpy (equilibrium air, $p = 0.1$ to $10$ atm.).

have been carried out for constant external flows with Lewis-Semenov numbers different from one. And it is in this case that the reference enthalpy method cannot justifiably be applied.

**B. Stagnation point solutions.** Near a stagnation point of an inviscid flow the exact similar solutions which are possible depend for their existence upon the fact that all fluid properties except velocity have maxima at the stagnation point and may be taken to be approximately constant. In this case the boundary layer equations (8.2.14) and (8.2.15) reduce to

$$(8.3.14) \qquad (Nf'')' + ff'' + (1+j)^{-1}\left(\frac{\rho_\delta}{\rho} - f'^2\right) = 0,$$

$$(8.3.15) \qquad \left(\frac{N}{Pr}g'\right)' + fg' + \left[\frac{N(Le-1)}{Pr}\sum(h_i - h_i^0)\left(\frac{dc_i}{dh}\right)g'\right]' = 0.$$

The coefficient $(1+j)^{-1}$ in the momentum equation is obtained from the conditions that in the region of a stagnation point $r_b = x$ and $u_\delta = x(du_\delta/dx)_0$, so that from (8.2.9a) $\xi \propto x^{2(1+j)}/2(1+j)$ as $x \to 0$.

The simultaneous numerical solution of this system of equations for a perfect gas with constant specific heats, $\rho_\delta/\rho = g$, $Le = 1$, and $N = 1$ was carried out on a differential analyzer by Levy [1] for $j = 0$ and $j = 1$ with $Pr = 0.7$ and 1. At about the same time Cohen and Reshotko [1] made digital calculations for $Pr = 1$ which Reshotko and Cohen [1] later extended to $Pr = 0.7$. In addition Li and Nagamatsu [2] performed analogue computations for the two-dimensional stagnation point with $Pr = 1$.

In order to summarize some of their results we note that with the gas a perfect one and the enthalpy a function of temperature alone the heat transfer at the wall may be expressed as

$$(8.3.16a) \qquad -\dot{q}_0 = \left(\frac{k}{c_p}\frac{\partial h}{\partial y}\right)_b = \frac{k_b\rho_b r_b^j u_\delta H_\delta}{c_{p_b}\sqrt{2\xi}}g_b',$$

or

$$(8.3.16b) \qquad -\dot{q}_0 = \frac{\sqrt{1+j}H_\delta k_b}{c_{p_b}}\left[\frac{\rho_b}{\mu_b}\left(\frac{du_\delta}{dx}\right)_0\right]^{1/2}g_b',$$

with the aid of (8.2.9) and (8.2.10). It is convenient to introduce a Nusselt number and a Reynolds number based on wall conditions, defined for the stagnation region by

$$(8.3.17a) \qquad (Nu_0)_b = \frac{-\dot{q}_0 c_{p_b} x}{k_b(h_r - h_b)},$$

$$(8.3.17b) \qquad (Re_0)_b = \frac{\rho_b}{\mu_b}\left(\frac{du_\delta}{dx}\right)_0 x^2.$$

Note that for stagnation point flows $h_r = H_\delta = h_\delta$. We shall usually deal with the combination $Nu/\sqrt{Re}$, and the relation between this combined quantity based on wall conditions and the more conventional similar quantity based on conditions outside the boundary layer (with the subscript $\delta$ understood) is given by

(8.3.18) $$\left(\frac{Nu_0}{\sqrt{Re_0}}\right)_b = \frac{Pr_b}{Pr_\delta}\sqrt{\frac{\rho_\delta\mu_\delta}{\rho_b\mu_b}}\frac{Nu_0}{\sqrt{Re_0}}.$$

If $N = 1$ and $Pr = constant$ the factor multiplying $Nu_0/\sqrt{Re_0}$ in (8.3.18) is one. The Nusselt number based on wall conditions is expressed from (8.3.16) by the relation

(8.3.19) $$\left(\frac{Nu_0}{\sqrt{Re_0}}\right)_b = \sqrt{1+j}\left(\frac{g_b'}{1-g_b}\right).$$

The quantity in the brackets is a function of $j$, of $Pr$, of $g_b$, and of the function $N(\eta)$, with the Lewis-Semenov number equal to one. In the calculations we are discussing we have $N(\eta) = 1$.

On Fig. 8–2 we have plotted the results of these authors for the heat transfer parameter $g_b'/(1 - g_b)$ for two-dimensional and axisymmetric flow as a function of the wall cooling ratio $g_b$ for different values of the Prandtl number. We have also included on this graph the axisymmetric incompressible calculations ($g_b = 1$) of Sibulkin [1] and the two-dimensional flow solutions of Squire taken from Goldstein [1, pp. 631–632]. Squire and Sibulkin observed from their results that the effect of the constant Prandtl number on $Nu_0/\sqrt{Re_0}$ could be closely represented by the empirical relation

(8.3.20) $$\left(\frac{Nu_0}{\sqrt{Re_0}}\right)_{b\ or\ \delta} = \sqrt{1+j}(Pr)^{0.4}\left(\frac{g_b'}{1-g_b}\right)_{Pr=1}.$$

This approximate expression is found to be extremely good in all the cases shown in Fig. 8–2. We also observe that the effect of pressure gradient, which depends on whether the flow is two-dimensional or axisymmetric, is smaller with the wall cooling greater. Furthermore, wall cooling or heating by itself has only a limited effect on the heat transfer parameter $g_b'/(1 - g_b)$, since for a given value of the Prandtl number the difference of this parameter from its incompressible value ($g_b = 1$) is never more than 8 percent.

An extension of these stagnation point calculations to a dissociated gas flow was carried out by Mark [1] for the axisymmetric case of air in equilibrium, with the Lewis-Semenov number implicitly assumed equal to one. Unfortunately he employed the same incorrect fluid properties that Romig and Dore [1] used. As with the flat plate solutions, Romig [1] again succeeded in correlating, this time to within 5 percent, all of Mark's stagnation point results by using the reference enthalpy method. The result for the heat transfer parameter with an appropriate average Prandtl number is

$$(8.3.21) \qquad \frac{Nu_0}{\sqrt{Re_0}} = 0.763(Pr)^{0.4} \sqrt{\frac{\rho^* \mu^*}{\rho_\delta \mu_\delta}}.$$

In this case, since $h_r = h_\delta$ in (8.3.8), the reference enthalpy is just the arithmetic mean of the external and wall enthalpies. We note that the constant 0.763 is the incompressible axisymmetric result given in Fig. 8–2 multiplied by the Mangler factor $\sqrt{2}$.

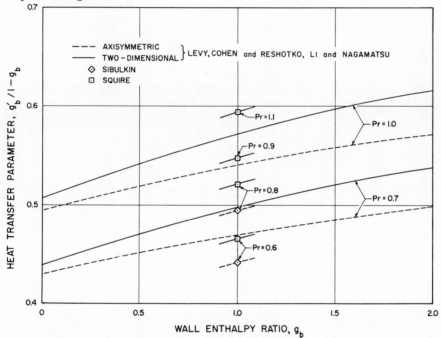

FIG. 8–2. Stagnation point heat transfer parameter as a function of wall enthalpy ratio for constant $\rho\mu$ and $Pr$.

Although the similar solutions we have discussed are of significant interest, none of them considers the question important in hypersonic flight of the difference between heat transfer by conduction and by diffusion with $Le$ not equal to one. The importance of diffusion in producing energy transfer in reacting mixtures has been recognized for a long time by physical chemists. In boundary layer theory the importance of the parameter was recognized by Lees [4] in the case of frozen flow, and by Fay and Riddell [1] (see also Fay, Riddell, and Kemp [1]) in more general problems including the equilibrium case. Fay and Riddell carried out a very complete set of solutions of

(8.3.14) and (8.3.15) for the axisymmetric stagnation point. Their digital calculations covered a range of wall temperatures from 300°K to 3000°K and stagnation enthalpies from 670 to 10,400 BTU/lb, which correspond to values of $N_\delta$ from 0.17 to 1. The Lewis-Semenov numbers used in their calculations ranged from 1 to 2 and were always taken to be constant across the boundary layer. The other fluid and transport properties they employed are those shown on Fig. 8–1.

For an equilibrium flow with $Le \neq 1$ the local heat transfer rate $-\dot{q}$ is determined by the sum of the conductive and diffusive transport and is given by

$$(8.3.22) \qquad -\dot{q} = \left[ k \frac{\partial T}{\partial y} + \rho D_{12} \sum (h_i - h_i^0) \frac{\partial c_i}{\partial y} \right]_b,$$

or

$$(8.3.23) \qquad -\dot{q} = \left[ \frac{k}{\bar{c}_p} \frac{\partial h}{\partial y} + \frac{k}{\bar{c}_p} (Le - 1) \sum (h_i - h_i^0) \frac{\partial c_i}{\partial y} \right]_b.$$

Analogous to (8.3.16a) this becomes, in terms of a dimensionless enthalpy distribution,

$$(8.3.24) \qquad -\dot{q} = \frac{k_b \rho_b u_\delta r_b^j H_\delta}{\bar{c}_{p_b} \sqrt{2\xi}} \left[ g' + (Le - 1) \sum c_{i\delta} \frac{(h_i - h_i^0)}{H_\delta} z_i' \right]_b.$$

This expression for the heat transfer can in turn be reduced to the same form as (8.3.19) for the axisymmetric stagnation point with $Pr = constant$, to give

$$(8.3.25) \qquad \left( \frac{Nu_0}{\sqrt{Re_0}} \right)_b = \sqrt{\frac{\rho_\delta \mu_\delta}{\rho_b \mu_b}} \frac{Nu_0}{\sqrt{Re_0}}$$

$$= \frac{\sqrt{2}}{1 - g_b} \left[ g' + (Le - 1) \sum c_{i\delta} \frac{(h_i - h_i^0)}{H_\delta} z_i' \right]_b.$$

On evaluating (8.3.25), Fay and Riddell found that all their heat transfer calculations could be correlated for various values of the fluid property parameters $N_\delta$, $Le$, and $Pr$ with an accuracy of about 2 percent. Their empirical result based on these extensive numerical computations was

$$(8.3.26) \qquad \frac{Nu_0}{\sqrt{Re_0}} = 0.763(Pr)^{0.4} \left( \frac{\rho_b \mu_b}{\rho_\delta \mu_\delta} \right)^{0.1} \left[ 1 + (Le^{0.52} - 1) \frac{h_{d_\delta}}{H_\delta} \right],$$

where $h_{d_\delta}$ is the average atomic dissociation energy multiplied by the atom mass fraction at the edge of the boundary layer. What is most significant about this relation is that the numerical answers when expressed in this manner do not depend directly on the estimates of viscosity, which may be in error at the higher temperatures, but depend only on the shape of the curve for $\rho\mu$. This is probably reasonably accurately represented (see Fig. 8–1).

Indications are that the empirical representation (8.3.26) is good for surface temperatures less than or equal to the stagnation temperature. Note the factor $N_\delta^{-0.1}$ in (8.3.26). With large wall cooling $N_\delta$ can be of the order of 0.20, and thus this factor can be of the order of 0.85. The discrepancy between (8.3.21) and (8.3.26) can probably be ascribed primarily to the fact that in his calculations Mark employed widely varying values of the Prandtl number at lower values of the enthalpy.

It is of interest to see from (8.3.26) that the Lewis-Semenov number correction arises in a form not much different from what we would expect from the simplified analysis presented in Section 8.1. The exponent on $Le$ will be discussed further when we consider frozen flow solutions.

One of the most interesting aspects of the stagnation point similarity solutions in dissociated air is the comparison of (8.3.26) with the experimental heat transfer data obtained by Rose and Stark [1] in a shock tube at the stagnation point of a hemisphere-cylinder body. To determine the stagnation point velocity gradient these authors employed the modified Newtonian pressure distribution without the centrifugal correction, which gives for the velocity gradient $R_b(du_\delta/dx)_0 = (2p_0/\rho_0)^{1/2}$. Their results are presented in Fig. 8–3. These results simulate hypersonic flight at roughly 20,000, 70,000, and 120,000 ft altitudes. The simulated velocity range covered in the experiments extends from below the onset of dissociation (stagnation temperatures of about 5000°R) to about satellite velocity. The theoretical curves shown represent (8.3.26) calculated for a Lewis number of 1.4 and a Prandtl number of 0.71. From the comparison it is clear that good agreement is obtained between the experimental data and the curves obtained from the theoretical results of Fay and Riddell. The important point here is that inclusion of the diffusion effect is necessary for an acceptable agreement of the theoretical with the experimental results.

**C. Hypersonic solutions.** The only other exact similar solutions which can be found for physical flows are those obtained with $Pr = 1$ or in the limiting situation of a locally hypersonic flow where $u_\delta^2/H_\delta \to 2$. The similarity boundary layer differential equations are in the form

$$(8.3.27) \qquad (Nf'')' + ff'' + 2\frac{d\ln u_\delta}{d\ln\xi}\left(\frac{\rho_\delta}{\rho} - f'^2\right) = 0,$$

$$(8.3.28) \qquad \left(\frac{N}{Pr}g'\right)' + fg' + \frac{u_\delta^2}{H_\delta}\left[N\left(1 - \frac{1}{Pr}\right)f'f''\right]'$$

$$+ \left[\frac{N(Le - 1)}{Pr}\sum c_{i\delta}\frac{(h_i - h_i^0)}{H_\delta}z_i'\right]' = 0,$$

with $u_\delta^2/H_\delta = 2$ for our hypersonic solutions.

As it is written (8.3.27) is not in a form suitable for a similar solution. However, for a perfect gas a form suitable for obtaining a similar solution can be obtained by noting that the quantity in the bracket of (8.3.27) is expressible for a boundary layer as

$$(8.3.29) \qquad \frac{\rho_\delta}{\rho} - f'^2 = \frac{h}{h_\delta} - f'^2 = \frac{g - f'^2}{h_\delta/H_\delta}.$$

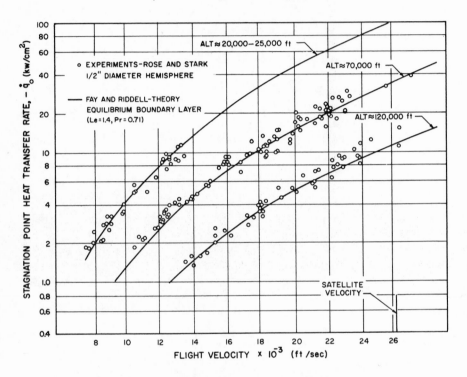

FIG. 8-3. Shock tube axisymmetric stagnation point heat transfer data in partially dissociated air (Rose and Stark [1]).

This replacement is equivalent to the Stewartson-Illingworth transformation. The coefficient of this bracket may be expressed as

$$(8.3.30) \qquad 2\frac{d\ln u_\delta}{d\ln \xi} = -2\left(\frac{p_\delta}{\rho_\delta}\right)\frac{\int_0^{} p u_\delta r_b^{2j}\,dx}{p^2 u_\delta^3 r_b^{2j}}\frac{dp}{dx};$$

here we have used (8.2.9) defining $\xi$, the fact that $p$ is constant across a boundary layer, and the requirement that the wall temperature be constant. For hypersonic flows we replace $\frac{1}{2}u_\delta^2$ in (8.3.30) by $H_\delta$ and $p_\delta/\rho_\delta$ by $(\gamma - 1)h_\delta/\gamma$, and set $u_\delta$ constant in the integral. The similarity condition (2) given at the beginning of this section may only be satisfied if the pressure obeys a law of the form

$$(8.3.31) \qquad p \propto \bar{x}^n$$

or an exponential form in $\bar{x}$ corresponding to $n = \infty$, where the variable $\bar{x}$ is given by

$$(8.3.32) \qquad \bar{x} = \int_0^\cdot r_b^{2j} \, dx.$$

If $j = 0$, $\bar{x} = x$. With the pressure satisfying (8.3.31) we may then rewrite (8.3.27) as

$$(8.3.33) \qquad (Nf'')' + ff'' + \beta(g - f'^2) = 0,$$

where $\beta$ is a constant given by

$$(8.3.34) \qquad \beta = -\left(\frac{\gamma - 1}{\gamma}\right)\left(\frac{n}{n+1}\right).$$

The quantity $\beta$ is equivalent to the classical Falkner-Skan constant. Note that (8.3.33) is in exactly the same form as is (8.3.14) for the stagnation point solutions, provided the gas is perfect and we may replace $\rho_\delta/\rho$ in (8.3.14) by $g$. In this stagnation point case, then we have $\beta = (1 + j)^{-1}$, or $\beta = 1$ in two-dimensional flow and $\beta = \frac{1}{2}$ in axisymmetric flow. For similarity we must also require in general that the Lewis-Semenov number is equal to one.

If the Lewis-Semenov number is different from one the assumption that the gas is a perfect one can at best be an approximation. No calculations have as yet been made with $Le \neq 1$. With $Le = 1$ and $Pr = 1$ the term in $u_\delta^2/H_\delta$ does not enter the equations. Available results for $Le = 1$ and $Pr = 1$ with various values of the parameter $\beta$ are discussed below.

For $Le = 1$ and $Pr \neq 1$, the only available calculation for $u_\delta^2/H_\delta = 2$ is that of Reshotko and Cohen [2], for the case $Pr = 0.7$ and $\beta = 1$. This solution is also discussed with the locally similar solutions. Solutions of this type with smaller values of the parameter $\beta$ are useful in interaction problems (see Section 9.3), and additional calculations are desirable.

A quite general independence principle exists for hypersonic boundary layers, under the assumption that $h_\delta/H_\delta \ll 1$, i.e. that $M_\delta \gg 1$. According to this principle, the solution in the principal part of the boundary layer is determined by the constant free stream total enthalpy $H_\delta$, the given pressure distribution, and the given body temperature distribution. This part of the solution is independent (in a limiting sense) of the actual value of $h_\delta/H_\delta$ or of $M_\delta$. The principal part of the boundary layer is separated from the cool inviscid external flow by a narrow transitional layer, the solution in which does depend upon $M_\delta$. This principle was developed by the authors too late for an analysis to be included in this book. For such an analysis, see Hayes and Probstein [1].

**D. Solutions with $Pr = 1$ and locally similar solutions.** As with the hypersonic solutions, for the mathematical solutions of the similar ordinary differential equations which we consider here there is an immediate problem in obtaining a suitable form for the momentum equation. If the gas is a perfect gas the approach given above will lead to (8.3.33), with

$$(8.3.35) \qquad \beta = 2 \frac{H_\delta}{h_\delta} \frac{d \ln u_\delta}{d \ln \xi}$$

for the Falkner-Skan constant. Alternative laws for the gas behavior can lead to a similar result. An empirical law suggested by Hayes [5] involves replacing (8.3.29) by a relation of the form

$$(8.3.36) \qquad \frac{\rho_\delta}{\rho} - f'^2 = \alpha(\bar{g} - f'^2),$$

where $\bar{g}$ is related linearly with $g$ through the relation

$$(8.3.37) \qquad g = b + (1 - b)\bar{g}.$$

At the edge of the boundary layer $\bar{g} = 1$ and (8.3.36) is automatically satisfied. With the two quantities $\alpha$ and $b$ which are functions of $\xi$ alone, we may empirically match the values of $\rho_\delta/\rho$ and its first derivative at the wall (according to (8.3.36)) with their correct values. The results of this fitting are the relations

$$(8.3.38) \qquad b = \frac{h_b - c_{p_b}/\kappa_b}{H_\delta}$$

and

$$(8.3.39) \qquad \alpha(\xi) = \frac{\rho_\delta}{\rho_b} \left[ 1 + \frac{H_\delta - h_b}{c_{p_b}/\kappa_b} \right],$$

where $\kappa$ is the coefficient of thermal expansion defined by

$$(8.3.40) \qquad \kappa = \rho \left( \frac{\partial(1/\rho)}{\partial T} \right)_p .$$

The quantity $b$ must be assumed to be constant, and if it is not strictly constant a suitable value must be chosen and the fitting accomplished with respect to only the value of $\rho_\delta/\rho$ at the wall. If the gas behaves as a perfect gas at the wall, $b$ is zero and $\alpha = \rho_\delta H_\delta/\rho_b h_b$.

With this empirical fitting for an imperfect gas, (8.3.33) is obtained, with

$$(8.3.41) \qquad \beta = 2\alpha \frac{d \ln u_\delta}{d \ln \xi}$$

and $\bar{g}$ in place of $g$. The energy equation for $\bar{g}$ is in exactly the same form as that for $g$, i.e. (8.2.15), (8.3.7), or (8.3.28), provided we take $Le = 1$ and replace $u_\delta^2/H_\delta$ by $u_\delta^2/(1 - b)H_\delta$. Note that for stagnation point flows $\beta$ is $\alpha(1 + j)^{-1}$ rather than $(1 + j)^{-1}$.

Up to this point we have considered calculations of solutions only for the cases $\beta = 0$, $\frac{1}{2}$, and 1. We may note that positive values of $\beta$ correspond to negative pressure gradients, while negative values of $\beta$ correspond to positive gradients. Solutions of (8.3.28) and (8.3.33) for $\beta$ ranging between values corresponding to separation and $\beta = 2$ were obtained by Levy [1], Cohen and Reshotko [1], and Li and Nagamatsu [2] for the special case of a perfect gas with $N$, $Pr$, and $Le$ all equal to one. By restricting their solutions to $Pr = 1$, these authors did not have to consider the viscous dissipation term in the energy equation. A summary of the results taken from Cohen and Reshotko [1] for the surface shear stress function at the wall $f_b''$ and the heat transfer parameter $g_b'/(1 - g_b)$ is shown in Fig. 8–4. It is of interest to observe that for large wall cooling these results show the direct influence of the pressure gradient to be small except near separation. The effects of the gas not being perfect are also relatively small with large wall cooling, since these effects appear primarily as a modification of the pressure gradient parameter.

In order to determine how the dissipation term influences these similarity solutions, Reshotko and Cohen [2] carried out some calculations for $Pr = 0.7$. They considered the cases $u_\delta^2/H_\delta = 1$ and $u_\delta^2/H_\delta = 2$, with the pressure gradient parameter $\beta = 1$ in both cases. An indication of the relatively small role the dissipation term plays, at least for Prandtl numbers close to one, can be had by examining Fig. 8–5(a), where their results for the shear function at the wall are plotted with $u_\delta^2/H_\delta = 0$, 1, and 2. In Fig. 8–5(b) the heat transfer function expressed in terms of the adiabatic recovery enthalpy, $g_b'/(h_r/H_\delta - g_b)$, is also shown for the same conditions. The effect of the dissipation term is clearly not a dominant one. This conclusion also follows from the fact that the dissipation parameter enters the differential equation as $(1 - Pr^{-1})$, a quantity which is small when the Prandtl number is not too different from unity.

Kemp, Rose, and Detra [1] have also calculated the effect of the dissipation term for the highly cooled equilibrium boundary layer in a dissociated flow. For the cases $Pr = 0.71$, $Le = 1$, $\beta = 0$ and $\frac{1}{2}$, and $u_\delta^2/H_\delta = \frac{1}{4}$, $\frac{1}{2}$, and $\frac{3}{4}$ they showed that the recovery factor was very close to the usual low speed value of $\sqrt{Pr}$. That is,

$$(8.3.42) \qquad \frac{h_r}{H_\delta} \approx 1 + (\sqrt{Pr} - 1)\frac{u_\delta^2}{2H_\delta}.$$

**E. Frozen solutions.** Although the number of calculations carried out for

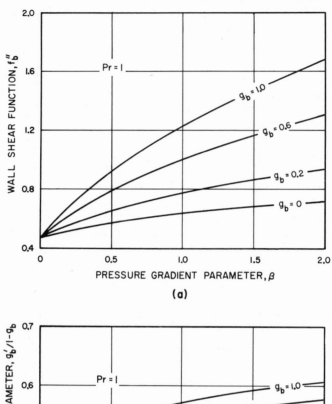

Fig. 8–4. Effect of wall cooling and pressure gradient on constant $\rho\mu$ similar solutions (Cohen and Reshotko [1]). (a) Wall shear function. (b) Heat transfer parameter.

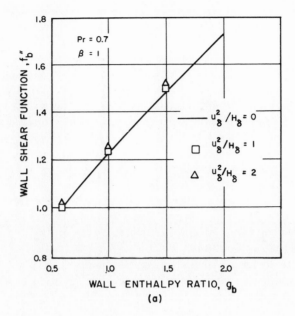

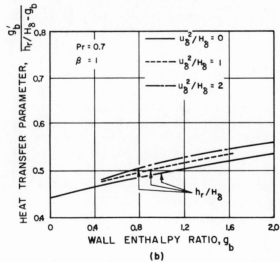

FIG. 8–5. Effect of $u_\delta^2/H_\delta$ on constant $\rho\mu$ similar solutions (Reshotko and Cohen [2]). (a) Wall shear function. (b) Heat transfer parameter.

equilibrium boundary layers has been large, the number carried out for the other limiting case of frozen boundary layers, where the recombination rates are so slow that the atoms pass through to the surface without recombining in the fluid, has been much smaller. In the frozen case two limiting assumptions can be made about the concentration boundary condition at the body: Either the wall is non-catalytic, in which case the atom concentration does not vary across the boundary layer (with $d \ln c_{i_\delta}/d \ln \xi = 0$) and the heat transfer is accomplished by conduction alone; or the wall is catalytic, in which case the $z_{i_b}$ must have their equilibrium values corresponding to the wall temperature. If the wall is cold $z_{i_b} = 0$ for the atoms in the catalytic case and all the atoms recombine at the surface and give up their dissociation energy. Under the last condition the diffusion of atoms toward the body can produce a large heat transfer when the free stream atom concentration is high. Other assumptions about the boundary condition on the concentrations at the wall may be made. Frozen boundary layer calculations for the axisymmetric stagnation point have been carried out by Fay and Riddell [1] for these two limiting cases.

In order to perform a similar stagnation point analysis for a catalytic wall, we require the concentration equation in addition to (8.3.14) and (8.3.15). For stagnation point conditions this equation can be obtained from (8.2.12) by setting $w_i$ and $dc_{i_\delta}/d\xi$ equal to zero, giving

$$(8.3.43) \qquad \left(\frac{N Le}{Pr} z_i'\right)' + f z_i' = 0.$$

The boundary conditions for this problem are $z_i(0) = 0$ for a cold wall and $z_i(\eta) \to 1$ as $\eta \to \infty$, with $z_i$ given for the atoms.

The concentration equation is identical with the energy equation (8.3.15) when $Le = 1$, as we have already noted in getting (8.3.4). Except for the difference in the dependence of $N$ on $z_i$ in one case and on $g$ in the other we can compare (8.3.43) for the frozen case with (8.3.15) for the equilibrium case. We would not expect this difference in dependence to be very large. The boundary conditions in the two cases are the same for a highly cooled surface where $g_b \to 0$. This suggests that the heat transfer rates we would obtain for a catalytic wall calculation with a frozen flow should be almost identical with the equilibrium results, depending on the amount of surface cooling. This observation was made by Lees [4] for the case $N = 1$ and is borne out by the Fay-Riddell calculations. Fay and Riddell obtained an empirical correlation identical to the one found for the equilibrium situation (8.3.26), except that in this case the Lewis-Semenov number is raised to the power 0.63 instead of 0.52.

We may briefly note at this point that the form of the result (8.3.26) can be found approximately by observing that the similarity between (8.3.43) and (8.3.15) noted above may be applied to a comparison in which $Le = 1$ in (8.3.15) and the Prandtl number is replaced by $Pr/Le$ (Schmidt number) in (8.3.43). This observation for $N = 1$ is due to Lees [4]. The solution of (8.3.15) at the body surface with $Le = 1$ and $g_b \to 0$ is given as $\sqrt{2}g_b' = 0.763(Pr)^{0.4}N_\delta^{0.4}$ for the axisymmetric case (see (8.3.26)). The analogous solution for the concentration gradient at the wall would be $\sqrt{2}z_{i_b}' = 0.763(Pr)^{0.4}(Le)^{-0.4}N_\delta^{0.4}$, with $z_{i_b} = 0$. It has been shown by Lees [4] that the heat transfer by conduction alone in the highly cooled boundary layer is given approximately by $k_b g_b'(H_\delta - h_{d\delta})/\bar{c}_{p_b}$ and the heat transfer by diffusion alone approximately by $(\partial \eta/\partial y)_b k_b \, Le \, z_{i_b}' h_{d\delta}/\bar{c}_{p_b}$. If we use the value of $z_{i_b}'$ just given the form of (8.3.26) follows directly, the only difference being that the Lewis number exponent is 0.6 instead of 0.63 or 0.52.

We shall not treat the problem of boundary layers in a dissociated gas with finite recombination rates. Fay and Riddell [1] have carried out calculations for an axisymmetric stagnation region with finite recombination rates, and find that the total rate of heat transfer to a catalytic wall is almost unchanged from the corresponding equilibrium value. This result we might have predicted from the comparison of the two limiting cases of frozen flow with a catalytic wall and of flow in thermodynamic equilibrium.

In concluding this section we point out a characteristic feature of hypersonic boundary layers (excepting the stagnation point solutions). This feature is that the maximum temperature or enthalpy in the boundary layer may be very much greater than that in the free stream, even though the body is extremely cold. In order to illustrate this feature, we turn to the case $Pr = 1$ and $Le = 1$ with zero pressure gradient, for which Crocco's integral (8.3.3) is available. If the parameter $u_\delta^2/H_\delta$ is less than $1 - g_b$ and $g_b \leqslant 1$ the maximum enthalpy occurs at the outer edge of the boundary layer. Thus we obtain

$$(8.3.44) \qquad \frac{h_{\max}}{H_\delta} = \frac{h_\delta}{H_\delta} = 1 - \tfrac{1}{2}\left(\frac{u_\delta^2}{H_\delta}\right); \qquad \frac{u_\delta^2}{H_\delta} \leqslant 1 - g_b.$$

If $g_b \leqslant 1$ but $u_\delta^2/H_\delta$ is greater than $1 - g_b$, the maximum enthalpy occurs within the boundary layer proper, and is given by

$$(8.3.45) \qquad \frac{h_{\max}}{H_\delta} = g_b + \frac{(1 - g_b)^2}{2u_\delta^2/H_\delta}; \qquad \frac{u_\delta^2}{H_\delta} \geqslant 1 - g_b \geqslant 0.$$

If the body is heated, of course, the maximum enthalpy occurs at the wall and is given by

$$(8.3.46) \qquad \frac{h_{\max}}{H_\delta} = g_b; \qquad 1 - g_b \leqslant 0.$$

As the Mach number in the external flow becomes larger, the parameter $u_\delta^2/H_\delta$ approaches 2 (cf. (8.2.16)) and the quantity $h_\delta/H_\delta$ approaches zero. With $u_\delta^2/H_\delta = 2$ the quantity $h_{max}/H_\delta$ is given from (8.3.45) as $\frac{1}{4}(1 + g_b)^2$ and cannot be less than $\frac{1}{4}$. Thus $h_{max}/h_\delta$ increases without limit as $u_\delta^2/H_\delta \to 2$.

### 4. Local similarity concept

Until now we have considered only those boundary layer solutions which can be obtained by a reduction of the basic partial differential equations to a system of ordinary differential equations. The computation of numerical solutions for the complete set of nonlinear partial differential equations of the boundary layer is an imposing task. Numerous approximate methods have been developed for solving the complete set of equations. With the exception of finite difference schemes all these techniques involve in one way or another the reduction of the equations to ordinary differential equations. The number of such approximate schemes appears to have grown markedly in recent years. Our considerations here will be restricted to those methods which seem most directly applicable to the boundary layer problems associated with hypersonic flight conditions.

Among the approximate approaches to the calculation of laminar boundary layers with arbitrary pressure and fluid property distributions, we can differentiate the following principal schemes:

1. The piecewise application of locally similar solutions, in which the history of the flow is ignored except insofar as it appears in a calculation of the variable $\xi$.

2. Integral methods, in which one or more assumptions are made as to the profiles of the flow variables, and in which the equations used are obtained by taking suitable integrals of the boundary layer equations across the boundary layer.

3. Series-expansion methods, in which the coefficients in the series in an $x$-dependent variable are obtained from the solution of ordinary differential equations and the expansion variable depends on the external flow conditions.

4. Perturbation methods, in which a perturbation of a known boundary layer solution is considered and an expansion is carried out in terms of a parameter. This approach is not considered in this chapter. An example of this method is given in Sections 9.2 and 9.3 in connection with boundary layer interaction problems.

5. Iteration methods, in which improved distributions of the various flow variables are obtained from the solution of simplified equations. Some of the quantities in these equations are not treated as unknowns but are based upon the last approximation. These methods are not treated here. A simplified example of an iteration method may be found in Probstein [3].

It is probably fair to say that the difficulty and accuracy of the first three techniques increases in the order listed.

In this section we shall discuss the first method—that of local similarity. The applicability of this technique relies essentially on the condition that the external and body flow properties vary sufficiently slowly with the $x$-dependent variable $\xi$, defined by (8.2.9). If this is the case, then derivatives with respect to $\xi$ of the boundary layer dependent variables are small compared to the corresponding $\eta$ derivatives, so that the right hand sides of the boundary layer equations (8.2.12) to (8.2.15) can be neglected. Those terms on the left hand sides of (8.2.12) to (8.2.15) which are functions of $\xi$ are assumed to take on their local values, and the boundary layer equations are considered as ordinary differential equations in $\eta$ with $\xi$ as a parameter. Because of the approximations involved, we might expect that in general this scheme possesses the lowest accuracy.

Local similarity thus represents a "patching together" of local solutions in which the "history" of the flow is involved only in the $\xi$ dependence of the definition of $\eta$ in (8.2.9). Presentations of this method are to be found, among others, in Lees [4], Kemp, Rose, and Detra [1], and Smith [1]. To illustrate the calculation technique in this scheme let us consider the estimation of the displacement thickness and heat transfer distribution about a body with an arbitrary pressure gradient.

According to (8.2.9b) the actual distance normal to the surface can be computed by means of the quadrature

$$(8.4.1) \qquad y = \frac{\sqrt{2\xi}}{r_b^j \rho_\delta u_\delta} \int_0^{} \frac{\rho_\delta}{\rho} \, d\eta,$$

while the displacement thickness is given by

$$(8.4.2) \qquad \delta^* = \int_0^\infty \left(1 - \frac{\rho u}{\rho_\delta u_\delta}\right) dy = \frac{\sqrt{2\xi}}{r_b^j \rho_\delta u_\delta} \int_0^\infty \left(\frac{\rho_\delta}{\rho} - \frac{u}{u_\delta}\right) d\eta.$$

In order to obtain the distributions of these quantities, we first require the properties of the inviscid flow around the body, together with the wall conditions. Then knowing these properties, we can compute at each body station the local distribution of $\rho_\delta/\rho$ and $u/u_\delta$ in $\eta$ corresponding to a similar solution for the local values of the parameters $u_\delta^2/H_\delta$, $g_b$, $N_\delta$, and $\beta$. Thus through successive patching, the boundary layer thickness, displacement thickness, etc. can be found approximately at every point on the body, with the history of the layer contained only in the evaluation of $\xi$.

To determine the heat transfer distribution about a blunt body by this technique, we take the general expression (8.3.24) divided by the same expression for the stagnation point (see (8.3.16)). It follows that the ratio

of the heat transfer rate at any point on the body to the stagnation point
heat transfer rate is

$$(8.4.3) \quad \frac{-\dot{q}}{-\dot{q}_0} = \frac{\rho_b \mu_b u_\delta r_b^j \left[ g' + (Le - 1) \sum c_{i_\delta} \frac{(h_i - h_i^0)}{H_\delta} z_i' \right]_b}{\sqrt{2 \xi \rho_{b_0} \mu_{b_0} (1 + j) \left( \frac{du_\delta}{dx} \right)_0} \left[ g' + (Le - 1) \sum c_{i_\delta} \frac{(h_i - h_i^0)}{H_\delta} z_i' \right]_{b_0}}.$$

We now assume that such effects as the influence of the Lewis-Semenov
number are accounted for by the stagnation point behavior. With this
assumption the heat transfer rate is expressed in terms of the heat transfer
rate calculated for $Le = 1$, as

$$(8.4.4) \quad \frac{-\dot{q}}{-\dot{q}_0} = \frac{\rho_b \mu_b u_\delta r_b^j}{\sqrt{2 \xi \rho_{b_0} \mu_{b_0} (1 + j) \left( \frac{du_\delta}{dx} \right)_0}} \left( \frac{g_b'}{g_{b_0}'} \right)_{Le=1}.$$

With the local similarity solutions known, it is a simple matter to calculate
the heat transfer at any point on the body once the heat transfer rate at the
stagnation point and the inviscid field have been determined.

For the case of a highly cooled wall ($g_b \approx 0$) with a sufficiently blunt body
a number of valuable conceptual simplifications were found by Lees [4].
The basic idea of Lees is that with a highly cooled body the quantity $\rho_\delta/\rho$ is
small, particularly near the wall. With $\rho_\delta/\rho$ small, the quantity $(\rho_\delta/\rho) - f_\eta^2$
is still smaller and may be neglected in (8.2.14) in seeking an approximate
solution. Thus, with a highly cooled wall, the effect of the pressure gradient
on the momentum equation may be dropped in this approximation. The
effect of the pressure gradient on the heat transfer appears only indirectly
in an integral of the velocity profile across the layer, and is even smaller than
the effect on the skin friction.

We can support this argument, as did Lees, by reference to the similar
solutions which have been carried out. For example, from Fig. 8–4 for the
results of perfect gas similar solutions with $N$, $Pr$, and $Le$ all equal to
one, it is clear that the assumption of a negligibly small direct influence of
pressure gradient for $g_b \approx 0$ is highly accurate for the surface heat transfer
rate and somewhat less accurate for the skin friction. The conclusions
drawn from these results can be considered fairly general since, as we have
already indicated, the effects of Lewis-Semenov number, of $Pr$, and of $u_\delta^2/H_\delta$
are all moderately small for blunt bodies. These generalizations have in fact
been substantiated by the equilibrium air calculations of locally similar
solutions by Kemp, Rose, and Detra [1].

From these arguments we may conclude that the non-dimensionalized
enthalpy gradient at the surface $g_b'$ can be taken sensibly constant over the
whole body; and since its value is independent of surface temperature

within this approximation, the method is applicable to nonisothermal surfaces. Thus the heat transfer rate on the body at any point is determined only by the stagnation point heat transfer rate and the external pressure distribution, so that from (8.4.4) for $g_b \approx 0$ we arrive at the relatively simple relation

$$(8.4.5) \qquad \frac{-\dot{q}}{-\dot{q}_0} = \frac{\rho_b \mu_b u_\delta r_b^j}{\sqrt{2 \xi \rho_{b_0} \mu_{b_0} (1 + j) \left(\dfrac{du_\delta}{dx}\right)_0}} .$$

A detailed study of the actual variation of $g_b'/g_{b_0}'$ has been carried out by Kemp, Rose, and Detra [1] by correlating equilibrium air similarity solutions for various values of $g_b$, $u_\delta^2/H_\delta$, $\beta$, and $N(\eta)$. They concluded from their numerical correlation that the variation of $g_b'/g_{b_0}'$ could be expressed as a function of the pressure gradient parameter $\beta$ alone by means of the empirical relation

$$(8.4.6) \qquad \frac{g_b'/(1 - g_b)}{g_{b_0}'/(1 - g_{b_0})} = \frac{1 + 0.096\sqrt{\beta}}{1 + 0.096(1 + j)^{-1/2}} .$$

On Fig. 8–6 are shown experimental heat transfer data obtained in dissociated air on a highly cooled hemisphere-cylinder body. These experiments were performed in a shock tube by Kemp, Rose, and Detra [1]; they represent a stagnation point simulation which corresponds to a flight velocity of 18,000 ft/sec at 80,000 ft altitude in the atmosphere. On the same graph we have shown the heat transfer distributions computed using the expression of Lees, (8.4.5), and that of Kemp, Rose, and Detra, (8.4.6) in conjunction with (8.4.4). In carrying out these computations the pressure distribution was taken to be given by the modified Newtonian relation without centrifugal correction, expressed as $p_b/p_0 = 1 - (1 - p_\infty/p_0) \cos^2 \theta_b$. For these experiments this relation was found experimentally to be of sufficient accuracy for the heat transfer calculation. From the comparison of the theoretical curves we see that the difference between them is small and that the agreement of the approximate theories with the experimental data is satisfactory.

Neither (8.4.4) nor (8.4.5) can give us any information about when we might expect the local similarity approach to break down. However as we shall see in more detail in the following section when we discuss integral methods, the criterion for the applicability of the local similarity concept is connected with the fact that the rate of change of $g_b'$ with $\xi$ must be small in comparison with $g_b'$ itself.

Our comments so far have been restricted to the equilibrium boundary layer. Lees [4] has pointed out that with a highly cooled hypersonic boundary layer a conceptual simplification is available which can give us approximate information on the heat transfer process in a frozen flow. An example is the approximate Lewis-Semenov number dependence obtained for (8.3.43) in the preceding section for the frozen stagnation point boundary layer.

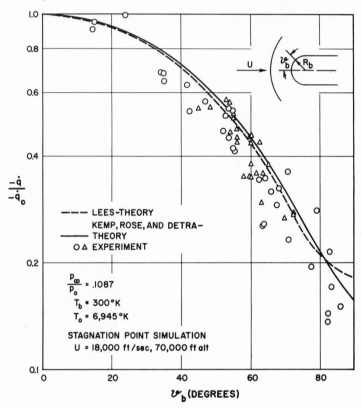

FIG. 8–6. Comparison of local similarity results and shock tube heat transfer data in partially dissociated air on a hemisphere-cylinder (Kemp, Rose, and Detra [1]).

## 5. Integral methods

We turn now to the approach using integral relations, following the classical concept of the von Kármán momentum integral. These methods have proved to be very useful in boundary layer theory, despite certain inherent limitations. The basic idea behind this approach is that certain assumptions are made as to the profiles of the unknown functions, and with the assumed profiles the partial differential equations are reduced to ordinary differential equations.

In this section we shall be emphasizing the use of similar or locally similar profiles for the assumed profiles in the integral methods. Accordingly, we shall define dimensionless displacement, momentum, and enthalpy-defect thicknesses using the variables introduced in Section 8.2. We shall assume that the gas is perfect, so that (8.3.29) holds. This relation may be replaced by the empirical relation (8.3.36) if appropriate.

When such similarity considerations as have been considered in the preceding sections are no longer valid, we might expect that an integral method should yield a somewhat better approximation technique. This, however, is not at all apparent, as can be seen by considering the integrated forms of the equilibrium momentum and energy equations. These equations are obtained by integrating (8.2.14) and (8.2.15) with respect to $\eta$, and with (8.3.29) assumed to hold are

$$(8.5.1) \qquad (\overline{f_{\eta\eta}})_b = \overline{\Theta} + 2\xi \frac{d\overline{\Theta}}{d\xi} + (\overline{\Delta^*} + \overline{\Theta}) \frac{2\xi}{u_\delta} \frac{H_\delta}{h_\delta} \frac{du_\delta}{d\xi},$$

$$(8.5.2) \qquad \left(\frac{\overline{g}_\eta}{Pr}\right)_b + \left[\frac{(Le-1)}{Pr} \sum c_{i\delta} \frac{(h_i - h_i^0)}{H_\delta} \overline{z}_{i\eta}\right]_b = \overline{\Lambda} + 2\xi \frac{d\overline{\Lambda}}{d\xi}.$$

In this section we shall take $Le = 1$, and the bracket of (8.5.2) is thus identically zero. Of course, the approach of this section can be applied with $Le \neq 1$ as well. Here the quantities $\overline{\Delta^*}$, $\overline{\Theta}$, and $\overline{\Lambda}$ are the dimensionless displacement, momentum, and enthalpy-defect thicknesses, defined as

$$(8.5.3a) \qquad \overline{\Delta^*} = \int_0^\infty (g - f_\eta) \, d\eta,$$

$$(8.5.3b) \qquad \overline{\Theta} = \int_0^\infty f_\eta (1 - f_\eta) \, d\eta,$$

$$(8.5.3c) \qquad \overline{\Lambda} = \int_0^\infty f_\eta (1 - g) \, d\eta.$$

Barred quantities have been used in these equations so that we may later employ unbarred quantities to denote a similarity value.

The dimensionless quantities $\overline{\Theta}$ and $\overline{\Lambda}$ are equal to the physical momentum and enthalpy-defect thicknesses times the factor $\rho_\delta \, d\eta / \rho \, dy$, which is a function of $x$ alone (see (8.2.9)). This is not true for $\overline{\Delta^*}$, where the physical displacement thickness (8.4.2) times $\rho_\delta \, d\eta / \rho \, dy$ is related to $\overline{\Delta^*}$ by

$$(8.5.4) \qquad \int_0^\infty \left(\frac{\rho_\delta}{\rho} - f_\eta\right) d\eta = \frac{H_\delta}{h_\delta} (\overline{\Delta^*} + \overline{\Theta}) - \overline{\Theta}.$$

An important point to be noted is that the variation of viscosity through the boundary layer, which can materially affect the heat transfer rate, does not appear in (8.5.1) or (8.5.2). This is most strikingly illustrated by the integral calculations of Beckwith [1], who carried out a Kármán-Pohlhausen solution of (8.5.1) and (8.5.2) for an equilibrium axisymmetric stagnation point (with $Le = 1$). The answer he obtained indicated almost no difference from the undissociated solution, a result which, as we have already seen from exact solutions, can be in error if the variations in $\rho\mu$ across the boundary layer are important. Note also that the viscous dissipation term associated with the parameter $u_\delta^2/H_\delta$ has disappeared from the energy equation (8.5.2) and no influence of this parameter appears directly.

Lal [1] has extended the Kármán-Pohlhausen approach to the simultaneous solution of the integrated boundary layer equations (8.5.1) and (8.5.2) for $g_b = constant$. In Lal's approach, as in most others of this type, the velocity and total enthalpy profiles are approximated by simple polynomial functions. Each of the boundary layer profiles can, by an appropriate scale transformation, be reduced to a function of one independent parameter; this is done by satisfying the boundary layer equations and a suitable number of boundary conditions at the wall. The $x$ dependence of the velocity and total enthalpy parameters is then determined by the simultaneous solution of the two ordinary differential equations (8.5.1) and (8.5.2). In these equations the coefficients are functions of the external velocity and its derivatives and the wall temperature and its derivatives, as well as any other quantities at the boundaries which vary with $x$ (e.g. $Pr_b$, etc.).

Except for a rough estimate of the $x$ dependence of the boundary layer solutions, it does not appear that the Kármán-Pohlhausen approach is satisfactory for a high temperature gas flow where fluid property variations are important. However, the integrated momentum and energy equations do give us some indication as to when the local similarity concept of Section 8.4 breaks down. For example, we observe from (8.5.2) that in calculating the heat transfer at the wall by local similarity we have essentially neglected the term $2\xi \, d\overline{\Lambda}/d\xi$, and in first approximation have considered that the relation $\overline{g_b'} = Pr_b\overline{\Lambda}$ holds. Clearly this is incorrect, and the degree to which it is not correct depends on how small $2\xi \, d\overline{g_b'}/d\xi$ is in comparison with $\overline{g_b'}$.

If we wish to improve on the local similarity analysis, it is evident that some combination of the integral method and local similarity would be appropriate. Such a concept was first introduced by Thwaites [1] for the case of incompressible flow with an arbitrary pressure gradient. His approach was to obtain a functional correlation between the shear stress at the wall, the local pressure gradient, and the ratio of displacement to momentum thickness. He did not make an assumption as to the type of profile as is done in the Kármán-Pohlhausen method, but rather obtained his correlation from the properties of the known incompressible similar solutions. By employing the Stewartson-Illingworth transformation (Stewartson [1] and

Illingworth [1]) for a perfect gas with $N = 1$, the approach of Thwaites was later extended by Rott and Crabtree [1] to the insulated body with $Pr = 1$, and by Cohen and Reshotko [2] to bodies with heat transfer with $Pr = 1$ and $g_b = constant$.

Cohen and Reshotko, in carrying over the incompressible analysis of Thwaites to compressible flow with heat transfer, used essentially the classical method of applying the momentum-integral technique. In this classical method the enthalpy equation is ignored and a relation between the basic correlation parameter and the velocity gradient is assumed. As we shall see, this leads in general to a basic inconsistency in the calculation of heat transfer.

To obtain the low speed form of the momentum equation similar to the one employed by Cohen and Reshotko [2], let us make the transformation on $\overline{\Delta^*}$ and $\overline{\Theta}$

$$(8.5.5a) \qquad \overline{\Delta^*} = \sqrt{\frac{H_\delta}{h_\delta}} \frac{u_\delta}{\sqrt{2\xi}} \overline{\delta^*},$$

$$(8.5.5b) \qquad \overline{\Theta} = \sqrt{\frac{H_\delta}{h_\delta}} \frac{u_\delta}{\sqrt{2\xi}} \bar{\theta}.$$

With this transformation the momentum equation reduces to essentially the low speed form

$$(8.5.6) \qquad \frac{d\bar{\theta}}{dx} + \frac{(H_F + 2)}{u_\delta} \frac{H_\delta}{h_\delta} \frac{du_\delta}{dx} \bar{\theta} = \sqrt{\frac{h_\delta}{H_\delta}} \frac{\tau_b r_b^j}{u_\delta^2},$$

where $H_F$ is the form factor equal to $\overline{\Delta^*}/\overline{\Theta} = \overline{\delta^*}/\bar{\theta}$, and $\tau_b$ is the shear stress at the wall. The quantity $\bar{\theta}$ is equal to $\rho_\delta r_b^j \sqrt{h_\delta/H_\delta}$ times the physical momentum thickness, while $\overline{\delta^*}$ is connected with the physical displacement thickness through the same factor and a relation of the form (8.5.4). Note that the quantity $H_\delta du_\delta/h_\delta u_\delta$ equals $dM_\delta/M_\delta$, in conformity with the Stewartson-Illingworth reduction of a compressible boundary layer to an equivalent incompressible one.

In the method of Thwaites a basic correlation parameter $n$ is defined analogous to the classical Pohlhausen parameter but with momentum thickness in place of displacement thickness. The parameter $n$ is used as a dependent variable. In our formulation $n$ would be defined by the relation

$$(8.5.7) \qquad n = -\bar{\theta}^2 u_\delta \left(\frac{H_\delta}{h_\delta}\right)^2 \frac{du_\delta}{d\xi}.$$

The quantity $H_F$ and a reduced shear stress at the wall are estimated as functions of $n$, and (8.5.6) becomes an ordinary differential equation in $n$

with $x$ as the independent variable. In the version of Cohen and Reshotko the quantity $g_b$ appears as an additional parameter.

Cohen and Reshotko also essentially assume that the quantity $(\partial g/\partial \eta)_b$ is a function of $n$ and $g_b$ given by the results of the similar solutions. With this assumption the heat transfer may be calculated, with no use made of the equation for the enthalpy defect (8.5.2). This energy equation (8.5.2), however, may also be used to calculate the heat transfer, and the two answers disagree in general. Thus a basic inconsistency appears in the use of the classical momentum-integral method for the calculation of the heat transfer.

The method of Thwaites is admirably suited for the approximate calculation of the skin friction in incompressible flows with no heat transfer. Its straightforward extension to high velocity flows and to flows with large heat transfer is on weaker ground and admits a large degree of arbitrariness.

To correct the deficiency of the Cohen and Reshotko method we will follow an alternative approach suggested by the work of Hayes [5], which combines the integral method with the similar solution development. As we have stated, we will consider only the equilibrium boundary layer with $Le = 1$, although the generalization to the case of $Le \neq 1$ introduces no new features. In this scheme the basic thickness used as a reference value is taken to be a function $G(\xi)$ which is considered to be unknown, rather than the momentum thickness used in the Thwaites method. We introduce the transformation

$$(8.5.8a) \qquad \overline{\Delta^*} = \frac{G}{\sqrt{2\xi}} \Delta^*,$$

$$(8.5.8b) \qquad \overline{\Theta} = \frac{G}{\sqrt{2\xi}} \Theta,$$

$$(8.5.8c) \qquad \overline{\Lambda} = \frac{G}{\sqrt{2\xi}} \Lambda,$$

$$(8.5.8d) \qquad \overline{(f_{\eta\eta})_b} = \frac{\sqrt{2\xi}}{G} (f_{\eta\eta})_b,$$

$$(8.5.8e) \qquad \overline{(g_\eta)_b} = \frac{\sqrt{2\xi}}{G} (g_\eta)_b.$$

The function $G(\xi)$ is taken to be the basic parameter; no assumption is made about its relation to the velocity distribution, but rather its value is to be determined from the basic equations.

With $\xi$ as the independent variable, the basic equations may now be written

$$(8.5.9) \qquad G^2 \frac{d\Theta}{d\xi} + \left[ G \frac{dG}{d\xi} + (1 + H_F) \frac{G^2 H_\delta}{u_\delta h_\delta} \frac{du_\delta}{d\xi} \right] \Theta = (f_{\eta\eta})_b,$$

$$(8.5.10) \qquad G^2 \frac{d\Lambda}{d\xi} + \left( G \frac{dG}{d\xi} \right) \Lambda = \left( \frac{g_\eta}{Pr} \right)_b.$$

One fundamental assumption, corresponding to Thwaites' correlation assumption, is that the variables $\Theta$, $H_F$, and $(f_{\eta\eta})_b$ in (8.5.9) and $\Lambda$ and $(g_\eta)_b$ in (8.5.10) are the same as they would be in a similar solution with the local values of $g_b$ and $u_\delta^2/H_\delta$, and with a suitable value of the Falkner-Skan constant $\beta$ which is as yet undetermined.

If the boundary layer were actually a similar boundary layer, we would have the relations

$$(8.5.11) \qquad G = \sqrt{2\xi},$$

$$(8.5.12) \qquad \beta = \frac{G^2}{u_\delta} \frac{H_\delta}{h_\delta} \frac{du_\delta}{d\xi}.$$

With these relations we would obtain

$$(8.5.13) \qquad (f_{\eta\eta})_b = [1 + \beta(1 + H_F)]\Theta,$$

$$(8.5.14) \qquad (g_\eta)_b = Pr_b \Lambda.$$

With our fundamental assumption we assume that (8.5.13) and (8.5.14) hold for our general boundary layer with our unknown $\beta$. Relations (8.5.11) and (8.5.12) are *not* assumed to hold in general except with the local similarity assumption of the previous section.

We use (8.5.13) and (8.5.14) to eliminate $(f_{\eta\eta})_b$ and $(g_\eta)_b$ from (8.5.9) and (8.5.10), and recast them in the form

$$(8.5.15) \qquad \frac{G^2}{\Theta} \frac{d\Theta}{d\xi} + G \frac{dG}{d\xi} - 1 + (1 + H_F) \left( \frac{G^2 H_\delta}{u_\delta h_\delta} \frac{du_\delta}{d\xi} - \beta \right) = 0,$$

$$(8.5.16) \qquad \frac{G^2}{\Lambda} \frac{d\Lambda}{d\xi} + G \frac{dG}{d\xi} - 1 = 0.$$

These are the basic equations in this approach.

If, as in the method of Cohen and Reshotko [2], we ignore the energy equation (8.5.16) we must specify the quantity $\beta$ using (8.5.12). Equation (8.5.15) is then an ordinary differential equation for the unknown function $G$, and with the assumption of similar profiles (8.5.14) may be used to calculate the heat transfer. On the other hand, $(g_\eta)_b$ may be calculated directly from (8.5.10), and yields the result

$$(8.5.17) \qquad (g_\eta)_b = Pr_b \Lambda \left[ 1 - G^2 \left( \frac{1}{\Theta} \frac{d\Theta}{d\xi} - \frac{1}{\Lambda} \frac{d\Lambda}{d\xi} \right) \right].$$

In general, (8.5.14) and (8.5.17) are fundamentally inconsistent, as $\Lambda$ will not be proportional to $\Theta$ over the entire range of parameters to be considered.

For the purpose of simplifying the presentation of the method, the quantities $\Theta$ and $\Lambda$ are now considered to be functions of $\beta$ and $g_b$ alone. The dependence on $u_\delta^2/H_\delta$ or $Pr_b$ can be treated in the same way as the dependence on $g_b$, while the variation of $N(\eta)$ or $Pr/Pr_b$ with $\xi$ would entail some additional complications. We define the following logarithmic partial derivatives with respect to $\beta$ and $g_b$:

$$(8.5.18a) \qquad \Theta_\beta^+ = \frac{1}{\Theta}\frac{\partial\Theta}{\partial\beta}, \qquad \Theta_{g_b}^+ = \frac{1}{\Theta}\frac{\partial\Theta}{\partial g_b},$$

$$(8.5.18b) \qquad \Lambda_\beta^+ = \frac{1}{\Lambda}\frac{\partial\Lambda}{\partial\beta}, \qquad \Lambda_{g_b}^+ = \frac{1}{\Lambda}\frac{\partial\Lambda}{\partial g_b}.$$

In terms of these derivatives (8.5.15) and (8.5.16) can be rewritten as

$$(8.5.19) \qquad G^2\left(\frac{d\beta}{d\xi}\Theta_\beta^+ + \frac{dg_b}{d\xi}\Theta_{g_b}^+\right) + G\frac{dG}{d\xi} - 1$$
$$+ (1 + H_F)\left(\frac{G^2}{u_\delta}\frac{H_\delta}{h_\delta}\frac{du_\delta}{d\xi} - \beta\right) = 0,$$

$$(8.5.20) \qquad G^2\left(\frac{d\beta}{d\xi}\Lambda_\beta^+ + \frac{dg_b}{d\xi}\Lambda_{g_b}^+\right) + G\frac{dG}{d\xi} - 1 = 0.$$

In principle the distribution problem can now be solved, since $u_\delta$ and $g_b$ are known functions of $\xi$ while $\Theta$, $\Lambda$, and $H_F$ are determined in terms of $\beta$ and $g_b$ from the similarity solutions. Thus (8.5.19) and (8.5.20) provide us with a pair of ordinary simultaneous differential equations which determine $\beta(\xi)$ and $G(\xi)$. Once $\beta(\xi)$ is found, the other pertinent quantities are specified from the known similar solutions. Several methods may be devised for solving the differential equations for $G$ and $\beta$ (see Hayes [5]). However, in order to carry out any numerical calculations following this approach, numerical results for the quantities $\Theta$, $\Lambda$, and $H_F$ are needed from the similar solutions. It would be desirable to have these numerical results tabulated.

## 6. Series-expansion methods

The last approach we shall discuss for solving the partial differential equations of the boundary layer is that of series expansions. In order to simplify the calculation we will, as before, restrict our considerations to thermodynamic equilibrium with $Le = 1$.

To employ any expansion scheme it is necessary that the fluid properties, such as the density ratio $\rho_\delta/\rho$, be expressed in an analytic form. For a perfect gas we may use relation (8.3.29). For a general fluid the empirical approximation of (8.3.36) and (8.3.37) may be more appropriate. With this approximation (8.2.14) and (8.2.15) take the form

$$(8.6.1) \qquad (Nf_{\eta\eta})_\eta + ff_{\eta\eta} + 2\alpha \frac{d \ln u_\delta}{d \ln \xi} (\bar{g} - f_\eta^2) = 2\xi(f_\eta f_{\eta\xi} - f_\xi f_{\eta\eta}),$$

$$(8.6.2) \qquad \left(\frac{N}{Pr}\bar{g}_\eta\right)_\eta + f\bar{g}_\eta + \frac{u_\delta^2}{(1-b)H_\delta}\left[\left(1 - \frac{1}{Pr}\right)Nf_\eta f_{\eta\eta}\right]_\eta = 2\xi(f_\eta \bar{g}_\xi - f_\xi \bar{g}_\eta).$$

In order to illustrate the series-expansion technique in the simplest manner possible, we will consider the case of axisymmetric flow in a perfect gas with $N = 1$, $Pr = constant$, and either a constant wall temperature or an insulated wall. In this case we have $\alpha = H_\delta/h_\delta$, $b = 0$, and $\bar{g} = g$. The underlying assumption of this technique as applied to this case, originally developed by Blasius (see, for example, Schlichting [1, pp. 131–138, 162–167]) for expansions in $x$, is that the external velocity distribution can be expressed in a power series of the form

$$(8.6.3) \qquad u_\delta = u_0\xi^{1/4} + u_1\xi^{3/4} + u_2\xi^{5/4} + \cdots = \sum_{k=0}^\infty u_k\xi^{\frac{2k+1}{4}},$$

where the $u_k$'s are constants determined by the inviscid velocity distribution. The principal new feature in (8.6.3) is the use of $\xi$ as the independent variable in place of $x$. The use of expansions in a variable equivalent to $\xi$ has been applied independently by Görtler [1] to two-dimensional incompressible boundary layers without considering heat transfer and, following Görtler's approach, by Sparrow [1] to the same problem with heat transfer. It should be pointed out that when the coordinate $\xi$ is transformed to the original $x$ coordinate, this series is exactly a Taylor expansion of the inviscid velocity in powers of $x$, with only odd powers of $x$ appearing. The first term in this expansion, $u_0\xi^{1/4}$, simply represents the behavior of the inviscid field in the neighborhood of an axisymmetric stagnation point where $u_\delta \propto x$. Görtler has pointed out that the main feature of the use of a series in a variable equivalent to $\xi$ is that the first term in the series solution for $f$ satisfies all the boundary conditions and may by itself be a good approximation to the whole solution quite far downstream.

Although a series-expansion scheme is satisfactory for blunt bodies, its usefulness becomes somewhat impaired in general for slender shapes, for which a large number of terms may be required to represent the inviscid velocity profile. The method does afford a means of calculating analytically the initial portion of a boundary layer with great accuracy.

With the external velocity distribution given by (8.6.3), the following expansions are appropriate for the non-dimensional velocity and enthalpy functions in axisymmetric flow:

$$(8.6.4) \qquad f = f_0 + f_1 \xi^{1/2} + f_2 \xi + \cdots = \sum_{k=0}^{\infty} f_k \xi^{k/2},$$

$$(8.6.5) \qquad g = g_0 + g_1 \xi^{1/2} + g_2 \xi + \cdots = \sum_{k=0}^{\infty} g_k \xi^{k/2},$$

where the $f_k$'s and $g_k$'s are assumed to depend on $\eta$ alone. Insertion of these series into the partial differential equations gives a set of ordinary differential equations. The equations of lowest order are the axisymmetric stagnation point equations equivalent to (8.3.14) and (8.3.15), solutions to which are already tabulated in this case. The simultaneous ordinary differential equations obtained for the succeeding approximations can be written in the form

$$(8.6.6) \qquad f_k''' + f_0 f_k'' - (1+k) f_0' f_k' + (1+k) f_0'' f_k + \tfrac{1}{2} g_k = F_k,$$

$$(8.6.7) \qquad g_k'' + Pr[f_0 g_k' - k f_0' g_k + (1+k) g_0' f_k] = G_k,$$

where the functions $F_k$ and $G_k$ depend on the solutions up to order $(k-1)$. Examples of $F_k$ and $G_k$ for $k=1$ and $2$ are

$$(8.6.8a) \qquad F_1 = \left( \frac{u_1}{u_0} + \frac{u_0^2}{4H_\delta} \right) (f_0'^2 - g_0),$$

$$(8.6.8b) \qquad F_2 = (\tfrac{3}{2} f_1'^2 - 2 f_1 f_1'') + \left( \frac{u_1}{u_0} + \frac{u_0^2}{4H_\delta} \right) (2 f_0' f_1' - g_1)$$
$$+ \left( 2 \frac{u_2}{u_0} - \frac{u_1^2}{u_0^2} + \frac{u_1 u_0}{H_\delta} + \frac{u_0^4}{8 H_\delta^2} \right) (f_0'^2 - g_0);$$

$$(8.6.9a) \qquad G_1 = (1 - Pr) \frac{u_0^2}{H_\delta} (f_0' f_0''' + f_0''^2),$$

$$(8.6.9b) \qquad G_2 = Pr(f_1' g_1 - 2 f_1 g_1') + (1 - Pr) \frac{u_0^2}{H_\delta} (f_0' f_1''' + 2 f_0'' f_1'' + f_0''' f_1')$$
$$+ 2(1 - Pr) \frac{u_0 u_1}{H_\delta} (f_0' f_0''' + f_0''^2).$$

In order to render the functional coefficients $f_k$ and $g_k$ independent of the particular properties of the inviscid profile—that is, the $u_k$'s—it is necessary to split them up in the following manner, at least for $k=1$ and $2$:

$$(8.6.10a) \qquad f_1 = \frac{u_0^2}{H_\delta} f_{1,1} + \frac{u_1}{u_0} f_{1,2},$$

$$(8.6.10b) \qquad f_2 = \frac{u_0^4}{H_\delta^2} f_{2,1} + \frac{u_0 u_1}{H_\delta} f_{2,2} + \frac{u_1^2}{u_0^2} f_{2,3} + \frac{u_2}{u_0} f_{2,4}.$$

These relations with $f$ replaced by $g$ are used to split the $g_k$ functions. Such a separation allows the reduction of the differential equations to the form of (8.6.6) and (8.6.7), where the subscript $k$ is now replaced by $(k, m)$, where the index $m$ goes from one to an integer equal to the number of terms into which $f_k$ and $g_k$ are split. For example, for $f_2$ the index $m$ goes from 1 to 4, while for $f_3$ the index $m$ goes from 1 to 7, and for $f_4$ the index $m$ goes from 1 to 12. In this separation, the terms $F_{k,m}$ and $G_{k,m}$ also become independent of the $u_k$'s. For every value of $m$, we must now solve simultaneously a linear third-order momentum equation and a linear second-order energy equation subject to the boundary conditions

(8.6.11a) $f_{k,m}(0) = 0, \quad f'_{k,m}(0) = 0, \quad g_{k,m}(0) = 0 \quad$ or $\quad g'_{k,m}(0) = 0,$

(8.6.11b) $\qquad\qquad f'_{k,m} \to 0, \quad g_{k,m} \to 0, \quad$ as $\quad \eta \to \infty.$

Of the boundary conditions on $g$ in (8.6.11a), the first is for a constant wall temperature and the second is for an insulated wall. We note that these boundary conditions are all homogeneous.

If the wall temperature is given and is not constant, $g_b(\xi)$ must be expanded in a suitable series, and additional terms must be included in the splitting of (8.6.10). For these additional terms the boundary condition on $g_{k,m}(0)$ is not homogeneous.

A further simplification can be achieved by means of the transformation

(8.6.12) $\qquad\qquad f_{k,m} = f'_0 f^*_{k,m}(\eta),$

(8.6.13) $\qquad\qquad g_{k,m} = g'_0 f^*_{k,m}(\eta) + g^*_{k,m}(\eta),$

which permits the reduction of the third-order equations to linear second-order equations in $f^{*\prime}_{k,m}$, while the energy equations are transformed to linear second-order equations in $g^*_{k,m}$. Although the problem is reduced to one of simultaneous solution of two second-order linear differential equations, the task is nonetheless quite formidable. At least in simple cases where the inviscid velocity profile can be represented by the first 2 or 3 terms, however, such a solution would afford us a basis for comparison with which to assess the validity of the local similarity concept and of integral methods.

## 7. The turbulent boundary layer

For hypersonic flow, as for other flow regimes, the boundary layer in general undergoes a transition from a laminar condition and becomes fully turbulent, if the Reynolds number is sufficiently high. Once this occurs, the local flow is no longer steady and the velocity components fluctuate in a random manner. The resultant turbulent mixing process will cause increases in the shear, heat transfer, and diffusion, above the corresponding values for laminar flow at the same Reynolds number. Because of the severe heating problems encountered in atmospheric hypersonic flight, it is of great importance to estimate the extent of these increases.

The Prandtl boundary layer concept is still applicable to a turbulent boundary layer, and a mathematical treatment can in principle be carried out by assuming the motion to be separable into a mean flow and a superposed turbulent fluctuation with zero mean values. On this basis one can obtain the appropriate differential equations of mean motion, energy, and continuity for the turbulent boundary layer in a compressible dissociating flow. These equations derived by Probstein, Adams, and Rose [1] (see also Rose, Probstein, and Adams [1]) for a dissociating flow permit us to determine how the general characteristics of a high temperature turbulent boundary layer differ from those of the relatively more familiar supersonic case at moderate temperatures. With methods analogous to the methods which have been used for ordinary low speed and supersonic flows, using similarity and semi-empirical arguments on the nature of the turbulent shear, we can also obtain some information on the surface shear and heat transfer rates. We will indicate that as with laminar flow the presence of dissociation phenomena should not markedly alter the results from those obtained in the undissociated case.

To simplify the analysis, we will consider once again the case of thermodynamic equilibrium with the laminar Lewis-Semenov and Prandtl numbers taken to be one. Later we will indicate appropriate empirical corrections for values of $Le$ and $Pr$ different from one. Following the classical approach for turbulent flows, each fluid property is written as the sum of a time averaged quantity which is dependent only on position and a fluctuating or primed quantity which is also a function of time (see, for example, Young [1]); then, for example, we have

$$(8.7.1) \qquad u = \bar{u} + u', \qquad h = \bar{h} + h', \qquad \rho = \bar{\rho} + \rho'.$$

In our analysis, certain terms will be dropped from the averaged equations on the basis of order-of-magnitude estimates from the boundary layer approximations. These terms will not be separately discussed.

If the expressions of (8.7.1) are substituted into the boundary layer continuity equation (8.2.1) (with a time-dependent term) and mean values are taken, the result for a steady state mean motion is

$$(8.7.2) \qquad \frac{\partial \bar{\rho} \bar{u} r^j}{\partial x} + \frac{\partial \bar{\rho} \bar{v} r^j}{\partial y} + \frac{\partial \overline{\rho' v'} r^j}{\partial y} = 0.$$

In carrying out the same analysis for the momentum equation (8.2.3), a term involving the fluctuation in the viscosity coefficient is neglected as small compared with a term in the mean viscosity. The resulting time averaged momentum equation can be written as

$$(8.7.3) \qquad \bar{\rho}\bar{u}\frac{\partial \bar{u}}{\partial x} + (\bar{\rho}\bar{v} + \overline{\rho'v'})\frac{\partial \bar{u}}{\partial y} = -\frac{\partial p}{\partial x} + \frac{\partial}{\partial y}\left[(\mu + \mu_T)\frac{\partial \bar{u}}{\partial y}\right],$$

where the eddy viscosity $\mu_T$ is defined by the relation $\mu_T = -\bar{\rho}\overline{u'v'}/(\partial\bar{u}/\partial y)$ in terms of the Reynolds stress $\bar{\rho}\overline{u'v'}$. The bars have been dropped on $p$ and $\mu$. If a number of terms involving the fluctuations in viscosity and heat conductivity are similarly neglected, the energy equation (8.2.7) for $Pr = 1$, $Le = 1$ and a steady mean motion becomes

$$(8.7.4) \qquad \bar{\rho}\bar{u}\frac{\partial \bar{H}}{\partial x} + (\bar{\rho}\bar{v} + \overline{\rho'v'})\frac{\partial \bar{H}}{\partial y} = \frac{\partial}{\partial y}\left[\frac{(k + k_T)}{\bar{c}_p}\frac{\partial \bar{H}}{\partial y}\right],$$

where here the eddy thermal conductivity $k_T$ has been taken to be $k_T = -\bar{\rho}\bar{c}_p\overline{v'h'}/(\partial\bar{h}/\partial y)$. This definition of the eddy thermal conductivity is consistent with its usual definition for a gas with a constant specific heat and no dissociation. Probstein, Rose, and Adams, however, showed that, just as the energy transported by ordinary conduction and diffusion in a dissociating gas is only $(k/\bar{c}_p)(\partial h/\partial y)$ for $Le = 1$, so too the rate of energy transport by turbulent conduction and diffusion is only given by $-\bar{\rho}\overline{v'h'} = (k_T/\bar{c}_p)(\partial\bar{h}/\partial y)$ when the turbulent Lewis-Semenov number is unity. Here we have defined the turbulent Lewis-Semenov number as $Le_T = D_T\bar{\rho}\bar{c}_p/k_T$, where $D_T$ represents the turbulent diffusion coefficient. Although no information on the magnitude of $Le_T$ exists, its value is probably closer to one than is the laminar Lewis-Semenov number $Le$. As is well known, the turbulent Prandtl number $Pr_T = \bar{c}_p\mu_T/k_T$ is closer to one than is the laminar Prandtl number $Pr$.

We observe that if both $Pr$ and $Pr_T$ are set equal to one, then the mean momentum and energy equations are similar to each other with a uniform external flow. Since the boundary conditions for an insulated body and for a constant surface enthalpy are also similar, we immediately obtain the familiar Crocco integral (8.3.3) between enthalpy and velocity,

$$(8.7.5) \qquad H = h_b + \frac{H_\delta - h_b}{u_\delta}u.$$

In (8.7.5) and the remainder of this section the bars are dropped on mean quantities. We shall not have occasion to refer again specifically to the quantity $\overline{\rho'v'}$.

Thus the relation between total enthalpy and velocity in the dissociated equilibrium turbulent boundary layer with $Pr = Pr_T = 1$ and $Le = Le_T = 1$ is exactly the same as in the laminar boundary layer. Therefore for this case the heat transfer rate and skin friction are again connected by Reynolds' analogy, which may be written as $St = \frac{1}{2}C_f$ (cf. (8.3.12)). From our work with the dissociating laminar boundary layer, such a result immediately leads us to expect that the heat transfer and surface shear in an equilibrium dissociating turbulent flow are not much different from those in an equivalent undissociated turbulent flow, despite the fact that the transfer processes themselves are considerably different. As in the laminar case, we must assume catalytic recombination at the wall for this conclusion, so that energy transfer is equivalent to heat transfer.

Two limiting cases appear to be of significance in connection with zero pressure gradient hypersonic turbulent boundary layers. The first, which is of particular interest in wind tunnel tests, is the case of an undissociated turbulent boundary layer at high Mach number on an insulated surface. The second, which corresponds more closely to conditions in hypersonic atmospheric flight, is the case of a highly cooled dissociated turbulent boundary layer on the flat after portion of a blunt body.

Let us consider the wind tunnel case first. Now we know that for a turbulent boundary layer, turbulent mixing donates the greatest contribution to the shear outside a narrow region near the wall. As Liepmann and Roshko [1] have pointed out, this process does not depend on temperature as directly as does the ordinary laminar viscous shear. Some evidence for this conclusion is the fact that the velocity profiles for high Mach number flows are much the same as for low Mach number flows (see Lobb, Winkler, and Persh [1]). Therefore for an *insulated* body we may expect that the dominant effect of Mach number would simply be to increase the temperature in the boundary layer, thereby reducing the density and increasing the boundary layer thickness. The result would be that the gradients are lowered, and hence that the skin friction is lowered. This fact is most strikingly illustrated by the compiled experimental wind tunnel results given by Liepmann and Roshko [1] and shown in Fig. 8–7. Here we have plotted, from relatively low temperature wind tunnel tests, the variation with Mach number of the ratio of the actual skin friction coefficient to the incompressible skin friction coefficient for an insulated constant-pressure surface; there is seen to be a marked decrease in the skin friction coefficient with increasing Mach number.

In order to obtain some idea of the variation of $C_f/C_{f_{inc}}$ with Mach number, let us use Eckert's empirical reference enthalpy method for the turbulent case in the same manner as we did for laminar flow.

For incompressible flow the turbulent skin friction coefficient on a flat plate for Reynolds numbers less than about $10^7$ is quite accurately represented by the Blasius formula

(8.7.6)                          $\frac{1}{2}C_{f_{inc}} = 0.029\, Re_x^{-0.2}$,

with both $C_f$ and $Re_x$ based on conditions external to the boundary layer.

From the discussion given in Section 8.3, it follows that the ratio $C_f/C_{f_{\text{inc}}}$ is

$$(8.7.7) \qquad \frac{C_f}{C_{f_{\text{inc}}}} = \left(\frac{\mu^*}{\mu_\delta}\right)^{0.2}\left(\frac{\rho^*}{\rho_\delta}\right)^{0.8},$$

where starred quantities again indicate fluid properties evaluated at the reference enthalpy. Let us now consider the case of an insulated wall with a constant specific heat ratio and with $Pr = 1$: from (8.3.8), on eliminating

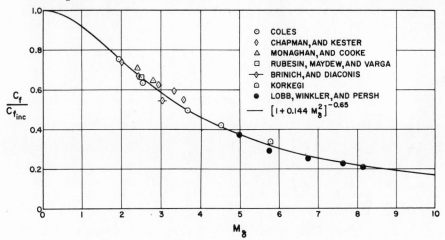

FIG. 8–7. Wind tunnel data for turbulent skin friction coefficient on an insulated constant pressure surface (data compiled by Liepmann and Roshko [1]).

the velocity by means of the relation $u_\delta^2/2c_p = T_b - T_\delta$, the reference temperature is found to be

$$(8.7.8) \qquad \frac{T^*}{T_\delta} = 1 + 0.72\left(\frac{T_b}{T_\delta} - 1\right) = 1 + 0.72\left(\frac{\gamma - 1}{2}\,M_\delta^2\right).$$

Hence for air, for which the viscosity relation for moderate temperatures is given very closely by $\mu/\mu_\delta = (T/T_\delta)^{0.75}$, we find that with $\gamma = 1.4$

$$(8.7.9) \qquad \frac{C_f}{C_{f_{\text{inc}}}} = (1 + 0.144 M_\delta^2)^{-0.65}$$

for the insulated plate. This empirical relation is also plotted on Fig. 8–7 and the agreement with experiment is seen to be quite good. It should be kept in mind that although this result is valid for high Mach numbers, it is true only for the case of an insulated body in a perfect gas with a constant specific heat ratio. This case is not particularly realistic for hypersonic flight. For a more detailed analysis of the undissociated case see, for example, Donaldson [1].

A more realistic limiting case than that just considered is that of the turbulent boundary layer on a blunt body with large wall cooling. Following Probstein, Adams, and Rose [1] (see also Rose, Probstein, and Adams [1]), let us conjecture how a turbulent flow would behave under these circumstances. If we assume a fully developed turbulent profile such as a power law velocity profile to be applicable, and this certainly appears reasonable from the existing experimental data (see Lobb, Winkler, and Persh [1]), then the fluid properties in the outer turbulent portion of the highly cooled boundary layer will be practically constant down to the edge of the narrow laminar

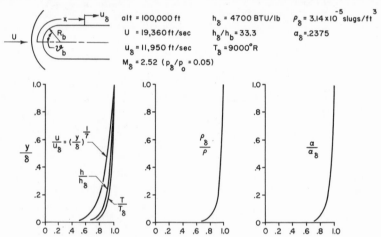

FIG. 8–8.  Approximate turbulent boundary layer profiles in partially dissociated air (Probstein, Rose, and Adams [1]).

sublayer. This conclusion follows directly from the Crocco relation between enthalpy and velocity.

To illustrate the nature of the highly cooled turbulent boundary layer, we have shown in Fig. 8–8 distributions of static enthalpy, temperature, and degree of dissociation $\alpha$ for a representative hypersonic flight condition on a blunt body. These curves were obtained by using the Crocco relation (8.7.5) and by assuming the boundary layer to be in thermodynamic equilibrium, with a velocity profile of the form $u/u_\delta = (y/\delta)^{1/7}$. We might point out, incidentally, that the general nature of the distributions is not extremely sensitive to the choice of velocity profile, as long as the profile is of the fully developed turbulent type. As with a laminar boundary layer, no maximum of the temperature appears with sufficiently large wall cooling, provided $u_\delta^2/H_\delta$ is less than one and the Crocco relation (8.7.5) holds (cf. (8.3.44)).

From the curves of Fig. 8–8 we can note that the density in the highly cooled turbulent boundary layer should be approximately constant outside the narrow sublayer, and the Mach number is not a significant factor. Therefore we may take the skin friction coefficient to be approximately given by the incompressible result in which the external fluid properties are used— that is, by the relation $C_f/C_{f_{inc}} = 1$. Such a relation relies on the fact that the turbulent boundary layer growth is essentially unaffected by the laminar sublayer, since only a small fraction of the total momentum is included in the sublayer.

We have shown, at least for zero pressure gradient and the Prandtl and

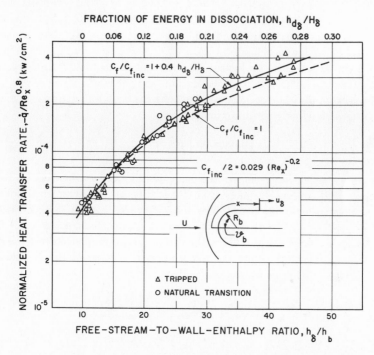

FIG. 8–9. Shock tube turbulent heat transfer data in partially dissociated air on cylindrical afterbody of a hemisphere-cylinder (Rose, Probstein, and Adams [1]).

Lewis-Semenov numbers equal to one, that Reynolds' analogy holds for a turbulent layer. By employing the approximation $C_f = C_{f_{inc}}$ for a highly cooled turbulent layer, we are able immediately to estimate the heat transfer provided we know $C_{f_{inc}}$. We must bear in mind, however, that for a dissociating gas it is necessary to make a correction for Lewis-Semenov numbers different from one, in much the same manner as an empirical correction is made for Prandtl numbers different from one. It has been found that an appropriate approximate form of the Prandtl number correction in a turbulent boundary layer is the same as for laminar flow, and is given by (8.3.12). It is also reasonable to expect that the Lewis-Semenov number correction would not be much different from that given by the laminar flow calculations (e.g. (8.3.26)). In any event, an upper limit on the Lewis-Semenov number correction is given by the result of the simple one-dimensional analysis presented in Section 8.1. Therefore for the case of zero pressure gradient, following Probstein, Adams, and Rose [1], we can write

$$(8.7.10) \qquad \frac{C_f}{C_{f_{\mathrm{inc}}}} = \frac{-\dot{q}}{-\dot{q}_{Le=1}} = 1 + (Le^\omega - 1)\frac{h_{d_\delta}}{H_\delta},$$

where $\omega$ is an exponent satisfying $0.5 < \omega < 1.0$. The exact determination of $\omega$ must lie with experiment.

From the arguments we have presented, using Reynolds' analogy, the Blasius incompressible skin friction relation, and the laminar Lewis-Semenov and Prandtl number corrections, we find that the heat transfer rate on a zero pressure gradient body is approximated by

$$(8.7.11) \qquad \frac{Nu}{Re_x^{0.8}} = 0.029 Pr^{1/3}\left[1 + (Le^\omega - 1)\frac{h_{d_\delta}}{H_\delta}\right].$$

On Fig. 8–9 we have shown the heat transfer measurements of Rose, Probstein, and Adams [1] taken in a shock tube on the cylindrical portion of a hemisphere-cylinder body. The solid curve represents (8.7.11) with a value of $(Le^\omega - 1) = 0.4$, so that $Le = 1.4$ corresponds to $\omega = 1$. The dashed curve represents (8.7.11) without the Lewis number correction, and it is clear that it falls below the experimental data when the fraction of energy in dissociation becomes appreciable.

# CHAPTER IX

# VISCOUS INTERACTIONS

## 1. Flow models and interaction parameters

In the last chapter we have examined viscous problems in which the boundary layer can be considered separate from the inviscid flow field. We now turn to a treatment of those problems in which the viscous-inviscid interaction can no longer be neglected. In treating interaction phenomena, we shall in general assume that the gas is a perfect one of constant $\gamma$ and shall not consider those properties peculiar to high temperature dissociating flows. We shall assume that the interaction solutions for a perfect gas can be corrected for imperfect gas behavior in a manner similar to that indicated by the results of Chapter VIII.

As we pointed out in Section 8.1, two principal types of interactions may be expected. One of these is the pressure interaction resulting from the relatively large outward streamline deflection induced by a thick boundary layer at hypersonic speeds. On slender bodies at subsonic or low supersonic speeds and high Reynolds numbers, the local streamline deflection induced by the boundary layer is of the order of the reciprocal of the square root of the local Reynolds number. In this case the effect on the pressure distribution may be shown to be inversely proportional to the square root of the Reynolds number, and is in general negligibly small (in the special case of a semi-infinite two-dimensional flat plate the pressure is inversely proportional to the Reynolds number itself). On the other hand, at hypersonic speeds the streamline deflection is of the order of its value at low supersonic speeds multiplied by $M_\infty^2$, and the induced pressure on a slender body due to the interaction of the new "effective" body shape with the Mach waves in the inviscid field is of the order of the streamline deflection times $M_\infty$. An interaction effect of this order of magnitude may be very important with $M_\infty$ large.

For sharp-nosed slender bodies the second type of interaction mentioned in Section 8.1, the vorticity interaction, comes from an effective blunting of the nose due to the initial boundary layer growth and is not generally of too great importance. Vorticity interaction may be especially important in the boundary layer on a blunted slender body, or in the flow on a blunt body at very low values of the Reynolds number. This type of interaction is treated in Section 9.6.

To treat pressure interaction and vorticity interaction phenomena correctly, we must know the exact nature of the development of the boundary layer from the leading edge, first because the initial boundary layer growth is required to determine the correct pressure level, and second because the initial shock wave shape is required to determine the downstream vorticity pattern.

The two types of interactions we have discussed may be recognized as involving characteristics of the external flow field. The pressure interaction may be considered to be an interaction involving the Mach waves in the inviscid flow; the characteristic relations for the Mach waves relate the flow deflection angle and the pressure. The vorticity interaction may be considered to be an interaction involving the streamlines; the characteristic relations for the streamlines relate the entropy and hence the vorticity with the stream function. Thus these interactions may be termed "characteristic" interactions.

Another type of boundary layer effect which may become particularly important at hypersonic speeds results from the curvature of the body. These "curvature" effects are very similar in nature to interaction effects, and may be classed together with them. In axisymmetric flows we may distinguish two such effects, a "longitudinal" curvature effect and a "transverse" curvature effect. In two-dimensional flows only the longitudinal curvature effect may appear. The appropriate parameter measuring the importance of these effects is the boundary layer thickness times the appropriate body curvature. On smooth slender bodies of revolution the longitudinal curvature effect will be much smaller than the transverse curvature effect, and we shall not discuss the longitudinal curvature effect in this book.

The interactions which we shall consider are the pressure interaction, the vorticity interaction, and the transverse curvature effect, of which the first is generally by far the most important. We may roughly classify boundary layer interactions as to their source as "boundary layer induced", "shock induced", and "bluntness induced". With a boundary layer induced interaction, the disturbance of the external flow field is entirely due to the distribution of displacement thickness of the boundary layer itself, and without viscous effects the flow field would be completely undisturbed. With a shock induced interaction, the flow field with no viscous effects would contain a shock wave which contacts the body at a point downstream of the leading edge; with viscous effects present a developed boundary layer is in existence at this inviscid point of contact. With a bluntness induced interaction, the boundary layer develops within the pressure and vorticity field created by the slightly blunted leading edge of an otherwise slender body. This classification is far from being either precise or exhaustive, but is probably suitable for most purposes.

Although shock induced interactions are very important in hypersonic flows on certain bodies (such as a body with a flared skirt), we shall not treat such interactions in this book. The primary reason for this omission is the lack of a developed and accepted theory. Probably the best theoretical presentation of the subject of shock induced interactions is due to Crocco [3]. Experimental results on shock induced interactions at hypersonic speeds are extremely scanty. More work has been done at supersonic speeds, and much of this work has been reported in Chapman, Kuehn, and Larson [1], Bogdonoff [1], and Holder and Gadd [1].

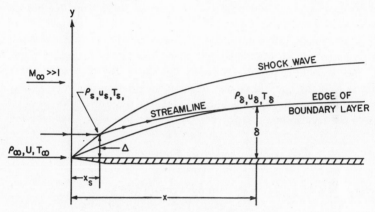

Fig. 9–1. Sketch of boundary layer induced flow field over a flat plate.

Most of this chapter will be devoted to the study of boundary layer induced interactions, which we shall sometimes term "self induced" interactions, with pressure and vorticity interactions usually considered to be independent. Bluntness induced interactions will be discussed in Section 9.5. We shall carry out our study within the framework of the classical Prandtl boundary layer concept, with the boundary layer considered as an entity distinct from the inviscid flow field. We shall restrict the discussion to laminar flow, since a suitable theory for turbulent boundary layers with arbitrary pressure gradient does not yet exist, even for subsonic speeds. In any event, we note that the induced pressure gradients for a turbulent boundary layer can be expected to be smaller than for a laminar boundary layer.

We may start by considering the pressure interactions resulting from the two-dimensional hypersonic flow past a flat plate with a sharp leading edge. In this case we mean by "sharp" that the leading edge has no essential effect on the inviscid pressure distribution along the surface. In other words, the leading edge radius is small enough to make the Reynolds number $Re_{t_\infty}$ based on the thickness sufficiently low (say less than 100) that the viscous effects far outweigh any inviscid effects associated with a finite leading edge radius at high Mach numbers.

The viscous boundary layer is considered to be distinct from the inviscid shock layer, and is shown schematically in Fig. 9–1. Such a model was discussed for the hypersonic interaction problem by Lees and Probstein [1], and was applied independently by the Langley Field hypersonic tunnel group of the NACA (see Becker [1]). If we at first assume that the boundary layer approximations are valid, so that variations in the pressure across the viscous layer are negligible, then it is easily shown for all real gases that in order to have a consistent approach the shock wave cannot coincide with the edge of the boundary layer.

To prove this, we first note that if the outer edge of the boundary layer were to coincide with the shock, the mass flow in the boundary layer must equal the mass flow passing through the shock (see Fig. 9–1). With the condition that the body have non-negative inclination to the free stream the mass flow passing through the shock is greater than or equal to $\rho_\infty U \delta$, and we have the condition

$$(9.1.1) \qquad \rho_\infty U \delta \leqslant \int_0^\delta \rho u \, dy.$$

Since $u < U$ and $\rho_\infty / \rho_\delta \approx \epsilon$, we may write (9.1.1) as

$$(9.1.2) \qquad \epsilon < \frac{\bar{\rho}}{\rho_\delta},$$

where $\bar{\rho}$ is a suitable average value of $\rho$. We set

$$(9.1.3) \qquad \frac{\bar{\rho}}{\rho_\infty} = \frac{\bar{p}}{p_\infty} \frac{T_\infty}{\bar{T}}$$

and note that at most

$$(9.1.4) \qquad \frac{\bar{p}}{p_\infty} \sim M_\infty^2 \left(\frac{d\delta}{dx}\right)^2 \sim M_\infty^2 \left(\frac{\delta}{x}\right)^2.$$

From the Crocco integral (8.3.3) and the strong shock approximation we have that $\bar{T}/T_\infty = O(\epsilon M_\infty^2)$ in a hypersonic flow. Combining the results above we obtain the approximate condition

$$(9.1.5) \qquad \frac{1}{\epsilon} \left(\frac{\delta}{x}\right)^2 > 1$$

for the outer edge of the boundary layer to coincide with the shock wave. In order that the Prandtl boundary layer concepts apply it is necessary that the relative change in the pressure across the layer be small and that the axial derivative terms in the viscous shear and heat transfer expressions are small. It may be readily shown that the condition for the validity of the boundary layer concepts with $\bar{T}/T_\infty = O(\epsilon M_\infty^2)$ is

$$(9.1.6) \qquad\qquad \frac{1}{\epsilon}\left(\frac{\delta}{x}\right)^2 \ll 1.$$

The incompatibility of (9.1.5) and (9.1.6) shows that the shock layer cannot be a boundary layer.

Thus the shock layer must contain an inviscid region of relatively cool high density flow outside the boundary layer. Following the classical concept of the displacement thickness we may replace the body and the boundary layer with an equivalent body in an inviscid flow for the purpose of calculating the correct external inviscid flow field. This equivalent body is simply the original body thickened by the displacement thickness distribution $\delta^*(x)$ defined in (8.4.2). With a hypersonic boundary layer, the density in the layer is very low and we may approximately equate $\delta$ and $\delta^*$. With this approximation the equivalent body lies along the outer edge of the boundary layer and we have

$$(9.1.7) \qquad\qquad \theta = \theta_\delta = \theta_b + \frac{d\delta^*}{dx}.$$

Without this approximation we would have (9.1.7) with $\theta_{\delta*}$ instead of $\theta_\delta$, where $\theta_{\delta*}$ is the streamline inclination for the inviscid flow on the equivalent body.

Therefore as long as $(\delta/x)^2 \ll \epsilon$, the interaction problem is to determine the solutions for a classical Prandtl boundary layer subjected to an external pressure gradient and vorticity field which is not known in advance, but which depends, through the hypersonic inviscid flow relations, on the rate of growth of the boundary layer itself.

In the work of Lees and Probstein [1; 2] and Lees [1] it was found that the pressure interaction could be divided quite naturally into asymptotic regions called strong and weak interaction zones, at least for the case in which the flow would be uniform if there were no boundary layer. This conclusion was based on an approximate pressure-flow deflection relation for slender bodies at hypersonic speeds. Such a division is useful for characterizing the problem and bringing out the principal flow parameters. In addition, it makes the analysis somewhat more tractable because it is possible to obtain analytic results for these asymptotic regions.

According to this concept, in the weak interaction region the effects produced by the self induced pressure gradient are essentially perturbations superposed on an already existing uniform flow. The strong interaction region, on the other hand, is characterized by the fact that the streamline inclination induced by the viscous layer becomes large (larger, say, than the wedge angle if the flow is the flow over a wedge), and the pressure gradient and viscous stress gradient terms are of the same order of magnitude. On a flat plate this strong interaction zone would be close to the leading edge, while the weak interaction zone would be farther downstream. Of course, there will also be an intermediate or transition region in which the interaction is neither weak nor strong and in which the solutions are not of an asymptotic nature.

In both the weak and strong interaction regions, we can easily derive the parameters on which the induced pressure depends by employing the approximate tangent-wedge expressions for the inviscid surface pressure distribution in the two limiting cases $K^2 \ll 1$ and $K^2 \gg 1$. Here $K$ is the local hypersonic similarity parameter for the effective body and is defined as

$$(9.1.8) \qquad K = M_\infty \left( \theta_b + \frac{d\delta^*}{dx} \right).$$

We shall use the symbol $K_b$ for $M_\infty \theta_b$.

For the weak interaction case the flow deflection resulting from the growth of the boundary layer must be sufficiently small; for this condition either $K$ is less than or of the order of one, or $d\delta^*/dx < \theta_b$ with $M_\infty \theta_b$ arbitrary. In the first case, with $K$ sufficiently small, the induced pressure is given approximately by (7.3.2) as

$$(9.1.9) \qquad \frac{p}{p_\infty} \approx 1 + \gamma K.$$

If we again use bars to denote average values of the fluid properties in the boundary layer, then the order of the boundary layer thickness on a flat plate follows from the fact that

$$(9.1.10) \qquad \delta^2 \sim \left( \frac{\bar{\mu} x}{\bar{\rho} U} \right) \sim \left( \frac{\bar{\mu}}{\mu_\infty} \right) \left( \frac{\rho_\infty}{\bar{\rho}} \right) \left( \frac{\mu_\infty x}{\rho_\infty U} \right).$$

Making use of a linear viscosity-temperature relation of the form $\mu/\mu_\infty = C_\infty T/T_\infty$, where $C_\infty$ is a constant, and employing the fact that $\rho_\infty/\bar{\rho} \approx \bar{T}/T_\infty$ and $\bar{T}/T_\infty \sim \frac{1}{2}(\gamma - 1)M_\infty^2$ (note that $\epsilon_{\lim} = O[\frac{1}{2}(\gamma - 1)]$), we find that

$$(9.1.11) \qquad \frac{\delta^*}{x} \sim \frac{\delta}{x} \sim \frac{\gamma - 1}{2} \frac{M_\infty^2 \sqrt{C_\infty}}{\sqrt{Re_{x_\infty}}},$$

where the Reynolds number $Re_{x_\infty}$ is based on free stream conditions. Therefore for the weak interaction on a flat plate ($\theta_b = 0$), the induced pressure is given from (9.1.7) and (9.1.9) as

$$(9.1.12) \qquad \frac{p}{p_\infty} - 1 \approx \gamma M_\infty \frac{d\delta^*}{dx} \sim \frac{\gamma - 1}{2} \frac{M_\infty^3 \sqrt{C_\infty}}{\sqrt{Re_{x_\infty}}} = \frac{\gamma - 1}{2} \bar{\chi}.$$

The fundamental interaction parameter $\bar{\chi}$ is defined by (9.1.12). For $\bar{\chi}$ appreciably less than one the effect will be small; for values of $\bar{\chi}$ of the order of one or greater, the induced pressures are significant.

In the strong interaction case, $K^2 \gg 1$ and $d\delta^*/dx > \theta_b$. From (7.3.1) the pressure is then given approximately by

$$(9.1.13) \qquad \frac{p}{p_\infty} \approx \frac{\gamma(\gamma+1)}{2} K^2.$$

Using (9.1.3) again, we have

$$(9.1.14) \qquad \delta^2 \sim \left(\frac{\bar{\mu}}{\mu_\infty}\right)\left(\frac{\bar{T}}{T_\infty}\right)\left(\frac{p_\infty}{p}\right)\left(\frac{\mu_\infty x}{\rho_\infty U}\right).$$

Since for a flat plate with $\theta_b = 0$, $p/p_\infty \sim M_\infty^2(\delta/x)^2$, then

$$(9.1.15) \qquad \frac{\delta^*}{x} \sim \frac{\delta}{x} \sim \left[\frac{\gamma-1}{2}\frac{M_\infty\sqrt{C_\infty}}{\sqrt{Re_{x_\infty}}}\right]^{1/2}$$

and

$$(9.1.16) \qquad \frac{p}{p_\infty} \sim \frac{\gamma-1}{2}\frac{M_\infty^3\sqrt{C_\infty}}{\sqrt{Re_{x_\infty}}} = \frac{\gamma-1}{2}\bar{\chi}.$$

These relations will hold for those cases in which $\bar{\chi}$ is sufficiently large in comparison with one. The important point to be observed here is that the pressure is inversely proportional to $\sqrt{x}$ and the boundary layer grows like $x^{3/4}$ (not like $\sqrt{x}$ as in the weak interaction). It is, however, also important to observe from (9.1.12) and (9.1.16) that the relative change in pressure in both weak and strong interactions is a function of the same hypersonic interaction parameter $\bar{\chi}$.

Let us now examine the question of the vorticity interaction. The existence and importance of this type of interaction was originally pointed out by Ferri and Libby [1]. The main idea of vorticity interaction lies in the outer boundary condition which must be satisfied. Without external vorticity the velocity at the outer edge of the boundary layer equals the velocity at the inner edge of the inviscid flow were there no boundary layer. With external vorticity the velocity at the outer edge of the boundary layer must equal the velocity in the inviscid flow at the same value of the stream function. With the vorticity such that the inviscid velocity increases outward from the body, the effect of vorticity interaction is to increase the skin friction and heat transfer.

A parameter $\Omega$ characterizing the importance of vorticity interaction may be defined (see Li [1]) as the ratio of the external inviscid vorticity to the average vorticity in the boundary layer. This vorticity interaction parameter may be approximately defined for a low speed boundary layer as

$$(9.1.17) \qquad\qquad \Omega = \frac{\zeta_{\text{inv}}}{u_{\text{inv}}/\delta} \, ,$$

where $\delta$ is a suitable measure of the boundary layer thickness and the subscript "inv" refers to the edge of the equivalent inviscid flow. If the parameter $\Omega$ is small the effect of vorticity interaction may be considered to be negligible. If this parameter is of order one vorticity interaction is not negligible and should be taken into account. If this parameter is large the shear stress in the boundary layer is of the same order of magnitude as the supposedly negligible shear stress in the external inviscid flow, and the problem requires a re-examination of the basic boundary layer concepts. A more precise definition of $\Omega$ will be given in Section 9.6.

A rough analysis given in Section 9.6 shows that vorticity interaction should have little importance in the strong interaction region. It is clear that its importance decreases in the intermediate and weak interaction regions and must be negligible at a sufficiently large downstream distance. The case of the vorticity interaction for the boundary layer in the stagnation region of the flow on a blunt body of revolution is treated in Section 9.6.

In discussing all these interaction effects, the question naturally arises whether slip phenomena will enter under the same conditions as the interaction phenomena. Now an approximate criterion for slip is that the mean free path at the wall be small compared with the boundary layer thickness. The estimates of Section 1.7 may be applied approximately for a stagnation region on a blunt body or to the weak interaction region, but a separate approximate analysis is needed for the strong interaction region. These questions are discussed in Section 10.1. In general, we may say that within the regions of validity of the boundary layer concept, rarefied gas effects such as slip do not enter, even though the boundary layers are thick enough so that the interaction effects we are discussing are important. This is particularly true for the slip effect at the wall if the body is cooled.

A notational difficulty arises in interaction problems in making a distinction between the inviscid part of a flow with a boundary layer and the inviscid flow which would occur if there were no viscous effects and no boundary layer whatsoever. This distinction is unimportant in boundary layer problems not involving interaction effects. To resolve this notational difficulty we consider the flow with no viscous effects and no boundary layer as an "original" flow and we shall use the term "original" to refer to it. Quantities defined at the body in the original flow or defined in terms of such quantities will bear the subscript "orig". An exception will be the local hypersonic similarity parameter $K_b = M_\infty \theta_b$, which will always be defined using $M_\infty$, and will never have the subscript "orig". The pressure is always assumed to be constant through a boundary layer, and this pressure is indicated by $p$ without subscript. Other quantities defined with a boundary layer present bear the subscripts $\delta$ or $b$ as usual. When we consider vorticity interaction we shall use the subscript "inv" to indicate the edge of the equivalent body in an inviscid flow. Only with vorticity interaction important need we distinguish between the subscripts $\delta$ and "inv".

## 2. Weak pressure interactions

It was pointed out in the previous section that the weak pressure interaction region is characterized essentially by a perturbation on the original flow conditions produced by the hypersonic boundary layer. At first, in order to strip away as much of the complication as possible, we will consider the case of flow over an inclined wedge or flat plate, so that we need discuss only a perturbation on an initially uniform inviscid parallel flow. Later we will briefly discuss more general body shapes and three-dimensional flows.

Weak interaction effects enter when $K$ is less than or of the order of one or when $d\delta^*/dx < \theta_b$ with $M_\infty\theta_b$ arbitrary. Based on these criteria, weak interaction effects should appear on thin wedges at low angles of attack if the Reynolds number is high at high Mach numbers or if the Mach number is moderately supersonic at lower Reynolds numbers. They should appear also at high Mach numbers on thick wedges or on the compression surface of any wedge at sufficiently high angles of attack.

The original theoretical and experimental estimates of the weak interaction effect for steady plane supersonic flow past an insulated flat plate were made by the NACA hypersonic research group at Langley Field and reported by Becker [1]. Lees and Probstein [1] (see also Probstein and Lees [1]) carried out detailed theoretical calculations of the weak interaction over a flat plate with arbitrary heat transfer, including the first-order perturbation on the velocity and enthalpy distributions for a linear viscosity-temperature relation. Independently and at about the same time, Maslen [1] performed a similar analysis, in which he included the effect of an arbitrary viscosity law. A more approximate treatment of this problem was also given by Bertram [1]. Somewhat later the weak interaction study was extended to the case of wedge flow by Lees and Probstein [2] in a monograph which did not receive wide distribution. For an insulated surface and a linear viscosity law with $Pr = 1$, Kuo [1] treated the same flat plate problem with a technique which involved an attempted extension of Lighthill's method for rendering solutions uniformly valid. To consistent orders of magnitude it is readily shown that the results of Kuo for the weak interaction region of this case reduce to those given earlier by Lees and Probstein [1] and Maslen [1]. Although Kuo attempted to extend his analysis through the strong interaction region to the leading edge, there seems to be no justification for the procedure used and his results are clearly in error here; we refer the reader to Maslen [2] for a discussion of this point. More recently, Pan and Kuo [1] also studied for the boundary layer on a wedge the interaction correction arising from reflections from the shock of the outgoing waves. Their calculations for $\gamma = 1.4$ indicate that the correction is completely negligible even though the wedge shock is strong. It is clear from Sections 7.2 and 9.1 that a number of other interaction effects of small order should be at least as important as the one Pan and Kuo investigated.

Although there are several alternative approaches to the problem of the weak pressure interaction on a wedge at an angle of attack, we will adopt the method given by Lees and Probstein [2]. It was assumed in that method that since the pressure is a unique function $p(\theta)$ of the local total flow deflection, it may be expressed as a Taylor series expansion in powers of $d\delta^*/dx$. This expansion is of the form

$$(9.2.1) \qquad \frac{p}{p_{\text{orig}}} = 1 + \frac{1}{p_{\text{orig}}/p_\infty} \left(\frac{dp/p_\infty}{d\theta}\right)_{\theta=\theta_b} \left(\frac{d\delta^*}{dx}\right)$$

$$+ \frac{1}{2p_{\text{orig}}/p_\infty} \left(\frac{d^2p/p_\infty}{d\theta^2}\right)_{\theta=\theta_b} \left(\frac{d\delta^*}{dx}\right)^2 + \cdots.$$

Here $\theta$ is the total flow deflection angle given by $\theta = \theta_b + d\delta^*/dx$, where $\theta_b$ is the geometric slope of the body surface (equal to $\theta_w \pm \alpha$ for a wedge). If the wedge is a slender one we may use the hypersonic small disturbance result (7.3.1) for the original pressure on the wedge $p_{\text{orig}}$.

In order to evaluate the coefficients of $(d\delta^*/dx)$ in (9.2.1) it is necessary to know the function $p(\theta)$. For this relation we use the tangent-wedge approximation, without centrifugal correction. The shock-expansion method of Section 7.2 cannot be used, because the shock is highly curved near the leading edge. With such a highly curved initial shock the accuracy of the shock-expansion method is poor and there is no way of establishing the initial shock angle needed for the method. The tangent-wedge approximation has none of these difficulties with the initial shock curvature, and gives answers which are of the correct order of magnitude over the entire range of inclination angles. Its validity increases with decreasing values of $\gamma - 1$, while the shock-expansion method grows worse. In addition, the shock-expansion method does not yield a unique function $p(\theta)$ for all cases, while the tangent-wedge approximation does. Such a unique function permits us to carry out a unified approach on interaction problems, with consistent formulas used for all interaction regions.

The first two coefficients of (9.2.1), as evaluated from (7.3.1) for a perfect gas of constant $\gamma$, are found to be of the form

$$(9.2.2a) \qquad \left(\frac{dp/p_\infty}{d\theta}\right)_{\theta=\theta_b} = \gamma M_\infty \left(\frac{p_{\text{orig}}}{p_\infty}\right) J_1(K_b),$$

$$(9.2.2b) \qquad \left(\frac{d^2p/p_\infty}{d\theta^2}\right)_{\theta=\theta_b} = \frac{\gamma(\gamma+1)}{2} M_\infty^2 \left(\frac{p_{\text{orig}}}{p_\infty}\right) J_2(K_b).$$

Here

$$(9.2.3a) \qquad J_1(K_b) = \left(\frac{p_\infty}{p_{\text{orig}}}\right)\left[\frac{\gamma+1}{2} K_b + \frac{1 + 2\left(\frac{\gamma+1}{4}\right)^2 K_b^2}{\sqrt{1 + \left(\frac{\gamma+1}{4}\right)^2 K_b^2}}\right],$$

$$(9.2.3b) \qquad J_2(K_b) = \left(\frac{p_\infty}{p_{\text{orig}}}\right)\left[1 + \frac{\left(\frac{\gamma+1}{4}\right)K_b\left[\left(\frac{\gamma+1}{4}\right)^2 K_b^2 - \frac{3}{2}\right]}{\left[1 + \left(\frac{\gamma+1}{4}\right)^2 K_b^2\right]^{3/2}}\right],$$

where $p_\infty/p_{\text{orig}}$ is to be evaluated from (7.3.1). In terms of the quantities $J_1(K_b)$ and $J_2(K_b)$ thus defined, the general expression for the induced pressure becomes

$$(9.2.4) \qquad \frac{p}{p_{\text{orig}}} = 1 + \gamma\left(M_\infty \frac{d\delta^*}{dx}\right)J_1 + \frac{\gamma(\gamma+1)}{4}\left(M_\infty \frac{d\delta^*}{dx}\right)^2 J_2 + \cdots.$$

For a flat plate at zero angle of attack $K_b = 0$ and $J_1(0) = J_2(0) = 1$. On the other hand for $K_b^2 \gg 1$ we have $J_1 \approx 2/\gamma K_b$ and $J_2 \approx 4/\gamma(\gamma+1)K_b^2$.

We begin the development of the perturbation scheme for the weak interaction region by taking $d\delta^*/dx$ equal to the value given by the usual zero pressure gradient boundary layer solution for an inclined wedge or a flat plate. As we shall see, the induced pressure has no first-order effect on the slope of the edge of the boundary layer, but only causes a uniform reduction in thickness. Therefore, if $d\delta^*/dx$ is known for the non-interacting flow, (9.2.4) gives the induced pressure distribution correct to second order.

From the zero pressure gradient solutions derived by Crocco [2] with a linear viscosity-temperature law and constant $Pr$, the displacement thickness for a constant specific heat with $Pr = 1$ can be shown to be given by

$$(9.2.5a) \qquad \delta^*\sqrt{\frac{1}{x}\left(\frac{u}{\nu C}\right)_{\text{orig}}} = 1.730\,\frac{T_b}{T_{\text{orig}}} + 0.664\left(\frac{\gamma-1}{2}\right)M_{\text{orig}}^2;$$

with $Pr = 0.725$ the displacement thickness is given by

$$(9.2.5b) \qquad \delta^*\sqrt{\frac{1}{x}\left(\frac{u}{\nu C}\right)_{\text{orig}}} = 1.937\,\frac{T_b}{T_{\text{orig}}} + 0.578\left(\frac{\gamma-1}{2}\right)M_{\text{orig}}^2 - 0.207.$$

Here again the subscript $b$ refers to properties evaluated at the surface of the body, and the subscript "orig" refers to the original conditions associated with the uniform inviscid flow at the wedge (or flat plate) surface with no boundary layer. The constant $C_{\text{orig}}$ in the linear viscosity-temperature law is determined by matching the viscosity relation, usually evaluated at the surface temperature, with the exact value of the viscosity. Thus for an inclined wedge,

$$(9.2.6) \qquad C_{\text{orig}} = \left(\frac{\mu_b}{\mu_{\text{orig}}}\right)\left(\frac{T_{\text{orig}}}{T_b}\right).$$

In the special case of a surface parallel to the oncoming stream, the wedge conditions are replaced by the respective free stream conditions, and $C_{\text{orig}}$ in our notation may be replaced by $C_\infty$. In (9.2.5) the terms in $(\gamma - 1)M_{\text{orig}}^2$

TABLE 9–1

*Coefficients for rate of change of displacement thickness*

| $Pr$ | $A$ | $B$ | $D$ |
|------|-----|-----|-----|
| 1.0 | 0.865 | 0.166 | 0.599 |
| 0.725 | 0.968 | 0.145 | 0.556 |

are large compared with one for a hypersonic boundary layer. Unless $T_b/T_{\text{orig}}$ is itself large compared with one the term in $T_b/T_{\text{orig}}$ may be neglected. In addition, the term $-0.207$ in (9.2.5b) may be considered negligible. For an insulated plate $T_b/T_{\text{orig}}$ is of the same order as $(\gamma - 1)M_{\text{orig}}^2$.

From (9.2.5) with the term $-0.207$ neglected, we may write

$$(9.2.7) \qquad \frac{d\delta^*}{dx} = d_{\text{orig}}\sqrt{C_{\text{orig}}}\,\frac{M_{\text{orig}}^2}{\sqrt{Re_{x_{\text{orig}}}}} = d_{\text{orig}}\frac{\bar{\chi}_{\text{orig}}}{M_{\text{orig}}},$$

with

$$(9.2.8) \qquad d_{\text{orig}} = \frac{A(Pr)}{M_{\text{orig}}^2}\frac{T_b}{T_{\text{orig}}} + (\gamma - 1)B(Pr),$$

where $A$ and $B$ are functions of $Pr$. For an insulated body the approximation for $Pr \neq 1$

$$(9.2.9a) \qquad \frac{T_b}{T_{\text{orig}}} \approx 1 + \sqrt{Pr}\,\frac{\gamma - 1}{2}\,M_{\text{orig}}^2$$

may be used, and yields

$$(9.2.9b) \qquad d_{\text{orig}} = (\gamma - 1)D(Pr),$$

with a term $0.865/M_{\text{orig}}^2$ dropped. The coefficients $A$, $B$, and $D$ are given for $Pr = 1$ and 0.725 in Table 9–1. The influence of a very cold wall in reducing the induced pressure can be seen quite clearly from (9.2.8), where for

(9.2.10a)
$$\frac{T_b}{T_{\text{orig}}} = O(1)$$

we may consistently approximate

(9.2.10b)
$$d_{\text{orig}} = (\gamma - 1)B(Pr).$$

Thus the effect in the cold wall case is about one quarter of that in the insulated case common to wind tunnel tests.

By combining the preceding relations, we can obtain the following expression for the induced pressure distribution:

(9.2.11a)
$$\frac{p}{p_{\text{orig}}} = 1 + \gamma \left(\frac{M_\infty}{M_{\text{orig}}}\right) J_1 \, d_{\text{orig}} \bar{\chi}_{\text{orig}}$$
$$+ \frac{\gamma(\gamma + 1)}{4} \left(\frac{M_\infty}{M_{\text{orig}}}\right)^2 J_2 \, d_{\text{orig}}^2 \bar{\chi}_{\text{orig}}^2 + \cdots,$$

or

(9.2.11b)
$$\frac{p}{p_{\text{orig}}} = 1 + \gamma E_1 \bar{\chi}_{\text{orig}} + \frac{\gamma(\gamma + 1)}{4} E_2 \bar{\chi}_{\text{orig}}^2 + \cdots.$$

Here $\bar{\chi}_{\text{orig}}$ is the hypersonic interaction parameter based on wedge conditions, defined by

(9.2.12)
$$\bar{\chi}_{\text{orig}} = \frac{M_{\text{orig}}^3 \sqrt{C_{\text{orig}}}}{\sqrt{Re_{x_{\text{orig}}}}}.$$

The quantity $M_\infty/M_{\text{orig}}$ is a function of $K_b$ and $\gamma$ alone.

In the special cases when the body is very cold or the body is insulated, $d_{\text{orig}}$ is independent of the Mach number and of $K_b$; then since $\bar{\chi}_{\text{orig}}/\bar{\chi}$ is a function of $K_b$, the induced pressure rise is a function only of the usual hypersonic similarity parameter $K_b$ and the free stream hypersonic interaction parameter $\bar{\chi}$. For $K_b^2 \gg 1$ (say $M_\infty \theta_b > 3$), we have $J_1 \approx 2/\gamma K_b$ and $M_{\text{orig}} \theta_b \approx \sqrt{2/\gamma(\gamma - 1)}$. Since $\mu_{\text{orig}} \propto M_\infty^2 \theta_b^2$ if $\mu \propto T$, then

(9.2.13)
$$\frac{M_\infty}{M_{\text{orig}}} \frac{\bar{\chi}_{\text{orig}}}{K_b} \sim \frac{\bar{\chi}}{K_b^2},$$

and we find from (9.2.11) that

(9.2.14)
$$\frac{p}{p_{\text{orig}}} - 1 \sim d_{\text{orig}} \frac{\bar{\chi}}{K_b^2}.$$

Because of the strong inviscid pressure field, the viscous interaction effects on an inclined wedge are considerably smaller than those for the flat plate at zero angle of attack. Note that for a flat plate $(p/p_{\text{orig}}) - 1$ from (9.2.11) is approximately $\gamma \, d_{\infty} \bar{\chi}$ rather than the value given by (9.2.14).

According to our discussion in Section 9.1, the edge of the boundary layer is very nearly a streamline. Hence the external inviscid velocity and temperature field can be obtained from the Bernoulli equation and the condition of isentropic flow, using the value of $p/p_{\text{orig}}$ we have just derived. Expressed to the first order, these equations are

$$(9.2.15\text{a}) \qquad \frac{u_{\delta}}{u_{\text{orig}}} = 1 - \frac{E_1}{M_{\text{orig}}^2} \bar{\chi}_{\text{orig}} + O(\bar{\chi}_{\text{orig}}^2)$$

or

$$(9.2.15\text{b}) \qquad \frac{u_{\delta}}{u_{\text{orig}}} = 1 - \frac{J_1}{M_{\text{orig}}^2} \left( M_{\infty} \frac{d\delta^*}{dx} \right) + O\left[ \left( M_{\infty} \frac{d\delta^*}{dx} \right)^2 \right],$$

$$(9.2.16\text{a}) \qquad \frac{T_{\delta}}{T_{\text{orig}}} = 1 + (\gamma - 1)E_1 \bar{\chi}_{\text{orig}} + O(\bar{\chi}_{\text{orig}}^2)$$

or

$$(9.2.16\text{b}) \qquad \frac{T_{\delta}}{T_{\text{orig}}} = 1 + (\gamma - 1)J_1 \left( M_{\infty} \frac{d\delta^*}{dx} \right) + O\left[ \left( M_{\infty} \frac{d\delta^*}{dx} \right)^2 \right].$$

These relations are written both in terms of $\bar{\chi}_{\text{orig}}$ and of $d\delta^*/dx$. The use of the interaction parameter $\bar{\chi}_{\text{orig}}$ implies a linear viscosity-temperature relation, and a relation written in terms of $d\delta^*/dx$ is more general.

From the form of the inviscid flow variables it seems quite natural to expect that all flow quantities in both the external inviscid and internal viscous field are expressible as asymptotic series in ascending powers of $d\delta^*/dx$ or $\bar{\chi}_{\text{orig}}$. In such a scheme the lowest-order approximation is the usual zero pressure gradient wedge or flat plate solution. Thus for the boundary layer solution we write

$$(9.2.17\text{a}) \qquad \frac{u}{u_{\text{orig}}} = u_0(\eta) + u_1(\eta)\bar{\chi}_{\text{orig}} + \cdots,$$

$$(9.2.17\text{b}) \qquad \frac{T}{T_{\text{orig}}} = T_0(\eta) + T_1(\eta)\bar{\chi}_{\text{orig}} + \cdots,$$

where $\eta$ is the transformed normal distance defined by (8.2.9), and $u_0(\eta)$ and $T_0(\eta)$ are the classical solutions for zero pressure gradient, non-dimensionalized with respect to $u_{\text{orig}}$ and $T_{\text{orig}}$ respectively.

Were we to consider the fluid properties as variable, the expansions, including all temperature dependent quantities such as $\mu(T)$ and $Pr(T)$, would be carried out in powers of $M_{\infty} \, d\delta^*/dx$. As will be shown, the results obtained by assuming a linear viscosity-temperature law and constant $Pr$ are directly applicable to the variable fluid property case by a simple generalization. Hence for simplicity, only the case of a linear viscosity-temperature law and constant $Pr$ is considered here.

By substituting the asymptotic expansions (9.2.11) and (9.2.15) to (9.2.17) into the boundary layer equations (8.2.14) and (8.2.15), the equations for each order higher than zero are reducible to two independent ordinary inhomogeneous second-order equations, with variable coefficients which are functions only of lower-order solutions in the expansion.

The momentum and energy equations for $u_0$ and $T_0$ take on the familiar flat plate forms:

$$(9.2.18) \qquad f_0''' + f_0 f_0'' = 0,$$

$$(9.2.19) \qquad T_0'' + Pr\, f_0 T_0' = -(\gamma - 1) Pr\, M_{\text{orig}}^2 f_0''^2,$$

where primes denote differentiation with respect to $\eta$, and where $u_0 = f_0'$.

The reduced momentum equation for $u_1$ is

$$(9.2.20) \quad u_1'' + \left(\frac{u_0'}{u_0} + f_0\right) u_1' + \left(u_0'' - \frac{u_0'^2}{u_0}\right) u_1 = -\frac{E_1}{M_{\text{orig}}^2}(T_0 - \gamma M_{\text{orig}}^2 f_0 u_0'),$$

while the energy equation for $T_1$ expressed in terms of the quantity $\Upsilon_1$ is

$$(9.2.21) \quad \Upsilon_1'' + Pr\, f_0 \Upsilon_1' + Pr\, u_0 \Upsilon_1$$

$$= \frac{E_1}{M_{\text{orig}}^2} \frac{d}{d\eta}\left[\left(\int_0^\eta T_0\, d\eta - \sqrt{2} E_1 M_{\text{orig}}^2\right)\left(\frac{T_0'}{u_0'} + (\gamma - 1) M_{\text{orig}}^2 Pr\, u_0\right)\right],$$

where

$$(9.2.22) \qquad T_1 = \frac{T_0' u_1}{u_0'} + \Upsilon_1.$$

Now the solutions of the homogeneous portions of (9.2.20) and (9.2.21) can be given in closed form, leading to the following complete solutions:

$$(9.2.23) \quad u_1(\eta) = \frac{u_0'}{u_0}\left[a + b\int_0^\eta \frac{u_0}{u_0'}\, d\eta - \gamma E_1 f_0 - \frac{E_1}{2M_{\text{orig}}^2}\int_0^\eta T_0\, d\eta\right],$$

$$(9.2.24) \quad \Upsilon_1(\eta) = (u_0')^{Pr}\left[m + n\int_0^\eta \frac{d\eta}{(u_0')^{Pr}}\right.$$

$$\left. + \frac{E_1}{M_{\text{orig}}^2}\int_0^\eta \frac{\left(\int_0^\eta T_0\, d\eta - \sqrt{2}E_1 M_{\text{orig}}^2\right)}{(u_0')^{Pr}}\left(\frac{T_0'}{u_0'} + (\gamma - 1)M_{\text{orig}}^2 Pr\, u_0\right) d\eta\right].$$

The integration constants $a$, $b$, $m$, and $n$ must be determined by the boundary conditions, which at the outer edge of the boundary layer are $u_1(\infty) = -E_1/M_{\text{orig}}^2$ and $T_1(\infty) = (\gamma - 1)E_1$. The no slip condition at the surface implies $u_1(0) = 0$. If the wall temperature is specified, $T_1(0) = \Upsilon_1(0) = 0$; if the surface is insulated, $T_1'(0) = \Upsilon_1'(0) = 0$. It can be shown (see Maslen [1] and Probstein and Lees [1]) that in order to satisfy these boundary conditions, we must have $a = m = n = 0$ and $b = E_1^2/\sqrt{2}$. This leads directly to the result that *the local heat transfer rate and equilibrium wall temperature are unaltered to first order* by the self induced pressure gradient. Thus Busemann's conclusion that the recovery temperature is unaffected by the pressure gradient for $Pr = 1$ is here generalized to arbitrary $Pr$, at least to terms of order $\bar{\chi}_{\text{orig}}$ for a weak pressure interaction in hypersonic flow. In addition, this result has been shown by Maslen [1] to hold with an arbitrary variation of fluid properties with temperature.

Although the interaction contributes nothing to the heat transfer, it nevertheless has an effect on the local skin friction coefficient as evidenced by the fact that $b \neq 0$. By the use of the solution (9.2.23) for $u_1(\eta)$, it follows that the skin friction coefficient to first approximation is given by

$$(9.2.25) \qquad C_f^{(1)} \sqrt{\frac{Re_{x_{\text{orig}}}}{C_{\text{orig}}}} = \sqrt{2}(u_0')_b + 2E_1^2 \bar{\chi}_{\text{orig}}.$$

Here $\sqrt{2}(u_0')_b$ is equal to the flat plate value of 0.664. Thus for a linear viscosity-temperature relation, the change in the local value of the skin friction coefficient from the zero pressure gradient value is

$$(9.2.26) \qquad \frac{C_f^{(1)} - C_f^{(0)}}{C_f^{(0)}} = \frac{E_1^2 \bar{\chi}_{\text{orig}}}{0.332}.$$

It can be shown that the skin friction can be generalized to an arbitrary viscosity-temperature relation simply by expressing the answer in terms of $d\delta^*/dx$ through the definition of $E_1$ (9.2.11b) and the relation (9.2.7) between $d\delta^*/dx$ and $\bar{\chi}_{\text{orig}}$. The resulting general expression is

$$(9.2.27) \qquad C_f^{(1)} = C_f^{(0)} + \frac{2J_1^2}{M_{\text{orig}}^3}\left(M_\infty \frac{d\delta^*}{dx}\right)^2,$$

where $C_f^{(0)}$ is the lowest-order solution for variable fluid properties (cf. Maslen [1]).

Because of the favorable (negative) induced pressure gradient, we would expect the boundary layer thickness to be reduced in a first approximation. We should not however conclude that this reduction in thickness has a first-order effect on the flow inclination induced in the external field by the viscous layer. If we expand $\delta^*$ in $\bar{\chi}_{\text{orig}}$ we obtain a result of the form

$$(9.2.28) \qquad \delta^{*(1)} = \delta^{*(0)}(1 + c\bar{\chi}_{\text{orig}}) = \delta^{*(0)} + C,$$

where $c$ and $C$ are negative constants. Thus we have $d\delta^{*(1)}/dx = d\delta^{*(0)}/dx$, and find there is no first-order effect on the slope of the edge of the layer,

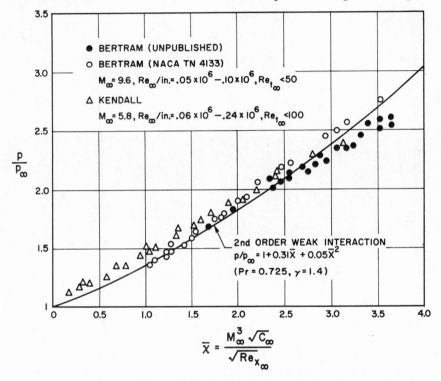

FIG. 9–2. Weak interaction induced pressure on an insulated flat plate in air.

only a uniform reduction in thickness. We conclude that the induced pressure formula (9.2.4), employing the zero pressure gradient value of $d\delta^*/dx$, is valid to second order.

In order to compare with experiment the weak interaction theory just presented, we have shown on Fig. 9–2 the experimental pressure distributions on an insulated flat plate at zero angle of attack, obtained in wind tunnel tests with air. These measurements were carried out by Bertram [2] at a nominal Mach number of 9.6 and by Kendall [1] at a nominal Mach number of 5.8. In Bertram's tests the Reynolds number based on the leading edge thickness was less than 50, while in Kendall's tests this Reynolds number was less than 100. Therefore it is probably reasonable to say that in both sets of experiments the leading edge had little or no effect on the pressure distribution. Both sets of experiments covered a wide range of Reynolds numbers. Also shown on Fig. 9–2 are additional as-yet unpublished data obtained by Bertram at zero angle of attack. We might mention that in this

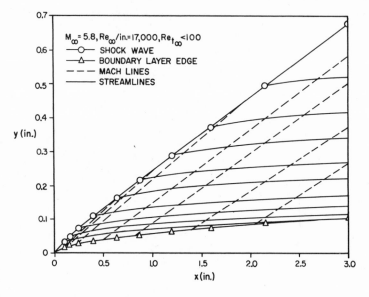

FIG. 9–3. Experimentally determined flow field for weak interaction on an insulated flat plate in air (Kendall [1]).

same unpublished work, Bertram has obtained data on a plate at nonzero angles of attack which are consistent with the data at zero angle of attack. Because of the profusion of the data, not all the experimental points of these authors are indicated; a sufficient number are plotted, however, to give a representative idea of the scatter. We also note that in Bertram's experiments there were a mild temperature gradient and a certain amount of heat transfer along the surface of the plate. A correction was made by Bertram to the displacement thickness for this effect, and the data were reduced to equivalent data for an insulated plate pressure distribution.

On Fig. 9–2 is also shown the second-order weak interaction result for an insulated flat plate, obtained from (9.2.11) for $\gamma = 1.4$ and $Pr = 0.725$. This relation is given by

$$(9.2.29) \qquad \frac{p}{p_\infty} = 1 + 0.31\bar{\chi} + 0.05\,\bar{\chi}^2.$$

The agreement between experiment and theory is seen to be quite good. The deviation of the experimental points from the theoretical curve starts at a value of $\bar{\chi}$ between 3 and 4, which from (9.2.29) is about where one might expect it to occur.

Kendall [1] in his experiments also checked the tangent-wedge approximation and showed it to be remarkably accurate. For the conditions of Kendall's test we should expect the tangent-wedge approximation to be very good and essentially identical with the shock-expansion approximation. He also determined the entire flow field, including the shock wave shape. He compared this shape with the shape obtained from the shock-expansion theory for the equivalent body defined by his measured displacement thickness. In Fig. 9–3 we have shown this experimentally determined flow field for one value of the Reynolds number per inch. From this figure it is quite clear that the shock-expansion approximation, which is consistent with our pressure distribution to second order, is in fact just what is found experimentally.

The average skin friction coefficient along the plate was also determined by Kendall in his experiments. The local skin friction coefficient as given by (9.2.25) is not directly integrable to provide a theoretical estimate of the average coefficient. However, Kendall took the experimentally determined value of the average skin friction coefficient at a downstream station and computed its variation ahead of this station using the theoretical relation (9.2.25). Theory and experiment were found to agree within 2 per cent up to quite near the leading edge.

In principle the treatment of weak pressure interactions is also applicable to arbitrary two- and three-dimensional flows, provided the lowest-order solution is known. Further discussion of the solution of pressure interaction problems for arbitrary two-dimensional bodies will be reserved for Section 9.4.

An analysis of the weak interaction on an unyawed right circular cone analogous to that given for two-dimensional wedge flow was carried out by Probstein [1]. Independently T. C. Lin, S. A. Schaaf, and F. S. Sherman (see Talbot [1]) computed the first-order induced pressure, although their results were somewhat in error due to the fact that the linearized theory was used for determining the inviscid cone pressure. These calculations were later corrected and reported on by Talbot [1] in connection with his experimental cone probe studies. In the most recent work on this problem Talbot, Koga, and Sherman [1] again computed the weak interaction induced pressures for the flow over a cone. Their method was a numerical-graphical iteration scheme, thus differing from the analytical treatment of Probstein. In their calculation the sum of the induced and inviscid cone pressures was determined by calculating the local pressure corresponding to an effective local cone angle $\theta_c + d\delta^*/dx$. The determination of the pressure sum was made by means of the tangent-cone method (Section 7.3), employing the Taylor-Maccoll results as computed by Kopal [1].

In our discussion of this problem we will follow the analysis of Probstein [1] in which the boundary layer equations are reduced to the two-dimensional form by use of the Mangler transformation. By this means the analysis parallels that for the wedge, except that the tangent-cone relation is employed to evaluate the coefficients in the pressure expansion (9.2.1). If the tangent-cone approximation is used, then if $K_b^2 = M_\infty^2 \theta_c^2 \gg 1$ and $\epsilon$ is small the inviscid pressure ratio $p_{orig}/p_\infty$ and the derivatives in (9.2.1) can be estimated from (4.2.26). For $K_b^2 \ll 1$ Talbot, Koga, and Sherman [1] have given an empirical modification of the Kármán-Moore slender body result which may be used. In the intermediate region $K_b = O(1)$, the inviscid cone pressure and the derivatives should be evaluated numerically from the Taylor-Maccoll solution.

According to the Mangler transformation for axisymmetric flow over an unyawed cone,

$$(9.2.30) \qquad \frac{d\delta^*}{dx} = \frac{d_{orig}}{\sqrt{3}} \frac{M_{orig}^2 \sqrt{C_{orig}}}{\sqrt{Re_{x_{orig}}}},$$

where $d_{orig}$ is the same function defined by (9.2.7). Thus if we define a quantity $J_{c_1}$ as we did for the wedge case (9.2.3a), then

$$(9.2.31) \qquad \frac{p}{p_{orig}} = 1 + \gamma J_{c_1} \left(\frac{M_\infty}{M_{orig}}\right) \frac{d_{orig}}{\sqrt{3}} \bar{\chi}_{orig} + O(\bar{\chi}_{orig}^2).$$

Talbot, Koga, and Sherman [1] have measured the induced pressure distributions on sharp-nosed cones ($Re_{t_\infty} < 10$) in a low-density wind tunnel for Mach numbers up to about 5.7 and values of $\bar{\chi}_{orig}$ up to 3.5. At $\bar{\chi}_{orig} = 2$, Probstein's second-order theory gives $p/p_{orig} = 1.38$, while the mean of the experimental data is about 1.25. This difference between the theory and experiment appears to increase with larger values of $\bar{\chi}_{orig}$. On the other hand, Talbot, Koga, and Sherman's numerical method yields a curve which is linear in $\bar{\chi}_{orig}$ and which appears to correlate the experimental data reasonably well, although it is also slightly high. For further details regarding the changes in the skin friction coefficient and the heat transfer rate due to the induced pressure (for axisymmetric flow there is a nonzero first-order contribution to the heat transfer as a result of the induced pressure) we refer the reader to the paper of Probstein.

Now it must be borne in mind for slender cones where the induced pressure gradient effect is largest, that the boundary layer thickness may no longer be small compared to the radius of the body cross-section, and the transverse curvature effect neglected in the Mangler transformation may have to be taken into account. Probstein and Elliott [1] and Probstein [1] have considered this point and find that although the transverse curvature increases the local skin friction coefficient, it does not alter the displacement thickness in a first approximation. Therefore the effects of the induced pressure gradient and transverse curvature are separable, at least when the boundary layer thickness is of the order of the body cross-sectional radius. In fact it turns out that for a cone, the main increases in local skin friction and heat transfer rate come primarily from the transverse curvature effect and not from the induced pressure gradient. These results have been checked experimentally by Ipsen [1] in measurements of the skin friction coefficient on cones in low-density supersonic flow.

## 3. Strong pressure interactions

In section 9.1 we have shown that a strong pressure interaction region exists for the flow over flat plates at not too high angles of attack when the Mach number is sufficiently large and the local Reynolds number is sufficiently small. For more general body shapes the strong interaction region can be characterized by the facts that $d\delta^*/dx > \theta_b$ and $K^2 \gg 1$, with $K$ given by (9.1.8). The first analysis of this region for a wedge or a flat plate with zero heat transfer was carried out by Shen [1]. He applied the von Kármán momentum equation to the entire flow field between the shock wave and body surface, and applied the strong oblique shock relation

$$(9.3.1) \qquad \frac{p}{p_\infty} = \frac{2\gamma}{\gamma + 1} M_\infty^2 \left(\theta_b + \frac{d\delta}{dx}\right)^2 = \frac{2\gamma}{\gamma + 1} (M_\infty \sigma)^2$$

to relate the pressure to the slope of the shock wave. He represented the velocity profile by a straight line and solved the von Kármán momentum-integral equation approximately. For an insulated flat plate with a sharp leading edge Shen obtained the results that $\delta \propto x^{3/4}$ and $p/p_\infty \propto x^{-1/2}$ for $\bar\chi \gg 1$. Later Li and Nagamatsu [1] extended Shen's analysis by approximating the velocity profile by a quartic, as in the usual Kármán-Pohlhausen approach, and obtained expressions for $\delta(x)$ and $C_f$ for an insulated flat plate. Unfortunately, Li and Nagamatsu's calculations were in error numerically. But more important was the fact that the approach of Shen and the extension of Li and Nagamatsu contained a conceptual error. This in turn led to a modest numerical error.

The difficulty with Shen's treatment lies not so much in the general results, which we have already shown to be correct by simple order of magnitude considerations (Section 9.1), but rather in the basic inconsistency of the flow model resulting from the assumption that the shock and the boundary layer edge are coincident. This inconsistency with conditions of continuity was first pointed out by Lees [1]. Lees observed, as we have shown in Section 9.1, that in the strong interaction region the shock wave cannot coincide with the outer edge of the boundary layer. In the model employed by Lees and Probstein [1; 2] and Lees [1] this inconsistency is avoided because the shock wave and the boundary layer are regarded as distinct.

Now we will at first approach the solution of the strong interaction problem for arbitrary bodies by adopting one of the approximate forms of the hypersonic inviscid flow relations. Later we will show for the particular cases of a flat plate or a $\frac{3}{4}$ power body that to the lowest order of approximation ($M_\infty \to \infty$), exact matching similar solutions can be obtained in both the external inviscid and internal viscous fields. These solutions are just the inviscid similar solution of Section 2.6, sometimes referred to as a blast wave solution, and the hypersonic similar solution for the viscous field of Section 8.3. We should note that these similar solutions are not general ones for the interaction problem and apply only to the zeroth-order strong interaction result and to particular bodies. On the other hand, by using an approximate inviscid flow relation of the form $p(\theta)$ a very general scheme is developed, which can in principle be employed for studying the strong pressure interaction on arbitrary bodies with arbitrary free stream Mach numbers.

To analyze the strong pressure interaction we use again the tangent-wedge approximation, following the method given by Lees and Probstein [2]. In order to simplify the presentation, we shall consider first only two-dimensional bodies with a linear viscosity-temperature law. It is to be emphasized that none of these restrictions is essential. Later we shall illustrate how they can be removed.

For the strong pressure interaction over an inclined flat plate or wedge, to any order higher than zero the geometric flow inclination $\theta_b$ cannot be neglected in comparison with the induced flow deflection $d\delta^*/dx$. This therefore suggests that the oblique shock relation (7.3.1) be expanded in inverse powers of $M_\infty \theta$. Carrying out the expansion, the following form of the tangent-wedge approximation is obtained:

$$(9.3.2a) \qquad \frac{p}{p_\infty} = \frac{\gamma(\gamma + 1)}{2} K^2 + \frac{3\gamma + 1}{\gamma + 1} - \frac{8\gamma}{(\gamma + 1)^3} K^{-2} + O(K^{-4}),$$

or

$$(9.3.2b) \qquad \frac{p}{p_\infty} = \frac{\gamma(\gamma + 1)}{2}\left(M_\infty \frac{d\delta^*}{dx}\right)^2\left(1 + \frac{\theta_b}{d\delta^*/dx}\right)^2 + \frac{3\gamma + 1}{\gamma + 1}$$

$$- \frac{8\gamma}{(\gamma + 1)^3}\left(M_\infty \frac{d\delta^*}{dx}\right)^{-2}\left(1 + \frac{\theta_b}{d\delta^*/dx}\right)^{-2} + O\left[\left(M_\infty \frac{d\delta^*}{dx}\right)^{-4}\right].$$

The external flow relation was expressed in this form by Lees [2].

As shown in (9.1.15) and (9.1.16), for the flat plate at zero angle of attack with $\gamma - 1$ not small, $p/p_\infty \sim \bar\chi$ and $M_\infty d\delta^*/dx \sim \bar\chi^{1/2}$, with $\bar\chi \gg 1$. In the case of the wedge, this suggests the generating parameter

$$(9.3.3) \qquad \frac{\theta_b}{d\delta^*/dx} \sim \frac{K_b}{\bar\chi^{1/2}},$$

where $K_b = M_\infty \theta_b$ as before. The static pressure along the outer edge of the boundary layer (equal to the surface pressure) is then represented by an asymptotic series of the form

$$(9.3.4) \qquad \frac{p}{p_\infty} = p_0 \bar\chi \left[ 1 + \frac{p_1 K_b}{\bar\chi^{1/2}} + \frac{p_2 + p_3 K_b^2}{\bar\chi} + O(\bar\chi^{-3/2}) \right].$$

The subscript 0 here does not refer to stagnation conditions. When $K_b = 0$, as for the flat plate at zero incidence, (9.3.4) reduces to

$$(9.3.5) \qquad \frac{p}{p_\infty} = p_0 \bar\chi + p_2 + O(\bar\chi^{-1}).$$

The boundary layer displacement thickness, just as the pressure, can be expressed as an asymptotic series of the form

$$(9.3.6) \qquad \frac{\delta^*}{x} = \delta_0 \frac{\bar\chi^{1/2}}{M_\infty} \left[ 1 + \frac{\delta_1 K_b}{\bar\chi^{1/2}} + \frac{\delta_2 + \delta_3 K_b^2}{\bar\chi} + O(\bar\chi^{-3/2}) \right],$$

where the constants $\delta_m$ are connected with the $p_m$ of (9.3.4). By calculating $d\delta^*/dx$ from (9.3.6), substituting the results into (9.3.2), and equating the pressure to the series expansion given by (9.3.4), we find that

$$(9.3.7a) \qquad p_0 = \tfrac{9}{32} \gamma(\gamma + 1)\delta_0^2,$$

$$(9.3.7b) \qquad p_1 = \frac{8}{3}\left(\delta_1 + \frac{1}{\delta_0}\right),$$

$$(9.3.7c) \qquad p_2 = \tfrac{10}{3}\delta_2 + \frac{32}{9}\frac{(3\gamma + 1)}{\gamma(\gamma + 1)^2}\frac{1}{\delta_0^2},$$

$$(9.3.7d) \qquad p_3 = \tfrac{10}{3}\delta_3 + \frac{16}{9}\left(\delta_1 + \frac{1}{\delta_0}\right)^2.$$

Thus only one set of independent constants exists, and these constants are to be determined from the solutions of the boundary layer equations.

For the boundary layer, we use the results of Section 8.3 for similar hypersonic solutions, with $p \propto x^n$ from (8.3.31). For the lowest-order strong interaction solution, $n = -\tfrac{1}{2}$ and $\delta^* \propto x^{3/4}$. If we had a pressure variation following (8.3.31) with a general value of $n$, the similar hypersonic boundary layer solution would yield

$$(9.3.8) \qquad \delta^* \propto x^{1/2}p^{-1/2} \propto x^{(1-n)/2}.$$

We now consider that the equivalent body is a power-law body for which a similar inviscid solution of the type treated in Section 2.6 applies. With this assumption we must have

$$(9.3.9) \qquad y_b + \delta^* \propto x^k \propto x^{(2+n)/2}.$$

In order that we may have a consistent solution both (9.3.8) and (9.3.9) must hold and $\delta^* \propto x^{3/2-k}$. If $y_b = 0$ and the body is a flat plate, consistency is obtained with $k = \frac{3}{4}$ and $n = -\frac{1}{2}$ in the lowest-order strong interaction solution. Consistency is also obtained with $y_b \propto x^{3/4}$, with a three-quarter power body. If $k$ is to be greater than $\frac{3}{4}$, $\delta^*$ must be larger than $y_b + \delta^*$ if $x$ is sufficiently small, and $y_b$ must there be negative. With this possibility rejected, we see that the boundary layer cannot have an initial behavior corresponding to $k > \frac{3}{4}$. If $k$ is to be less than $\frac{3}{4}$, $\delta^*$ must be small compared with $y_b$ for sufficiently small $x$, and the initial interaction may be considered to be of the weak type. Such a weak interaction is not of the type treated in the previous section but is of the blunt-nosed type to be discussed in Section 9.5. In this case we must keep in mind the difficulties discussed in Section 2.6 concerning the initiation of similar solutions with $k$ close to the constant-energy solution value ($k = \frac{2}{3}$ in two-dimensional flow). This discussion distinguished the hot core of the idealized similar inviscid solution from the cool core of the steady solution on a blunt body. This distinction affects principally the pressure distribution very near the nose. Thus, though a complete similar solution with $k < \frac{3}{4}$ may be considered and may be of interest, we should recognize that it has certain inherent difficulties associated with it.

The case $k = \frac{3}{4}$ with $n = -\frac{1}{2}$ is clearly the case of primary importance in the strong interaction problem, and we shall consider only this case. The fact that a complete similar solution was available for the two-dimensional flat plate was recognized by Stewartson [2 ; 3], who gave numerical results based on a momentum integral calculation of the boundary layer. Stewartson's results for the similar inviscid solution with $k = \frac{3}{4}$ are the only numerical ones available to the authors, and give pressures on the body somewhat higher than those given by the tangent-wedge approximation for $\gamma = \frac{7}{5}$ and $\frac{5}{3}$. Stewartson obtains for the first coefficient in (9.3.2) the value 1.987 in place of 1.680 (tangent-wedge) for $\gamma = \frac{7}{5}$ and the value 2.947 in place of 2.222 (tangent-wedge) for $\gamma = \frac{5}{3}$. Stewartson's numerical results for these coefficients have been checked by Oguchi [1]. We follow here the less accurate course of continuing to use the tangent-wedge approximation. As long as it is not too greatly in error, the tangent-wedge approximation is preferable because of the unified approach it offers for the general interaction problem. The leading term for the pressure in the strong interaction solution which we present for $\gamma = 1.4$ may be easily changed to conform with Stewartson's similar inviscid solution by multiplying by $(1.987/1.680)^{1/2} = 1.088$.

For the similar boundary layer we require solutions of (8.3.28) and (8.3.33) with the Falkner-Skan parameter of (8.3.34) given by

$$(9.3.10) \qquad\qquad \beta = \frac{\gamma - 1}{\gamma}$$

as was noted by Lees [1]. For $Le = 1$ and $Pr = 1$ a number of these solutions have been calculated and are discussed in Section 8.3. From the treatment of Section 8.3 it is clear that the strong interaction similar solutions are not necessarily restricted to linear viscosity-temperature relations or to $Le = 1$.

From the results we have obtained it would seem logical to seek analytic solutions of the boundary layer equations in the form

$$(9.3.11) \qquad \frac{u(x, y)}{u_\delta(x)} = \frac{\partial f}{\partial \eta} = u_0(\eta) + \frac{K_b u_1(\eta)}{\bar\chi^{1/2}} + \frac{u_2(\eta) + K_b^2 u_3(\eta)}{\bar\chi} + \dots,$$

and

$$(9.3.12) \qquad \frac{H(x, y)}{H_\delta} = g = g_0(\eta) + \frac{K_b g_1(\eta)}{\bar\chi^{1/2}} + \frac{g_2(\eta) + K_b^2 g_3(\eta)}{\bar\chi} + \dots.$$

Here the zeroth-order differential equations for $u_0$ and $g_0$ are simply (8.3.28) with $Le = 1$ and (8.3.33) with $\beta = (\gamma - 1)/\gamma$ and $u_\delta^2/H_\delta = 2$. The boundary conditions on these equations are the familiar ones already discussed in Section 8.3.

By inserting the series (9.3.4), (9.3.11), and (9.3.12) into the complete boundary layer equations, the differential equations governing the functions $u_m(\eta)$ and $g_m(\eta)$ may be found to any desired order. It turns out that the $u_m$'s and $g_m$'s satisfy simultaneous linear second-order differential equations with coefficients depending only on the previous terms in the expansion. For all $m \geqslant 1$, the boundary conditions are that $u_m(\eta)$ and $g_m(\eta)$ are zero both at the surface and the edge of the viscous layer.

Once the solutions $u_m(\eta)$ and $g_m(\eta)$ to the differential equations are obtained, the physical distance normal to the surface can be computed by means of a single quadrature. Since the solutions contain the constants $p_m$ (or $\delta_m$), the $\delta_m$'s are determined from the expression for $\delta^*$ by means of a series of purely algebraic relations. For example, from (8.2.9), (8.2.10), and

(9.3.4) to (9.3.7), we can show after considerable algebraic manipulation that

$$(9.3.13) \quad \delta_0^2 = \frac{4(\gamma-1)}{3\sqrt{\gamma(\gamma+1)}} \left[ \sqrt{2} \int_0^\infty (g_0 - u_0^2) d\eta \right] = \frac{4(\gamma-1)}{3\sqrt{\gamma(\gamma+1)}} G(g_b, Pr, \beta),$$

and

$$(9.3.14) \quad \delta_1 = \sqrt{2} \int_0^\infty \left[ g_1 - \left(1 + \frac{g_0}{u_0^2}\right) u_0 u_1 \right] d\eta - p_1 G(g_b, Pr, \beta).$$

Here we have employed the density relation (8.3.29) with $H_\delta/h_\delta \approx \frac{1}{2}(\gamma-1)M_\delta^2$, and have taken $u_0$ to be small compared to $\frac{1}{2}(\gamma-1)M_\delta^2 u_0^2$ in the integrand of (9.3.13), in which case we have in effect $\delta^* \approx \delta$ (see (8.4.1) and (8.4.2)). By using (9.3.7), the corresponding relations for the $p_m$'s can also be found.

With the skin friction coefficient defined by

$$(9.3.15) \qquad C_{f_\infty} = \frac{2}{\rho_\infty U^2} \left(\mu \frac{\partial u}{\partial y}\right)_b$$

we can show that

$$(9.3.16) \quad C_{f_\infty} = \sqrt{\frac{p^{(0)}}{p_\infty}} \sqrt{\frac{C_\infty}{Re_{x_\infty}}} (u_0')_b \left[1 + \frac{C_{f_1} K_b}{\bar{\chi}^{1/2}} + \frac{C_{f_2} + C_{f_3} K_b^2}{\bar{\chi}} + O(\bar{\chi}^{-3/2})\right],$$

where

$$(9.3.17) \qquad \sqrt{\frac{p^{(0)}}{p_\infty}} = \sqrt{p_0 \bar{\chi}} = \tfrac{3}{8}\delta_0 \sqrt{2\gamma(\gamma+1)}\ \bar{\chi}^{1/2}.$$

The coefficients $C_{f_m}$ will involve the solutions to the differential equations for $u_m$. To first order, for example,

$$(9.3.18) \qquad C_{f_1} = \left(\frac{u_1 u_0' + u_0 u_1'}{u_0 u_1'}\right)_b + p_1.$$

Similarly for constant $c_p$ the local Stanton number (8.3.12) defined by

$$(9.3.19) \qquad St_\infty = \frac{-\dot{q}}{\rho_\infty U c_p (T_r - T_b)}$$

may be written as

$$(9.3.20) \qquad St_\infty = \frac{C_{f_\infty}}{2Pr} \frac{(\partial g/\partial \eta)_b}{(\partial u/\partial \eta)_b} \frac{1}{h_r/H_\delta - g_b},$$

where $h_r/H_\delta = 1$ for $Pr = 1$.

The important point to be observed from this formulation is that the major effect of the pressure in the strong interaction region is to contract the scale of distance normal to the surface by a factor proportional to $p^{1/2}$

(cf. (9.3.8)), and thereby to increase the local skin friction and heat transfer coefficients by the same factor. Furthermore, unlike the weak interaction solution, we see that the expression for the local skin friction coefficient in the strong interaction region is integrable and the total skin friction drag is finite.

TABLE 9–2

*Values of $G$, $p_0$, $\delta_0$, $C_{f_0}$, and $St_0$ for $\rho\mu = constant$, $\gamma = 1.4$ ($\beta = 0.286$), $Pr = 1$*
*(Li and Nagamatsu [3])*

| $g_b$ | $G$ | $p_0$ | $\delta_0$ | $C_{f_0}$ | $St_0$ |
|---|---|---|---|---|---|
| 0 | 0.540 | 0.149 | 0.397 | 0.208 | 0.0788 |
| 0.2 | 0.842 | 0.232 | 0.495 | 0.279 | — |
| 0.6 | 1.37 | 0.377 | 0.632 | 0.412 | 0.155 |
| 1.0 | 1.87 | 0.514 | 0.738 | 0.549 | 0.187 |

To summarize our preceding results, we have to zeroth order for the wedge or flat plate

$$(9.3.21) \qquad \frac{p^{(0)}}{p_\infty} = \tfrac{9}{32}\gamma(\gamma + 1)\delta_0^2\bar{\chi} = p_0\bar{\chi},$$

$$(9.3.22) \qquad M_\infty \frac{\delta^{(0)}}{x} \approx M_\infty \frac{\delta^{*(0)}}{x} = \delta_0\bar{\chi}^{1/2},$$

$$(9.3.23) \qquad C_{f_\infty}^{(0)} \sqrt{\frac{Re_{x_\infty}}{C_\infty}} = \tfrac{3}{8}\,\delta_0\sqrt{2\gamma(\gamma+1)}(u_0')_b\bar{\chi}^{1/2} = C_{f_0}\bar{\chi}^{1/2},$$

$$(9.3.24) \qquad St_\infty^{(0)} = \frac{3}{16}\frac{\delta_0\sqrt{2\gamma(\gamma+1)}}{(h_r/H_\delta - g_b)Pr}\frac{(g_0')_b}{(u_0')_b}\bar{\chi}^{1/2} = St_0\bar{\chi}^{1/2}.$$

Here the constant $\delta_0$ defined by (9.3.13) and the velocity and enthalpy gradients at the wall depend on $\gamma$ through the pressure gradient parameter $\beta$.

The function $G(g_b, Pr, \beta)$ defined in (9.3.13) which determines $\delta_0$ has been calculated by Li and Nagamatsu [3] from their similar solutions (Li and Nagamatsu [2]) for $Pr = 1$ and $\rho\mu = constant$. Their results are presented in Tables 9–2 and 9–3, together with values for the corresponding constants $p_0$, $\delta_0$, $C_{f_0}$, and $St_0$. A couple of minor errors of Li and Nagamatsu in the values of $St_0$ have been corrected here. There appear to remain certain inconsistencies in their data. For example, for $\beta = 0.286$ and $g_b = 1$ we find from curves of the dimensionless displacement and momentum thicknesses calculated by Pretsch [1] for the classical Falkner-Skan profiles that $G = 1.72$ instead of 1.87. These inconsistencies may arise from the fact that Li and Nagamatsu used an analogue computer for their basic boundary layer calculations. Additional calculations would be desirable.

From the results presented in Tables 9–2 and 9–3 it can be seen that, just as in the weak interaction case, cooling of the surface causes a marked

TABLE 9–3

Values of $G$, $p_0$, $\delta_0$, $C_{f_0}$, and $St_0$ for $\rho\mu = constant$, $\gamma = 1.667$ ($\beta = 0.400$), $Pr = 1$
(Li and Nagamatsu [3])

| $g_b$ | $G$ | $p_0$ | $\delta_0$ | $C_{f_0}$ | $St_0$ |
|-------|-------|-------|-------|-------|-------|
| 0     | 0.496 | 0.261 | 0.457 | 0.287 | 0.125 |
| 0.2   | 0.764 | 0.403 | 0.568 | 0.395 | —     |
| 0.6   | 1.25  | 0.696 | 0.726 | 0.602 | 0.210 |
| 1.0   | 1.75  | 0.921 | 0.858 | 0.820 | 0.252 |
| 2.0   | 2.86  | 1.51  | 1.10  | 1.36  | 0.342 |

reduction of all the interaction effects. The primary effect of the cooling is to thin the boundary layer and hence to reduce the induced pressure. The skin friction and the heat transfer rates are reduced because of the effect of the decreased wall temperature on $\mu$. Approximate solutions for other values of the Prandtl number can be obtained quite easily for the case when the surface temperature is much lower than the equilibrium temperature. For this case, as we observed in Section 8.4, the direct effect of the pressure gradient is relatively small and we can obtain a good approximation to the solution by dropping the pressure gradient term in the momentum equation. If we do this, $u_0(\eta)$ satisfies the Blasius equation for any value of the Prandtl number if $N = 1$, and the solution $g_0(\eta)$ is identical to that found by Crocco [2]. This approximation was first used by Lees [1] for the strong interaction problem.

Except for an insulated flat plate at zero angle of attack with $Pr = 1$, calculations beyond the zeroth order have so far not been carried out. For the insulated flat plate problem, Nagakura and Naruse [1] and Lees [3] have calculated the constant $p_2$ in (9.3.5) by a momentum-integral method. The result of Nagakura and Naruse for $\gamma = 1.4$ has been checked and is believed to be the more accurate of the two calculations. They obtain the result $p_2 = 0.759$. Therefore for zero heat transfer with $Pr = 1$ and $\gamma = 1.4$, the strong interaction induced pressure on an insulated flat plate becomes

$$(9.3.25) \qquad \frac{p}{p_\infty} = 0.514\bar{\chi} + 0.759 + O(\bar{\chi}^{-1}),$$

based on the tangent-wedge approximation.

On Fig. 9–4 we have plotted the strong interaction induced pressure relation given by (9.3.25). Also shown are the experimental data of Bertram for a flat plate. These data are from the same tests discussed previously in connection with the weak interaction problem, except that they are shown for higher values of $\bar{\chi}$. As can be seen, the agreement between theory and

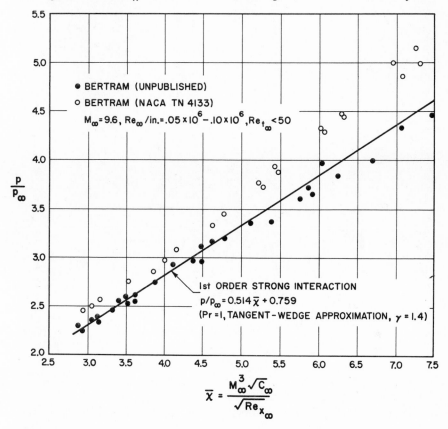

$$\bar{\chi} = \frac{M_\infty^3 \sqrt{C_\infty}}{\sqrt{Re_{x_\infty}}}$$

Fig. 9–4. Strong interaction induced pressure on an insulated flat plate in air.

experiment is well within the scatter of the experimental data. A more striking illustration of how the asymptotic results represented by the strong and weak interaction solutions check with experiment is shown in Fig. 9–5. Here we have plotted results of both the first-order strong ($Pr = 1$, tangent-wedge approximation) and the second-order weak ($Pr = 0.725$) interaction theories. We have also taken the liberty of drawing in an extrapolated second-order strong interaction curve which includes a contribution of order

$\bar{\chi}^{-1}$ in the pressure according to (9.3.25). This curve is only a sample to indicate the effect of such an additional term, the magnitude of which has not been calculated. Between the curves corresponding to the two asymptotic theories is an intermediate or transition region, which would appear from Fig. 9–5 to be reasonably narrow. We shall reserve further discussion

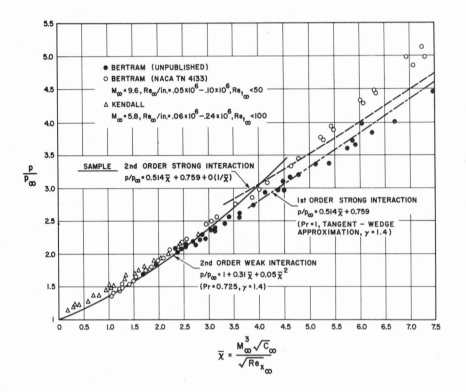

Fig. 9–5. Composite of weak interaction and strong interaction pressure results on an insulated flat plate in air.

of this intermediate region for the following section, in which a different approach is presented.

Equations (9.3.7a) and (9.3.13) are the equations which yield the desired solution for the flat plate. For a $\frac{3}{4}$ power body these equations are changed, with $p_0$ and $\delta_0$ still defined as in (9.3.4) and (9.3.6). In place of (9.3.7a) we must have, from (9.3.2b), the relation

$$(9.3.26) \qquad p_0 = \tfrac{9}{32}\gamma(\gamma+1)\delta_0^2\left(1+\frac{y_b}{\delta^*}\right)^2.$$

The relation we need in place of (9.3.13) is

$$(9.3.27) \qquad \delta_0^2 = \frac{4(\gamma - 1)}{3\sqrt{\gamma(\gamma + 1)}} \frac{G(g_b, Pr, \beta)}{1 + y_b/\delta^*} .$$

The form of (9.3.27) is evident from (9.3.13) when we note that $\delta_0$ is proportional to $p_0^{-1/2}$. The additional parameter $y_b/\delta^*$ which appears in (9.3.26) and (9.3.27) is not known a priori in a physical problem. We must use the relation derivable from (9.3.6) that

$$(9.3.28) \qquad \delta_0 \left( \frac{y_b}{\delta^*} \right) = \frac{M_\infty}{\bar{\chi}^{1/2}} \frac{y_b}{x} .$$

The quantity on the right hand side of (9.3.28) is a constant which is known for a given $\frac{3}{4}$ power body in a given flow. The solution is obtained by combining (9.3.27) and (9.3.28) into

$$(9.3.29) \qquad \delta_0^2 + \left( \frac{M_\infty}{\bar{\chi}^{1/2}} \frac{y_b}{x} \right) \delta_0 - \frac{4(\gamma - 1)}{3\sqrt{\gamma(\gamma + 1)}} G = 0,$$

which has one positive root for $\delta_0$. If $y_b/\delta^*$ is large, we may express the pressure in the more convenient form

$$(9.3.30) \qquad \frac{p}{p_\infty} = \frac{9\gamma(\gamma + 1)}{32} M_\infty^2 \left( \frac{y_b}{x} \right)^2 \left( 1 + \frac{\delta^*}{y_b} \right)^2 ,$$

in which the interaction effect is evident.

For axisymmetric flow we may use the tangent-cone approximation for interaction problems on bodies of revolution, in a manner directly analogous to that in which the tangent-wedge approximation may be used for two-dimensional bodies. Here we shall not use the tangent-cone approximation, but shall only look at the interaction solutions obtainable from the similar inviscid solutions. For the similar inviscid solutions of Section 2.6, the pressure on the body is expressible in the form

$$(9.3.31) \qquad \frac{p_b}{p_\infty} = \Pi(\gamma, k) M_\infty^2 \left( \frac{dr_b}{dx} \right)^2$$

for a body of revolution, or in a similar form with $y_b$ in place of $r_b$ for a two-dimensional body.

An analysis based on the Mangler transformation shows that while $p$ is still proportional to $x^{-1/2}$ and $k = \frac{3}{4}$ for a completely similar axisymmetric solution, $p$ is proportional to $\bar{x}^{-1/5}$ where $\bar{x}$ is defined in (8.3.32). The quantity $\beta$ from (8.3.34) is now

$$(9.3.32) \qquad \beta = \frac{\gamma - 1}{4\gamma} .$$

Since this quantity is quite small we may use results for $\beta = 0$ without great error, particularly if the wall is cooled. Calculations analogous to those we have given for the two-dimensional case may be made for a $\frac{3}{4}$ power body of revolution provided $\delta^*/r_b$ is sufficiently small.

The requirement that $\delta^*/r_b$ be sufficiently small is necessary in order that we may neglect the transverse curvature effect and use the two-dimensional boundary layer results through the Mangler transformation. Probstein and Elliott [1] and Yasuhara [2] have pointed out that a completely similar solution is still obtained on a $\frac{3}{4}$ power body of revolution with the transverse curvature effect included, and Yasuhara presented numerical solutions for the interaction problem with the transverse curvature effect for the case $\gamma = 1.4$, $Pr = 1$, $g_b = 1$. In general, the transverse curvature effect has an important influence on the skin friction and the heat transfer, but has a weak effect on the induced pressure.

For axisymmetric flow the function $\Pi(\gamma, \frac{3}{4})$ appearing in (9.3.31) has been calculated by Grodzovskii [1] and Yasuhara [1] for $\gamma = 1.4$ and by Kubota [1] for a range of $\gamma$ from 1 to $\frac{5}{3}$. For $\gamma = 1.4$ Grodzovskii and Kubota obtain $\Pi = 1.274$ while Yasuhara obtains $\Pi = 1.296$.

In applying the similar boundary layer and similar inviscid solution results to the problem of determining the flow on a $\frac{3}{4}$ power body of revolution we may use the approach given for the two-dimensional body. The quantity $\frac{1}{2}\gamma(\gamma + 1)$ is replaced by $\Pi$, and $\gamma - 1$ is replaced by $\frac{1}{2}(\gamma - 1)$. We obtain in place of (9.3.27)

$$(9.3.33) \qquad \delta_0^2 = \frac{(\gamma - 1)\sqrt{2}}{3\sqrt{\Pi}} \frac{G(g_b, Pr, \beta)}{1 + r_b/\delta^*},$$

and in place of (9.3.28)

$$(9.3.34) \qquad \delta_0\left(\frac{r_b}{\delta^*}\right) = \frac{M_\infty}{\bar{\chi}^{1/2}} \frac{r_b}{x}.$$

The quantity $\delta_0$ is solved from a quadratic of the form of (9.3.29). The pressure may be expressed in a form analogous to (9.3.26),

$$(9.3.35) \qquad p_0 = \tfrac{9}{16}\Pi\delta_0^2\left(1 + \frac{r_b}{\delta^*}\right)^2,$$

or in the form

$$(9.3.36) \qquad \frac{p}{p_\infty} = \tfrac{9}{16}\Pi M_\infty^2\left(\frac{r_b}{x}\right)^2\left(1 + \frac{\delta^*}{r_b}\right)^2$$

analogous to (9.3.30). Since $\delta^*/r_b$ must be sufficiently small if the transverse curvature effect is to be neglected, the latter form is preferable.

In the special case of an insulated surface ($g_b = 1$) and $Pr = 1$ the Busemann integral (8.3.2) is available, as are the classical Falkner-Skan solutions. From the calculations of Pretsch [1] for the dimensionless displacement and momentum thicknesses we obtain with $\beta = .0715$ $(\gamma = 1.4)$ the result $G = 2.17$. We may calculate $\delta_0(1 + r_b/\delta^*)^{1/2} = 0.60$ and $p_0(1 + r_b/\delta^*)^{-1} = 0.26$ from (9.3.33) and (9.3.35), and obtain the results

$$(9.3.37) \qquad \frac{p}{p_\infty} = 0.26\left(1 + \frac{r_b}{\delta^*}\right)\bar{\chi},$$

$$(9.3.38) \qquad M_\infty \frac{\delta^*}{x} = \frac{0.60\bar{\chi}^{1/2}}{(1 + r_b/\delta^*)^{1/2}}$$

from (9.3.4) and (9.3.6). The transverse curvature effect is not included in these results. A comparison of the results of (9.3.37) and (9.3.38) with the corresponding numerical results of Yasuhara [2] which include the transverse curvature effect shows but little difference.

## 4. Integral and inverse methods

Up to this point we have discussed only the asymptotic behavior of the interacting boundary layer, in the sense that we have considered the limiting regimes of weak and strong pressure interactions. An approximate solution, such as that given by an integral technique, can be constructed in which a continuous transition is achieved from the strong to the weak pressure interaction region. The difficulty with such a scheme is that in general it requires solving simultaneously the integrated momentum and energy equations and the inviscid flow relation describing the pressure along the curve $y = \delta^*(x)$.

The only integral solutions which have so far been carried out employ the Kármán-Pohlhausen technique, with the exception of a method given by Ferrari [2]. Furthermore, all these solutions have been restricted to an insulated surface with $Pr = 1$, with a linear viscosity-temperature relation. Under these conditions the energy integral is given exactly by the Busemann integral (8.3.2) and the energy equation can be eliminated. This permits a simultaneous solution of the inviscid flow relation, which can be expressed in the form $p/p_\infty = f(d\delta^*/dx)$, and the momentum equation, which involves $\delta^*$, $p/p_\infty$, and their derivatives with respect to $x$.

Nagakura and Naruse [1] have shown for the case of two-dimensional flow over an insulated surface with $\mu \propto T$ and $Pr = 1$, that with $M_\infty^2 \gg 1$ the momentum-integral equation can be integrated approximately to give

$$(9.4.1) \qquad \frac{d\delta^*}{dx} = \frac{d}{dx}\left[\frac{C_\infty \mu_\infty M_\infty^4}{\rho_\infty U} a\left(\frac{p}{p_\infty}\right)^{-b} \int_{x_0} \left(\frac{p}{p_\infty}\right)^{b-1} dx + \text{constant}\right]^{1/2}.$$

Here $a$ and $b$ are constants given by

$$(9.4.2) \qquad a = 2 - 2.43\frac{\gamma - 1}{\gamma}; \qquad b = 1.455(\gamma - 1)^2.$$

By employing the tangent-wedge relation (7.3.1) with the effective body angle $\theta_b + d\delta^*/dx$, we obtain two simultaneous relations to solve for $\delta^*$ and $p/p_\infty$. For the case of the flat plate ($\theta_b = 0$), Nagakaru and Naruse have carried out such a simultaneous solution numerically for $\gamma = 1.4$ and determined the induced pressure distribution. The results they obtain check approximately with those given for the weak and strong interaction regions and provide a continuous passage from one region to the other.

Other direct integral solutions are those of Stewartson [2] for the strong interaction over a flat plate, and Yasuhara [1], for the strong interaction over an axisymmetric $\frac{3}{4}$ power body. In both these cases the inviscid pressure relation used was that given by the similar inviscid solution. For two-dimensional flow in the weak interaction region Ferrari [2] has also presented an integral scheme. These authors all used the simplicity afforded by the Busemann integral $(Pr = 1)$, and a linear viscosity-temperature relation.

Another method for obtaining a solution in which a continuous transition is achieved from the strong to the weak pressure interaction region is the inverse method which determines the body shape associated with a prescribed pressure field. Two approaches to this problem have been given: one by Ferrari [2] for the weak interaction region alone, and the other by Li [3] following a suggestion of H. S. Tsien (see Lees and Probstein [2]) which is valid over the entire range. In our discussion we will present a scheme which is based on the tangent-wedge approximation and the approximate boundary layer solutions given by the local similarity concept of Section 8.4.

According to the inverse method, an arbitrary pressure distribution $p(x)/p_\infty$ is specified along the edge of the boundary layer; the first step in the problem is to determine the equivalent effective body of local slope $\theta = d(y_b + \delta^*)/dx$ associated with this pressure. If the inviscid pressure-flow deflection relation is represented for simplicity by the uncorrected tangent-wedge approximation with constant $\gamma$, then it is possible to solve directly for $dy_b/dx$ as a function of $p/p_\infty$ and $d\delta^*/dx$:

$$(9.4.3) \quad \frac{dy_b}{dx} = \frac{1}{M_\infty}\left(\frac{p}{p_\infty} - 1\right)\left[\frac{\gamma(\gamma+1)}{2}\frac{p}{p_\infty} + \frac{\gamma(\gamma-1)}{2}\right]^{-1/2} - \frac{d\delta^*}{dx}.$$

From the above relation it is evident that the required body shape can be determined if $\delta^*(x)$ can be related to the prescribed pressure distribution.

The important point to recognize is that in the direct problem described previously ($y_b$ given) it is necessary to solve for $p$ and $\delta^*$ simultaneously, whereas in the inverse problem ($p$ given) $\delta^*$ is obtained directly from one of the approximate boundary layer approaches given in Sections 8.4 and 8.5, and (9.4.3) is used to compute $y_b$. In this point lies the fundamental simplification of the inverse method.

Such a scheme has the desired character of giving a result which provides a smooth transition between the strong and weak interaction regions, as long as a realistic pressure function is chosen to represent the external flow field. With the pressure distribution specified the displacement thickness may be calculated using (8.4.2). As an example, we note that with local similarity assumed the relation for the displacement thickness takes the form

$$(9.4.4) \qquad \delta^* = \frac{\gamma - 1}{2} M_\delta^2 \left[ \left( \frac{\mu C}{\rho u} \right)_\delta \frac{\int_0^{} (p/p_\infty) dx}{p/p_\infty} \right]^{1/2} G(g_b, Pr, \beta)$$

with $\beta$ determined locally. If $p$ is taken to be proportional to $x^{-1/2}$ in the nose region our strong interaction solution on a $\frac{3}{4}$ power body is obtained, with the flat plate as a special case. With the pressure too low bodies of negative slope will be obtained. Li [3] has calculated various examples using an approximate momentum-integral approach to determine the displacement thickness.

With the local similarity approach and with the pressure distribution given we can explicitly integrate (9.4.4), employing the similarity solution values for $G(g_b, Pr, \beta)$. As we have previously noted, the quantity $G$ for $Pr = 1$ is given for two values of $\beta$ in Tables 9–2 and 9–3, and can be calculated under different conditions from the other similarity solutions discussed in Section 8.3. With $\delta^*$ known, it is then a simple matter to compute the body shape directly from (9.4.3)

## 5. Bluntness induced interactions on slender bodies

In our presentation of viscous interactions we have so far tacitly assumed that the leading edge or nose of the body with which we were dealing was infinitely sharp. In practical design for flight at hypersonic speeds, slender bodies must in general be blunt-nosed to some extent in order to solve the heating problem. The question naturally arises as to the relative importance of the inviscid pressure field associated with a blunt leading edge or nose and the self induced pressure field generated by the boundary layer growth. When the Reynolds number based on the leading edge thickness or nose diameter is no longer sufficiently small, the inviscid pressure field associated with the blunt leading edge or nose is dominant over the forward portion of the body, and this field determines the initial growth of the boundary layer. In spite of this fact, sufficiently far downstream of the nose viscous interaction phenomena again come into play.

In order to illustrate the relative magnitudes of these two effects we compare the pressure on a two-dimensional blunt-nosed slender body in an inviscid flow with that induced on a flat plate in viscous flow with strong interaction. We take $l$ to be a measure of the distance along both bodies for which the pressures are of the same magnitudes. The pressure on a blunt-nosed body may be estimated on the basis of the constant-energy solution of Section 2.6. This is done by equating the energy $E$ of (2.6.15) with the nose drag $\rho_\infty U^2 t$, using the relation (2.6.4) defining the constant $B$ with $\lambda = \lambda_s$, and applying (2.6.3c) for the pressure. The pressure on the flat plate in the viscous flow is given by (9.3.21) as of the order of $p_\infty \bar{\chi}$. Equating these pressures on an order-of-magnitude basis yields

$$(9.5.1) \qquad p \sim \frac{\rho_\infty U^2}{M_\infty^2} \frac{M_\infty^3 \sqrt{C_\infty}}{\sqrt{Re_{l_\infty}}} \sim \rho_\infty \left[ \frac{\rho_\infty U^2 t}{\rho_\infty l/U} \right]^{2/3}.$$

For the ratio $l/t$ we obtain the result

$$(9.5.2) \qquad \frac{l}{t} \sim \left( \frac{Re_{t_\infty}}{M_\infty^2 C_\infty} \right)^3,$$

or for $Re_{t_\infty}$ in terms of $\bar{\chi}$ for $x = l$,

$$(9.5.3) \qquad Re_{t_\infty} \sim \frac{M_\infty^3 C_\infty}{\bar{\chi}^{1/2}}.$$

Essentially the same result was obtained by Lees and Kubota [1] following a different argument. We have implicitly assumed in the foregoing comparison that $\epsilon$ is not small; as was pointed out in Section 2.6 the constant-energy solution is not applicable if $\gamma - 1$ and hence $\epsilon$ are very small.

We infer that the inviscid surface pressures generated by a blunt nose on a body in a viscous flow are larger than the induced pressures produced by the boundary layer growth over a distance from the nose which is of the order of magnitude $l$. With the extent of the strong interaction region on the flat plate defined approximately by $\bar{\chi} = 4$ (cf. Fig. 9–5), we note that if $Re_{t_\infty}$ is of the order of $M_\infty^3$ there can be no such entity as a strong interaction region for a blunt-nosed body in a viscous flow. Only if $Re_{t_\infty}$ is very much less than $M_\infty^3$ can we expect a fully developed strong interaction region to be observable without a marked effect of the blunt nose. In the experiments of Hammitt and Bogdonoff [1] and Hammitt, Vas, and Bogdonoff [1] in helium the quantity $Re_{t_\infty}/M_\infty^3$ was of the order of $\frac{1}{10}$ or larger and the influence of the blunt nose is appreciable. In the experiments of Bertram (unpublished data and [3]) in air the ratio $Re_{t_\infty}/M_\infty^3$ was of the order of $\frac{1}{20}$ or less, and no effect of the blunt nose is discernible. In the experiments of Vas [1] in helium, which covered a wide range of the parameter $Re_{t_\infty}$, a strong effect of $M_\infty$ on the value of $Re_{t_\infty}$ at which viscous effects predominate is evident.

One can similarly deduce for bodies of revolution the result for the distance from the blunt nose at which the pressure due to viscous interaction is comparable with the inviscid pressure on the cylindrical afterportion of a blunted slender body, provided $r_b/\delta^*$ is of the order of one. We use again the constant-energy solution with $k = \frac{1}{2}$ and the nose drag of the order of $\rho_\infty U^2 t^2$, together with the results of Section 9.3. Here $t$ is the diameter of the blunt nose. In place of (9.5.2) we obtain

$$(9.5.4) \qquad \frac{l}{t} \sim \left( \frac{Re_{t_\infty}}{M_\infty^2 C_\infty} \right),$$

or in place of (9.5.3)

$$(9.5.5) \qquad Re_{t_\infty} \sim \frac{M_\infty^4 C_\infty}{\bar{\chi}}.$$

In this case as $Re_{t_\infty}$ increases, the inviscid effect spreads downstream somewhat more slowly than in the two-dimensional case because of the more rapid decay of the inviscid pressure field relative to the viscous induced pressures. Here only if $Re_{t_\infty}$ is very much less than $M_\infty^4$ can we expect a fully developed strong interaction region to be observable without a marked effect of the blunt nose. If $Re_{t_\infty}$ is of the order of $M_\infty^4$ no strong interaction region should be identifiable. This estimate is borne out in part by experiments on blunt-nosed cones carried out by Bertram [2], in which $Re_{t_\infty}/M_\infty^4$ is of the order of 2 or larger and no viscous interaction effect is discernible.

If the inviscid pressure distribution on a blunt-nosed body were known exactly, then one could in principle calculate the boundary layer growth utilizing in first approximation the ordinary boundary layer equations, and in turn determine the induced pressure based on the distribution of displacement thickness obtained. In general such a calculation is very difficult, however, because of the various competing effects which can enter simultaneously. For example, although it is clear that a measure of the viscous interaction effects on a blunt-nosed curved body of revolution is given, say, by the ratio of $d\delta^*/dx$ to $dr_b/dx$ or by $\delta^*/r_b$ (the transverse curvature parameter—see Probstein and Elliott [1]), it is not clear that when this parameter approaches the order of one, the pressure interaction phenomena can be divorced from other interaction phenomena such as vorticity interaction and the effect of transverse curvature.

Although all the effects we have mentioned can be taken into account by a suitable modification of boundary layer theory, it does not appear that under such circumstances simple analytic generalizations can be given regarding the magnitude of the combined interaction effects. Furthermore when all these phenomena enter, the entire question must again be raised regarding the validity of the separation of viscous and inviscid layers, and it may be impossible to distinguish a boundary layer as a distinct identifiable entity (cf. Fig. 1–3 and the discussion of it).

Because of the difficulty of obtaining analytic solutions to the blunt-nosed slender body problem, empirical relations have been suggested for correlating the pressure distribution. For example in Hammitt, Vas, and Bogdonoff [1] and Hammitt and Bogdonoff [1] an attempt is made to correlate data on blunted flat plates in helium on the basis of a relation which is a linear combination of the parameters which result from the pressure interaction theory and the similar solution theory (Section 2.6). These authors assume a pressure relation of the form

$$(9.5.6) \qquad \frac{p}{p_\infty} = 1 + a\bar{\chi} + b\,\frac{M^2_\infty}{(x/t)^{2/3}},$$

with the constants of proportionality determined by experiment. Note that the last term (9.5.6) is of the same form as the expression given in (9.5.1). Creager [1] employed a similar form of the pressure relation and found moderately good correlation of a wide variety of tests on flat plates with blunt leading edges. Because of the empirical nature of this approach, however, we shall not discuss it further.

## 6. Vorticity interactions

One of the basic Prandtl boundary layer assumptions is that the layer is so thin that the structure of the external flow does not affect the structure of the boundary layer except through the external velocity (or pressure) distribution. As we have noted, if the vorticity in the external flow is sufficiently large, it may influence the boundary layer structure even though the layer is relatively thin.

We shall define the vorticity interaction parameter $\Omega$ in terms of quantities defined at the edge of the equivalent body in the equivalent inviscid flow. The vorticity and the velocity at this point are denoted $\zeta_{inv}$ and $u_{inv}$, respectively, with the vorticity positive if the velocity $u$ increases away from the body. The average vorticity in the layer is defined by the ratio of this velocity to a suitable boundary layer thickness. Our considerations of Chapter VIII indicate that for a consistent estimate, the suitable boundary layer thickness must be defined in terms of the Howarth-Dorodnitsyn variable. We shall define this thickness as corresponding to the value $\eta = 1$, where $\eta$ is the variable defined in (8.2.9). Thus we define the vorticity interaction parameter as

$$(9.6.1) \qquad \Omega = \frac{\zeta_{inv}}{\rho_{inv} u_{inv}} \int_0^{\eta=1} \rho \, dy$$

(cf. (9.1.17)). In analyzing boundary layers following the approach of Chapter VIII but with vorticity in the free stream, the subscript $\delta$ should be replaced by the subscript "inv" to indicate the edge of the equivalent body in the inviscid flow.

If we now express the inviscid flow field in terms of $\eta$ we obtain

$$(9.6.2) \qquad f_\eta = \frac{u}{u_{\mathrm{inv}}} = 1 + \Omega\eta + O(\eta^2),$$

in which the term of $O(\eta^2)$ arises from variation in the vorticity with $y$. We shall assume that this term is negligibly small within the region of interest for the boundary layer calculation. This assumption may not be justified in certain special cases, such as a case in which the vorticity is zero at the wall in an inviscid flow but must be taken into account in the free stream. For example, the vorticity in the flow on a blunt two-dimensional cylinder is zero at the wall (cf. Section 4.3) but is nonzero elsewhere.

The basic principle which is used in treating boundary layers with vorticity interaction is that, in comparing the inviscid flow which would exist with no boundary layer present and the inviscid part of the flow with a boundary layer, the relation between velocity and stream function must be kept fixed. The relation between the velocity and the streamline on which it is measured is assumed to be unaffected by the presence of the boundary layer.

In applying this principle to the linear profile of (9.6.2) with the term of $O(\eta^2)$ neglected, we first form the inviscid expression for the reduced stream function $f$

$$(9.6.3) \qquad f = \eta + \tfrac{1}{2}\Omega\eta^2,$$

and eliminate $\eta$ between (9.6.2) and (9.6.3). The result is due to Hayes [5] and is

$$(9.6.4) \qquad f_\eta^2 = 1 + 2\Omega f,$$

and is essentially simply a relation between velocity and stream function. This relation must hold in the inviscid part of the flow with the boundary layer present, and replaces the usual boundary condition $f_\eta = 1$ at the outer edge of the boundary layer.

The boundary condition $f_\eta = 1 + \Omega\eta$ is incorrect, as it neglects the change in the outer velocity field arising from the displacement thickness. An analysis based on the flow around the correct equivalent body would not have this error, but would involve the use of the displacement thickness which is unknown a priori. If the parameter $\Omega$ is small so that the effect of vorticity interaction may be treated as a perturbation, the displacement thickness may be approximated by that for the boundary layer without interaction, as was pointed out by Glauert [1] in disputing the results of Li [1; 2]. The influence of the displacement thickness in the outer boundary condition was also neglected by Mark [2].

Hayes [5] has pointed out that if we seek similar boundary layer solutions including the vorticity interaction, similarity conditions must be imposed on the external vorticity which are, in general, inconsistent with the steady flow conditions on the inviscid external flow. He observed that a similarity solution including the vorticity interaction can be obtained at the stagnation point of a blunt body. For a two-dimensional stagnation point the vorticity is zero at the surface and the parameter $\Omega$ as defined is zero. In the axisymmetric case the vorticity at the wall is finite, however, and does not follow the similarity requirements except in the stagnation region.

According to the approximate constant-density result (4.4.18), the inviscid axisymmetric stagnation point velocity profile is given by

$$(9.6.5) \qquad \frac{uR_s}{Ux} = \sqrt{\tfrac{8}{3}\epsilon}\left[\,1 + \frac{y(1 - \tfrac{8}{3}\epsilon)}{\sqrt{\tfrac{8}{3}\epsilon}\,\epsilon R_s}\right],$$

where $R_s$ is the radius of curvature of the shock wave. If from (8.2.9) we introduce our boundary layer variable $\eta$ evaluated at an axisymmetric stagnation point, we may write $\Omega$ as

$$(9.6.6) \qquad \Omega = \frac{1}{\sqrt{2}\epsilon(\tfrac{8}{3}\epsilon)^{3/4}}\left(\frac{\rho_b}{\rho_{\mathrm{inv}}}\right)\sqrt{\frac{\mu_b}{\rho_b U R_s}}\,(1 - \tfrac{8}{3}\epsilon).$$

The quantity $u_{\mathrm{inv}}$ of (9.6.1) and (9.6.2) is given by (9.6.5) with $y = 0$. The solution for the boundary layer may now be obtained from (8.3.14) and (8.3.15) with the altered boundary condition (9.6.4).

Unpublished results of Probstein for the case of the stagnation region of an axisymmetric blunt body in air with a highly cooled wall show an increase of the skin friction by the factor $1 + 0.49\,\Omega$ and an increase of the heat transfer by the factor $1 + 0.19\,\Omega$. These factors should be generally applicable within the scope of the calculations of Fay and Riddell [1].

In general, with $\Omega > 0$ and the inviscid velocity $u$ accordingly increasing from the body to the shock (cf. the papers of Li [1], Glauert [1], and Mark [2]), the values of $f_b''$ and $g_b'$ and the corresponding skin friction and heat transfer at the wall are increased. Similarly for $\Omega < 0$ the skin friction and heat transfer at the wall are decreased. As we have already seen (in Section 8.4), the coupling between the momentum and energy equations is weak, and we do not expect the effect on the heat transfer rate to be as large as on the shear.

In the case of the axisymmetric blunt body discussed above, the effect of vorticity interaction on the skin friction is roughly $2\frac{1}{2}$ times that on the heat transfer.

If the parameter $\Omega$ is small, its effect may be calculated by a perturbation procedure. If $\Omega$ is of the order of one a direct analysis is needed with the boundary condition (9.6.4). If $\Omega$ is large compared with one, the shear stress in the supposedly inviscid free stream is of the same order of magnitude as the shear stress in the boundary layer. To be consistent, we must either consider the entire flow field inviscid or the entire flow field viscous. In either case the conventional concept of the boundary layer breaks down and a completely different approach must be taken.

In the case of the flow in the stagnation region of a blunt body, the entire shock layer must be considered to be viscous if the parameter $\Omega$ is large. This approach and its limitations are treated in Section 10.2.

For the sharp-nosed flat plate we shall present an analysis to estimate the order of magnitude of the vorticity interaction effect in the strong interaction region. From (1.5.12) the vorticity immediately behind the shock is given approximately as

$$(9.6.7) \qquad \zeta_s = \frac{U}{\epsilon} \left( \frac{d^2\Delta}{dx^2} \right)_s \sim \frac{U}{\epsilon} \left( \frac{d^2\delta}{dx^2} \right)_s \sim \frac{U\delta_s}{\epsilon x_s^2},$$

in which we have used the fact that in the similar strong interaction solution $\delta_s \sim \Delta_s$. At a point on the same streamline farther downstream the vorticity is given by the relation

$$(9.6.8) \qquad \zeta_{\mathrm{inv}} = \frac{\zeta_s p}{p_s}.$$

The subscript $s$ here refers to conditions at the point of entry of a streamline. This relation is obtained from an application of Crocco's vorticity law and the perfect gas law. We shall use (9.6.8) at a point at the outside of the boundary layer, and shall require a correspondence relating the point of entry of a streamline into the shock layer and the point of entry of the same streamline into the boundary layer (see Fig. 9–1).

A continuity argument is used to determine where a given streamline crossing the shock wave enters the boundary layer. The mass flow entering is $\rho_\infty U \Delta_s$, and is of the order of magnitude of $\rho_\infty U \delta_s$. The mass flow in the boundary layer corresponding to the same streamline is of the order of $\bar{\rho} U \delta$, where $\bar{\rho}$ is of the order of $\rho_\infty \epsilon^{-1}(\delta/x)^2$. Equating these two mass flows gives the relation

$$(9.6.9) \qquad \frac{\delta_s}{\delta} \sim \frac{1}{\epsilon}\left(\frac{\delta}{x}\right)^2.$$

We also need certain results from the fact that the solution is similar, in particular that

(9.6.10)
$$\frac{\delta_s}{x_s^{3/4}} = \frac{\delta}{x^{3/4}}$$

and that

(9.6.11)
$$\frac{p}{p_s} \sim \left(\frac{x_s}{x}\right)^{1/2}.$$

Combining the approximate results stated above gives for $\Omega$

(9.6.12)
$$\Omega \sim \frac{\zeta_{\text{inv}} \bar{\rho} \delta}{U \rho_\delta} \sim \epsilon \left[\frac{1}{\epsilon}\left(\frac{\delta}{x}\right)^2\right]^{1-(2/3\gamma)}.$$

The quantity in the brackets is of the order of $M_\infty^{-2}\bar{\chi}$ and must be small from condition (9.1.6). We may conclude that in general, $\Omega$ will be small in the strong interaction problem except perhaps very near the front edge of the strong interaction region. It will certainly be very small when $\bar{\chi}$ is of order one in a hypersonic flow, as the weak interaction region is approached. It will certainly also be small within the weak interaction region. A parameter similar in form to that given in (9.6.12) was derived by Lees [5] in an approximate analysis of this problem. Lees indicates a very significant effect of the vorticity interaction, appreciably larger than appears to be reasonable from our order-of-magnitude estimates.

Oguchi [1] has made a careful and thorough study of the strong interaction problem in a perfect gas on an insulated flat plate, including effects to first order in the vorticity interaction parameter indicated in (9.6.12). The estimate of Lees interpreted as an upper bound is substantiated by Oguchi. However, Oguchi shows that a simplifying assumption made by Lees is responsible for his estimate being too high. Our order-of-magnitude estimates are consistent with Oguchi's results, which show the effect to be small.

CHAPTER X

# FREE MOLECULE AND RAREFIED GAS FLOWS

## 1. General features of rarefied gas flows

Because of the importance of high altitudes in practical hypersonic flight, no presentation of hypersonic flow theory could be considered complete without a discussion of rarefied gas flows, i.e. flows at relatively low values of the Reynolds number. In Chapter IX we have seen that at hypersonic flight speeds with the Reynolds number sufficiently low, such effects as pressure interaction, vorticity interaction, and transverse curvature can be important. It must be kept in mind that the calculations for all these effects were carried out using boundary layer theory, which in itself is a high Reynolds number theory based on continuum concepts. Completely apart from the question of whether the medium is a continuum, we should expect that some of the concepts derived from our high Reynolds number calculations must be modified when the Reynolds numbers become sufficiently small (say of the order of 10–100). And if the Reynolds numbers involved are small enough, the assumption that the gas is a continuum may not be valid. An early investigation in this realm of rarefied gas flow was that of Zahm [1].

Tsien [2] and others (see, e.g., Siegel [1]) have proposed a division of fluid mechanics into various regimes according to the degree of rarefaction as measured by the value of the Knudsen number. This basic parameter is defined as the ratio of the mean free path $\lambda$ to a characteristic flow length $L$. Tsien used as a flow length either a characteristic body dimension or the boundary layer thickness. Of the various realms into which he and others categorized gasdynamics in general, only two are reasonably well defined: ordinary continuum gasdynamics, where the density is sufficiently high that intermolecular collisions dominate ($\lambda/L \ll 1$) over collisions with the boundaries; and free molecule flow, where the gas is sufficiently rarefied that collisions with the boundaries dominate ($\lambda/L \gg 1$) over collisions between molecules. Between these two limiting regimes there is of course a wide class of flows of varying character. It is generally accepted (see e.g. Liepmann and Roshko [1, p. 381]) that if $\lambda/L$ is of the order of one or greater, a gas flow may properly be called rarefied. But the concept of the Knudsen number must be applied in context, in connection with the particular characteristic scale used and the particular phenomenon of interest. For example, if the feature of interest is the structure of a strong shock and the characteristic scale is the thickness of the shock, the flow is always to be considered rarefied.

In the general literature on low-density flows (see, e.g., Schaaf and Chambré [1]) it is usually stated that continuum gasdynamic considerations must be inapplicable for a rarefied gas flow and that flow problems in this regime necessarily require treatment from the point of view of kinetic theory. On the other hand, Liepmann and Roshko [1] point out that such a statement is too strong and very often is made on the basis of a comparison of a rarefied gas flow experiment with a solution of the Navier-Stokes equations which does not apply to the problem. For example, boundary layer theory is valid for high Reynolds numbers and cannot be expected to be applied to a rarefied gas flow, which is usually a low Reynolds number flow. It is for this reason that the use of the ratio of the mean free path to the boundary layer thickness is not completely satisfactory for defining the regimes of rarefied gas flows at high Mach numbers. Furthermore, regardless of the characteristic length used, it has been usual to compare this length with the mean free path in the free stream. This too is not always satisfactory, since the mean free path may change appreciably in the flow field. As Adams and Probstein [1] have pointed out, at hypersonic flight speeds the compression of the gas across the shock wave and at the body increases the local density appreciably and the mean free path behind the shock and in the stagnation region is generally appreciably smaller than its free stream value. Even in a hot boundary layer the mean free path may be less than in the free stream. With this point in mind, we shall attempt to determine the pertinent parameters defining regimes of low-density flow and limits to the continuum concept, following an analysis analogous to that given by Adams and Probstein [1].

In order to determine the parameters defining the regimes of low-density flow, let us estimate the changes in the mean free path from its free stream value which arise when we consider different parts of the flow field. At first we shall restrict our considerations to the stagnation region of an axisymmetric blunt body, although later we shall indicate how these concepts are readily extended to slender bodies. With the assumption that the temperatures of interest are high, we may assume that $\mu \propto T^{1/2}$ approximately. This assumption corresponds to the rigid sphere model of kinetic theory, for which $\lambda\rho$ is a constant. We shall use this assumption consistently in this section for simplicity; for precise results the actual dependence of $\mu$ on $T$ may have to be taken into account.

According to (1.7.2) the free stream mean free path $\lambda_\infty$ is proportional to $\mu_\infty/\rho_\infty a_\infty$, so that the free stream Knudsen number can be expressed in terms of the free stream Mach and Reynolds numbers as

(10.1.1)
$$\frac{\lambda_\infty}{L} \sim \frac{M_\infty}{Re_{L_\infty}}.$$

With $\lambda \rho$ approximately a constant we have the relation $\lambda_s \approx \epsilon \lambda_\infty$. Behind a shock wave, then, we have

(10.1.2)
$$\frac{\lambda_s}{L} \sim \epsilon \, \frac{M_\infty}{Re_{L_\infty}} \, .$$

For the case of a weak shock wave with $\epsilon \approx 1$, (10.1.2) and (10.1.1) are equivalent.

For the mean free path at the body, we may write

(10.1.3)
$$\frac{\lambda_b}{L} \sim \frac{\rho_\infty}{\rho_b} \, \frac{M_\infty}{Re_{L_\infty}} \, .$$

with our assumption that $\lambda \rho$ is constant. If we also require that the surface temperature of the body is of the order of the free stream temperature, the ratio $\rho_\infty / \rho_b$ is of the order of $p_\infty/p_b$. Then since $p_b/p_\infty \sim \rho_\infty U^2/p_\infty \sim M_\infty^2$, we have

(10.1.4)
$$\frac{\lambda_b}{L} \sim \frac{1}{M_\infty Re_{L_\infty}} \, .$$

Of course the surface temperature may be expected to be greater than the free stream temperature in hypersonic flight; but if the surface temperature can be considered to be of the same order of magnitude as the absolute temperature in the free stream, the mean free path at the body is of the same order of magnitude as that given by (10.1.4). For example, with $T_b = 2000°F$, $\lambda_b$ is roughly five times larger than the value given by (10.1.4).

Let us now look at what the previous results imply in terms of the actual flow field in the neighborhood of the stagnation region of a convex blunt axisymmetric body at hypersonic speeds. Assuming a continuum flow we can use the results of Section 4.4 for the thickness $\Delta$ of the shock layer at the stagnation point, with some suitable convention as to where the outside edge of the shock layer is. With the established result for bodies of finite curvature that $R_s \sim R_b$, the quantity $\Delta$ may be expressed from (4.4.16) as

(10.1.5)
$$\frac{\Delta}{R_b} \sim \epsilon.$$

The effect of viscosity here does not change the order-of-magnitude result of (10.1.5) as long as the shock wave is an identifiable entity and there is some appreciable part of the flow which may be considered as a continuum.

At hypersonic speeds the mean free path in the free stream is a completely inessential parameter; this result follows from the Mach number independence principle of Section 1.6 (q.v.). The only characteristic scale that is appropriate for a shock wave is the mean free path behind the shock. A general result for very strong shock waves without relaxation is that the shock thickness is of the order of this mean free path $\lambda_s$, or rather of the order of a few mean free paths. We shall use $\lambda_s$ as a measure of the shock wave thickness. With re-laxational effects present the situation is more complicated, and a new characteristic scale equal to a flow velocity divided by a relaxation time appears. We may note that the atomic and molecular processes which lead to a small value of $\epsilon$ may also produce relaxation phenomena.

With relaxational effects negligible or with a suitable relaxational scale used in place of $\lambda_s$, the shock thickness will be small compared to its radius of curvature as long as $\lambda_s/R_b$ is small compared with one. We shall assume relaxational effects are negligible here, but must recognize their importance. If relaxational effects are important, appreciable modifications may need to be made in the treatment of this section. In Section 10.2 we will briefly discuss the problem of a fluid in which there is a relaxation phenomenon behind the shock.

For the stagnation region of a blunt axisymmetric body we may write, with the assumption $\mu \propto T^{1/2}$, the equivalence

$$(10.1.6) \qquad \frac{\lambda_s}{\Delta} \sim \frac{\lambda_\infty}{R_b} \sim \frac{M_\infty}{Re_{R_b\infty}}.$$

The parameter $\lambda_s/\Delta$ is a basic one which serves to measure the degree of rarefaction or the degree of departure from continuum conditions of the flow in the shock layer.

If the body is cold, with a surface temperature of the order of magnitude of the free stream temperature, the conditions at the surface of the body should be examined. An approximate analysis shows that the fraction of the total energy flux $\frac{1}{2}\rho_\infty U^3$ incident upon the shock layer which is absorbed by the body as heat is of the order of $\sqrt{\lambda_s/\Delta}$. We may obtain this result using (8.3.16b), (10.1.2), (10.1.5), and the fact that the velocity gradient in the equivalent inviscid flow is approximately $\sqrt{\frac{8}{3}\epsilon}\, U/R_s$. This yields the result

$$(10.1.7) \qquad \frac{-\dot{q}_0}{\frac{1}{2}\rho_\infty U^3} \sim \sqrt{\frac{\lambda_s}{\Delta}} \frac{g_b'}{Pr_b} \sqrt{\frac{\rho_b\mu_b}{\rho_s\mu_s}}.$$

The Prandtl number is taken to be of the order of one, and $g_b'\sqrt{\rho_b\mu_b/\rho_s\mu_s}$ is seen to be of the order one from (8.3.25) and (8.3.26) if the term $N_\delta^{0.1}$ may be neglected. Thus we have

$$(10.1.8) \qquad \frac{-\dot{q}_0}{\frac{1}{2}\rho_\infty U^3} \sim \sqrt{\frac{\lambda_s}{\Delta}}$$

The physical significance of this result is that the heat transfer to the body is determined or controlled by processes occurring in parts of the layer with temperature of the order of $T_s$, and is affected only weakly by the fluid properties very near a very cold wall.

At the cold wall the temperature gradient is determined by the energy flux, or by the relation

$$(10.1.9) \qquad k_b \left(\frac{\partial T}{\partial y}\right)_b \sim \tfrac{1}{2}\rho_\infty U^3 \sqrt{\frac{\lambda_s}{\Delta}}.$$

For a characteristic scale $\delta$ we use not the boundary layer thickness as a whole but a distance across which the change in $T$ is of the order of $T_b$. We replace $k_b$ by $c_{p_b}\mu_b$ (with $Pr_b \sim 1$) and approximate $c_{p_b}$ by $\epsilon^{-1}$ times the gas constant $\mathscr{R}$. We can then rewrite (10.1.9) as

$$(10.1.10) \qquad \frac{\mathscr{R}\mu_b}{\epsilon}\frac{T_b}{\delta} \sim \rho_\infty U^3 \sqrt{\frac{\lambda_s}{\Delta}}.$$

We now replace $\mathscr{R}T_b$ by $\rho_\infty U^2/\rho_b$, and $\mu_b$ by $\rho_b a_b \lambda_b$. The result obtained is

$$(10.1.11) \qquad \frac{\lambda_b}{\delta} \sim \epsilon \frac{U}{a_b}\sqrt{\frac{\lambda_s}{\Delta}} \sim \epsilon^{1/2}\sqrt{\frac{T_s}{T_b}}\sqrt{\frac{\lambda_s}{\Delta}} \sim \epsilon M_\infty \sqrt{\frac{T_\infty}{T_b}}\sqrt{\frac{\lambda_s}{\Delta}}.$$

If $\epsilon M_\infty$ is not very large, if $T_\infty/T_b$ is of order one, and if $\sqrt{\lambda_s/\Delta}$ is small, the flow at the wall can be considered to be a continuum flow. However, we observe in (10.1.10) that if we take a limiting process in which $T_b \to 0$, the flow very near the wall cannot be a continuum flow. We term the existence of this phenomenon the "continuum cold wall paradox", which may be stated in other words that no continuum flow of a perfect gas past a body at absolute zero temperature may exist. This paradox is of no real practical significance, as the skin friction and heat transfer are generally controlled by processes at higher temperatures and are not affected by the details of the solution very near the wall.

In the conventional description of the phenomena described as slip and temperature jump (see, for example, Schaaf and Chambré [1, p. 718]), the velocity and temperature are assumed to jump discontinuously from their values 0 and $T_b$ in the body surface to their different values $u(0)$ and $T(0)$ in the fluid flow at the body surface. Omitting a term in the temperature gradient along the wall, the velocity jump can be expressed as

$$(10.1.12) \qquad u(0) = \lambda \left(\frac{\partial u}{\partial y}\right)_{y=0},$$

where $\lambda$ is a mean free path at the wall which is of the order of $\lambda_b$.

We now express as the condition for the phenomenon of slip to be negligible in our low-density stagnation region flow, that $u(0) \ll u_s$. In a layer which is viscous enough so that slip may be important the velocity $u_b = Ux/R_s$ is the only characteristic velocity which is available. We multiply the inequality by $\rho_b a_b$ to obtain a shear stress, and express the condition as

$$(10.1.13) \qquad \tau_b \sim \rho_b a_b \lambda_b \left(\frac{\partial u}{\partial y}\right)_{y=0} \ll \rho_b a_b u_s.$$

The shear is assumed to be approximately independent of local conditions near the wall, so that we may approximate $\tau_b \sim \rho_s a_s \lambda_s u_s/\Delta$. This gives the condition

$$(10.1.14) \qquad \frac{\lambda_s}{\Delta} \ll \frac{\rho_b a_b}{\rho_s a_s} \sim \sqrt{\frac{T_s}{T_b}}.$$

If the shock layer as a whole is completely in the continuum range, $\lambda_s/\Delta \ll 1$ and slip cannot be important in the stagnation region even if the body is insulated. If the body is highly cooled (10.1.14) is satisfied even if the flow in the shock layer cannot be considered as a continuum, as long as an identifiable shock layer exists. Thus, particularly with a cold body, slip cannot be considered to be an important phenomenon in the stagnation region in affecting skin friction and heat transfer. This is not to say that slip does not exist here as an identifiable phenomenon.

The temperature jump has a behavior which is closely analogous to slip, and in general is important or is unimportant as slip is important or unimportant. Thus, particularly with a cold body, the temperature jump cannot be considered to be important in affecting the heat transfer on a blunt axisymmetric body. Again, this is not to say that the temperature jump phenomenon does not exist.

In assessing the limits of continuum theory to the problem of the stagnation region on an axisymmetric blunt body we take as the basic condition for continuum flow the condition

$$(10.1.15) \qquad \frac{\lambda_\infty}{R_b} \sim \frac{\lambda_s}{\Delta} \ll 1.$$

We shall investigate continuum solutions for the shock layer in more detail in Section 10.2, and shall give approximate classifications of solution regimes at the end of this section. If the body is highly cooled we need never consider the slip and temperature jump phenomena. The continuum cold wall paradox may invalidate the solutions obtained in the immediate vicinity of the wall as far as correctness of detailed kinetic theory descriptions, but this fact does not affect the calculation of skin friction and heat transfer. With condition (10.1.15) the shock thickness is small compared with the shock layer thickness, and the shock wave still exists as an identifiable entity separate from the shock layer even though we may not be able to consider it as infinitesimally thin. If the shock thickness is of the order of the shock layer thickness, so that $\lambda_s/\Delta = O(1)$, condition (10.1.15) is violated and we cannot properly consider the flow as a continuum flow. We shall discuss this region further in Section 10.2 when we consider continuum solutions for rarefied flows.

The situation with a two-dimensional blunt body is quite different. With $\epsilon$ small the shock layer thickness is much larger than on a corresponding axisymmetric body in a highly viscous flow as well as in an inviscid flow, and different estimates of orders of magnitude are indicated. For example, there is zero vorticity at the wall in an inviscid flow, so that $\Omega = 0$ and there is no vorticity interaction in the sense of Section 9.6. If the vorticity inter-action is to be considered it must be of a type involving the normal derivative of the vorticity, a type which we have not treated. We shall not go into an analysis of the stagnation region on a two-dimensional body in this section. The same general approach we used for the axisymmetric case should be applicable, and the same continuum condition (10.1.15) should be appro-priate.

The questions which arise in a rarefied gas flow on either a sharp-nosed slender body or a blunt-nosed slender body are considerably more difficult than those which arise in stagnation regions on blunt bodies. The principal difficulty which arises is that in the region of interest there are large pressure gradients across the shock layer and classical boundary layer theory is no longer valid. The variations in density are much larger on a slender body than in a stagnation region, and no analogue of the local similarity so helpful in the stagnation region case has been found.

The approximate estimates of (1.7.3a) and (1.7.4a) do not apply for a hypersonic boundary layer in the strong interaction region and can be applied without modification only to boundary layers with moderate values of the external Mach number $M_\delta$ and with at most weak interaction. With a sharp-nosed flat plate we must take the boundary layer thickness $\delta$ to be of the same order of magnitude as the shock layer thickness $\Delta$ in any region forward of the strong interaction region treated in Section 9.3. Thus we have

$$(10.1.16) \qquad \frac{\delta}{\Delta} \sim 1$$

for this case. The inclination angle of the shock may be taken roughly as of the order of this thickness divided by $x$, or

$$(10.1.17) \qquad \sin \sigma \sim \frac{\Delta}{x}.$$

The shock wave is assumed to be an identifiable entity of small thickness within the region of interest. The density behind the shock is simply $\epsilon^{-1}\rho_\infty$, and the mean free path there $\lambda_s$ is $\epsilon \lambda_\infty$ if we assume $\mu \propto T^{1/2}$. The density within the shock layer varies considerably from that behind the shock. If we assume that the average velocity in the layer is of the same order of magnitude as $U$, we obtain from a continuity argument that the average density $\bar{\rho}$ is given as

$$(10.1.18) \qquad \bar{\rho} \sim \rho_\infty.$$

We now note that the pressure immediately behind the shock is of the order $p_\infty M_\infty^2 \sin^2 \sigma$, and assume that the pressure is of the same order of magnitude throughout the layer. From our experience with hypersonic boundary layers we estimate that the maximum temperature in the layer is of the order of magnitude of the recovery temperature $T_\infty \epsilon M_\infty^2$ even if the wall is cooled. This is certainly true if the wall is insulated. We conclude that the minimum density in the layer is of the order of

$$(10.1.19) \qquad \rho_{\min} \sim \rho_\infty \epsilon^{-1} \sin^2 \sigma.$$

The minimum density must be less than the average density, and we obtain a maximum value of $\sigma$, given by

$$(10.1.20) \qquad \sin \sigma_{\max} \sim \epsilon^{1/2}.$$

This implies that the solution near the forward part of the plate approaches one with a constant shock angle, within the region in which the shock may be considered thin.

With the assumption that $\mu \propto T^{1/2}$ we can now estimate the maximum value of $\lambda$ within the layer as

$$(10.1.21) \qquad \lambda_{\max} \sim \frac{\epsilon \lambda_\infty}{\sin^2 \sigma},$$

with the condition that $\lambda_{\max}$ cannot be less than $\lambda_\infty$. For the continuum concept to be valid throughout the layer we require that

$$(10.1.22) \qquad \frac{\lambda_{\max}}{\Delta} \sim \frac{\epsilon M_\infty}{\sin^3 \sigma \, Re_{x_\infty}} \ll 1.$$

We have used (10.1.17) in the above. If this condition is satisfied we also may write

$$(10.1.23) \qquad \frac{M_\infty}{\epsilon^{1/2} Re_{x_\infty}} \ll 1.$$

We now turn to the question of the thickness of the shock wave, which is of the order of $\lambda_s$. The ratio of shock thickness to shock layer thickness is given approximately by

$$(10.1.24) \qquad \frac{\lambda_s}{\Delta} \sim \frac{\epsilon M_\infty}{\sin \sigma \, Re_{x_\infty}}.$$

It is clear that if the continuum condition (10.1.22) is satisfied the shock wave must be extremely thin and may be considered as a discontinuity.

For an estimate of the importance of slip let us require that $u(0)$ be small compared with $u_s \sim U$ in order that slip may be neglected. We estimate roughly that $(\partial u/\partial y)_{y=0}$ is of the same order of magnitude as is $U/\Delta$, and obtain the condition

$$(10.1.25) \qquad\qquad \frac{\lambda_b}{\Delta} \ll 1.$$

If we take $\mu \propto T^{1/2}$ we obtain

$$(10.1.26) \qquad\qquad \frac{\lambda_{\max}}{\Delta} \ll \frac{T_{\max}}{T_b} \sim \epsilon M_\infty^2 \frac{T_\infty}{T_b} .$$

We conclude that if the continuum condition (10.1.22) is met slip will not be important with a slender body in affecting the skin friction and heat transfer, particularly if the body is cooled. Similar arguments apply to the effect of the temperature jump. Again, we are not concluding that slip or temperature jump do not exist as identifiable phenomena within the range we are considering.

As with the stagnation region discussed above, a continuum cold wall paradox applies to slender bodies. Again, the existence of this difficulty would not affect any estimates of skin friction or heat transfer made on a continuum basis for a flow which is a continuum flow over most of its extent. We shall not investigate the slender body case of this phenomenon.

In Sections 10.3 through 10.5 we shall develop the theory of free molecule flow, defined by the assumptions that collisions between molecules may be neglected and with the additional assumption that the reflection or re-emission of molecules from the body surface may be satisfactorily described through accommodation coefficients. The basic requirement for free molecule flow is that the Knudsen number $\lambda_\infty/L$ is very large, where $L$ is a characteristic dimension of the body. In the free molecule flow over an isolated body there is no implication that collisions between molecules do not exist, but only that most of them occur so far away from the body that there is no influence on the body.

The basic requirement $\lambda_\infty/L \gg 1$ is not sufficient to ensure free molecule flow if the body is cold. To see this let us consider a flow at very great velocity impinging on a body with a density of $n_\infty$ molecules per unit volume and a velocity of $U$. The number of molecules captured by the body per unit projected area is $n_\infty U$. We assume that the molecules are re-emitted with a velocity distribution corresponding to the body temperature $T_b$, corresponding to the case of diffuse reflection defined in Section 10.3. The molecules are re-emitted with an average velocity which is of the order of $\sqrt{\mathscr{R}T_b}$. With finite angle of incidence the density of the stream of re-emitted molecules near the body is of the order of $n_\infty U/\sqrt{\mathscr{R}T_b}$ molecules per unit volume. With $\lambda\rho$ constant, corresponding to a rigid sphere molecular model, the correct order of magnitude of the mean free path of an incident molecule passing through the cloud of re-emitted molecules near the body is given by

$$(10.1.27) \qquad\qquad \lambda = \lambda_\infty \frac{\sqrt{\mathscr{R}T_b}}{U}.$$

The mean free path of the re-emitted molecules with respect to the molecules in the free stream is of the same order of magnitude. The Knudsen number with respect to this mean free path must be much larger than one for the free molecule concept to be valid, or

$$(10.1.28) \qquad\qquad \frac{\lambda_\infty}{L} = \frac{M_\infty}{Re_{L_\infty}} \gg \frac{U}{\sqrt{\mathscr{R}T_b}}.$$

With the body cooled this condition is more stringent than the condition $\lambda_\infty/L \gg 1$.

We are led to a "free molecule cold wall paradox", which may be stated that no steady free molecule flow past a body at absolute zero temperature may exist. We note that with $\lambda_\infty$, $L$, and $U$ fixed the condition (10.1.28) is always violated with $T_b$ sufficiently small. In contradistinction to the continuum cold wall paradox discussed above, the free molecule cold wall paradox is of fundamental importance and represents an essential limitation to the concept of free molecule flow. It can be avoided only by requiring $\lambda_\infty$ to increase as $T_b$ is decreased, so that (10.1.28) may be satisfied. This difficulty must be kept in mind in interpretating the results of Sections 10.3 through 10.5. We shall treat free molecule flow there without further consideration of the limits of validity.

We close this section with a suggested classification of flow regimes, from continuum flows at high Reynolds numbers to free molecule flows at extremely low Reynolds numbers. This classification is intended to be reasonably general and suggestive rather than exhaustive and specific.

1. *Boundary layer regime.* At sufficiently high Reynolds numbers viscous effects may be taken into account using classical boundary layer theory, with suitable modification for pressure interaction if appropriate.

2. *Vorticity interaction regime.* If the vorticity in the inviscid flow is high, the classical boundary layer concepts must be modified. For a blunt axisymmetric body the vorticity interaction parameter $\Omega$ from (9.6.6) is of the order of

$$(10.1.29) \qquad\qquad \Omega \sim \frac{1}{\epsilon} \sqrt{\frac{\lambda_\infty}{R_b}} \left(\frac{T_s}{T_b}\right)^{1/4},$$

with $\mu \propto T^{1/2}$. If $\mu \propto T$ the factor $(T_s/T_b)^{1/4}$ is not present. If $\Omega$ is very small compared with one, vorticity interaction need not be taken into account and we are in the boundary layer regime. The limit of the vorticity interaction regime depends upon the shape of the velocity profile and upon the number of terms taken into account in the theory. With only the single term in $\Omega$ taken into account, we must restrict ourselves in general to the condition that $\Omega^2$ must be less than one. In the case of the blunt axisymmetric body the inviscid velocity profile is almost linear and the vorticity interaction theory involving only the parameter $\Omega$ may be carried to large values of $\Omega$.

3. *Viscous layer regime.* With the Reynolds numbers less than required for validity of a vorticity interaction approach, we may apply the complete Navier-Stokes equations (including the Fourier heat conduction equation) to the entire shock layer with the assumption that the shock wave may be treated as a discontinuity. In order that the classical shock wave relations be applicable and that the classical boundary conditions in terms of the velocity components behind the shock may be used, it is necessary that the viscous stresses and the conductive heat transfer be small in the shock layer at the shock boundary. In general, this condition also ensures that the shock wave be extremely thin. To assess the limit imposed by the condition that the viscous shear be small, we require that $\mu\, \partial u/\partial y$ be much less than the tangential momentum transport $\rho uv$ at the shock. For the blunt axisymmetric body we may take the velocity gradient as of the order of $u/\Delta$ and $a_s$ as of the order of $\epsilon^{1/2}U$ and obtain.

$$(10.1.30) \qquad \frac{\lambda_\infty}{R_b} \sim \frac{\lambda_s}{\Delta} \ll \epsilon^{1/2}$$

for the condition that we may use the viscous layer concept.

4. *Incipient merged layer regime.* Here we consider that the shock layer is still a continuum, so that we have condition (10.1.15) as a limiting condition for this regime. But we now may no longer consider the shock as a discontinuity following the classical Hugoniot relations. Two courses are open for the treatment of the shock: We may consider the shock as a discontinuity obeying conservation laws in which the viscous stresses and heat conduction are taken into account. Or we may use the complete Navier-Stokes equations to give us a solution which includes the shock wave structure and has free stream conditions as outer boundary conditions. In the first course we cannot assume that the density ratio is given by the relations of Section 1.4 and we may not assume that the tangential velocity component is constant through the shock. In the latter course we must recognize that the shock structure obtained is not valid because the Navier-Stokes equations cannot be considered valid for very strong shocks. Our use of the Navier-Stokes equations here is as a model which must satisfy the overall conservation

laws and which we can be certain will give a reasonably accurate picture of the density and mean velocity profiles of the gas passing through the shock.

5. *Fully merged layer and transitional layer regimes.* This major regime is delimited by the limits for the incipient merged layer regime and the first-order collision theory regime discussed below. A strict treatment of a flow in this regime requires the full formulation of kinetic theory, using the Boltzmann equation or some sufficiently valid equivalent. We may roughly divide this regime into an almost-continuum or fully merged layer regime defined by $\lambda_\infty/R_b$ less than about one and a noncontinuum or transitional layer regime defined by $\lambda_\infty/R_b$ greater than about one. This distinction appears somewhat arbitrary, but perhaps may be useful in dividing a rather large class of flows of differing character. The fully merged layer regime will be discussed in Section 10.2.

6. *First-order collision theory regime.* If the Knudsen number $\lambda/R_b$ (see (10.1.27)) is large but not large enough to ensure the full validity of the free molecule flow concept, we may be able to make an analysis based upon kinetic theory taking only first-order collisions into account. A first-order collision in this sense is a collision between a free stream molecule and a re-emitted molecule. Each molecule may have one collision, but all second or subsequent collisions are neglected (see, for example, Lunc and Lubonski [1], Baker and Charwat [1], Hammerling and Kivel [1], and Willis [1]). We shall not treat this theory in this book.

7. *Free molecule flow regime.* In this regime we require condition (10.1.28) and neglect all intermolecular collisions. This regime is the subject of Sections 10.3 through 10.5.

## 2. Continuum solutions for rarefied gas flows

The flow within the shock layer in the viscous layer or incipient merged layer regimes is a continuum, and is properly described by the compressible Navier-Stokes equations. The near-continuum part of regime 5 discussed at the end of the last section, the fully merged layer regime, is definitely not a continuum regime. However, for purposes of obtaining estimates for skin friction and heat transfer and of obtaining a picture of density and mean velocity distributions which should be reasonably accurate we may postulate the complete Navier-Stokes equations as a model for this regime. In the sense that we use the term, the Navier-Stokes equations include the linear heat conduction law of Fourier, and are the appropriate equations for a fluid continuum in thermodynamic quasi-equilibrium.

The belief that a Navier-Stokes model should be a satisfactory one for the purposes mentioned is not an arbitrary one, but is based on certain known results. One of these is the fact that experimental evidence (Sherman [1]) shows excellent agreement of actual shock wave structure with Navier-Stokes shock structure at normal Mach numbers high enough ($M_\infty \approx 1.8$) that the shock thickness is of the order of a mean free path behind the shock. For shocks of this strength we would conclude according to the criteria used in the last section that the flow is definitely not a continuum flow. There is other evidence from the fields of acoustics and viscous flows that the Navier-Stokes equations have an appreciably wider range of empirically justified validity than their theoretically defendable range of validity. Experiments (see, for example, the results of Chiang [1] reported briefly in Schaaf and Chambré [1] and of Kuhlthau [1]) indicate a wide range of experimental validity for the Navier-Stokes equations with slip taken into account for the problem of Couette flow in a rarefied gas. This wide range of experimentally verified validity extends only to mean properties of the flow. F. S. Sherman (private communication) has pointed out to the authors that the Navier-Stokes velocity distributions in a strong shock are anomalous in yielding negative values for the distribution function, despite the eminent reasonableness of the Navier-Stokes results for the mean flow quantities. In the cold blunt-body case a simple analysis shows that the heat transfer at the stagnation point as calculated by the Navier-Stokes equations is always less than that calculated on the basis of the theory of free molecule flow (cf. Adams and Probstein [1]). This is one indication that no anomalies in mean quantities are to be expected from a Navier-Stokes model when applied to extremely rarefied flows.

In taking the course of including the shock structure in the incipient merged layer region and in using the Navier-Stokes model for the fully merged layer we may treat them together in a single analysis for the merged layer. We may note that for the fully merged layer if the body is cold, slip and temperature jump cannot be considered to be important phenomena in affecting the skin friction and heat transfer (cf. (10.1.14) and (10.1.26)). However if the body is insulated both slip and temperature jump will have to be considered even for calculating mean quantities at the surface, at least with the fully merged layer. The limits of validity for such an analysis in predicting skin friction and heat transfer must be considered as unknown. The results will certainly be quite accurate for some distance into the fully merged layer regime, and may possibly be very accurate well into the transitional layer regime. For engineering purposes no better approach is available within the fully merged layer and transitional layer regimes. Calculations and experimental results here are needed and should be forthcoming.

We have thus posed ourselves two classes of problems involving solutions to the Navier-Stokes equations, one for a viscous layer with a discontinuous shock and negligible viscous stresses and heat conduction behind the shock, and the other for a merged layer with the shock structure and shock layer structure treated together. We shall consider the viscous layer and merged layer problems for the stagnation region of an axisymmetric or two-dimensional body. We may note that the local similarity on which our attack on this problem is based applies also to a general stagnation point, in analogy with the inviscid solution of Section 4.5.

As with the inviscid solutions of Sections 4.3 and 4.4 the thickness of the shock layer must be small in comparison with the radius of curvature of the blunt body in order that local similarity may exist. We may now follow either of two approaches with regard to choice of coordinate system. In one approach we use cylindrical or spherical coordinates, take the body to be a cylinder or sphere, and seek a complete solution analogous to the solution of Whitham and of the authors presented in Section 4.3 and the solution of Lighthill presented in Section 4.4. Here we must assume not only that $\epsilon$ is constant across a shock discontinuity but also that the density is a function of the radius alone, the viscosity coefficients are proportional to $\cos \vartheta$, and the pressure and temperature are each a function of radius alone plus another function of radius alone times $\sin^2 \vartheta$. This approach is described by Probstein [6], and Probstein and N. H. Kemp (unpublished) have obtained numerical results for the viscous layer on a sphere with the assumption of constant density in the shock layer (approximating the case of the insulated body).

In the other approach we take advantage of the fact that the shock layer must be thin for local similarity to apply and use a coordinate system of the boundary layer type similar to that introduced in Section 5.1. The assumptions needed for a complete solution with cylindrical or spherical symmetry are unjustifiable in general and may be anomalous for sufficiently large $\vartheta$. Hence the validity of both approaches is the same, and requires that the shock layer be thin. We shall here follow the approach using a coordinate system of the boundary layer type.

We start with the inviscid equations (5.1.6) with one important change. In order to be consistent with the conventions of boundary layer theory we take the body surface as the reference surface and take $v$ and $y$ positive directed outward from the surface. This change effectively changes the sign of $K$ in (5.1.1) and (5.1.6). We drop the factor $\mathscr{H}$ except in (5.1.6a) in which a derivative of $\mathscr{H}$ appears, and replace $r$ by $\mathscr{H}x$. And we must, of course, add appropriate viscous terms. The resultant equations are

$$(10.2.1) \qquad \frac{\partial \rho u}{\partial x} + \frac{j \rho u}{x} + \frac{\partial \rho v}{\partial y} + (1 + j) K \rho v = 0,$$

$$(10.2.2) \qquad u \frac{\partial u}{\partial x} + v \frac{\partial u}{\partial y} + Kuv + \frac{1}{\rho} \frac{\partial p}{\partial x} = \frac{1}{\rho} \frac{\partial}{\partial y}\left(\mu \frac{\partial u}{\partial y}\right),$$

$$(10.2.3) \qquad u \frac{\partial v}{\partial x} + v \frac{\partial v}{\partial y} - Ku^2 + \frac{1}{\rho} \frac{\partial p}{\partial y} = \frac{1}{\rho} \frac{\partial}{\partial y}\left(\mu'' \frac{\partial v}{\partial y}\right) + \Xi,$$

where $\mu''$ is the longitudinal coefficient of viscosity defined by

$$(10.2.4) \qquad \mu'' = \tfrac{4}{3}\mu + \mu'$$

in terms of the dilatational or bulk coefficient of viscosity $\mu'$. The term $\Xi$ is an additional viscous acceleration term which will be dropped for most purposes. It is defined by

$$(10.2.5) \qquad \Xi = \frac{1}{\rho}\frac{\partial}{\partial y}\left[(\mu' - \tfrac{2}{3}\mu)\frac{\partial u}{\partial x}\right] + \frac{\mu}{\rho}\frac{\partial^2 u}{\partial x \partial y}.$$

These equations do not represent complete Navier-Stokes equations, as a number of terms have been dropped because they are small in a thin layer analysis. The analysis of orders of magnitude which justifies dropping these terms is somewhat lengthy but straightforward.

We recognize (10.2.2) immediately as being the same as the boundary layer momentum equation (plus a curvature term), and the analysis of orders of magnitude indicating which viscous term is kept is essentially identical to the classical one for the boundary layer equations. The usual boundary layer assumption $\partial p/\partial y = 0$ may not generally be made for our continuum solutions, as, for example, within the structure of the shock wave. The analysis leading to the choice of viscous terms retained in (10.2.3) is analogous in all respects to the classical analysis underlying (10.2.2).

While (10.2.1) through (10.2.5) have been written for a stagnation region, it is of interest to note that (10.2.2) and (10.2.3) are the appropriate equations for a thin shock layer on a slender body in the continuum part of the rarefied flow regime. As with the stagnation region, it is necessary that the shock layer thickness be small compared with the radii of the curvature of the body. For the continuity equation (5.1.6a) is appropriate in this case.

An equation for the energy is needed, in place of the entropy equation (5.1.7). With consistent approximations this equation is

$$(10.2.6) \qquad u\frac{\partial H}{\partial x} + v\frac{\partial H}{\partial y} = \frac{1}{\rho}\frac{\partial}{\partial y}\left(k\frac{\partial T}{\partial y} + \mu''v\frac{\partial v}{\partial y}\right),$$

where $H$ is the total enthalpy.

A direct approach to solving (10.2.1) through (10.2.6) for the flow in the stagnation region is to expand $u$ as a series in odd powers of $x$ with coefficients which are functions of $y$ and to expand the other dependent variables similarly in even powers of $x$. This approach leads to a succession of ordinary differential equations in $y$. There is a basic difficulty in this approach. To illustrate this we note that in solving (10.2.1) and (10.2.2) with $\rho$ assumed constant for the first coefficients in $u$ and $v$ we need the second coefficient of $p$. Calculation of this coefficient of $p$ from (10.2.3) involves the second coefficient of $v$, which is in turn related to the $x^3$ component of $u$ by (10.1.1). There is no way of stopping this argument within a finite number of terms.

The resolution of this difficulty lies in the thinness of the shock layer and in the fact that we may make a number of simplifications based on the assumption that $K\Delta$ is small compared with one, where $\Delta$ is a measure of the thickness of the layer.

For our thin viscous or merged layer we take $K = R_b^{-1}$ to be constant, and make a number of assumptions as to the functional form of the various dependent variables. These assumptions are somewhat analogous to those needed in an analysis with full cylindrical or spherical symmetry, and involve the inclusion of some terms which are small for the sole purpose of making the analysis neater. The assumed forms are

(10.2.7a)      $\rho = \rho_0(y)$,

(10.2.7b)      $u = xu_1(y)$,

(10.2.7c)      $\mu = \mu_0(y)$,

(10.2.7d)      $\Xi = \Xi_0(y)$,

(10.2.7e)      $v = (1 - \tfrac{1}{2}K^2x^2)v_0(y)$,

(10.2.7f)      $\mu'' = (1 - \tfrac{1}{2}K^2x^2)\mu_0''(y)$,

(10.2.7g)      $k = (1 - \tfrac{1}{2}K^2x^2)k_0(y)$,

(10.2.7h)      $p = (1 - K^2x^2)p_0(y) - \tfrac{1}{2}x^2p_2(y)$,

(10.2.7i)      $h = (1 - K^2x^2)h_0(y)$,

(10.2.7j)      $T = (1 - K^2x^2)T_0(y)$.

In (10.2.7) there is no attempt to obtain full self-consistency. Consistency is required only for the lowest-order terms in an expansion in $x$.

The equation of state for the fluid is applied with the quantities $p_0$, $\rho_0$, $h_0$, and $T_0$ in place of their counterparts without subscripts. The quantities $\mu_0''$ and $k_0$ are assumed to be the same functions of thermodynamic state as are their counterparts without subscripts. The influence of $p_2$ in the equation of state is neglected. Thus we take the equation of state correctly along the stagnation streamline.

We now rewrite the basic equations (10.2.1) through (10.2.3) and (10.2.6) with the forms above, to consistent orders of magnitude in $x$, as

$$(10.2.8) \qquad (1 + j)\rho_0 u_1 + \frac{d\rho_0 v_0}{dy} + (1 + j)K\rho_0 v_0 = 0,$$

$$(10.2.9) \qquad u_1^2 + v_0\frac{du_1}{dy} + Ku_1v_0 - \frac{2K^2p_0 + p_2}{\rho_0} = \frac{1}{\rho_0}\frac{d}{dy}\left(\mu_0\frac{du_1}{dy}\right),$$

$$(10.2.10) \qquad v_0\frac{dv_0}{dy} + \frac{1}{\rho_0}\frac{dp_0}{dy} = \frac{1}{\rho_0}\frac{d}{dy}\left(\mu_0''\frac{dv_0}{dy}\right) + \Xi_0,$$

$$(10.2.11) \qquad 2Ku_1^2 + 2K^2u_1v_0 + \frac{1}{\rho_0}\frac{dp_2}{dy} = 0,$$

$$(10.2.12) \qquad v_0\frac{d(h_0 + \tfrac{1}{2}v_0^2)}{dy} = \frac{1}{\rho_0}\frac{d}{dy}\left(k_0\frac{dT_0}{dy} + \mu_0''v_0\frac{dv_0}{dy}\right).$$

Not all the terms appearing in the equations above will be used in all applications. We may note that if $\rho_0 v_0$ is taken to be constant and $\Xi_0$ equal to zero, (10.2.10) and (10.2.12) are the classical equations for the Navier-Stokes structure of a shock wave. If the gas is a perfect gas, the longitudinal Prandtl number $Pr''$ is one, and the body is insulated we obtain immediately Becker's integral

$$(10.2.13) \qquad\qquad H = h_0 + \tfrac{1}{2} v_0^2 = \text{constant}$$

as valid for our stagnation region flow as well as for a shock wave. Except for (10.2.11), equations (10.2.8) through (10.2.12), with terms which are relatively small dropped, are essentially the same as those considered by Adams and Probstein [1].

In the merged layer, the exterior boundary conditions in the free stream are simply that $v_0 = -U$, $u_1 = KU$, $p_2 = 0$, $\rho_0 = \rho_\infty$, $p_0 = p_\infty$, and $h_0 = h_\infty$. The last two conditions are not independent because of the relation afforded by the equation of state. The boundary conditions at the body are three in number,

$$(10.2.14a) \qquad\qquad u_1 = 0,$$

$$(10.2.14b) \qquad\qquad v_0 = 0,$$

$$(10.2.14c) \qquad\qquad h_0 = h_b.$$

The term in $K$ appearing in (10.2.8), the term in $K$ in (10.2.9), and the term in $K^2$ in (10.2.11) are generally small compared with other terms in the two equations except near free stream conditions; they are included above only so that free stream boundary conditions may be satisfied. The quantity $p_\infty$ must be very small so that it may be neglected in applying (10.2.9) in the free stream. The term $\Xi_0$ in (10.2.10) may be neglected in a merged layer analysis.

These conclusions are based upon an analysis of orders of magnitude which is not given here in detail. In outline, we choose a parameter of the order of $\epsilon$ which is assumed to be small. For the viscous layer we take $\Delta/R_b$, $\rho_\infty/\rho_0$, $v_0/U$, and $\mu_0/\rho_\infty U R_b$ to be of the order of $\epsilon$; and we take $u_1 R_b/U$, $p_0/\rho_\infty U^2$, and $h_0/U^2$ to be of the order of one. The Prandtl number is taken to be of the order of one. Besides the conclusions made above, we conclude that $R_b^2 p_2/\rho_\infty U^2$ and $R_b \rho_\infty^{-1} U^{-2} dp_0/dy$ are of the order of one, and that the term in $2K^2 p_0 + p_2$ in (10.2.9) is negligible except where $u_1$ is small. For the merged layer we allow $v_0/U$ to be of the order of one, but subject to the limitation that $\rho_0 v_0/\rho_\infty U$ is of the order of one. Here $R_b \rho_\infty^{-1} U^{-2} dp_0/dy$ may be of the order of $\epsilon^{-1}$. We shall not treat the merged layer further in this book, and shall restrict ourselves now to the relatively much simpler viscous layer.

With a viscous layer we have an infinitesimally thin shock, for which $\epsilon$ is approximately constant and very small. With $\epsilon$ small, the pressure behind the shock is given by the shock relation

$$(10.2.15) \qquad p_{0_s} = p_\infty + (1 - \epsilon)\rho_\infty U^2.$$

With $\epsilon$ small the pressure within the layer does not vary much from this value. With the assumptions underlying the viscous layer regime we may drop the right-hand side of (10.2.10) as long as great accuracy in $p_0$ is not needed. The quantity $\frac{1}{2}v_0^2$ is small compared with $h_0$ within the layer and terms in $v_0$ in (10.2.12), and the term in $K^2$ in (10.2.11) may be dropped.

We are now left with the five equations (10.2.8) through (10.2.12) somewhat simplified. We may solve these equations as they stand, with the boundary conditions (10.2.14) at the body and the boundary conditions

$$(10.2.16a) \qquad u_{1_s} = KU,$$

$$(10.2.16b) \qquad v_{0_s} = -\epsilon U,$$

$$(10.2.16c) \qquad h_{0_s} = h_\infty + \tfrac{1}{2}U^2, \; \rho_{0_s} = \epsilon^{-1}\rho_\infty,$$

$$(10.2.17) \qquad p_{2_s} = 0,$$

together with (10.2.15) applied at the shock. These equations and their boundary conditions form a reasonably self-consistent set, and may be used to obtain solutions for the viscous layer.

A further simplification of the equations may be made within our assumption of a thin shock layer, with perhaps some expense in accuracy. The pressure variation across the layer may be neglected in the equation of state and the density $\rho_0(p_0, h_0)$ may be taken to be a known function of $h_0$. Consistent with this assumption we must drop the terms in $K$ appearing in (10.2.8), (10.2.9), and (10.2.11). This leads to our dropping both equations (10.2.10) and (10.2.11) from consideration. We are left with the three ordinary differential equations for our "constant-pressure" viscous layer

$$(10.2.18) \qquad (1 + j)\rho_0 u_1 + \frac{d\rho_0 v_0}{dy} = 0,$$

$$(10.2.19) \qquad u_1^2 + v_0 \frac{du_1}{dy} - \frac{2K^2 p_0 + p_2}{\rho_0} = \frac{1}{\rho_0}\frac{d}{dy}\left(\mu_0 \frac{du_1}{dy}\right),$$

$$(10.2.20) \qquad v_0 \frac{dh_0}{dy} = \frac{1}{\rho_0}\frac{d}{dy}\left(\frac{\mu_0}{Pr}\frac{dh_0}{dy}\right).$$

The boundary conditions at the body are still given by (10.2.14) and those at the shock by (10.2.16).

The difficulty which remains here is that $p_2$ is unknown. Both $p_0$ and $p_2$ in (10.2.19) are considered as constants, and $p_0$ is established accurately enough by its value behind the shock. The total variation in $p_2$ across the layer is of the same order of magnitude as $K^2 p_0$ and we may not necessarily take $p_2$ equal to its value behind the shock given by (10.2.17) as zero. This difficulty is resolved by the observation borrowed from the analogous solutions of Section 4.3 and 4.4 that the greatest accuracy in $p_2$ in (10.2.19) is needed near the wall. Thus we must take $p_2$ approximately equal to its value at the wall $p_{2_b}$. To obtain $p_{2_b}$ we must obtain an approximate quadrature of (10.2.11). The primary contribution to $p_{2_b}$ from (10.2.11) comes from the outer parts of the shock layer where $u_1$ is high, from the parts of the layer in which viscosity is least important. As a suitable approximation we take the Newtonian velocity distribution for this purpose, and obtain the Newtonian result (3.3.4) with (3.3.9). Thus we set

$$(10.2.21) \qquad p_2 = \frac{2}{2+j} K^2 p_0$$

in (10.2.19).

We take $p_0$ equal to $\rho_\infty U^2$ and introduce the quantity $u_{\text{inv}}$ equal to

$$(10.2.22) \qquad u_{\text{inv}} = \sqrt{\frac{2\epsilon(3+j)}{2+j}} \, KU.$$

This quantity is the velocity gradient at the body in an inviscid flow, and the subscript "inv" is equivalent to that used in Section 9.6. We now drop the subscript 0 and introduce the variables $\eta$ and $f(\eta)$ defined by the relations

$$(10.2.23a) \qquad \eta = \sqrt{\frac{(1+j)u_{\text{inv}}}{\rho_b \mu_b}} \int_0^r \rho \, dy,$$

$$(10.2.23b) \qquad u = u_1 x = u_{\text{inv}} x f_\eta,$$

$$(10.2.23c) \qquad v = -(1+j)u_{\text{inv}} \left(\frac{dy}{d\eta}\right) f.$$

The continuity equation (10.2.18) is automatically satisfied by this choice. With equation (8.2.13) defining $N$ as $\rho\mu/\rho_b\mu_b$ and (8.2.10b) defining $g$ as $H/H_s = h/h_s$ we obtain from (10.2.19) and (10.2.20) the stagnation point boundary layer equations (8.3.14) and (8.3.15). The only difference now lies in the outer boundary conditions.

The outer boundary conditions (10.2.16) are taken at the shock, the location of which is unknown. This fact accounts for what would otherwise be an extraneous boundary condition in our problem. Thus the problem is different from the classical boundary layer problem of Section 8.3.

An interesting observation may be made in the axisymmetric case. If we use the values of $f_s$ and $f_{\eta_s}$ given by the boundary conditions (10.2.16) behind the shock, we find that they satisfy the relation

$$(10.2.24) \qquad f_{\eta_s}^2 = 1 + 2\Omega f_s$$

there, where $\Omega$ is the vorticity interaction parameter defined in (9.6.6). This means that the vorticity interaction theory is identical with the theory of the constant pressure viscous layer, as (10.2.24) is precisely the outer boundary condition required with vorticity interaction. ·This result is not a coincidence, because for the inviscid velocity profile in the axisymmetric case the relation $f_\eta = 1 + \Omega\eta$ is appropriate over the entire layer and because boundary layer theory is a constant pressure (in $y$) theory. Unpublished calculations of Probstein and N. H. Kemp for vorticity interaction and for the complete viscous layer indicate good agreement between the two approaches within the range of validity of the viscous layer, and serve to support the constant pressure approximation.

We also note that equation (8.3.14) with $\rho_\delta/\rho$ equal to one and the first term involving $N$ dropped is an appropriate equation for the inviscid constant-density solutions of Sections 4.3 and 4.4, within the limits of validity of that theory. These equations are similar to those obtained by Li and Geiger [1] for this problem with $p_2 = 0$.

For an accurate estimation of the stagnation pressure we must integrate (10.2.10) in full with the viscous terms included and with (10.2.15) used as the outer boundary condition. This may be done as a quadrature using the functions $v_0$, $\rho_0$, $\mu_0''(T_0)$, and $u_1$ already obtained from a separate analysis made either with or without the constant pressure approximation. This calculation is the only one in which the use of the term $\Xi$ is essential.

A related problem which we have not treated is the problem of a fluid in which there is a relaxation phenomenon going on behind the shock. Solutions in the stagnation region may be obtained with the constant pressure state approximation if a suitable law describing the changes in density due to relaxational effects is available. If the layer is essentially inviscid only the function $\rho(t)$ describing the change of density at constant total enthalpy and pressure is needed. If the layer is viscous and heat transfer is important we need a law for the time rate change of the density due to relaxation as a function of total enthalpy at the given pressure. In either case the local similarity of the solution in the stagnation region is maintained as long as the layer is thin.

Considering relaxation in an essentially inviscid layer we must express the time a particle has spent in the layer as

$$(10.2.25) \qquad\qquad t = \int_{y_s}^{} \frac{dy}{v_0},$$

and the density is a known function of this time $\rho(t)$. To express this as a differential relation we write

$$(10.2.26) \qquad\qquad \frac{d\rho_0}{dy} = \frac{\rho'(t)}{v_0}$$

as an added equation to replace the constant-density assumption. An analogous but more complicated expression appears in the viscous layer with nonconstant enthalpy.

Freeman [2] has calculated detachment distances on a blunt body of revolution in a relaxing inviscid fluid, using the Newtonian theory for the purpose of estimating velocity distributions. The total value of the Howarth-Dorodnitsyn variable in his analysis is that given by (3.5.3).

## 3. Free molecule transfer theory

As we pointed out in Section 10.1, when a flow is sufficiently rarefied that the mean free path is everywhere very much greater than a characteristic body dimension, such a flow is termed a free molecule flow. By this we mean that the molecules scattered and re-emitted from the surface do not disturb the equilibrium free stream velocity distribution until "far from the body", so that the distortion of the free stream velocity distribution due to the presence of the body is negligible.

One of the basic postulates of free molecule flow is that the distribution of molecular velocities in the oncoming stream may be taken as Maxwellian superposed on the macroscopic uniform velocity of the free stream. The justification for this follows from the fact that when the mean free path is large in comparison with a characteristic body dimension, the probability that either party to a collision between an impinging free stream molecule and a re-emitted molecule will strike the body at all is small, and the probability that it will strike the body without first having had its original Maxwellian velocity restored by collision with other impinging molecules is even smaller. Because of this assumption the calculation of the heat transfer and aerodynamic characteristics of a body in a free molecule field is greatly simplified; the flows of the incident and re-emitted molecules can be treated separately.

When the incident molecules of the free stream impinge on the body surface, a transfer of both momentum and energy from the gas to the body takes place. The actual transfer processes are, however, tied up with the fact that the molecules are re-emitted or reflected in some manner. As a consequence of this re-emission of the molecules, a portion of the momentum imparted to the surface is due to this emission. Similarly, the energy transferred to the surface is reduced by the energy of the re-emitted molecules. On the other hand, since the velocity of emission itself depends on the surface temperature, the mechanisms of energy and momentum transfer are not independent.

At present the actual physical processes of re-emission are only incompletely understood, and a complete specification of these phenomena would require a knowledge of the velocity distribution function of the re-emitted molecules, given their incident velocities. In spite of this difficulty, it is possible to formulate a theory of free molecule flow utilizing certain average parameters which measure the extent to which the mean energy and momentum of the molecules are accommodated to the conditions existing at the body surface.

Let us first consider the so-called thermal accommodation coefficient. This coefficient is a measure of the extent to which the mean energy of the molecules that hit the surface and are reflected or re-emitted is accommodated toward an energy corresponding to the temperature of the wall. The thermal accommodation coefficient is defined by the equation

$$(10.3.1) \qquad a_e = \frac{E_i - E_r}{E_i - E_b},$$

where $E_i$ is the incident energy per unit surface area per second, $E_r$ is the reflected or re-emitted energy carried away by the molecules as they leave the body, and $E_b$ is the energy the re-emitted or reflected stream would have if all the incident molecules were re-emitted with a Maxwellian velocity distribution corresponding to the surface temperature $T_b$. For complete accommodation $a_e = 1$, while for the case of no energy exchange with the surface (i.e. $E_i = E_r$) we would have $a_e = 0$. Although not stated, it is implicitly assumed in this definition that all the energies—translational, rotational, vibrational, etc.—associated with the molecular degrees of freedom which enter into energy exchange with the surface, are accommodated to the same degree.

Since the thermal accommodation coefficient measures the ability of the molecules to adjust to the body temperature during their time of contact, it is evident from a more rigorous point of view that we should define individual accommodation coefficients for each energy mode. As far as the accommodation coefficients for translation and rotation are concerned, there is experimental evidence (see Herzfeld [1]) which indicates that they are approximately the same. On the other hand it is clear that vibrational energy and other forms of energy such as dissociation energy should require a greater adjustment time, and the assumption of a single coefficient for all forms of energy is probably incorrect. Such an "absorption relaxation" effect should show a dependence on the temperature of the body which would appear in the functional dependence of the average coefficient $a_e$. Because of lack of experimental evidence on this point we shall, in common with other writers on the subject, not consider such refinements.

Measurements of the thermal accommodation coefficient under low velocity conditions have been carried out by many authors (see, for example, the references in Estermann [1], Stalder and Jukoff [1], and Schaaf and Chambré [1]). The values found for various metallic surfaces varied between 0.1 and

1.0. Tests of Wiedmann and Trumpler [1] indicate that under static conditions the thermal accommodation coefficient for air on various typical engineering surfaces lies between 0.87 and 0.97.

It is reasonable to expect that the thermal accommodation coefficient varies not only with the nature of the surface and its orientation with respect to the stream, but also with the velocity of impingement and the gas and surface temperatures. Amdur [1] has suggested that there is also a variation of the thermal accommodation coefficient with pressure due to adsorption, in which the accommodation coefficient decreases as the pressure decreases. It is also likely that the thermal accommodation coefficient decreases as the velocity of impingement increases.

In addition to energy transfer, we must consider the process of momentum transfer. In the original treatment of Maxwell it is assumed that there are two types of reflection processes which occur for the molecules striking the surface of the body. The first and simplest is that of "specular" reflection, in which a molecule is assumed to hit a smooth hard surface and leave with its normal velocity component reversed and with its tangential velocity component unchanged. Essentially all experimental evidence indicates that such a process is completely unrealistic. We should consider the case of specular reflection only for purposes of comparison and not with any expectation of obtaining a practically useful result. The case of specular reflection was first considered by Newton (see Section 3.1).

From the molecular point of view typical engineering surfaces are not smooth. Maxwell recognized that some of the impinging molecules should be trapped by the surface and then re-emitted. Any such rebound process which is not specular is called "diffuse" reflection. A reasonable assumption for this diffuse reflection is that the molecules issue with a Maxwellian velocity distribution corresponding to a temperature which is close to that of the surface.

In Maxwell's original concept it is assumed that $(1 - f)$ of the impinging molecules are reflected specularly and the remainder diffusely, where $f$ is a dimensionless coefficient. Only the fraction $f$ of molecules contributes to the tangential momentum transfer. From the experimental work of Hurlbut [1; 2], however, it has become clear that the molecular surface interaction is not as simple as described by Maxwell, and that the parameter $f$ may not be sufficient to describe the reflection process for momentum adequately. In order to remedy this deficiency at least partially, Schaaf [1] and Hurlbut [1; 2] have suggested that both the tangential and normal force components of the reflected flux be specified through two different coefficients for the transport of momentum to and from a surface in the directions normal and parallel to the surface, respectively. Analogous to the definition of the thermal accommodation coefficient, these authors define a tangential accommodation coefficient as

$$(10.3.2) \qquad\qquad f_t = \frac{\tau_i - \tau_r}{\tau_i},$$

and a normal accommodation coefficient as

$$(10.3.3) \qquad\qquad f_n = \frac{p_i - p_r}{p_i - p_b},$$

where $p_b$ is the normal momentum component of the molecules which are re-emitted with a Maxwellian distribution at the surface temperature $T_b$. The terms "reflection coefficient" or "scattering coefficient" are often used for $1 - f_t$ or $f_t$.

From our preceding discussion it is clear that we may consider two limiting cases. One of these is the unrealistic case of completely specular reflection in which it is assumed that the surface is "ideally smooth" and that the impinging molecules are reflected from the surface as from a mirror. For this case all the accommodation coefficients are zero and $a_e = f_t = f_n = 0$. The other limiting case is the relatively realistic case of fully diffuse reflection in which the molecules are assumed to be completely accommodated to the surface conditions and $a_e = f_t = f_n = 1$.

Values of $f_t$ have been measured for air on various surfaces; the references to these measurements may be found in Estermann [1] or Schaaf and Chambré [1]. Most of the measured values of the tangential accommodation coefficient $f_t$ lie in the range between 0.8 and 1.0.

At present there is no experimental evidence regarding the normal accommodation coefficient. Both $a_e$ and $f_t$ appear to be close to one as determined from low velocity static or low speed tests, and this fact may be interpreted as an indication that the molecules are re-emitted nearly diffusely from a surface. If this is so then $f_n$ should also be close to one. For the purposes of our treatment, we will consider the overall average accommodation coefficients which have been defined as constants. However, it must be borne in mind that this is probably not the case, and any quoted values for these quantities must be considered in this light. We may note that any simple model for the reflection and re-emission process which is more general than the specular or diffuse models yields a dependence of the accommodation coefficients on incidence angle and body temperature.

Before determining the aerodynamic coefficients at hypersonic speeds for any specific shape, let us calculate the general macroscopic mass, force, and energy transfer expressions at the surface of a body in a free molecule flow under the assumption that the molecular velocity distributions are Maxwellian, but without any assumption that the flow is hypersonic. In our calculations we consider a unit element of surface area in a steady flow of a gas which has a macroscopic mean velocity $U$. We use a cartesian coordinate system fixed with respect to the body as shown in Fig. 10–1, with the $x$-axis normal to the surface at the origin and with $\theta$ the angle the macroscopic velocity vector makes with the element. The quantity $\theta$ is equivalent to the quantity $\theta_b$ used elsewhere in this book.

We denote the velocity components of a single molecule in the $x$, $y$, and $z$ directions by $c_x$, $c_y$, and $c_z$ respectively. It has been established (see, for

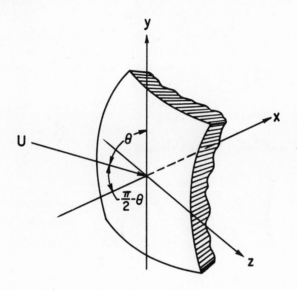

FIG. 10–1. Coordinate system for surface element in free molecule flow.

example, Kennard [1, p. 45]) that the Maxwellian distribution function for the molecular velocities including a superimposed mean velocity is given by

$$(10.3.4) \quad f(c_x, c_y, c_z) =$$
$$\frac{n_\infty}{(2\pi \mathscr{R} T_\infty)^{3/2}} \exp\left[ - \frac{(c_x - U \sin\theta)^2 + (c_y + U \cos\theta)^2 + c_z^2}{2\mathscr{R} T_\infty} \right].$$

Here $f$ is the number density, defined so that $f \, dc_x dc_y dc_z$ is the number of molecules per unit volume having velocity components between $c_x$ and $c_x + dc_x$, $c_y$ and $c_y + dc_y$, $c_z$ and $c_z + dc_z$. The quantity $\mathscr{R}$ is the gas constant equal to the universal gas constant divided by the molecular weight. In accordance with kinetic theory, the gas we are considering is a perfect gas. The quantity $n_\infty$ is the total number of incident molecules per unit volume of gas and is equal to $\rho_\infty/m$, where $m$ is the mass of a single molecule. We implicitly assume that the flow consists of molecules only of a single species.

From the geometry of the problem it can be shown that the number of molecules with velocities between $c_x$ and $c_x + dc_x$, etc. which will strike a unit area per unit time is $c_x f dc_x dc_y dc_z$. In order to find the total number of molecules striking the unit area per second, we must integrate over all velocities to give

$$(10.3.5) \qquad N_i = \int_{-\infty}^{\infty} \int_{-\infty}^{\infty} \int_{0}^{\infty} c_x f dc_x dc_y dc_z.$$

The lower limit of zero on $c_x$ simply says that no molecules with negative velocity in the $x$ direction can strike the front side of the surface. This relation can be integrated, with the result that

$$(10.3.6) \qquad N_i = n_{\infty} \sqrt{\frac{\mathscr{R}T_{\infty}}{2\pi}} \{ e^{-(\mathscr{S}\sin\theta)^2} + \sqrt{\pi}(\mathscr{S}\sin\theta)[1 + \mathrm{erf}\,(\mathscr{S}\sin\theta)] \},$$

where "erf" is the error function defined as

$$(10.3.7) \qquad \mathrm{erf}\,(t) = \frac{2}{\sqrt{\pi}} \int_{0}^{t} e^{-t^2}\, dt.$$

The quantity $\mathscr{S}$ is called the "speed ratio" and is the ratio of the mass velocity $U$ to the most probable random speed in the free stream $c_{mp}$, where $c_{mp}^2 = 2\mathscr{R}T_{\infty}$. Expressing $\mathscr{S}$ in terms of the free stream Mach number we have

$$(10.3.8) \qquad \mathscr{S} = \frac{U}{c_{mp}} = \frac{U}{\sqrt{2\mathscr{R}T_{\infty}}} = \sqrt{\frac{\gamma}{2}}\, M_{\infty}.$$

We use the quantity $\mathscr{S}$ in place of $M_{\infty}$ because of the simplicity this choice gives to the equations, and we should consider the two parameters as essentially equivalent.

In a similar manner we can calculate the momentum transfer from the impinging molecules to the surface of the plate. We must however bear in mind that the force on the surface element consists of a component due to the incident molecules and a component due to the re-emitted molecules. In computing the force on the plate it is convenient to resolve the resultant stress or force per unit area into its normal component, which is termed the pressure $p$, and its tangential component, which is the shear $\tau$. Now the number of molecules which have velocities between $c_x$ and $c_x + dc_x$, etc. transport an amount of momentum normal to the surface equal to $mc_x$ per molecule. The contribution to the normal pressure due to the momentum transport by the incident molecules is readily shown to be

$$(10.3.9) \qquad p_i = m \int_{-\infty}^{\infty} \int_{-\infty}^{\infty} \int_{0}^{\infty} c_x^2 f dc_x dc_y dc_z$$

$$= \frac{\rho_\infty U^2}{2\sqrt{\pi}\mathscr{S}^2} \{(\mathscr{S}\sin\theta)e^{-(\mathscr{S}\sin\theta)^2}$$

$$+ \sqrt{\pi}[\tfrac{1}{2} + (\mathscr{S}\sin\theta)^2][1 + \mathrm{erf}\,(\mathscr{S}\sin\theta)]\}.$$

From the definition of the normal accommodation coefficient (10.3.3), the total normal pressure acting on the surface is given by

$$(10.3.10) \qquad p = p_i + p_r = (2 - f_n)p_i + f_n p_b.$$

To calculate the total pressure, it is necessary to compute the normal pressure at the body exerted by those molecules which leave the surface with a Maxwellian velocity distribution corresponding to thermal equilibrium at the surface temperature and zero mean velocity. Since only molecules with $c_x$ negative are considered the actual mean velocity is not zero. In the calculation one may think of the reflected molecules as issuing from a hypothetical gas at rest on the reverse side of the surface. From (10.3.6). with $\mathscr{S} = 0$, $T_\infty$ replaced by $T_b$, and $n_\infty$ replaced by $n_b$, we have that

$$(10.3.11) \qquad N_b = n_b \sqrt{\frac{\mathscr{R}T_b}{2\pi}}.$$

Since for a steady state condition the number of incident molecules must equal the number reflected, it follows with $p_b = \rho_b \mathscr{R} T_b$ and $n_b = \rho_b/m$ that

$$(10.3.12) \qquad p_b = mN_i \sqrt{\frac{\pi\mathscr{R}T_b}{2}}.$$

Finally by combining (10.3.9), (10.3.10), and (10.3.12), the total normal pressure due to the reflected and incident molecules is found to be

$$(10.3.13) \qquad p = \frac{\rho_\infty U^2}{2\mathscr{S}^2} \left\{ \left[ \frac{(2-f_n)}{\sqrt{\pi}}(\mathscr{S}\sin\theta) + \frac{f_n}{2}\sqrt{\frac{T_b}{T_\infty}} \right] e^{-(\mathscr{S}\sin\theta)^2} \right.$$

$$\left. + \left[ (2-f_n)(\mathscr{S}^2\sin^2\theta + \tfrac{1}{2}) + \frac{f_n}{2}\sqrt{\pi}\sqrt{\frac{T_b}{T_\infty}}(\mathscr{S}\sin\theta) \right][1 + \mathrm{erf}\,(\mathscr{S}\sin\theta)] \right\}.$$

To calculate the shear acting at the surface we note that the molecules having velocities between $c_x$ and $c_x + dc_x$, etc. transport a tangential component of momentum of amount $-mc_y$ per molecule to the surface, so that the incident tangential shear from all the molecules is

$$(10.3.14) \quad \tau_i = -m \int_{-\infty}^{\infty} \int_{-\infty}^{\infty} \int_{0}^{\infty} c_x c_y f \, dc_x dc_y dc_z$$

$$= \frac{\rho_\infty U^2 \cos \theta}{2\sqrt{\pi} \mathscr{S}} \{e^{-(\mathscr{S} \sin \theta)^2} + \sqrt{\pi}(\mathscr{S} \sin \theta)[1 + \operatorname{erf}(\mathscr{S} \sin \theta)]\}.$$

But from the definition of the tangential accommodation coefficient (10.3.2), the total shear is given by
$$(10.3.15) \qquad\qquad \tau = \tau_i - \tau_r = f_t \tau_i,$$

so that the shear is obtained simply by multiplying (10.3.14) by $f_t$.

The remaining quantity to be calculated is the energy transfer to the body. With $-\dot{q}$ the heat transferred to the surface per unit time per unit area, we require that
$$(10.3.16) \qquad\qquad -\dot{q} = E_i - E_r,$$

or in terms of the thermal accommodation coefficient defined by (10.3.1) that

$$(10.3.17) \qquad\qquad -\dot{q} = a_e(E_i - E_b).$$

The quantity $-\dot{q}$ is equivalent to the same quantity of Chapters VIII and IX.

The calculation of the incident energy is simplified by breaking it up into the contribution due to translation $E_{i,\text{tr}}$ and that due to the internal degrees of freedom $E_{i,\text{int}}$. Thus with the kinetic energy per molecule equal to $\frac{1}{2}m(c_x^2 + c_y^2 + c_z^2)$, the total flux of translational energy per unit area per second into the element can be shown to be

$$(10.3.18) \quad E_{i,\,\text{tr}} = \frac{m}{2} \int_{-\infty}^{\infty} \int_{-\infty}^{\infty} \int_{0}^{\infty} c_x(c_x^2 + c_y^2 + c_z^2) f \, dc_x dc_y dc_z$$

$$= p_\infty \sqrt{\frac{\mathscr{R}T_\infty}{2\pi}} \{(\mathscr{S}^2 + 2)e^{-(\mathscr{S} \sin \theta)^2}$$

$$+ \sqrt{\pi}(\mathscr{S}^2 + \tfrac{5}{2})(\mathscr{S} \sin \theta)[1 + \operatorname{erf}(\mathscr{S} \sin \theta)]\}.$$

For a monatomic gas (10.3.18) is a sufficient description of the incident energy since only translational energies are involved. However, for a diatomic gas at moderate temperatures there is an additional internal energy contribution of an amount $m\mathscr{R}T_\infty$ per molecule due to rotation. More generally, with the assumption of classical equipartition of energy, each of the molecules carries an amount $\frac{1}{2}j_{\text{int}}m\mathscr{R}T_\infty$ of internal energy on the average, where $j_{\text{int}}$ denotes the number of internal degrees of freedom which partake in energy exchange. Now the total number of classical degrees of freedom which are excited is given by $j = 3 + j_{\text{int}}$. For our perfect gas $j = 2/(\gamma - 1)$ and $j_{\text{int}} = (5 - 3\gamma)/(\gamma - 1)$. Thus we may write the incident flux of internal energy under this assumption as

$$(10.3.19) \qquad E_{i,\text{int}} = \frac{5 - 3\gamma}{\gamma - 1} \frac{m\mathscr{R}T_\infty}{2} N_i.$$

The contribution of the reflected energy flux can be obtained from (10.3.18) and (10.3.19) by considering the gas to be issuing from the surface as before with a Maxwellian distribution at a temperature $T_b$ with $\mathscr{S} = 0$. If this is done, then from (10.3.18) and (10.3.6) we have

$$(10.3.20) \qquad E_{b,\text{tr}} = 2m\mathscr{R}T_b N_b,$$

while from (10.3.19)

$$(10.3.21) \qquad E_{b,\text{int}} = j_{\text{int}} \frac{m\mathscr{R}T_b}{2} N_b.$$

Since for a steady state condition $N_b = N_i$, it follows that

$$(10.3.22) \qquad E_b = (4 + j_{\text{int}}) \frac{m\mathscr{R}T_b}{2} N_i = \frac{\gamma + 1}{\gamma - 1} \frac{m\mathscr{R}T_b}{2} N_i.$$

From (10.3.17) to (10.3.19) and (10.3.22) the heat transfer per unit area per second is then found to be

$$(10.3.23) \quad -\dot{q} = a_e p_\infty \sqrt{\frac{\mathscr{R}T_\infty}{2\pi}} \left\{ \left[ \mathscr{S}^2 + \frac{\gamma}{\gamma - 1} - \frac{\gamma + 1}{2(\gamma - 1)} \frac{T_b}{T_\infty} \right] \right.$$
$$\left. \left( e^{-(\mathscr{S}\sin\theta)^2} + \sqrt{\pi}(\mathscr{S}\sin\theta)[1 + \text{erf}\,(\mathscr{S}\sin\theta)] \right) - \tfrac{1}{2} e^{-(\mathscr{S}\sin\theta)^2} \right\}.$$

By integrating over the surface of a given body we can in principle now determine from our general mass, force, and energy transfer expressions all the required aerodynamic coefficients for an arbitrary body in a free molecule flow.

## 4. Infinite speed ratio flows

One special case of interest in connection with hypersonic free molecule flows occurs when the molecular speed ratio $\mathscr{S}$ is extremely large, corresponding to the limiting process $\mathscr{S} \to \infty$. In this case we take the macroscopic velocity $U$ to be very large in comparison with the mean random velocity of the molecules in the free stream. We consider first the case in which the body is highly cooled, so that $U$ is also very large in comparison with the mean velocity of a particle re-emitted diffusely from the surface.

For this limiting condition we may consider that the transfer of mass, momentum, and energy to the surface is due only to those particles which are intercepted by the body in its travel, with the reflected molecular contributions considered negligible. Such a flow model is related to that given by Newton (see Section 3.1); Newton's assumptions for the flow of a rare medium correspond to a free molecule flow with infinite $\mathscr{S}$ and zero surface temperature. Because of the free molecule cold wall paradox discussed in Section 10.1 we must require the medium to be sufficiently rare that condition (10.1.28) is satisfied. This condition imposes a severe limitation on the infinite speed ratio model with a cooled body.

If the body is slender we must make the assumption that $\mathscr{S} \sin \theta$ is large, both in comparison with one and in comparison with $\sqrt{T_b/T_\infty}$. The basic assumption needed is thus analogous to the strong shock approximation of Section 1.3, with the high cooling of the body as an additional assumption. Using these two assumptions, we find from (10.3.6), (10.3.12), (10.3.14), and (10.3.23) that the number of incident molecules, pressure, shear, and heat transfer rate per unit area per second, respectively, may be expressed as

(10.4.1)
$$N_i = n_\infty U \sin \theta,$$

(10.4.2)
$$p = (2 - f_n)\rho_\infty U^2 \sin^2 \theta,$$

(10.4.3)
$$\tau = f_t \rho_\infty U^2 \sin \theta \cos \theta,$$

(10.4.4)
$$-\dot{q} = \tfrac{1}{2} a_e \rho_\infty U^3 \sin \theta.$$

For the hypothetical case of completely specular reflection where $a_e = f_t = f_n = 0$, there is, of course, no energy transfer to the body and the shear is zero. The pressure at the body is proportional to the square of the velocity and to the square of the sine of the angle of incidence. This corresponds exactly to Case 1 in Newton's Proposition 35 (see Section 3.1), where the impact is considered to be completely elastic. Newton's Case 2 corresponds to the case $f_t = 0, f_n = 1$, and $T_b$ small, with no specification as to $a_e$. This case is also unrealistic..

A more realistic limiting case is that of completely diffuse reflection, for which $a_e = f_t = f_n = 1$. For this case the pressure is half that for specular reflection and is the familiar Newtonian result without the centrifugal correction. We note, however, that this case differs from Newton's Case 2, in which there is no shear stress. With completely diffuse reflection the pressure, shear, and heat transfer rate are given by

(10.4.5)
$$p = \rho_\infty U^2 \sin^2 \theta,$$

(10.4.6)
$$\tau = \rho_\infty U^2 \sin \theta \cos \theta,$$

(10.4.7)
$$-\dot{q} = \tfrac{1}{2} \rho_\infty U^3 \sin \theta.$$

The maximum aerodynamic heat transfer rate per unit projected cross-sectional area perpendicular to the flight path (area times $\sin \theta$) is $\frac{1}{2}\rho_\infty U^3$, while the rate at which energy is dissipated in the flight of a body is given by the drag of the body times its velocity, or $\rho_\infty U^3$ per unit projected area. The heat transfer is measured in a coordinate system fixed in the body, while the energy dissipated by drag is measured in a coordinate system fixed in the free stream fluid. Thus the two energy dissipation rates are not directly comparable. In the coordinate system fixed in the free stream fluid the kinetic energy given to the "re-emitted" molecules is $\frac{1}{2}\rho_\infty U^3$ per unit projected area if the wall is cold, and this energy transfer plus the heat transfer equals the total energy dissipated in terms of drag. We note that in general the heat transfer to a body cannot be greater than half the dissipation in terms of drag in an infinite speed ratio flow.

So far, by requiring that $\mathscr{S} \sin \theta$ be large compared to $\sqrt{T_b/T_\infty}$, we have considered only the case of a highly cooled surface for which the reflected molecular flux can be neglected. If the surface temperature is very much larger than the free stream temperature (at least of the order of $T_\infty \mathscr{S}^2 \sin^2 \theta$), the random velocities of the molecules at the surface are no longer small in comparison with the free stream velocity, and the effect of molecular reflection cannot be neglected even with $\mathscr{S} \sin \theta \gg 1$. With $\mathscr{S} \sin \theta \gg 1$, but with $\mathscr{S}$ not necessarily large compared with $\sqrt{T_b/T_\infty}$, we find that

$$(10.4.8) \qquad p = \rho_\infty U^2 \sin^2 \theta \left[ (2 - f_n) + \frac{f_n}{2} \sqrt{\pi} \sqrt{\frac{T_b}{T_\infty}} \frac{1}{\mathscr{S} \sin \theta} \right],$$

$$(10.4.9) \qquad -\dot{q} = \frac{1}{2} a_e \rho_\infty U^3 \sin \theta \left[ 1 - \frac{1}{2}\left(\frac{\gamma+1}{\gamma-1}\right)\left(\frac{T_b}{T_\infty}\right)\frac{1}{\mathscr{S}^2} \right],$$

with the shear still given by (10.4.3). If the surface temperature becomes so high that these additional temperature ratio terms must be considered, then it is apparent that the flow no longer depends only on the surface coefficients and the free stream density and velocity, but also on the ratio $\sqrt{T_b/T_\infty}$.

One result of interest which comes from (10.4.9) is that the temperature for zero heat transfer, the adiabatic recovery temperature, is given by

$$(10.4.10) \qquad \frac{T_r}{T_\infty} = \frac{2(\gamma-1)}{\gamma+1} \mathscr{S}^2,$$

and is independent of the angle $\theta$. On the other hand, at high values of the speed ratio, the free stream stagnation temperature is given by

$$(10.4.11) \qquad \frac{T_0}{T_\infty} = \frac{\gamma-1}{\gamma} \mathscr{S}^2.$$

Since $2 > (\gamma + 1)/\gamma$ for $\gamma > 1$, we see that the recovery temperature in a free molecule flow is higher than the free stream stagnation temperature by the factor $2\gamma/(\gamma + 1)$. In contrast, in a boundary layer continuum flow with $Pr < 1$ the recovery temperature is less than or at least no greater than the stagnation temperature.

The explanation of the higher free molecule recovery temperature was first given by Stalder, Goodwin, and Creager [1] for a general value of the speed ratio $\mathscr{S}$. Our interpretation of this phenomenon follows a different line of reasoning, and is limited to the case of infinite speed ratio. Internal degrees of freedom do not enter the argument, and we shall consider only the case of a monatomic gas. In a stagnation process in a continuum originally at very high Mach number the kinetic energy per unit mass of the flow is converted into enthalpy following the relation

$$(10.4.12) \qquad \tfrac{1}{2}U^2 = \tfrac{5}{2}\mathscr{R}T_0.$$

The pressure term in the enthalpy arises from the fact that energy is stored in the form of pressure times volume. On an insulated surface in a free molecule flow, on the other hand, the entering kinetic energy per unit mass is balanced by energy emitted according to the relation

$$(10.4.13) \qquad \tfrac{1}{2}U^2 = 2\mathscr{R}T_r,$$

obtainable from (10.3.20). We observe that $T_r$ is larger than $T_0$ by the factor $\tfrac{5}{4}$. The explanation, very simply put, is that in the continuum case some energy is absorbed in building up the pressure of the gas and does not contribute to increasing the temperature. In the free molecule case there is an analogous effect, giving the difference between $2\mathscr{R}T$ and $\tfrac{3}{2}\mathscr{R}T$, but this effect is smaller than in the continuum case.

The particular case we have been considering of infinite speed ratios provides us with an example of the application of the Mach number independence principle of Section 1.6 to include real fluid effects involving heat transfer and shear. Based on our previous justification we see that with $\mathscr{S} \gg 1$ and $\mathscr{S} \sin \theta \gg 1$ the flow around any body should depend only upon the density $\rho_\infty$, the uniform velocity $U$ of the gas in the free stream, the temperature of the body, and the accommodation coefficients, and should be independent of $T_\infty$. We note that $\mathscr{S}\sqrt{T_\infty}$ is independent of $T_\infty$ if $U$ is fixed and that the independence is borne out in (10.4.3), (10.4.8), and (10.4.9). As in a continuum hypersonic flow, as long as $\mathscr{S}$ is finite there is a point at which this independence principle breaks down if $\theta$ becomes sufficiently small. The fact that the independence principle is valid for a hypersonic free molecule flow suggests that there is a hypersonic free molecule similitude for finite speed ratio flows; we shall exploit this idea further in the following section.

## 5. Free molecule similitude and finite speed ratio flows

In the hypothetical free molecule flow with specular reflection the shear and heat transfer are zero and the flow is essentially inviscid. For this case, as we have previously pointed out, the normal velocity component of a molecule striking the surface is simply reversed upon reflection so that the pressure at the surface is twice the incident pressure, whereas the tangential component of momentum is unchanged. Let us now consider a family of slender bodies with related shapes given by

$$(10.5.1) \qquad\qquad f(\bar{\tau}x, y, z) = 0$$

to be placed in such a flow. Here $(x, y, z)$ is a system of coordinates fixed with respect to the body, and, as in the analysis of hypersonic similitude, $\bar{\tau}$ is considered to be the thickness ratio or angle of attack of the body and is assumed to be small. (The symbol $\bar{\tau}$ is used here to avoid confusion with the symbol $\tau$ which is used for the shear.) In this case the inclinations of the individual particle paths to the free stream direction are also small.

For the family of related bodies (10.5.1) a similitude analogous to that for hypersonic continuum flow (Section 2.2) exists for specular reflection in free molecule flow. The free stream flow has a given macroscopic free stream velocity $U$, density $\rho_\infty$, and pressure $p_\infty$. The general functional dependence of the pressure on the body $p_{\text{spec}}$ is given from (10.3.9) by

$$(10.5.2) \qquad\qquad C_{p_{\text{spec}}} = C_{p_{\text{spec}}}(x, y, z, \bar{\tau}, \mathscr{S})$$

for all bodies of the given family whether slender or not, with $\bar{\tau}x$, $y$, and $z$ connected by (10.5.1). If $\bar{\tau}$ is small, however, the lateral velocity is simply proportional to $U\bar{\tau}$, while the axial perturbation velocity is proportional to $U\bar{\tau}^2$, just as in a hypersonic continuum flow. As a result, the number of independent variables is reduced by one and the pressure coefficient taken only on the body is expressible in the same manner as (2.2.12) without the parameter $\gamma$, namely

$$(10.5.3) \qquad\qquad C_{p_{\text{spec}}} = \bar{\tau}^2 \Pi(\bar{\tau}x, y, z, \mathscr{S}\bar{\tau}).$$

The pressure in Newton's hypothetical Case 2 is simply half that in the specular case and follows the same law if the body is very cold.

By prescribing a free molecule flow with specular reflection, we have in essence characterized the fluid and its functional dependence. Hence, in contrast to hypersonic continuum similitude, it is not necessary to add $\gamma$ as an independent parameter to describe the equation of state. As with continuum theory, because of the self-similar properties of the free molecule flow, it is not necessary to include the variables $p_\infty$ and $\rho_\infty$ explicitly in expressing the functional dependence of $C_{p_\text{spec}}$. Analogously we may write the lift and drag coefficients as

$$(10.5.4) \qquad C_{L_\text{spec}} = \bar{\tau}^2 \Lambda(\mathscr{S}\bar{\tau}),$$

$$(10.5.5) \qquad C_{D_\text{spec}} = \bar{\tau}^3 \Delta(\mathscr{S}\bar{\tau}),$$

with the lift and drag coefficients based on a lateral projected area. Thus, except for the absence of the parameter $\gamma$, the form of the specular reflection similarity law is not different from that for a perfect gas in classical hypersonic similitude. A similitude of this general form always exists if $f_t = 0$ and $T_b$ is small.

For completely diffuse reflection or reflection with $f_t$ finite the previous similarity considerations must be altered, since both the shear and the heat transfer are nonzero. With such reflection processes the lateral velocity is no longer proportional to $U\bar{\tau}$ alone, but rather is proportional to the sum of $U\bar{\tau}$ and the most probable random speed at the surface for the fraction of molecules which are re-emitted diffusely. Hence the body temperature must be taken into account. For diffuse or partially diffuse reflection and a slender body we have from (10.3.13) that

$$(10.5.6) \qquad C_p = \bar{\tau}^2 \Pi\left(\bar{\tau}x, y, z, \mathscr{S}\bar{\tau}, \sqrt{\frac{T_b}{T_\infty}}, f_n\right),$$

with $\bar{\tau}x$, $y$, and $z$ again connected by (10.5.1). Clearly the similarity is dependent not only on the surface conditions but also on the fraction of molecules which are re-emitted diffusely. If $f_n\sqrt{T_b/T_\infty}$ is small, $C_p/(2 - f_n)$ obeys (10.5.6) with no dependence on $\sqrt{T_b/T_\infty}$ or $f_n$.

For diffuse or partially diffuse reflection, unlike specular reflection, tangential momentum is transferred to the surface by the absorption of some fraction of the molecules. This results in a finite shear at the wall which is independent of the surface temperature and directly proportional to the tangential accommodation coefficient (see (10.3.14) and (10.3.15)). The shear is proportional to $f_t$ and it is convenient to define a modified skin friction coefficient as

$$(10.5.7) \qquad C_f' = \frac{\tau}{\frac{1}{2} f_t \rho_\infty U^2}.$$

This coefficient is essentially a friction coefficient expressed only for the fraction $f_t$ of molecules which are tangentially accommodated. It follows that

$$(10.5.8) \qquad C_f' = \bar{\tau}\Phi(\bar{\tau}x, y, z, \mathscr{S}\bar{\tau}),$$

with (10.5.1) again imposed to ensure we are on the body.

Since the drag force associated with the normal pressure is proportional to $\bar{\tau}^3$, it can be neglected in comparison with the drag due to shear which is proportional to $\bar{\tau}$ if $f_t$ is finite. Thus for small $\bar{\tau}$ the similarity law for the drag coefficient becomes

$$(10.5.9) \qquad C'_D = f_t^{-1} C_D = \bar{\tau}\Delta(\mathscr{S}\bar{\tau}),$$

in place of (10.5.5). The contribution to the lift associated with the shear is proportional to $\bar{\tau}$ times the shear, so that from (10.5.6) and (10.5.8) we may express

$$(10.5.10) \qquad C_L = \bar{\tau}^2\Lambda\left(\mathscr{S}\bar{\tau}, \sqrt{\frac{T_b}{T_\infty}}, f_n, f_t\right).$$

From the last two equations it can be seen that for diffuse reflection the lift-drag ratios will be poorer by a large order of magnitude than for the hypothetical case of specular reflection, because of the high drag force associated with the shear on the surface.

The remaining quantity to be considered in connection with our similitude is the heat transfer rate; here we will restrict our considerations for simplicity to surfaces at constant temperature. In continuum flow the appropriate dimensionless parameter for the heat transfer is the Stanton number, which may be defined as the ratio of the local surface heat transfer to a reference heat transfer $\rho_\infty U c_p$ times a thermal potential $(T_r - T_b)$. As with the skin friction coefficient, we shall modify the definition of the Stanton number by introducing the thermal accommodation coefficient $a_e$ to account for the fraction of molecules thermally accommodated. Furthermore, since at high speed ratios the recovery temperature is $2\gamma/(\gamma + 1)$ times the stagnation temperature, we shall introduce this factor to account for the effective decrease of the available thermal potential over that in a continuum flow. In this manner we set

$$(10.5.11) \qquad St' = \frac{2\gamma}{\gamma + 1}\frac{-\dot{q}}{a_e\rho_\infty U c_p(T_r - T_b)}.$$

Except for a factor of 2 and the fact that it is defined locally, this definition of the Stanton number is identical to that given by Oppenheim [1]. On the basis of (10.3.23) with terms of order $\mathscr{S}^{-2}$ dropped the similarity law takes the form

$$(10.5.12) \qquad St' = \bar{\tau}\Omega(\bar{\tau}x, y, z, \mathscr{S}\bar{\tau}),$$

with (10.5.1) again imposed.

The preceding similarity conditions for hypersonic free molecule flow are based on the general relations derived in Section 10.3. In Fig. 10–2 we have plotted the quantity $C_p/\theta^2$ calculated from (10.3.13) for the case of completely diffuse reflection ($f_n = 1$) for various values of the temperature ratio $T_b/T_\infty$. The marked influence of the temperature ratio on the pressure coefficient should be noted. In Fig. 10–3 the modified skin friction coefficient is plotted;

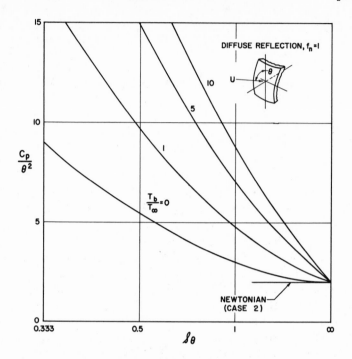

FIG. 10–2.  Pressure coefficient for completely diffuse reflection.

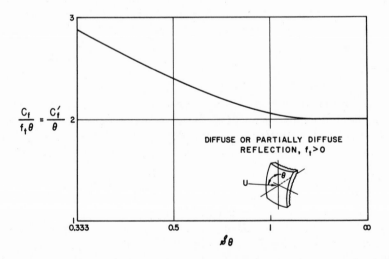

FIG. 10–3.  Modified local skin friction coefficient for free molecule flow.

an interesting result here is the fact that for $\mathscr{S}\theta$ only slightly greater than one, $C_f'/\theta$ has almost reached its value for infinite $\mathscr{S}\theta$.

To illustrate the hypersonic free molecule similarity law as applied to lift and drag, let us consider the example of a flat plate at a small angle of attack $\alpha$, since for this case it is possible to find the exact values of these quantities easily. The lift and drag per unit area for the flat plate can be obtained from the formulas

$$(10.5.13) \qquad L = [p(\alpha) - p(-\alpha)] \cos \alpha - [\tau(\alpha) + \tau(-\alpha)] \sin \alpha,$$

$$(10.5.14) \qquad D = [p(\alpha) - p(-\alpha)] \sin \alpha + [\tau(\alpha) + \tau(-\alpha)] \cos \alpha.$$

Using (10.3.13) to (10.3.15) for the pressure and shear at the surface, the lift and drag coefficients are found to be given without the assumption $\mathscr{S} \gg 1$ and $\sin \alpha \ll 1$ by

$$(10.5.15) \qquad \tfrac{1}{2} C_{L_{\text{exact}}} = \frac{\cos \alpha}{\mathscr{S}^2} \left\{ \frac{2 - f_n - f_t}{\sqrt{\pi}} (\mathscr{S} \sin \alpha) e^{-(\mathscr{S} \sin \alpha)^2} \right.$$

$$+ \frac{f_n}{2} \sqrt{\pi} \sqrt{\frac{T_b}{T_\infty}} (\mathscr{S} \sin \alpha) + (2 - f_n - f_t)(\mathscr{S} \sin \alpha)^2 \operatorname{erf} (\mathscr{S} \sin \alpha)$$

$$\left. + \tfrac{1}{2}(2 - f_n) \operatorname{erf} (\mathscr{S} \sin \alpha) \right\},$$

$$(10.5.16) \qquad \tfrac{1}{2} C_{D_{\text{exact}}} = \tfrac{1}{2} C_{L_{\text{exact}}} \tan \alpha$$

$$+ \frac{f_t}{\sqrt{\pi}\mathscr{S}} e^{-(\mathscr{S} \sin \alpha)^2} + f_t \sin \alpha \operatorname{erf} (\mathscr{S} \sin \alpha).$$

If terms of order $\mathscr{S}^{-2}$ are neglected in comparison with one, and $\sin \alpha \ll 1$, then we see that the above relations reduce to the similarity forms given previously. More specifically, for specular reflection

$$(10.5.17) \qquad \frac{C_{L_{\text{spec}}}}{\alpha^2} = \frac{C_{D_{\text{spec}}}}{\alpha^3} = \frac{4}{\sqrt{\pi}(\mathscr{S}\alpha)^2} \left\{ \mathscr{S}\alpha e^{-(\mathscr{S}\alpha)^2} \right.$$

$$\left. + \sqrt{\pi}[\tfrac{1}{2} + (\mathscr{S}\alpha)^2] \operatorname{erf} (\mathscr{S}\alpha) \right\},$$

while for completely diffuse reflection

$$(10.5.18) \qquad \frac{C_{L_{\text{diff}}}}{\alpha^2} = \frac{1}{(\mathscr{S}\alpha)^2} \left[ \operatorname{erf} (\mathscr{S}\alpha) + \sqrt{\pi} \sqrt{\frac{T_b}{T_\infty}} \mathscr{S}\alpha \right],$$

$$(10.5.19) \qquad \frac{C_{D_{\text{diff}}}}{\alpha} = \frac{2}{\sqrt{\pi}\mathscr{S}\alpha} \left[ e^{-(\mathscr{S}\alpha)^2} + \sqrt{\pi}(\mathscr{S}\alpha) \operatorname{erf} (\mathscr{S}\alpha) \right].$$

On Fig. 10–4 the specular reflection lift and drag coefficients for the flat plate are plotted. Figures 10–5 and 10–6 show the corresponding lift and drag coefficients for completely diffuse reflection. Here, as with the skin friction coefficient, the drag coefficient can be seen nearly to approach its asymptotic limit for values of $\mathscr{S}\alpha$ only slightly greater than one. An interesting feature of the lift coefficient curve for diffuse reflection is that the downward component of the shear completely cancels the lift due to pressure in the limiting case $\mathscr{S}\alpha \to \infty$, although the lift can be materially increased by raising the temperature of the body.

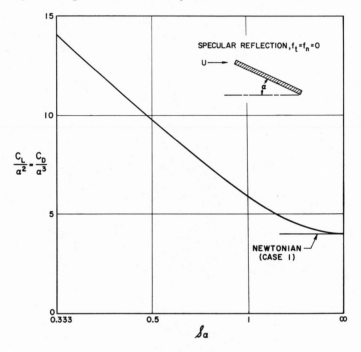

FIG. 10-4. Flat plate lift and drag coefficients for specular reflection.

The modified local Stanton number and the modified local skin friction coefficient are connected if $\mathscr{S} \gg 1$ by a general relation which may be expressed

$$(10.5.20) \quad St' = \tfrac{1}{2}C_f' = \frac{\sin \theta}{2\sqrt{\pi}(\mathscr{S} \sin \theta)}\left\{e^{-(\mathscr{S}\sin\theta)^2}\right.$$
$$\left. + \sqrt{\pi}\,(\mathscr{S} \sin \theta)[1 + \operatorname{erf}(\mathscr{S} \sin \theta)]\right\}.$$

This relation between $St'$ and $C_f'$ does not depend upon the body being slender, but does require that the speed ratio be large. Thus we find the rather interesting result that for a hypersonic free molecule flow, a modified Reynolds analogy exists locally at any angle of attack. For a slender body

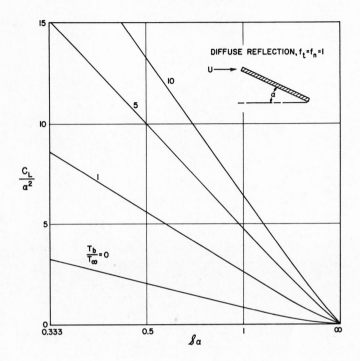

FIG. 10–5. Flat plate lift coefficient for completely diffuse reflection.

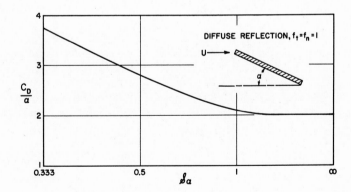

FIG. 10–6. Flat plate drag coefficient for completely diffuse reflection.

at constant temperature with $a_e$ and $f_t$ constant, the analogous result holds between $St'$ and $\frac{1}{2}f_t^{-1}C_D$, where $St'$ here is the average modified Stanton number for the total heat transfer to the body based on total surface area.

So far we have spoken primarily of slender bodies. In the case of free molecule flow all the aerodynamic coefficients for most simple geometrical shapes, either blunt or slender, can be obtained from a direct integration of the basic relations given in Section 10.3. For a summary of lift and drag

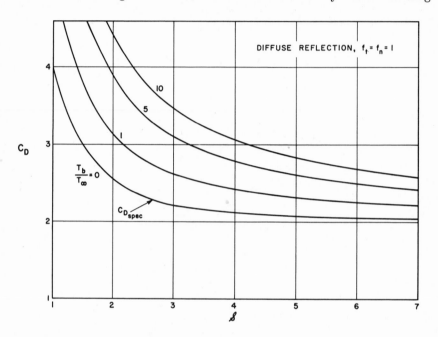

Fɪɢ. 10–7. Drag coefficient based on projected area for a sphere with completely diffuse or specular reflection.

results for various bodies we refer the reader to Ashley [1]; a compilation of many heat transfer calculations is to be found in the paper of Oppenheim [1].

To illustrate the general behavior of blunt bodies in hypersonic free molecule flow we present here expressions for the drag coefficients for a sphere. The drag coefficients for completely diffuse and specular reflection, valid for all speed ratios, are

$$(10.5.21) \quad C_{D_{\text{spec}}} = \frac{2\mathscr{S}^2 + 1}{\sqrt{\pi}\mathscr{S}^3} \, e^{-\frac{1}{2}\mathscr{S}^2} + \frac{4\mathscr{S}^4 + 4\mathscr{S}^2 - 1}{2\mathscr{S}^4} \, \text{erf}\,(\mathscr{S}),$$

$$(10.5.22) \quad C_{D_{\text{diff}}} = C_{D_{\text{spec}}} + \frac{2}{3}\frac{\sqrt{\pi}}{\mathscr{S}}\sqrt{\frac{T_b}{T_\infty}},$$

where the drag coefficient is based on the projected area of the sphere (see, for example, Ashley [1]). The corresponding heat transfer rate expressed in terms of the average modified Stanton number based on the total surface area was given by Sauer [1] as

$$(10.5.23) \quad St' = \frac{1}{4\mathscr{S}^2}\left[\mathscr{S}^2 - \mathscr{S} + \frac{1}{\sqrt{\pi}}\,e^{-\mathscr{S}^2} + (\mathscr{S} + \tfrac{1}{2})\,\mathrm{erf}\,(\mathscr{S})\right].$$

A pertinent feature of these equations is that for hypersonic or even moderate

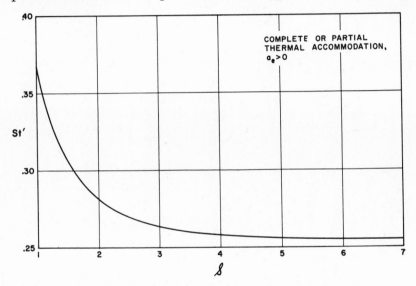

FIG. 10–8   Modified average Stanton number based on total surface area for a sphere in free molecule flow.

supersonic speed ratios, say for $\mathscr{S}$ greater than about 4 or 5, the drag and heat transfer coefficients are very nearly constant, and are close to their respective asymptotic limits for $\mathscr{S} = \infty$. This is shown in Figs. 10–7 and 10–8, on which are plotted the drag coefficients and average modified Stanton number. As in hypersonic continuum flow, the Mach number independence principle is operative at much lower speed ratios for blunt bodies than for slender bodies.

# CITED REFERENCES

In the references cited we have used, as far as possible, the abbreviations for journals and reports used by *Mathematical Reviews*. A list of these abbreviations may be found in any recent index number of *Mathematical Reviews*.

Except where a distinguishing reference to a superseded more informal report was desired, we have consistently referenced the final published version of a paper if available. It may be noted that often more than one *NACA Tech. Note* are lumped together and superseded by a single *NACA Rep.*, sometimes with a different combination of listed authors.

Transliteration of Russian names has followed the system used by *Applied Mechanics Reviews* and *Science Abstracts*, but with no distinction between e, ë, and э or between и and й, and with *y* used for ы. Russian titles have been translated into English. Where an original Russian reference was in English, this fact is indicated. The Russian references listed as having been "transl. by Friedman" have been translated by M. D. Friedman, Inc., Needham Heights, Mass.

Adams, M. C.
    See Probstein, Adams, and Rose.
    See Rose, Probstein, and Adams.
Adams, M. C., and Probstein, R. F.
    [1] On the validity of continuum theory for satellite and hypersonic flight problems at high altitudes, *Jet Propulsion* **28,** 86–89 (1958).
Amdur, I.
    [1] Pressure dependence of accommodation coefficients, *J. Chem. Phys.* **14,** 339–343 (1946).
Ashley, H.
    [1] Applications of the theory of free molecule flow to aeronautics, *J. Aero. Sci.* **16,** 95–104 (1949).
Ashley, H., and Zartarian, G.
    [1] Piston theory—a new aerodynamic tool for the aeroelastician, *J. Aero. Sci.* **23,** 1109–1118 (1956).
Baker, R. M. L., Jr., and Charwat, A. F.
    [1] Transitional correction to the drag of a sphere in free molecule flow, *Phys. Fluids* **1,** 73–81 (1958).
Bam-Zelikovich, G. M., Bunimovich, A. I., and Mikhailova, M. P.
    [1] Slender body motion at high supersonic speeds, *Collection of Papers no. 4, Teoretich. Gidromekhanika.* Oborongiz, SSSR, 1949.

Bechert, K.
[1] Über die Differentialgleichungen der Wellenausbreitungen in Gasen, *Ann. Physik* **39**, 357–372 (1941).

Becker, J. V.
[1] Results of recent hypersonic and unsteady flow research at the Langley Aeronautical Laboratory, *J. Appl. Phys.* **21**, 619–628 (1950).

Beckwith, I. E.
[1] The effect of dissociation in the stagnation region of a blunt-nosed body, *J. Aero. Sci.* **20**, 645–646 (1953).

Belotserkovskii, O. M.
[1] Flow past a circular cylinder with a detached shock, *Dokl. Akad. Nauk SSSR* **113**, 509–512 (1957). Transl. by Friedman. See also *Prikl. Mat. Mekh.* **22**, 206–219 (1958), and *Vychisl. Mat., 1958*, no. *3*, 149–185.

Bertram, M. H.
[1] An approximate method for determining the displacement effects and viscous drag of laminar boundary layers in two-dimensional hypersonic flow, *NACA Tech. Note* no. 2773 (1952).
[2] Tip-bluntness effects on cone pressures at $M = 6.85$, *J. Aero. Sci.* **23**, 898–900 (1956).
[3] Boundary-layer displacement effects in air at Mach numbers of 6.8 and 9.6, *NACA Tech. Note* no. 4133 (1957).

Bird, R. B.
See Hirschfelder, Curtiss, and Bird.

Bogdonoff, S. M.
[1] Some experimental studies of the separation of supersonic turbulent boundary layers, *Preprints 1955 Heat Transfer and Fluid Mech. Inst.*, Univ. of California, Los Angeles, Calif., Paper no. V, 1–23 (1955).
See Hammitt and Bogdonoff.
See Hammitt, Vas, and Bogdonoff.
See Vas, Bogdonoff, and Hammitt.

Bowen, E. N.
See Ivey, Klunker, and Bowen.

Bunimovich, A. I.
See Bam-Zelikovich, Bunimovich, and Mikhailova.

Busemann, A.
[1] Flüssigkeits-und-Gasbewegung, *Handwörterbuch der Naturwissenschaften*, Vol. IV, 2nd. Edition, pp. 244–279. Gustav Fischer, Jena, 1933.

Bush, W. B.
[1] Magnetohydrodynamic-hypersonic flow past a blunt body, *J. Aero/Space Sci.* **25**, 685–690, 728 (1958).

Cabannes, H.
[1] Détermination théorique de l'écoulement d'un fluide derrière une onde de choc détachée, *O.N.E.R.A. Note Tech.* no. 5 (1951).
[2] Tables pour la détermination des ondes de choc détachées, *Rech. Aéro.* no. 49, 11–15 (1956).

Chambré, P. L.
See Schaaf and Chambré.

Chapman, D. R., Kuehn, D. M., and Larson, H. K.

[1] Investigation of separated flows in supersonic and subsonic streams with emphasis on the effect of transition, *NACA Tech. Note* no. 3869 (1957).

Charwat, A. F.

See Baker and Charwat.

Cheng, H. K.

[1] Similitude of hypersonic flows over thin and slender bodies—an extension to real gases, *Rep.* no. AD-1052-A-6, Cornell Aero. Lab., Buffalo, N.Y., 1958.

Cheng, H. K., and Pallone, A. J.

[1] Inviscid leading-edge effect in hypersonic flow, *J. Aero. Sci.* **23**, 700–702 (1956).

Chernyi, G. G.

[1] Hypersonic flow around a body by an ideal gas, *Izv. Akad. Nauk SSSR Otd. Tekhn. Nauk, 1957*, no. 6, 77–85. See also *Dokl. Akad. Nauk SSSR* **107**, 221–224 (1956). Both transl. by Friedman.

[2] One-dimensional unsteady motion of a perfect gas with a strong shock wave, *Dokl. Akad. Nauk SSSR* **107**, 657–660 (1956). Transl. by Friedman.

[3] Problem of the point explosion, *Dokl. Akad. Nauk SSSR* **112**, 213–216 (1957).

[4] Hypersonic flow past an airfoil with a slightly blunted leading edge, *Dokl. Akad. Nauk SSSR* **114**, 721–724 (1957). Transl. by Friedman.

[5] Hypersonic flow around a slender blunt cone, *Dokl. Akad. Nauk SSSR* **115**, 681–683 (1957). Transl. by Friedman.

[6] The effect of tip bluntness on hypersonic flow around a body, *Izv. Akad. Nauk SSSR Otd. Tekhn. Nauk, 1958*, no. 4, 54–66.

See Gonor and Chernyi.

Chester, W.

[1] Supersonic flow past a bluff body with a detached shock. Part I. Two-dimensional body, *J. Fluid Mech.* **1**, 353–365 (1956).

[2] Supersonic flow past a bluff body with a detached shock. Part II. Axisymmetrical body, *J. Fluid Mech.* **1**, 490–496 (1956).

Chiang, S. F.

[1] Drag on a rotating cylinder at low pressures, *Tech. Rep.* no. HE-150–100, Inst. of Eng. Res., Univ. of California, Berkeley, Calif., 1952.

Chisnell, R. F.

[1] The motion of a shock wave in a channel, with applications to cylindrical and spherical shock waves, *J. Fluid Mech.* **2**, 286–298 (1957).

Chu, B. T.

[1] On weak interaction of strong shock and Mach waves generated downstream of the shock, *J. Aero. Sci.* **19**, 433–446 (1952).

[2] Wave propagation and the method of characteristics in reacting gas mixtures with applications to hypersonic flow, *WADC Tech. Note* no. 57–213, Div. of Eng., Brown Univ., Providence, R.I., 1957.

Cline, C. W.

See Ivey and Cline.

Coburn, N.

[1] Intrinsic form of the characteristic relations in the steady supersonic flow of a compressible fluid, *Quart. Appl. Math.* **15**, 237–248 (1957).

Codd, J.

See Maccoll and Codd.

Cohen, C. B.
See Reshotko and Cohen.

Cohen, C. B., and Reshotko, E.
[1] Similar solutions for the compressible laminar boundary layer with heat transfer and pressure gradient, *NACA Rep.* no. 1293 (1956). Supersedes *Tech. Note* no. 3325 (1955).
[2] The compressible laminar boundary layer with heat transfer and arbitrary pressure gradient, *NACA Rep.* no. 1294 (1956). Supersedes *Tech. Note* no. 3326 (1955).

Cole, J. D.
[1] Newtonian flow theory for slender bodies, *J. Aero. Sci.* **24**, 448–455 (1957).

Courant, R., and Hilbert, D.
[1] *Methods of Mathematical Physics*, Vol. I. Interscience, New York, 1953.

Crabtree, L. F.
See Rott and Crabtree.

Cranz, C.
[1] *Lehrbuch der Ballistik*, Vol. I (*Äussere Ballistik*), 5th Edition. Julius Springer, Berlin, 1925. Reprinted by Edwards Bros, Ann Arbor, 1943.
[2] *Lehrbuch der Ballistik, Ergänzungsband.* Julius Springer, Berlin, 1936. Reprinted by Edwards Bros., Ann Arbor, 1943.

Creager, M. O.
[1] Effects of leading-edge blunting on the local heat transfer and pressure distributions over flat plates in supersonic flow, *NACA Tech. Note* no. 4142 (1957).
See Stalder, Goodwin, and Creager.

Crocco, L.
[1] Singolarita della corrente gassosa iperacustica nell'intorno di una prora a diedro, *Aerotecnica* **17**, 519–534 (1937).
[2] Lo strato limite laminare nei gas, *Monografie Scientifiche di Aeronautica* No. 3, Rome, 1946. Transl. as *Rep.* no. AL-684, Aerophys. Lab., North American Aviation Inc., Los Angeles, Calif., 1948.
[3] Considerations on the shock-boundary layer interaction, *in Proceedings of the Conference on High-Speed Aeronautics* (A. Ferri, N. J. Hoff, and P. A. Libby, eds.), pp. 75–112. Polytechnic Inst. of Brooklyn, Brooklyn, N.Y., 1955.

Culler, G. J., and Fried, B. D.
[1] The propagation of shock waves. I, *Rep.* no. ARL-6-20, Aero. Res. Lab., The Ramo-Wooldridge Corp., Los Angeles, Calif., 1956.

Curtiss, C. F.
See Hirschfelder, Curtiss, and Bird.

Daskin, W. and Feldman, L.
[1] The characteristics of two-dimensional sails in hypersonic flow, *J. Aero. Sci.* **25**, 53–55 (1958).

Dennis, D. H.
See Eggers, Resnikoff, and Dennis.
See Syvertson and Dennis.

Detra, R. W.
See Kemp, Rose, and Detra.

Donaldson, C. du P.
[1] Skin friction and heat transfer through turbulent boundary layers for incompressible and compressible flows, *Preprints* 1952 *Heat Transfer and Fluid Mech. Inst.*, Univ. of California, Los Angeles, Calif., 19–35 (1952).

Dore, F. J.
See Romig and Dore.

Dorodnitsyn, A. A.
[1] Laminar boundary layer in compressible fluid, *Dokl. Akad. Nauk SSSR* **34**, 213–219 (1942) (in English).
[2] On a method of numerical solution of some nonlinear problems of aero-hydro-dynamics, *Proc. 9th Internatl. Congr. Appl. Mech.*, Brussels, Vol. I, 485 (1957).
[3] Method of the integral relations for the numerical solution of partial differential equations, *Rep.* Inst. of Exact Mechanics and Computing Technique, Akad. Nauk SSSR, 1958 (in English).

Drebinger, J. W.
[1] Detached shock waves, *Ph.D. Thesis*, Faculty of Arts and Sci., Harvard Univ., Cambridge, Mass., 1950.

Eckert, E. R. G.
[1] Survey on heat transfer at high speeds, *WADC Tech. Rep.* no. 54–70, Wright Air Dev. Cent., Wright-Patterson Air Force Base, Ohio, 1954.
[2] Engineering relations for friction and heat transfer to surfaces in high velocity flow, *J. Aero. Sci.* **22**, 585–587 (1955).

Eggers, A. J., Jr., Resnikoff, M. M., and Dennis, D. H.
[1] Bodies of revolution having minimum drag at high supersonic airspeeds, *NACA Rep.* no. 1306 (1957). Supersedes *Tech. Note* no. 3666 (1956).

Eggers, A. J., Jr., and Savin, R. C.
[1] Approximate methods for calculating the flow about non-lifting bodies of revolution at high supersonic airspeeds, *NACA Tech. Note* no. 2579 (1951).
[2] A unified two-dimensional approach to the calculation of three-dimensional hypersonic flows, with application to bodies of revolution, *NACA Rep.* no. 1249 (1955). Supersedes *Tech. Note* no. 2811 (1952).

Eggers, A. J., Jr., Savin, R. C., and Syvertson, C. A.
[1] The generalized shock-expansion method and its application to bodies traveling at high supersonic air speeds, *J. Aero. Sci.* **22**, 231–238, 248 (1955).

Eggers, A. J., Jr., and Syvertson, C. A.
[1] Inviscid flow about airfoils at high supersonic speeds, *NACA Tech. Note* no. 2646 (1952). Superseded by Eggers, Syvertson, and Kraus [1].

Eggers, A. J., Jr., Syvertson, C. A., and Kraus, S.
[1] A study of inviscid flow about airfoils at high supersonic speeds, *NACA Rep.* no. 1123 (1953). Supersedes Eggers and Syvertson [1] and Kraus [1].

Ehret, D. M., Rossow, V. J., and Stevens, V. I.
[1] An analysis of the applicability of the hypersonic similarity law to the study of flow about bodies of revolution at zero angle of attack, *NACA Tech. Note* no. 2250 (1950).

Elliott, D.
See Probstein and Elliott.

Epstein, P. S.

[1] On the air resistance of projectiles, *Proc. Nat. Acad. Sci. U.S.A.* **17**, 532–547 (1931).

Estermann, I.

[1] Gases at low densities, *in Thermodynamics and Physics of Matter* (F. D. Rossini, ed.), Sect. I, pp. 736–778 (Vol. I of *High Speed Aerodynamics and Jet Propulsion*). Princeton Univ. Press, Princeton, 1955.

Evans, M. E.

See Mangler and Evans.

Fay, J. A., and Riddell, F. R.

[1] Theory of stagnation point heat transfer in dissociated air, *J. Aero. Sci.* **25**, 73–85, 121 (1958).

Fay, J. A., Riddell, F. R., and Kemp, N. H.

[1] Stagnation point heat transfer in dissociated air flow, *Jet Propulsion* **27**, 672–674 (1957).

Feldman, L.

See Daskin and Feldman.

Feldman, S.

[1] *Hypersonic gas dynamic charts for equilibrium air.* Avco Research Lab., Everett, Mass., 1957.

[2] Some shock tube experiments on the chemical kinetics of air at high temperatures, *J. Fluid Mech.* **3**, 225–242 (1957).

[3] Hypersonic conical shocks for dissociated air in thermodynamic equilibrium, *Jet Propulsion* **27**, 1253–1255 (1957).

Ferrari, C.

[1] Campo aerodinamico a velocita iperacustica attorno a un solido di rivoluzione a proro acuminata, *Aerotecnica* **16**, 121–130 (1936). *Transl.* no. A9-T-18, Grad. Div. Appl. Math., Brown Univ., Providence, R.I., 1948.

[2] Sullo strato limite laminare in corrente ipersonica, *Aerotecnica* **36**, 68–94 (1956).

Ferri, A.

[1] The method of characteristics, *in General Theory of High Speed Aerodynamics* (W. R. Sears, ed.), Sect. G, pp. 583–669 (Vol. VI of *High Speed Aerodynamics and Jet Propulsion*). Princeton Univ. Press, Princeton, 1954.

[2] Supersonic flows with shock waves, *in General Theory of High Speed Aerodynamics* (W. R. Sears, ed.), Sect. H, pp. 670–747 (Vol. VI of *High Speed Aerodynamics and Jet Propulsion*). Princeton Univ. Press, Princeton, 1954.

See Vaglio-Laurin and Ferri.

Ferri, A., and Libby, P. A.

[1] Note on an interaction between the boundary layer and the inviscid flow, *J. Aero. Sci.* **21**, 130 (1954).

Fowler, J. E., and French, D. M.

[1] A graphical correlation based on the Taylor-Maccoll results of the air conditions just outside the boundary layer of a cone as related to the conditions of the undisturbed air, *Data Folder* no. 85501, General Electric Company, Schenectady, N. Y., 1946.

Fraenkel, L. E.

[1] The hypersonic flow of a polyatomic gas past bodies of finite thickness, *Proc. 9th Internatl. Congr. Appl. Mech.*, Brussels, Vol. I, 255–265 (1957).

Freeman, N. C.
[1] On the theory of hypersonic flow past plane and axially symmetric bluff bodies, *J. Fluid Mech.* **1**, 366–387 (1956).
[2] Non-equilibrium flow of an ideal dissociating gas, *J. Fluid Mech.* **4**, 407–425 (1958). See also *Rep.* no. 133, Advisory Group for Aero. Res. and Dev., N.A.T.O., Paris, 1957.

French, D. M.
See Fowler and French.

Fried, B. D.
See Culler and Fried.

Gadd, G. E.
See Holder and Gadd.

Garabedian, P. R.
[1] Numerical construction of detached shock waves, *J. Math. Phys.* **36**, 192–205 (1957).

Garabedian, P. R., and Lieberstein, H. M.
[1] On the numerical calculation of detached bow shock waves in hypersonic flow, *J. Aero. Sci.* **25**, 109–118 (1958).

Geiger, R. E.
See Li and Geiger.

Glauert, M. B.
[1] The boundary layer in simple shear flow past a flat plate (with author's reply by T. Y. Li), *J. Aero. Sci.* **24**, 848–850 (1957).

Goldstein, S., editor
[1] *Modern Developments in Fluid Mechanics*, Vol. II. Clarendon Press, Oxford, 1938.

Goldsworthy, F. A.
[1] Two-dimensional rotational flow at high Mach number past thin airfoils, *Quart. J. Mech. Appl. Math.* **5**, 54–63, (1952).

Gonor, A. L., and Chernyi, G. G.
[1] On minimum drag bodies at hypersonic speeds, *Izv. Akad. Nauk SSSR Otd. Tekh. Nauk, 1957,* no. 7, 89–93. Transl. by Friedman.

Goodwin, G.
See Stalder, Goodwin, and Creager.

Görtler, H.
[1] A new series for the calculation of steady laminar boundary layer flows, *J. Math. Mech.* **6**, 1–66 (1957).

Green, J. R., and Southwell, R. V.
[1] Relaxation methods applied to engineering problems, IX. High-speed flow of compressible fluid through a two-dimensional nozzle, *Philos. Trans. Roy. Soc. London. Ser. A* **239**, 367–386 (1944).

Grodzovskii, G. L.
[1] Certain peculiarities of the flow around bodies at high supersonic velocities, *Izv. Akad. Nauk SSSR Otd. Tekhn. Nauk, 1957,* no. 6, 86–92. Transl. by Friedman.

Guderley, G.
[1] Starke kugelige und zylindrische Verdichtungsstösse in der Nähe des Kugel-mittelpunktes bzw. der Zylinderachse. *Luftfahrtforschung* **19**, 302–312 (1942).

Guiraud, J. P.

  [1] Sur la méthode de choc-détente, *C. R. Acad. Sci. Paris* **245**, 1778–1780 (1957).

  [2] Écoulement hypersonique d'un fluide parfait sur une plaque plane comportant un bord d'attaque d'épaisseur finie, *C. R. Acad. Sci. Paris* **246**, 2842–2845 (1958).

Hadamard, J.

  [1] *Lectures on Cauchy's Problem in Linear Partial Differential Equations.* Yale Univ. Press, New Haven, 1923. Reprinted by Dover, New York, 1952.

Hamaker, F. M., Neice, S. E., and Wong, T. J.

  [1] The similarity law for hypersonic flow and requirements for dynamic similarity of related bodies in free flight, *NACA Rep.* no. 1147 (1953). Supersedes Hamaker and Wong [1] and *Tech. Note* no. 2443 (1951).

Hamaker, F. M., and Wong, T. J.

  [1] The similarity law for nonsteady hypersonic flows and requirements for the dynamical similarity of related bodies in free flight, *NACA Tech. Note* no. 2631 (1952). Superseded by Hamaker, Neice, and Wong [1].

Hammerling, P., and Kivel, B.

  [1] Heat transfer to a sphere at the transition from free molecule flow, *Phys. Fluids* **1**, 357–358 (1958).

Hammitt, A. G.

  See Vas, Bogdonoff, and Hammitt.

Hammitt, A. G., and Bogdonoff, S. M.

  [1] Hypersonic studies of the leading edge effect on the flow over a flat plate, *Jet Propulsion* **26**, 241–246, 250 (1956).

Hammitt, A. G., Vas, I. E., and Bogdonoff, S. M.

  [1] Leading edge effects on the flow over a flat plate at hypersonic speeds, *Rep.* no. 326. Dept. of Aero. Eng., Princeton Univ., Princeton, N. J., 1955.

Hansen, C. F.

  [1] Note on the Prandtl number for dissociated air, *J. Aero. Sci.* **20**, 789–790 (1953).

  [2] Approximations for the thermodynamic and transport properties of high-temperature air, *NACA Tech. Note* no. 4150 (1958).

Hantzsche, W., and Wendt, H.

  [1] Die laminare Grenzschicht der ebenen Platte mit und ohne Wärmeübergang unter Berücksichtigung der Kompressibilität, *Jbuch. Deutschen Luftfahrtforschung*, Part I, 40–50 (1942). Univ. of California Eng. Proj. Transl., 1947.

Hasimoto, Z.

  [1] Some local properties of plane flow behind a curved shock wave, Dept. Math. and Phys. *Rep.*, Ritumeikan Univ., Kyoto, Japan, 1956.

Hastings, S. M.

  See Korobkin and Hastings.

Hayes, W. D.

  [1] On hypersonic similitude, *Quart. Appl. Math.* **5**, 105–106 (1947).

  [2] Pseudotransonic similitude and first-order wave structure, *J. Aero. Sci.* **21**, 721–730 (1954).

  [3] Some aspects of hypersonic flow, The Ramo-Wooldridge Corp. *Rep.*, Los Angeles, Calif., 1955.

  [4] Hypersonic flow fields at small density ratio (and its continuation), The Ramo-Wooldridge Corp. *Rep.*, Los Angeles, Calif., 1955.

  [5] On laminar boundary layers with heat transfer, *Jet Propulsion* **26**, 270–274 (1956).

[6] The vorticity jump across a gasdynamic discontinuity, *J. Fluid Mech.* **2**, 595–600 (1957).

[7] The basic theory of gasdynamic discontinuities, *in Fundamentals of Gas Dynamics* (H. W. Emmons, ed.), Sect. D, pp. 416–481 (Vol. III of *High Speed Aerodynamics and Jet Propulsion*). Princeton Univ. Press, Princeton, (1958). See Rockett and Hayes.

Hayes, W. D., and Probstein, R. F.

[1] Viscous hypersonic similitude, *Rep.* no. 59–63, Inst. of Aero. Sci., New York, N.Y., 1959.

Heims, S. P.

[1] Prandtl-Meyer expansion of chemically reacting gases in local chemical and thermodynamic equilibrium, *NACA Tech. Note* no. 4230 (1958).

Herzfeld, K. F.

[1] Freie Weglänge und Transporterscheinungen in Gasen, *Hand-und-Jahrbuch der Chemischen Physik*, Vol. 3, Part II, Sect. IV. Akademische Verlagsgesellschaft, Leipzig, 1939.

Hilbert, D.
See Courant and Hilbert.

Hirschfelder, J. O., Curtiss, C. F., and Bird, R. B.

[1] *Molecular Theory of Gases and Liquids*. Wiley, New York, 1954.

Holder, D. W., and Gadd, G. E.

[1] The interaction between shock waves and boundary layers and its relation to base pressure in supersonic flow, *Boundary Layer Effects in Aerodynamics*, *Natl. Phys. Lab. Symposium*, pp. 8.1–8.65. H.M.S.O., London, 1955, and Philosophical Library, New York, 1957.

Holt, M.

[1] The method of characteristics for steady supersonic rotational flow in three dimensions, *J. Fluid Mech.* **1**, 409–423 (1956).

Hord, R. A.

[1] An approximate solution for axially symmetric flow over a cone with an attached shock wave, *NACA Tech. Note* no. 3485 (1955).

Howarth, L.

[1] Concerning the effect of compressibility on laminar boundary layers and their separation, *Proc. Roy. Soc. London. Ser. A* **194**, 16–42 (1948).

Hurlbut, F. C.

[1] An experimental molecular beam investigation of the scattering of molecules from surfaces, *Tech. Rep.* no. HE-150-118, Inst. of Eng. Res., Univ. of California, Berkeley, Calif., 1953.

[2] Studies of molecular scattering at the solid surface, *J. Appl. Phys.* **28**, 844–850 (1957).

Illingworth, C. R.

[1] Steady flow in the laminar boundary layer of a gas, *Proc. Roy. Soc. London. Ser. A* **199**, 533–558 (1949).

Il'yushin, A. A.

[1] The law of plane sections in the aerodynamics of high supersonic speeds, *Prikl. Mat. Mekh.* **20**, 733–755 (1956).

Ipsen, D. C.

[1] Experiments on cone drag in a rarefied air flow, *Jet Propulsion* **26**, 1076–1077 (1956).

Isenberg, J. S., and Lin, C. C.

[1] The method of characteristics in compressible flow, Part I (Steady supersonic flow), *Tech. Rep.* no. F-TR-1173A-ND (GDAM A9-M 11/1), Air Materiel Command, Wright-Patterson Air Force Base, Ohio, 1947. See also Part IA (Tables and charts), and Part IB (Numerical Examples), 1947.

Ivey, H. R., and Cline, C. W.

[1] Effect of heat-capacity lag on the flow through oblique shock waves, *NACA Tech. Note* no. 2196 (1950).

Ivey, H. R., Klunker, E. B., and Bowen, E. N.

[1] A method for determining the aerodynamic characteristics of two- and three-dimensional shapes at hypersonic speeds, *NACA Tech. Note* no. 1613 (1948).

Ivey, H. R., and Morrissette, R. R.

[1] An approximate determination of the lift of slender cylindrical bodies and wing-body combinations at very high supersonic speeds, *NACA Tech. Note* no. 1740 (1948).

Janssen, E.

See Young and Janssen.

Johannsen, N. H., and Meyer, R. E.

[1] Axially-symmetrical supersonic flow near the center of an expansion, *Aero. Quart.* **2,** 127–142 (1950).

Johnson, H. A.

See Rubesin and Johnson.

Jukoff, D.

See Stalder and Jukoff.

Kantrowitz, A.

[1] A survey of physical phenomena occurring in flight at extreme speeds, *in Proceedings of the Conference on High-Speed Aeronautics* (A. Ferri, N. J. Hoff, and P. A. Libby, eds.), pp. 335–339. Polytechnic Inst. of Brooklyn, Brooklyn, N. Y., 1955.

Kemp, N. H.

[1] On hypersonic stagnation-point flow with a magnetic field, *J. Aero. Sci.* **25,** 405–407 (1958).

See Fay, Riddell, and Kemp.

Kemp, N. H., Rose, P. H., and Detra, R. W.

[1] Laminar heat transfer around blunt bodies in dissociated air, *Res. Rep.* no. 15, Avco Research Lab., Everett, Mass., 1958. Also *J. Aero/Space Sci.* **26** (1959), to be published.

Kendall, J. M., Jr.

[1] An experimental investigation of leading-edge shock-wave–boundary-layer interaction at Mach 5.8, *J. Aero. Sci.* **24,** 47–56 (1957).

Kennard, E. H.

[1] *Kinetic Theory of Gases.* McGraw-Hill, New York, 1938.

Kirkwood, J. G.

See Wood and Kirkwood.

Kivel, B.

See Hammerling and Kivel.

Klunker, E. B.

See Ivey, Klunker, and Bowen.

Klunker, E. B., and McLean, F. E.

[1] Effect of thermal properties on laminar-boundary-layer characteristics, *NACA Tech. Note* no. 2916 (1953).

Koga, T.

See Talbot, Koga, and Sherman.

Kogan, A.

[1] On inviscid flow near an airfoil leading edge or an ogive tip at high supersonic Mach numbers, *J. Aero. Sci.* **23,** 794–795 (1956).

[2] On supersonic rotational flow behind strong shock waves, II. Flow past ogives of revolution, *Tech. Rep.*, Technion Res. and Dev. Found. Ltd., Haifa, Israel, 1956.

[3] An application of Crocco's stream function to the study of rotational supersonic flow past airfoils, *Quart. J. Mech. Appl. Math.* **11,** 1–23 (1958).

Kopal, Z.

[1] Tables of supersonic flow around cones, *Tech. Rep.* No. 1, Dept. of Elect. Eng., Mass. Inst. Tech., Cambridge, Mass., 1947.

Korobkin, I., and Hastings, S. M.

[1] Mollier chart for air in dissociated equilibrium at temperatures of 2000°K to 15,000°K, *NAVORD Rep.* no. 4446, U. S. Naval Ord. Lab., White Oak, Md., 1957.

Krasheninnikova, N. L.

[1] On the unsteady motion of a gas displaced by a piston, *Izv. Akad. Nauk SSSR Otd. Tekh. Nauk 1955*, no. *8*, 22–36.

Kraus, S.

[1] An analysis of supersonic flow in the region of the leading edge of curved airfoils, including charts for determining surface-pressure gradient and shock-wave curvature, *NACA Tech. Note* no. 2729 (1952). Superseded by Eggers, Syvertson, and Kraus [1].

Kubota, T.

[1] Investigation of flow around simple bodies in hypersonic flow, *Memo.* no. 40, Hypersonic Research Project, Guggenheim Aero. Lab., California Inst. of Tech., Pasadena, Calif., 1957.

See Lees and Kubota.

Kuehn, D. M.

See Chapman, Kuehn, and Larson.

Kuhlthau, A. R.

[1] The application of high rotational speed techniques to low density gasdynamics, *Proc. 3rd Midwestern Conf. on Fluid Mech.*, Univ. of Minnesota, Minneapolis, Minn., 495–514 (1953).

Kuo, Y. H.

[1] Viscous flow along a flat plate moving at high supersonic speeds, *J. Aero. Sci.* **23,** 125–136 (1956).

[2] Dissociation effects in hypersonic viscous flows, *J. Aero. Sci.* **24,** 345–350 (1957).

See Pan and Kuo.

Lal, S.

[1] Heat transfer in compressible laminar boundary layers, *J. Aero. Soc. India* **8,** 1–17, 19–34 (1956).

Landahl, M. T.

[1] Unsteady flow around thin wings at high Mach numbers, *J. Aero. Sci.* **24,** 33–38 (1957).

Larson, H. K.

See Chapman, Kuehn, and Larson.

Latter, R.

[1] Similarity solution for a spherical shock wave, *J. Appl. Phys.* **26,** 954–960 (1955).

Lees, L.

[1] On the boundary-layer equations in hypersonic flow and their approximate solutions, *J. Aero. Sci.* **20,** 143–145 (1953).

[2] Hypersonic viscous flow over an inclined wedge, *J. Aero. Sci.* **20,** 794–796 (1953).

[3] Hypersonic flow, *Proc. 5th Internatl. Aero. Conf., Los Angeles,* Inst. Aero. Sci., New York, 241–276 (1955).

[4] Laminar heat transfer over blunt-nosed bodies at hypersonic flight speeds, *Jet Propulsion* **26,** 259–269, 274 (1956).

[5] Influence of the leading-edge shock wave on the laminar boundary layer at hypersonic speeds, *J. Aero. Sci.,* **23,** 594–600, 612 (1956).

See Probstein and Lees.

Lees, L., and Kubota, T.

[1] Inviscid hypersonic flow over blunt-nosed slender bodies, *J. Aero. Sci.* **24,** 195–202 (1957).

Lees, L., and Probstein, R. F.

[1] Hypersonic viscous flow over a flat plate, *Rep.* no. 195, Dept. of Aero. Eng., Princeton Univ., Princeton, N. J., 1952.

[2] *Hypersonic Flows of a Viscous Fluid* (unpublished monograph with limited circulation), 1953. Copies available through the Brown University Library, Brown Univ., Providence, R.I.

Levy, S.

[1] Effect of large temperature changes (including viscous heating) upon laminar boundary layers with variable free-stream velocity, *J. Aero. Sci.* **21,** 459–474 (1954).

Li, T. Y.

[1] Simple shear flow past a flat plate in an incompressible fluid of small viscosity, *J. Aero. Sci.* **22,** 651–652 (1955). See also 724–725.

[2] Effects of free-stream vorticity on the behavior of a viscous boundary layer, *J. Aero. Sci.* **23,** 1128–1129 (1956).

[3] An inverse problem in hypersonic viscous flow, *Proc. 5th Midwestern Conf. on Fluid Mech.,* Univ. of Michigan, Ann Arbor, Mich., 201–223 (1957).

Li, T. Y., and Geiger, R. E.

[1] Stagnation point of a blunt body in hypersonic flow, *J. Aero. Sci.* **24,** 25–32 (1957).

Li, T. Y., and Nagamatsu, H. T.

[1] Shock-wave effects on the laminar skin friction of an insulated flat plate at hypersonic speeds, *J. Aero. Sci.* **20,** 345–355 (1953).

[2] Similar solutions of compressible boundary-layer equations, *J. Aero. Sci.* **22,** 607–616 (1955).

[3] Hypersonic viscous flow on noninsulated flat plate, *Proc. 4th Midwestern Conf. on Fluid Mech.,* Purdue Univ., Lafayette, Ind., 273–287 (1955).

Libby, P. A.
  See Ferri and Libby.
Lieberstein, H. M.
  See Garabedian and Lieberstein.
Liepmann, H. W., and Roshko, A.
  [1] *Elements of Gasdynamics.* Wiley, New York, 1957.
Lighthill, M. J.
  [1] The flow behind a stationary shock, *Phil. Mag.* **40**, 214–220 (1949).
  [2] Oscillating airfoils at high Mach number, *J. Aero. Sci.* **20**, 402–406 (1953).
  [3] Dynamics of a dissociating gas. Part I. Equilibrium flow, *J. Fluid Mech.* **2**, 1–32 (1957).
Lin, C. C.
  [1] On a perturbation theory based on the method of characteristics, *J. Math. Phys.* **33**, 117–134 (1954).
  [2] Note on Garabedian's paper "Numerical construction of detached shock waves," *J. Math. Phys.* **36**, 206–209 (1957).
  See Isenberg and Lin.
  See Shen and Lin.
Lin, C. C., Reissner, E., and Tsien, H. S.
  [1] On two-dimensional non-steady motion of a slender body in a compressible fluid, *J. Math. Phys.* **27**, 220–231 (1948).
Lin, C. C., and Rubinov, S. I.
  [1] On the flow behind curved shocks, *J. Math. Phys.* **27**, 105–129 (1948).
Lin, C. C., and Shen, S. F.
  [1] An analytic determination of the flow behind a symmetrical curved shock in a uniform stream, *NACA Tech. Note* no. 2506 (1951).
Lin, S. C.
  [1] Cylindrical shock waves produced by instantaneous energy release, *J. Appl. Phys.* **25**, 54–57 (1954).
Linnell, R. D.
  [1] Two-dimensional airfoils in hypersonic flows, *J. Aero. Sci.* **16**, 22–30 (1949).
Lobb, R. K., Winkler, E. M., and Persh, J.
  [1] Experimental investigation of turbulent boundary layers in hypersonic flow, *J. Aero. Sci.* **22**, 1–9, 50 (1955).
Lock, C. N. H., and Tomlinson, R. C.
  [1] The use of tensor notation to develop characteristic equations of supersonic flow, *Aero. Res. Council. Rep. and Memo.* no. 2632 (1954).
Lubonski, J.
  See Lunc and Lubonski.
Lunc, M., and Lubonski, J.
  [1] Sur une solution approchée du problème de l'écoulement d'un gaz raréfié autour d'un obstacle, *Arch. Mech. Stos.* **8**, 597–616 (1956).
Maccoll, J. W.
  See Taylor and Maccoll.
Maccoll, J. W., and Codd, J.
  [1] Theoretical investigations of the flow around various bodies in the sonic region of velocities, *Theor. Res. Rep.* no. 17/45, Armament Res. Dept., Ministry of Supply, Fort Halstead, Kent, 1945.

Mahony, J. J.

[1] A critique of shock-expansion theory, *J. Aero. Sci.* **22**, 673–680, 720 (1955).

Mahony, J. J., and Skeat, P. R.

[1] The flow around a supersonic airfoil, *Aero. Note* no. 147, Res. and Dev. Branch, Aero. Res. Lab., Melbourne, Australia, 1955.

Mangler, K. W., and Evans, M. E.

[1] The calculation of the inviscid flow between a detached bow wave and a body, *Tech. Note* no. Aero 2536, Roy. Aircraft Est., Farnborough, 1957.

Mark, R. M.

[1] Compressible laminar heat transfer near the stagnation point of blunt bodies of revolution, *Rep.* no. ZA-7-016, Convair, San Diego, Calif., 1955.

[2] Effect of externally generated vorticity on laminar heat transfer, *J. Aero. Sci.* **24**, 923–924 (1957).

Maslen, S. H.

[1] Second approximation to laminar compressible boundary layer on flat plate in slip flow, *NACA Tech. Note* no. 2818 (1952).

[2] On the supersonic flow of a viscous fluid past a flat plate, *J. Aero. Sci.* **23**, 800–802 (1956).

Maslen, S. H., and Moeckel, W. E.

[1] Inviscid hypersonic flow past blunt bodies, *J. Aero. Sci.* **24**, 683–693 (1957).

McCall, F.

See Mitchell and McCall.

McLean, F. E.

See Klunker and McLean.

Meyer, R. E.

[1] The method of characteristics, *in Modern Developments in Fluid Dynamics, High Speed Flow* (L. Howarth, ed.), Vol. I, pp. 71–104. Oxford, London, 1953.

[2] On supersonic flow behind a curved shock, *Quart. Appl. Math.* **14**, 433–436 (1957).

See Johannsen and Meyer.

Mikhailova, M. P.

See Bam-Zelikovich, Bunimovich, and Mikhailova.

Milne-Thomson, L. M.

[1] *Theoretical Hydrodynamics*, 3rd Edition. Macmillan, New York, 1955.

Mitchell, A. R.

[1] Application of relaxation to the rotational field of flow behind a bow shock wave, *Quart. J. Mech. Appl. Math.* **4**, 371–383 (1951).

Mitchell, A. R., and McCall, F.

[1] The rotational field behind a bow shock wave in axially symmetric flow using relaxation methods, *Proc. Roy. Soc. Edinburgh. Sect. A* **53**, 371–380 (1952).

Moeckel, W. E.

[1] Approximate method for predicting form and location of detached shock waves, *NACA Tech. Note* no. 1921 (1949).

[2] Oblique-shock relations at hypersonic speeds for air in chemical equilibrium, *NACA Tech. Note* no. 3895 (1957).

See Maslen and Moeckel.

Moore, L. L.

[1] A solution of the laminar boundary-layer equations for a compressible fluid with variable properties, including dissociation, *J. Aero. Sci.* **19**, 505–518 (1952).

Morrissette, R. R.
See Ivey and Morrissette.

Munk, M. M., and Prim, R. C.
[1] Surface-pressure gradient and shock-front curvature at the edge of a plane ogive with attached shock front, *J. Aero. Sci.* **15**, 691–695 (1948).

Nagakura, T., and Naruse, H.
[1] An approximate solution of the hypersonic laminar boundary-layer equations and its application, *J. Phys. Soc. Japan* **12**, 1298–1304 (1957).

Nagamatsu, H. T.
See Li and Nagamatsu.

Naruse, H.
See Nagakura and Naruse.

Neice, S. E.
See Hamaker, Neice, and Wong.

Newman, D. J.
See Zlotnick and Newman.

Newton, I.
[1] *Mathematical principles of natural philosopy (Philosophiae naturalis principia mathematica)*, transl. by A. Motte (1729), revised by A. Cajori. Univ. of California Press, Berkeley, 1934. Reprinted 1946.

Oguchi, H.
[1] First-order approach to a strong interaction problem in hypersonic flow over an insulated flat plate, *Rep.* no. 330, Aero. Res. Inst., Univ. of Tokyo, Japan, 1958.

Oliver, R. E.
[1] An experimental investigation of flow over simple blunt bodies at a nominal Mach number of 5.8, *J. Aero. Sci.* **23**, 177–179 (1956).

Oppenheim, A. K.
[1] Generalized theory of convective heat transfer in a free-molecule flow, *J. Aero. Sci.* **20**, 49–58 (1953).

Oswatitsch, K.
[1] Similarity laws for hypersonic flow, *Tech. Note* no. 16, Institutionen för Flygteknik, Kungl. Tekniska Högskolan, Stockholm, 1950.
[2] Ähnlichkeitsgesetze für Hyperschallströmung, *Z. Angew. Math. Phys.* **2**, 249–264 (1951).

Pallone, A. J.
See Cheng and Pallone.

Pan, L. J., and Kuo, Y. H.
[1] Compressible viscous flow past a wedge moving at hypersonic speeds, *J. Math. Phys.* **35**, 179–193 (1956).

Penner, S. S.
[1] *Introduction to the Study of Chemical Reactions in Flow Systems.* Butterworths, London, 1955.

Persh, J.
See Lobb, Winkler, and Persh.

Pretsch, J.
[1] Die Stabilität einer ebenen Laminarströmung bei Druckgefälle und Druckanstieg. *Jbuch. Deutschen Luftfahrtforschung*, Part I, 158–175 (1941). British *Transl.* no. M.A.P.-VG-52 (Völkenrode), 1946.

Prim, R. C.
See Munk and Prim.

Probstein, R. F.
[1] Interacting hypersonic laminar boundary layer flow over a cone, *Tech. Rep.* no. AF 2798/1, Div. of Eng., Brown Univ., Providence, R. I., 1955.
[2] Inviscid flow in the stagnation point region of very blunt-nosed bodies at hypersonic flight speeds, *WADC Tech. Note* no. 56–395, Div. of Eng., Brown Univ., Providence, R. I., 1956.
[3] Methods of calculating the equilibrium laminar heat transfer rate at hypersonic flight speeds, *Jet Propulsion* **26**, 497–499 (1956).
[4] Inversion of the Prandtl-Meyer relation for specific heat ratios of 5/3 and 5/4, *J. Aero. Sci.* **24**, 316–317, 632 (1957).
[5] On the nature of the sonic line for supersonic and hypersonic flow over blunt bodies, *WADC Tech. Note* no. 57–349, Div. of Eng., Brown Univ., Providence, R. I., 1957.
[6] Continuum theory and rarefied hypersonic aerodynamics, *WADC Tech. Note* no. 58–145, Div. of Eng., Brown Univ., Providence, R. I., 1958. See also *Proc. 1ᵉʳ Symposium International sur l'Aérodynamique et l'Aérothermique des Gaz Raréfiés*, Centre Universitaire Méditerranéen, Nice, France, to be published (1959).
See Adams and Probstein.
See Hayes and Probstein.
See Lees and Probstein.
See Rose, Probstein, and Adams.
See Waldman and Probstein.

Probstein, R. F., Adams, M. C., and Rose, P. H.
[1] On turbulent heat transfer through a highly cooled partially dissociated boundary layer, *Jet Propulsion* **28**, 56–58 (1958).

Probstein, R. F., and Elliott, D.
[1] The transverse curvature effect in compressible axially symmetric laminar boundary-layer flow, *J. Aero. Sci.* **23**, 208–224, 236 (1956).

Probstein, R. F., and Lees, L.
[1] On the recovery factor for hypersonic flow with a self-induced pressure gradient, *J. Aero. Sci.* **20**, 291–292 (1953).

Reissner, E.
See Lin, Reissner, and Tsien.

Reshotko, E.
See Cohen and Reshotko.

Reshotko, E., and Cohen, C. B.
[1] Heat transfer at the forward stagnation point of blunt bodies, *NACA Tech. Note* no. 3513 (1955).
[2] Note on the compressible laminar boundary layer with heat transfer and pressure gradient, *J. Aero. Sci.* **22**, 584–585 (1955).

Resler, E. L.
[1] Characteristics and sound speed in nonisentropic gas flows with nonequilibrium thermodynamic states, *J. Aero. Sci.* **24**, 785–790 (1957).

Resnikoff, M. M.
See Eggers, Resnikoff, and Dennis.

Riddell, F. R.
See Fay and Riddell.
See Fay, Riddell, and Kemp.

Rockett, J. A., and Hayes, W. D.
[1] The method of characteristics in compressible flow, Part IC (Two-dimensional flow with large entropy changes), *Tech. Rep.* no. 102-AC 49/6-100, Air Materiel Command, Wright-Patterson Air Force Base, Ohio, 1949.

Romig, M. F.
[1] Stagnation point heat transfer for hypersonic flow, *Jet Propulsion* **26**, 1098–1101 (1956). Addendum, **27**, 1255 (1957).
[2] Conical flow parameters for air in dissociation equilibrium: final results, *Res. Note* no. 14, Convair Scientific Res. Lab., San Diego, Calif., 1958.

Romig, M. F., and Dore, F. J.
[1] Solutions of the compressible laminar boundary layer including the case of a dissociated free stream, *Rep.* no. ZA-7-012, Convair, San Diego, Calif., 1954.

Rose, P. H.
See Kemp, Rose, and Detra.
See Probstein, Adams, and Rose.

Rose, P. H., Probstein, R. F., and Adams, M. C.
[1] Turbulent heat transfer through a highly cooled partially dissociated boundary layer, *J. Aero/Space Sci.* **25**, 751–760 (1958).

Rose, P. H., and Stark, W. I.
[1] Stagnation point heat-transfer measurements in dissociated air, *J. Aero. Sci.* **25**, 86–97 (1958).

Roshko, A.
See Liepmann and Roshko.

Rossow, V. J.
[1] Applicability of the hypersonic similarity rule to pressure distributions which include the effects of rotation for bodies of revolution at zero angle of attack, *NACA Tech. Note* no. 2399 (1951).
See Ehret, Rossow, and Stevens.

Rott, N., and Crabtree, L. F.
[1] Simplified laminar boundary-layer calculations for bodies of revolution and for yawed wings, *J. Aero. Sci.* **19**, 553–565 (1952).

Rubesin, M. W., and Johnson, H. A.
[1] A critical review of skin-friction and heat-transfer solutions of the laminar boundary layer of a flat plate, *Trans. A.S.M.E.* **71**, 385–388 (1949).

Rubinov, S. I.
See Lin and Rubinov.

Sakurai, A.

[1] On the propagation and structure of the blast wave, I, *J. Phys. Soc. Japan* **8,** 662–669 (1953).

[2] On the propagation and structure of the blast wave, II, *J. Phys. Soc. Japan* **9,** 256–266 (1954).

Sänger, E.

[1] *Raketenflugtechnik.* R. Oldenburg, Munich, 1933.

Sauer, F. M.

[1] Convective heat transfer from spheres in a free-molecule flow, *J. Aero. Sci.* **18,** 353–354 (1951).

Savin, R. C.

See Eggers and Savin.

See Eggers, Savin, and Syvertson.

Schaaf, S. A.

[1] Theoretical considerations in rarefied-gas dynamics, *Heat Transfer Symposium University of Michigan,* pp. 237–260. Univ. of Michigan Press, Ann Arbor, 1953.

Schaaf, S. A., and Chambré, P. L.

[1] Flow of rarefied gases, *in Fundamentals of Gas Dynamics* (H. W. Emmons, ed.), Sect. H, pp. 687–739 (Vol. III of *High Speed Aerodynamics and Jet Propulsion*). Princeton Univ. Press, Princeton, 1958.

Schlichting, H.

[1] *Boundary Layer Theory* (transl. by J. Kestin). McGraw-Hill, New York, 1955.

Sedov, L. I.

[1] On certain unsteady motions of a compressible fluid, *Prikl. Mat. Mekh.* **9,** 293–311 (1945), *Transl.* no. T-57, The Rand Corp., Santa Monica, Calif., 1956. See also, On unsteady motions of a compressible fluid, *Dokl. Akad. Nauk SSSR* **47,** 91–93 (1945) (in English).

[2] Propagation of strong blast waves, *Prikl. Mat. Mekh.* **10,** 241–250 (1946). See also, Le mouvement d'air en cas d'une forte explosion, *Dokl. Akad. Nauk SSSR* **52,** 17–20 (1946).

[3] *Similarity and Dimensional Methods in Mechanics.* Gostekhizdat, SSSR. Third edition 1954, fourth edition 1957. English translation (M. Holt, ed.), Academic Press, New York, 1959, in press.

Serbin, H.

[1] The high speed flow of gas around blunt bodies, *Aero. Quart.* **9,** 313–330 (1958). Supersedes *Res. Memos.* nos. RM-1713 and RM-1772, The Rand Corp., Santa Monica, Calif., 1956.

Shen, S. F.

[1] An estimate of viscosity effect on the hypersonic flow over an insulated wedge, *J. Math. Phys.* **31,** 192–205 (1952).

See Lin and Shen.

Shen, S. F., and Lin, C. C.

[1] On the attached curved shock in front of a sharp-nosed axially symmetric body placed in a uniform stream, *NACA Tech. Note* no. 2505 (1951).

Sherman, F. S.

[1] A low-density wind tunnel study of shock-wave structure and relaxation phenomena in gases, *NACA Tech. Note* no. 3298 (1955).

Sherman, P. M.
    See Talbot, Koga, and Sherman.

Sibulkin, M.
    [1] Heat transfer near the forward stagnation point of a body of revolution, *J. Aero. Sci.* **19**, 570–571 (1952).

Siegel, K. M.
    [1] Boundaries of fluid mechanics, *J. Aero. Sci.* **17**, 191–192 (1950).

Skeat, P. R.
    See Mahony and Skeat.

Smith, A. M. O.
    [1] Rapid laminar boundary-layer calculations by piecewise application of similar solutions, *J. Aero. Sci.* **23**, 901–912 (1956).

Southwell, R. V.
    See Green and Southwell.

Sparrow, E. M.
    [1] The thermal boundary layer on a non-isothermal surface with non-uniform free stream velocity, *J. Fluid Mech.* **4**, 321–329 (1958).

Stalder, J. R., Goodwin, G., and Creager, M. O.
    [1] A comparison of theory and experiment for high-speed free-molecule flow, *NACA Rep.* no. 1032 (1951). Supersedes *Tech. Note* no. 2244 (1950).

Stalder, J. R., and Jukoff, D.
    [1] Heat transfer to bodies traveling at high speed in the upper atmosphere, *NACA Rep.* no. 944 (1949). Supersedes *Tech. Note* no. 1682 (1948).

Stanyukovich, K. P.
    [1] On automodel solutions of equations of hydrodynamics possessing central symmetry, *Dokl. Akad. Nauk SSSR* **48**, 310–312 (1945).
    [2] *Unsteady Motion of Continuous Media.* Gostekhizdat, SSSR, 1955.

Stark, W. I.
    See Rose and Stark.

Stevens, V. I.
    See Ehret, Rossow, and Stevens.

Stewartson, K.
    [1] Correlated incompressible and compressible boundary layers, *Proc. Roy. Soc. London. Ser. A* **200**, 84–100 (1949).
    [2] On the motion of a flat plate at high speed in a viscous compressible fluid. I. Impulsive motion, *Proc. Cambridge Philos. Soc.* **51**, 202–219 (1955).
    [3] On the motion of a flat plate at high speed in a viscous compressible fluid—II. Steady motion, *J. Aero. Sci.* **22**, 303–309 (1955).

Stocker, P. M.
    [1] Hypersonic flow. Part I. General considerations and two-dimensional inviscid flow theory, *Rep.* no. (B) 22–55, Armament Res. and Develop. Establish., Fort Halstead, Kent, 1955.

Syvertson, C. A.
    See Eggers, Savin, and Syvertson.
    See Eggers and Syvertson.
    See Eggers, Syvertson, and Kraus.

Syvertson, C. A., and Dennis, D. H.
[1] A second-order shock-expansion method applicable to bodies of revolution near zero lift, *NACA Rep.* no. 1328 (1957). Supersedes *Tech. Note* no. 3527 (1956).

Talbot, L.
[1] Viscosity corrections to cone probes in rarefied supersonic flow at a nominal Mach number of 4, *NACA Tech. Note* no. 3219 (1954).

Talbot, L., Koga, T., and Sherman, P. M.
[1] Hypersonic viscous flow over slender cones, *NACA Tech. Note* no. 4327 (1958).

Taylor, G. I.
[1] The formation of a blast wave by a very intense explosion, *Proc. Roy. Soc. London. Ser. A* **201,** 159–186 (1950).

Taylor, G. I., and Maccoll, J. W.
[1] The air pressure on a cone moving at high speeds, *Proc. Roy. Soc. London. Ser. A* **139,** 278–311 (1933).

Thwaites, B.
[1] Approximate calculation of the laminar boundary layer, *Aero. Quart.* **1,** 245–280 (1949).

Tomlinson, R. C.
See Lock and Tomlinson.

Truesdell, C.
[1] On curved shocks in steady plane flow of an ideal fluid, *J. Aero. Sci.* **19,** 826–828 (1952).

Trumpler, P. R.
See Wiedmann and Trumpler.

Tsien, H. S.
[1] Similarity laws of hypersonic flows, *J. Math. Phys.* **25,** 247–251 (1946).
[2] Superaerodynamics, mechanics of rarefied gases, *J. Aero. Sci.* **13,** 653–664 (1946).
See Lin, Reissner, and Tsien.

Uchida, S., and Yasuhara, M.
[1] The rotational field behind a curved shock wave calculated by the method of flux analysis, *J. Aero. Sci.* **23,** 830–845 (1956).

Vaglio-Laurin, R., and Ferri, A.
[1] Theoretical investigation of the flow field about blunt-nosed bodies in supersonic flight, *J. Aero/Space Sci.* **25,** 761–770 (1958).

Van Driest, E. R.
[1] Investigation of the laminar boundary layer in compressible fluids using the Crocco method, *NACA Tech. Note* no. 2597 (1952).
[2] The laminar boundary layer with variable fluid properties, *Rep.* no. AL-1866, North American Aviat. Inc., Downey, Calif., 1954.

Van Dyke, M. D.
[1] The combined supersonic-hypersonic similarity rule, *J. Aero. Sci.* **18,** 499–500 (1951).
[2] A study of hypersonic small-disturbance theory, *NACA Rep.* no. 1194 (1954). Supersedes *Tech. Note* no. 3173 (1954).
[3] Applications of hypersonic small-disturbance theory, *J. Aero. Sci.* **21,** 179–186 (1954).

[4] Supersonic flow past oscillating airfoils including nonlinear thickness effects, *NACA Rep.* no. 1183 (1954). Supersedes *Tech. Note* no. 2982 (1953).

[5] A model of supersonic flow past blunt axisymmetric bodies, with application to Chester's solution, *J. Fluid Mech.* **3**, 515–522 (1958).

[6] The supersonic blunt body problem—review and extensions, *J. Aero/Space Sci.* **25**, 485–496 (1958).

Vas, I. E.

[1] An experimental investigation of the pressure on a thin flat plate at hypersonic speeds, *WADC Tech. Note* no. 57–104, Dept. of Aero. Eng., Princeton Univ., Princeton, N. J., 1957.

See Hammitt, Vas, and Bogdonoff.

Vas, I. E., Bogdonoff, S. M., and Hammitt, A. G.

[1] An experimental investigation of the flow over simple two-dimensional and axial symmetric bodies at hypersonic speeds, *Jet Propulsion* **28**, 97–104 (1958).

von Kármán, T.

[1] The problem of resistance in compressible fluids, *Accad. d'Italia Roma, Fondazione Alessandro Volta, Proc. 5th Volta Cong., Rome*, 222–277 (1935).

Waldman, G. D., and Probstein, R. F.

[1] An analytic extension of the shock-expansion method, *WADC Tech. Note* no. 57–214, Div. of Eng., Brown Univ., Providence, R. I., 1957.

Wendt, H.

See Hantzsche and Wendt.

Whitham, G. B.

[1] A note on the stand-off distance of the shock in high speed flow past a circular cylinder, *Comm. Pure Appl. Math.* **10**, 531–535 (1957).

Wiedmann, M. L., and Trumpler, P. R.

[1] Thermal accommodation coefficients, *Trans. A.S.M.E.* **68**, 57–64 (1946).

Willis, D. R.

[1] On the flow of gases under nearly free molecular conditions, *Rep.* no. 442, Dept. of Aero. Eng., Princeton Univ., Princeton, N.J., 1958.

Winkler, E. M.

See Lobb, Winkler, and Persh.

Wong, T. J.

See Hamaker, Neice, and Wong.
See Hamaker and Wong.

Wood, W. W., and Kirkwood, J. G.

[1] The hydrodynamics of a reacting and relaxing fluid, *J. Appl. Phys.* **28**, 395–399 (1957).

Yasuhara, M.

[1] On the hypersonic viscous flow past slender bodies of revolution, *J. Phys. Soc. Japan* **8**, 878–886 (1956).

[2] An exact approach to the hypersonic viscous flow past a slender body of revolution, *Proc. 6th Japan Natl. Congr. Appl. Mech.*, Kyoto, Japan, 291–294 (1957).

See Uchida and Yasuhara.

Young, A. D.

[1] Boundary layers, *in Modern Developments in Fluid Dynamics, High Speed Flow,* Vol. I (L. Howarth, ed.), pp. 375–475. Oxford, London, 1953.

Young, G. B. W., and Janssen, E.

[1] The compressible boundary layer, *J. Aero. Sci.* **19,** 229–236, 288 (1952).

Zahm, A. F.

[1] Superaerodynamics, *J. Franklin Inst.* **217,** 153–166 (1934).

Zartarian, G.

See Ashley and Zartarian.

Zienkiewicz, H. K.

[1] Flow about cones at very high speeds, *Aero. Quart.* **8,** 384–394 (1957).

Zlotnick, M., and Newman, D. J.

[1] Theoretical calculation of the flow on blunt-nosed axisymmetric bodies in a hypersonic stream, *Tech. Rep.* no. 2–57–29, Research and Advanced Dev. Div., Avco Mfg. Corp., Lawrence, Mass., 1957.

# SYMBOL INDEX

Throughout the book we have tried wherever possible to use standard aerodynamic and mathematical notation. In order to maintain some degree of self-consistency and in order to avoid confusing repetition, it was necessary to use a few symbols different from those which are commonly accepted. We have also tried to avoid duplication within the obvious limitations imposed by common usage and the limited number of symbols available to us in the Roman and Greek alphabets. However, in symbols used only locally frequent repetition is to be found. In order to avoid as far as possible the use of dummy variables, we have consistently used the integral sign with one limit to represent an indefinite integral evaluated as zero at that limit.

Except as indicated all standard mathematical symbols are taken to have their usual meanings. No attempt has been made to include every symbol used in the book. In particular, we have generally not included symbols which are only employed locally and which are not referred to in other parts of the book.

In this index we refer primarily to the page where the symbol is introduced and defined; as a rule, we include also a reference to where the symbol is reintroduced in a different context. A verbal definition is usually included, and in addition where appropriate an equation number, mathematical definition, or both are given.

| | |
|---|---|
| $c_A$ | atom mass fraction, 286 |
| $c_i$ | mass fraction of $i^{th}$ component, 289 |
| $c_p$ | specific heat at constant pressure, 13, 213 |
| $\bar{c}_p$ | mean specific heat ratio of mixture, $\Sigma c_i c_{p_i}$, 287, 290 |
| $c_v$ | specific heat at constant volume, 13, 228 |
| $c_{x,y,z}$ | velocity component of a single molecule with subscript indicating direction, 399 |
| $C$ | constant in linear viscosity-temperature relation, (9.2.6), 338 |
| $C_D$ | drag coefficient, Drag/$\frac{1}{2}\rho_\infty U^2$, 40, 78 |
| $C_D'$ | modified drag coefficient for free molecule flow, 409 |
| $C_f$ | skin friction coefficient based on conditions at edge of boundary layer, (8.3.10), 296 |
| $C_f$ | modified skin friction coefficient for free molecule flow, (10.5.7), 408 |
| $C_{f_\infty}$ | skin friction coefficient based on free stream conditions, (9.3.15), 358 |
| $C_{f_0}$ | zeroth-order coefficient in expansion of skin friction coefficient for strong interaction, (9.3.23), 359 |
| $C_{f_m}$ | dimensionless coefficients in expansion of skin friction coefficient for strong interaction, (9.3.16), 358 |
| $C_L$ | lift coefficient, Lift/$\frac{1}{2}\rho_\infty U^2$, 40, 79 |
| $C_p$ | pressure coefficient, $(p - p_\infty)/\frac{1}{2}\rho_\infty U^2$, 39 |
| $C_\rho$ | density coefficient, (2.3.4), 43 |
| $d$ | see $a, b, c, d$, 245 |
| $d_{orig}$ | coefficient in expression for rate of change of displacement thickness, (9.2.7), 344 |
| $D(Pr)$ | coefficient in expression for rate of change of displacement thickness in insulated case, (9.2.9b), 344 |
| $D_A$ | atomic diffusion coefficient, 286 |
| $D_T$ | turbulent diffusion coefficient, 327 |
| $D_{12}$ | binary diffusion coefficient, 289 |
| $\mathscr{D}$ | quantity representing change in cross-sectional areas of streamtubes in thin shock layer analysis, (5.3.2), 182 |
| $e$ | specific internal energy, 11 |
| $E$ | total energy per unit area ($j = 0$) or per unit depth per radian ($j = 1$), (2.6.14), 57 |
| $E(\bar{\psi})$ | entropy function, (6.3.12), 217 |
| $E_b$ | energy flux of reflected or re-emitted molecules if completely accommodated, 396 |
| $E_i$ | energy flux of incident molecules at surface, 396 |
| $E_r$ | energy flux of reflected or re-emitted molecules at surface, 396 |
| $E_{1,2}$ | coefficients in pressure expansion for weak interaction, (9.2.11b), 345 |
| $f$ | body shape function, (2.1.5), (2.2.1), (2.4.1), (5.3.13), (10.5.1), 32, 38, 45, 184, 407 |
| $f$ | dimensionless stream function variable defining velocity in boundary layer, (8.2.10a), 290 |
| $f$ | frequency of a disturbance, 69 |
| $f(\eta)$ | detachment function, (4.1.6), 140 |
| $f_n$ | normal accommodation coefficient, (10.3.3), 398 |
| $f_t$ | tangential accommodation coefficient, (10.3.2), 398 |
| $f$ | Maxwellian distribution function, (10.3.4), 399 |
| $F$ | integrand in calculus of variations, (3.4.8), (3.4.40), 94, 105 |

$Y_1, Y_2$     real and imaginary parts of $Y$ coordinate, 248

$z$     see $x, y, z$

$z$     coordinate normal to body in constant-density solution with cross flow, (4.5.6), 164

$z$     variable dependent on shock angle in constant-streamtube-area analysis, (5.3.23), 185, 199

$z$     dimensionless square of speed of sound, (2.6.6), 54

$z'$     reduced lateral cartesian coordinate, (2.4.4), 45

$z_i$     dimensionless concentration of $i^{\text{th}}$ species, $c_i/c_{i\delta}$, 290

$Z$     compressibility factor in equation of state, $p = \rho \mathcal{R} T Z$, 262


$\alpha$     angle of attack, 40, 107

$\alpha$     exponent in constant-streamtube-area ogival body solution, (5.3.43), 190

$\alpha$     fraction of original molecules dissociated, $Z = 1 + \alpha$, 262

$\alpha(x)$     dimensionless variable in variable-streamtube-area analysis, (5.4.4), 196

$\alpha(\xi)$     parameter in empirical density relation, (8.3.36), 306

$\beta$     Prandtl-Glauert parameter, $\sqrt{M_\infty^2 - 1}$, 42

$\beta$     local Prandtl-Glauert parameter, $\sqrt{M^2 - 1}$, 260

$\beta$     pressure gradient parameter in boundary layer momentum equation equivalent to classical Falkner-Skan constant, (8.3.34), (8.3.35), (8.3.41), (9.3.10), (9.3.32), 305, 306, 357, 363

$\beta$     ratio of body thickness to forebody thickness, (3.4.26), 103

$\beta$     semiangle of cone, 125

$\beta(x)$     dimensionless variable in variable-streamtube-area approximation, (5.4.7), 197

$\gamma$     isentropic exponent or effective ratio of specific heats in free stream (actual specific heat ratio for perfect gas), $\rho_\infty a_\infty^2/p_\infty$, 13

$\gamma_e$     isentropic exponent or effective ratio of specific heats, $\rho a^2/p$, (1.4.22), 13

$\gamma_\epsilon$     ratio of enthalpy to internal energy, (1.4.20), 18

$\gamma_*$     thermodynamic coefficient analogous to $\gamma$, (1.4.24), 44

$\Gamma$     thermodynamic parameter, $\frac{1}{2}(\gamma_* + 1)$, (1.4.26), 20

$\Gamma$     interaction parameter in characteristic relations, (7.2.2), 267

$\delta$     differential width between two loci of entering streamlines, 120

$\delta$     increment of, 137

$\delta$     viscous characteristic distance across which change in $T$ is of order $T_b$, (10.1.10), 379

$\delta$     boundary layer thickness, 28

$\delta^*$     boundary layer displacement thickness, (8.4.2), 313

$\bar{\delta}^*$     dimensionless transformed displacement thickness, (8.5.5a), 319

$\delta_m$     dimensionless coefficients in expansion of displacement thickness for strong interaction, (9.3.6), 355

$\boldsymbol{\delta}_1$     infinitesimal distance vector, Newtonian flow, 120

$\Delta$     shock layer thickness, 28

$\Delta_0$     detachment or stand-off distance at stagnation point, 152, 221

$\Delta^*$     similar solution value of dimensionless displacement thickness, (8.5.8a), 320

$\bar{\Delta}^*$     dimensionless displacement thickness, (8.5.3a), 317

$\Delta s$     separation distance between two neighboring trajectories orthogonal to streamlines, 213

$\epsilon$        density ratio across shock, $\rho_\infty/\rho_s$, 7, 12

$\epsilon_{\text{lim}}$       limiting density ratio for strong shocks, (1.4.9), 13

$\epsilon_\infty$       free stream parameter analogous to $\epsilon_{\text{lim}}$, (1.4.10c), 13

$\zeta$         vorticity in two-dimensional or axisymmetric flow, (1.5.11), 23

$\zeta$         dimensionless radial coordinate in method of integral relations, $(R - R_b)/\Delta$, (6.3.26), 219

$\eta$         argument of detachment function, (4.1.5b), (4.2.19b), 140, 146

$\eta$         transformed $y$ coordinate in boundary layer, (8.2.9), 290

$\theta$         local streamline inclination angle (see also $\theta_\delta$), 147, 211, 255

$\theta$         angle macroscopic velocity vector makes with surface element, equivalent to $\theta_b$, 399

$\theta_b$        local inclination angle of body, 9

$\theta_c$        half-angle of cone, 351

$\theta_s$        flow deflection angle behind shock, 21

$\theta_w$        half-angle of wedge, 342

$\theta_\delta$        streamline inclination for inviscid flow on equivalent body, $\theta_b + d\delta^*/dx$, (9.1.7), 337

$\overline{\theta}$        transformed dimensionless momentum thickness, (8.5.5b), 319

$\vartheta$        polar angle, 143, 150, 158, 216

$\Theta$        similar solution value of dimensionless momentum thickness, (8.5.8b), 320

$\overline{\Theta}$        dimensionless momentum thickness, (8.5.3b), 317

$\kappa$        parameter in similar small-disturbance solutions, (2.6.8), 55

$\kappa$        parameter in various examples, (3.4.21), (3.6.19), (3.6.25), (4.3.8), (4.4.19), 102, 125, 127, 151, 161

$\kappa$        coefficient of thermal expansion, (8.3.40), 306

$\lambda$        mean free path, 27, 375

$\lambda$        dimensionless radial distance, constant on similarity line, (2.6.4), 54

$\lambda$        wave length or lateral scale of a disturbance, 69

$\lambda_S$       Lagrange multiplier for surface integral, (3.4.8), 94

$\lambda_V$       Lagrange multiplier for volume integral, (3.4.8), 94

$\Lambda$        similar solution value of dimensionless enthalpy-defect thickness, (8.5.8c), 320

$\overline{\Lambda}$        dimensionless enthalpy-defect thickness, (8.5.3c), 317

$\mu$        Mach angle, $\sin^{-1} 1/M$, 257

$\mu$        cosine of polar angle, $\cos \vartheta$, 143

$\mu$        viscosity coefficient, 27

$\mu'$        dilatational or bulk coefficient of viscosity, 389

$\mu''$       longitudinal coefficient of viscosity, (10.2.4), 388

$\mu_T$       eddy viscosity, $-\overline{\rho u'v'}/(\partial\overline{u}/\partial y)$, 327

$\nu$        kinematic viscosity, 27

$\nu$        Prandtl-Meyer turning angle, (7.1.14), 39, 258

$\xi$         polar variable, (4.2.16), 145

$\xi$         dimensionless $x$ coordinate in variable-streamtube-area analysis, (5.4.16), 199

$\xi(x)$       transformed $x$ coordinate in boundary layer, (8.2.9), 290

$\Xi$        viscous acceleration term, (10.2.5), 388

$\pi_{1,2}$       dimensionless pressure correction terms, (3.6.35), 129, 163

$\Pi(\gamma, k)$     parameter from similar inviscid solutions determining pressure on **axisymmetric** body, 363

## SUBSCRIPTS

det             shock detachment point, 142, 189
diff            completely diffuse reflection, 411
$f$             frozen state, 262
hom             homogeneous layer model, 80
$i$             with reference to $i$th species, 289
inc             incompressible value, 328
int             energy associated with internal degrees of freedom, 402
inv             edge of equivalent body in an inviscid flow with vorticity interaction, 340
max             maximum, 311, 382
$n$             normal, 11
orig            value of inviscid flow quantities if there were no viscous effects, 340
$p$-$g$           perfect gas value, 287
$s$             conditions immediately behind (downstream of) shock, 11
sing            point at which shock layer is sonic in an average sense, (5.4.12), 198
son             sonic conditions, 205
spec            completely specular reflection, 407
tr              energy associated with translational degrees of freedom, 402
$w$             wedge, 140
0               conditions at point of entry of particle under consideration, Newtonian flow, (3.2.12), 80
0               stagnation conditions or conditions on axis of body, 87, 184, 213
1               outer edge of shock layer, or rear of body, 78, 110
2-$d$            two-dimensional, 122
$\infty$             free stream conditions or conditions ahead (upstream of) shock, 11
$\delta$             conditions at edge of boundary layer, 290

## SUPERSCRIPTS

$*$             values of temperature dependent quantities in boundary layer evaluated at reference enthalpy, 296
$+$             logarithmic partial derivative, (8.5.18), 322
$'$             fluctuating quantity dependent on time and position in turbulent boundary layer analysis, (8.7.1), 326
$-$             dimensionless variables in method of integral relations, 216
$-$             time averaged quantity in turbulent boundary layer analysis, (8.7.1), 326
                average conditions in boundary layer, 336

## MATHEMATICAL AND SPECIAL SYMBOLS

$R$             aspect ratio, 40
$D/Dx$           partial derivative with respect to $x$ with $\psi$ held constant, 170
$O(\ )$           of order of or of small order than, in a limiting sense, 14
$\sim$             of the same order of magnitude as (requires dimensional consistency), 27
$\approx$             approximately equal to (requires dimensional consistency), 64
$\propto$             proportional to, 62
[ ]             difference between the quantity inside the brackets after the shock and the same quantity before the shock, 33

# AUTHOR INDEX

# SUBJECT INDEX

Absolute optimum shapes, 93–97, 105
  axisymmetric, 95, 105
  two-dimensional, 105
Absolute zero temperature, enthalpy at, 19, 261
Absorption relaxation, 396
Accommodation coefficients, 2, 383, 396–398
  dependence of, 398
  for each energy mode, 396
  for Newton's models, 72, 73
  normal, 398, 401
  tangential, 397, 398, 402
  thermal, 396, 397, 402
Adsorption, 397
Air, properties of (see Equilibrium air)
Almost-normal shock,
  on cone, 149
  on wedge, 143
Analogy,
  Artesian-well, 172–173
  Shower-bath, 172–173
Analytic continuation,
  into complex domain, 234, 245–248
  of flow field, 232
  upstream of shock, 231
Angle of attack, 31, 38, 40
Artesian-well analogy, 172–173
Aspect ratio, 38, 40, 45, 46, 69
Attached solutions on blunt ogive of revolution, 189–194
Automodel solutions, 53
Averaging process for turbulent flow, 326, 327
Axisymmetric and two-dimensional cases, difference between, 111, 161, 162, 183, 195, 201

Basic hypersonic assumption, 9, 34
Basic hypersonic limiting process, 9, 10, 13, 15, 22, 24
Becker integral for total enthalpy, 391
Bernoulli equation,

in constant-density flows, 144, 153–156, 159, 160, 163
in method of integral relations, 216
with relaxation techniques, 228, 229
Blasius equation, 232
Blasius turbulent skin friction formula, 328
Blast wave solutions, 57, 354
Blunt-body flows, 4, 5, 28, 75
  constant density, 150–165
  other methods for, 202–252
  rarefied, 378–381, 388–395
  with thin shock layers, 181–201
Blunt-nosed cone, flow about, 249–251
Blunt ogive of revolution, attached solutions on, 189–194
Blunted slender body, 7, 63, 272, 281
  boundary layer interaction on, 333, 367–370
  empirical pressure relation for, 370
  vorticity interaction on, 369, 370
Bluntness induced interactions, 334, 367–370
Body-oriented coordinate system, 171
Boltzmann equation, 27, 386
Boundary layer, 7, 26, 284–374
Boundary layer concepts, 284, 288
  in bluntness induced interactions, 369
  in rarefied gas flows, 340, 376, 381
  in strong interaction, 336
  in vorticity interaction, 340, 370, 373
Boundary layer coordinates,
  physical, 288
  transformed, 290
Boundary layer equations,
  laminar, 288–291
  turbulent, 326, 327
Boundary layer induced interactions, 29, 285, 334–367, 370–374
Boundary layer interaction, 29, 42, 284, 285, 333–374
Boundary layer regime, in flow classification, 384

# HYPERSONIC
# FLOW THEORY

# APPLIED MATHEMATICS AND MECHANICS

A Series of Monographs Prepared under the Auspices of the
Applied Physics Laboratory, The Johns Hopkins University

EDITOR-IN-CHIEF

## F. N. FRENKIEL

Applied Physics Laboratory,
The Johns Hopkins University, Silver Spring, Maryland

ADVISORY EDITORIAL BOARD

RICHARD COURANT      CARL ECKART

A. M. KUETHE      W. R. SEARS

ACADEMIC PRESS · NEW YORK and LONDON